The Theory and Practice of
Goldsmithing

The Theory and Practice of
Goldsmithing

Prof. Dr. Erhard Brepohl

―――――――――

TRANSLATED BY Charles Lewton-Brain
EDITED BY Tim McCreight

Brynmorgen Press

The Theory and Practice of Goldsmithing
by Erhard Brepohl

Translated by Charles Lewton-Brain and Roy Ysla
Drawings and photos by the author unless specified
Closeup photography by Robert Diamante
Design by Mark Jamra
Layout by Aaron Cheever
Cover design by Tim McCreight and Mark Jamra
Cover photo: Bracelet, Jewelry Studios
              Schullin & Seitner, Vienna (Austria)

Originally published as *Theorie und Praxis des Goldschmieds*
© Fachbuchverlag Leipzig GmbH 1994

Brynmorgen Press
Portland, Maine 04101 USA
© 2001 Brynmorgen Press
All rights reserved. Published in 2001
Printed in China.

10 9 8 7 6 5 4 3
Second Printing

Brynmorgen Press
34 Danforth Street
Portland, Maine 04101 USA
207 761 8217
www.brynmorgen.com

ISBN 0 9615984 9 2

CONTENTS

5

HANDWORKING SKILLS

ix

PREFACE

Since the first printing of this book in 1961, "the Brepohl" has become a standard text for the training of goldsmiths and a recognized general reference book for professional workshop practice. Thirteen editions have appeared in German and four in Russian and in each case the text was reworked and brought up to date. The preparations for the book in front of you were begun in 1987, and were given a tremendous boost on September 11, 1989, with the opening of the border between the two German states. It is a great pleasure to the author who lived in the former German Democratic Republic (East Germany) that in March 1994 this book, which from its beginning was widely known in both German states, appeared in a new form in a united Germany. This new version has won immediate acceptance by goldsmiths in Germany, Switzerland and Austria. With this English translation the book takes on a new dimension as it reaches out to goldsmiths in the United States, the United Kingdom and other colleagues who are able to read English.

I want to thank Charles Lewton-Brain for his excellent translation. He has managed to convey the sense of the difficult text. Also I want to thank Brynmorgen Press and especially Tim McCreight whose personal engagement has made this version a reality. It is my sincere hope that this new edition is as useful to its new audience as was its predecessor.

This edition represents an entirely new book, thoroughly revised to reflect the contemporary state of science and technology. The text has been completely reworked and significantly enlarged with the advice of experienced specialists. Its mission, however, remains the same: to instruct goldsmiths comprehensively in both the science and technology of the craft. As in the early versions, I have retained the close connection between scientific knowledge and practical work in that every problem is viewed from both viewpoints. Also as before, I have tried to make the theoretical context understandable, without neglecting the scientific approach.

Through the friendly support of authoritative companies, I am able to illustrate specialized tools representing the newest developments; special thanks are due to the J. Schmalz Company (Pforzheim), the Heraeus-Philico Company (Pforzheim), Degussa (Pforzheim), and Arno Lindner (Munich).

All metal alloys and chemical formulas were either self tested or derived from the advice of experienced colleagues. When not otherwise given, the percents and proportions of mixture are based on mass.

In this new edition I have included more examples of finished pieces than in earlier versions. These not only demonstrate the working techniques, but also show high quality jewelry in which skill in handwork and design are united. Most of the work shown is that of goldsmiths from the former German Democratic Republic; this is the work that was most available to me and I hope that it will be of interest to the rest of the world to see the level of work that has gone on here in recent times. Because few pieces of jewelry are made with a single technique, most of the examples illustrate not only the point at hand but the complexity and interrelatedness of techniques. All friends and colleagues are thanked for their readiness to submit photos.

It is my intention that *The Theory and Practice of Goldsmithing* can provide a foundation for the education of the goldsmith, metalsmith, stone setter, silversmith and engraver. I believe the book is appropriate for students of colleges, vocational schools and polytechnics, as well as for aspiring Masters candidates. But of greatest importance is that it should be useful to practicing goldsmiths in their workshops!

In this context I'd like to pass along some important advice. Every workshop develops its own interesting equipment and tools; each invents tricks and methods to make the work easier and more efficient and all of this cannot be assembled into a single book. The mutual exchange of experience is an important means of further education. Those who allow their colleagues to participate willingly in their own experiences will often get useful information in return.

I'd like to thank the many colleagues who supported and advanced my endeavor. I would particularly like to single out the following people for their critical contributions to important parts of the book: Diploma of Engineering Peter Neuburger (Arnstadt) Diploma of Engineering Volkmar Rössiger (Freiburg), the electroplaters Strohbach Senior and Junior (Dresden), gold and silversmithing Master Jochen Kaiser (Erfurt), and the following Masters of Goldsmithing:

Reinhold Bothner, Pforzheim
Siegfried Kapp, Bad Dürrenberg
Bruno Kawecki, Dessau
Arthur Kiek, Wolfen
Siegfried Meyer, Freiburg
Claus Winkelmann, Werningerode
Uwe Wrabetz, Haldensleben

Critical advice is also welcomed for the edition before you.

Prof. Dr. Erhard Brepohl
Bad Doberan, Germany
August 1999

EDITOR'S NOTE

When Charles Lewton-Brain approached me in June of 1987 with the suggestion that we collaborate on this project, I had no inkling of the complexity of the task. I neither read nor speak German, but a look at the charts and tables was enough to convince me that this was a book unlike any English language text currently available to our field. After lengthy negotiations with a publisher in East Germany, I received permission to produce an English version.

Charles had in his possession a 1985 copy of the book, and set to work rendering the text in English, more or less translating word for word. Because of the different structures of the languages, each paragraph then needed to be rephrased. When Dr. Brepohl rewrote the text in the early 90s, we set aside what had been done and started fresh. Throughout the 13 years it has taken to create this edition, Charles has been a diligent and patient translator. We are all in his debt. The text has been reviewed by experts in chemistry, physics, and metallurgy, as well as being thoroughly reviewed by the translator and the author, who reads English.

The book you hold in your hands is, from start to finish, a labor of love. All of us involved are pleased to offer this valuable resource to English-speaking metalsmiths around the world.

So many people have contributed so much to this book that to thank them all would be a task too daunting to attempt. It is important, though, that certain individuals be given special thanks.

Roy Ysla translated several chapters and was an invaluable help in the final years of work. For ongoing encouragement we'd like to thank Alan Revere, Oppi Untracht, and the dozens of goldsmiths who consistently expressed their enthusiasm for this edition. Mark Jamra designed the pages and has given us a preview of his newest font, Expo, which we see as prototypes in the chapter headings. Mark also designed Greek characters for the scientific references that we are pleased to premier in this edition. Aaron Cheever did a great job in laying out the complex text, always with good grace and intelligence. Robert Diamante's rich photographs introduce each chapter with a drama that still hits me, every time I see them. Aubrey McClellan provided service above and beyond the call in his careful indexing. When you find just what you're looking for, thank Aubrey.

And special thanks to Jenny Hall who devoted long hours to her meticulous editing – her penchant for accuracy has made this a better book.

And on a personal note, I would like to thank Dr. Brepohl for his patience, astounding eye for detail, and longstanding good humor.

T.M.
Portland, Maine
June 2001

Historical Overview

Rather than show again the works that might appear in other texts, I have selected some lesser known examples, in which both the quality of the design and the mastery of execution is particularly remarkable. Because goldsmithing techniques have remained essentially the same for many centuries, these pieces of jewelry from the past are suitable examples of the techniques and procedures described elsewhere in the text.

The history of jewelry may be traced back to the very earliest societies. More than 20,000 years ago, simply worked natural products were used as what we today call "body jewelry." Perhaps beauty and the joy of ornament as we understand these concepts today were present in early jewelry, but as primitive peoples struggled for survival against beasts of prey and natural forces, it is expected that ornament would be infused with this force. We can imagine that ornament was not simply a matter of vanity, but also had association of protection. In this sense, early jewelry was necessary for survival. Necklaces of bones, teeth and claws of predatory animals might be associated with skill or spiritual assistance in hunting, for instance. Amulets protected the body from the unexplained forces of nature and drove away evil spirits.

With the developing division of labor into herdsmen, farmers and artisans, an individual was able to produce more than he himself consumed. As society's technology and range of materials developed, the skills of the smith were increasingly important and he was kept busy producing tools, weapons and jewelry. The restructuring of society led to training in specialties (such as metalworking) and a system of education to pass along skills from one generation to the next. Over time there was an increased specialization in the field of metalsmithing, resulting in the creation of the role of goldsmith, a metalworker concerned especially with pieces of jewelry and fine decorative utensils of gold, silver, copper, bronze and iron. Because this specialization process stretched over a long period of time and occurred in different cultures at different times, it is impossible to say exactly how long there have been goldsmiths.

As long ago as the early Iron Age, that is before 3,000 years ago, technology was sufficiently developed to make mass production possible. This development opened the viability of slave labor and led to the practice of capturing rather than killing prisoners of war. The slave-owning society developed as the first example of the class system. The rich became continually richer and more powerful while the dependency of their remaining clan members often went so far that they themselves became slaves.

As the families of the ruling class wished to distinguish themselves outwardly from other clan members, their clothing became more splendid and they demonstrated their rank with costly jewelry. In this way, jewelry obtained an important new function in the class society as a sign of ruling majesty. In principle this close connection to the ruling class has not changed to the present time. Alongside this the magical function remained unchanged.

Outstanding examples of technical mastery can be found in metalwork of the Egyptians, Greeks, Thracians and Sycthians. Though the Romans are not remembered for advancing the goldsmith's art, they played an important role in preserving and cross-fertilizing the traditions developed in the Mediterranean region. With the internal collapse of the mighty Roman Empire in the early decades of the modern era, the stage was set for a conflict between the social system of the slave owning states and the advancing development of the forces of production, until finally in the 5th century AD, Slavic and German peoples succeeded in overthrowing the Roman Empire.

It came to pass that these peoples in Western Europe (who were barely a step above barbarism and held property as well as the instruments of production in common) made the transition to a feudal production mode. Instead of slaves, bondsmen and serfs were now exploited.

The Teuton peoples had developed a completely individual type of jewelry since the Bronze age. The contact with the Roman culture effected a significant enrichment of craftsmanship and design, but their own basic designs were retained. Outstanding works of the Teuton goldsmiths have been passed on from the time of the mass migrations. Particularly beautiful are the jewelry pieces from the graves of the lords of Franconia and Thuringia. Memorable too are the works of the Vikings, such as the renowned "Hiddensee" jewelry (see figure 8.25).

We can assume that what is true today was true in ancient times; that people wore jewelry not only to ornament themselves, but to express their individuality. This social and esthetic need was combined with the practical need of securing untailored garments, and accounts for the popularity of jewelry in general and fibulae in particular. And of course these dragon and animal-shaped images offered a protective device against the incomprehensible forces of nature and spirits in the ideological system of that time just as the amulets of earlier times served their cultures.

As Christianity spread in Middle Europe, and particularly as churches and ecclesiastic institutions took root, there was a shift in the work of the goldsmith. Ornamentation of the body and protection against evil spirits lost some importance, and was replaced by the desire to decorate the Christian altar and to meet the need for sacred utensils required for the religious service. Particularly in the Romanesque period, cloisters developed into spiritual and cultural centers. Workshops were often located close to and sometimes under the authority of these centers, and it was from here that fashion and education spread until the end of the 12th century. The first general goldsmithing text book was passed on to us from the time around 1120. In his work, the *On Divers Arts* the priest and monk Theophilus gave a distilled overview of the craft techniques of his time.

The transition from early to high feudalism was completed in the 12th century. The first towns and cities grew from settlements on well-placed trade routes and here the crafts were concentrated to an increasing degree. The need for uniform regulations and group solidarity led to the creation of trade guilds, and goldsmiths were important in this development. This coincided with and precipitated a move by goldsmiths from the ecclesiastic centers into the villages and cities. Along with sacred work, they made decorative objects and jewelry pieces as commissions for feudal lords and the increasingly rich middle class.

These shifting patterns of the Gothic period explain why secular as well as sacred works of the goldsmiths art have been passed down to us. Stylistically, work of this period often incorporated architectural forms.

With the Renaissance (which in Germany is determined by the Reformation) the established middle class developed alongside the aristocracy as primary clients of goldsmiths. Jewelry acquired an importance not known before that time as it responded to the radical changes in society. Magnificent decorative vessels and utensils were created to showcase the high level of development of the goldsmiths art. The goldsmiths' guilds of Augsburg, Nuremberg, Leipzig, Dresden, and Berlin stand out in particular; the creations of their masters spread throughout Europe and can be seen today in many museums.

The 30 Years War (1618-1648) led to a general economic and cultural decline in which the middle class was particularly affected – amid such want and misery the goldsmiths art became superfluous. On the other hand the rulers of the many German feudal principalities were able to confirm their power.

In the second half of the 17th century they would construct their courts using the model of the French king, Louis XIV, following the style of the newly arrived Baroque pomp and splendor, while their subjects lived in poverty and misery. Under such conditions the goldsmiths craft recovered slowly from the ravages of war.

Until the end of the 18th century, Absolutism determined societal relationships. The rule of August the Strong, Prince of Saxonia and King of Poland can serve as an example. He attracted first class artists to his court in order to realize his wide-ranging artistic plans. Among them was Johann Melchior Dinglingern who created works of immortal beauty for the Prince such as the tableau *The Court of Delhi on the Birthday of the Great Mogul Aureng Zeyb* and the splendid vessel *The Bath of Diana*. Alongside the works of these court goldsmiths in the "Green Chamber" in Dresden are works from many other talented goldsmiths of the Baroque and Renaissance periods.

Despite the feudal oppression, the development of the capitalist production system advanced in the

European states. After the English middle classes had fought for and gained extensive rights through the establishment of a constitutional monarchy, Absolutism was ended in France by revolution. In the small German states political advances could take place only slowly and the citizens revolution of 1848 failed. Esthetic developments were similarly slow to evolve, the German lower middle classes remained satisfied with the mannered romanticism of the Biedermeiers with the portrait medallion or the ring with the beloved's lock of hair.

It was not until the middle of the last century that the far reaching industrialization of Germany began, and with the unification carried out by Prussian leadership (1871), a powerful economic system developed. Some goldsmiths became factory owners themselves, but most were content to address the demands of their "Nouveau Riche" customers. Their overloaded jewelry pieces became a visible bank withdrawal; an ostentatious reflection of capital. Style elements of bygone epochs were often arbitrarily mixed with one another and it is significant that the arts and crafts schools that appeared at this time were generally associated with museums.

New industrial methods allowed for the creation of mass produced jewelry made of less costly materials. The Pforzheim industry produced doublé jewelry for the lower middle classes; from Galbonz (Jablonec), came the cheap jewelry pieces made of tombak with colored glass settings for the lower classes. Numerous progressive artists of the Art Nouveau movement tried to counter the general decline of taste by consciously incorporating the possibilities of the industrial techniques in their designs. At the same time, important one-of-a-kind pieces were also being created. For the first time since prehistory, materials of various kinds were brought together solely for design and creative reasons without regard to their material value. It's possible to trace contemporary attitudes about materials to this period of history. Handwork skills were refined to great virtuosity while at the same time it was shown that industrial methods could be used in the service of exciting jewelry design.

In our century both the world wars and their consequences, the revolutionary transformations, and the existence of two German states with different social structures have all affected the development of jewelry. After the First World War, the tradition of handwork was kept alive in the German Democratic Republic, and there emerged industrial factories for fashion and precious metal jewelry. Spreading out from the traditional centers of jewelry, the Federal Republic of Germany created a productive jewelry industry while simultaneously establishing a respected tradition of handworking skills. The rigid system of goldsmithing traditions was broken up: fusing, electroforming, adhesives, and in particular precision centrifugal casting opened up completely new creative possibilities. Parallel to this, there arose an increased desire for well designed jewelry.

Figure 0.1
Chest piece. Thin fine fold sheet with the decorative patterns pressed in with shaped stamps. Eutruscan, 8th century BC. (Staatl. Museen zu Berlin)

Figure 0.2
Medallion with a depiction of the Annunciation. Gold, with chased design in the middle; the frame is chased and pierced through with a chisel. East Roman, about 600 AD, found in Egypt. (Staatl. Museen zu Berlin)

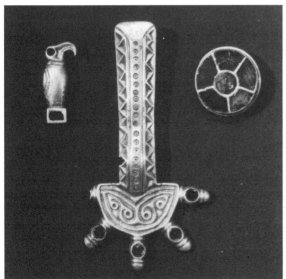

Figure 0.3
Bow and bird fibulas. Bronze, cast from wax models. Small push pin with an inlaid plates of almandine garnet. 6-7th century, found in Weimar. (Staatl. Museen zu Berlin)

Figure 0.4
Two brooches. Gold filigree work on the front side (left). Silver with engraved runic writing on the back (right). 7th century, found in Balingen. (Landesmuseum, Stuttgart)

Figure 0.6
Ring with the image of a god. Cast gold, with the image in cloisonné enamel. Romanesque, 11th century. (Nationalmuseum, Budapest)

Figure 0.5
Capsule. The lamb of God with the symbols of the evangelists. Bronze with a cast figurative image. Romanesque, beginning of the 12th century. (Domschatz Quedlinburg)

Figure 0.8
Pendant in the shape of a cross (back view). Mary as the queen of heaven. Silver, engraved. Gothic, 14th century. (Domschatz Quedlinburg)

Figure 0.7
A pendant with a fantastic creature. Bronze cast, fire gilt. Romanesque, 11th century, found on Burg Regenstein. (Harz)

Figure 0.9
Ornamental ideas for the goldsmith.
a) pendant with the allegory "Fortitudo" (bravery) and engraved or chased arabesques. Daniel Mignot, 1593.
b) Engraved, nielloed and chased arabesques, Daniell Hailler, 1604.

Figure 0.10
Pendant with a decorative chain. Saxon shield, inscribed "Sub umbra alarum tuarum" (under the shadow of your wings). Cast gold, champleve enamel. Saxon, 1611. (Staatl. Museen zu Berlin, Kunstgewerbemuseum).

Figure 0.11
Pendant depicting a siren. Gold, precious stones. Constructed using cast parts, enameled. Renaissance, 16th century. (Grünes Gewölbe, Dresden)

xix

Figure 0.12
Cover of a box. "Chinoiserie," miniature painting on enamel. Baroque, beginning of the 18th century. (Grünes Gewölbe, Dresden)

Figure 0.13
Decorative chain, cast iron. Berlin, beginning of the 19th century. (Museum für Kunsthandwerk, Dresden)

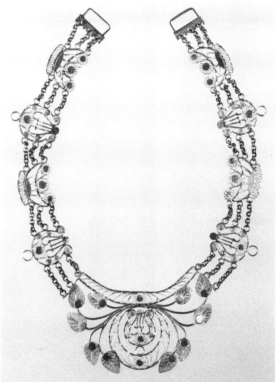

Figure 0.14
Neckpiece. Gold, filigree components connected with chains. About 1830. (Museum des Kunsthandwerks, Leipzig)

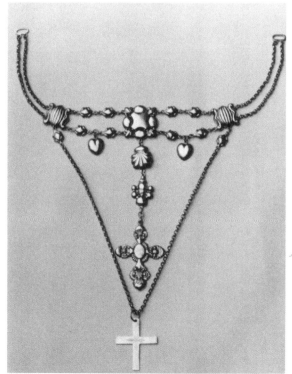

Figure 0.15
Neckpiece, folk wedding jewelry. Silver, stamped and chased components connected with chains, gold plated. Thüringia, 1849. (private collection)

Figure 0.16
Pendant. Gold, hollow
stamped, soldered closed.
About 1850. (private col-
lection)

Figure 0.17
Medallion. Gold, decora-
tive constructed design of
several colors of gold, on
a matte yellow colored
background. End of the
19th century. (private
collection)

Figure 0.18
Pendant in the shape of
a cross. Gold, fabricated
from two stamped halves.
End of the 19th century.
(private collection)

Figure 0.19
Brooch. Silver, matte flowers with leaves upon a stamped and decked
frame which is filled with pitch. Late 19th century. (private collection)

Figure 0.21
Three pendants. silver, precious gems, pearls, cast and stamped, fabri-
cated. About 1900 (Museum des Kunsthandwerks, Leipzig)

Figure 0.20
Belt buckle and theater bag. Cast silver. Art Nouveau, about 1900.
(Museum des Kunsthandwerks, Leipzig)

Figure 0.22
Pendant. Gold doublé, stamped parts, fabricated. About 1920. (private
collection)

Metals

1.1
Principal Characteristics of Metals

Of the 92 naturally occurring elements, 80 are metals. Only about a third have practical applications, as defined by these parameters: a useful metal must be present in nature in reasonable quantities and able to be removed from the earth with sufficient economy, it must be able to be formed using standard metalworking methods, and it must have characteristics such as strength or conductivity that contribute to a practical use.

Even with modern refining methods it is impossible to yield a totally pure metal: one that contains a single kind of atom. There are always some foreign atoms included, but whenever possible it is best to use alloys that have fixed degrees of purity, as established by government or industry standards. Metals are formable by chip removal or other methods. They are also opaque, reflect light when polished, and conduct heat and electricity.

Many characteristics of metals can be explained by similarities in their atomic structure. For instance, most metals have only a few electrons on the outer shell of the atomic structure, (usually only one or two) that are easily given up as valence electrons. The remaining atomic bodies form the crystal structure of the metal while the valence electrons move relatively freely between them. In chemical compounds, metals give up the valence electron when forming molecules with non-metal atoms; the non-metals turn into anions by incorporating these electrons.

Despite the similarity in principle between metals, there are considerable differences between the characteristics of density, hardness, tensile strength, melting temperature, and chemical activity.

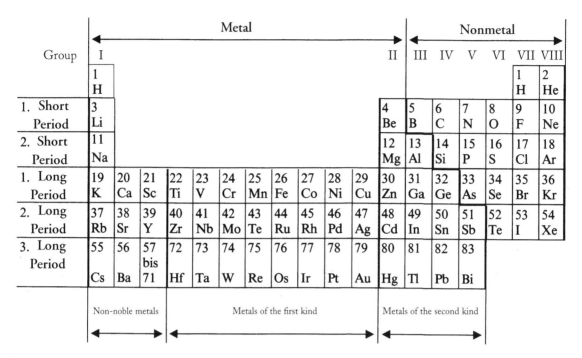

Figure 1.1
The Periodic Table of Elements.
above: entire table
below: important groups of elements.

11 Na		Basic elements of the most important bases.
19 K	20 Ca	

12 Mg	13 Al	14 Si

Aluminum alloys.

50 Sn	51 Sb
82 Pb	83 Bl

Lead alloys, soft solders.

	28 Ni	29 Cu	30 Zn
44 Ru	45 Rh	46 Pd	47 Ag	48 Cd
76 Os	77 Ir	78 Pt	79 Au	80 Hg

Noble metals and their alloy additives.

Basic elements of the most important acids.

5 B	6 C	7 N	8 O	9 F
	14 Si	15 P	16 S	17 Cl

22 Ti	23 V	24 Cr	25 Mn	26 Fe	27 Co	28 Ni

Steel

Non-ferrous alloys.

			13 Al
28 Ni	29 Cu	30 Zn	

50 Sn
82 Pb

4

1.2
Metals in the Periodic System

The connection between atomic structure and the characteristics of elements can be made clear by looking at the periodic chart (figure 1.1).

The elements are organized in Mendeleev's Periodic Table according to the sequence of their atomic charges; that is, the number of positively charged protons contained in their nucleus. As a rule, the number of protons is the same as the number of electrons that orbit the body of the atom.

Imagine the structure of the atom as a series of concentric spheres. Electrons (which are negatively charged) are distributed on individual shells or spheres, each of which can hold only a specific number of electrons. The inner shell (or first sphere) has to be filled to its capacity before electrons can be deposited on the next layer. Reading horizontally, the top tier of the chart contains hydrogen (H) with one electron and helium (He) with two. This fills up the first sphere, which is called the K shell. Another shell is indicated on the chart by moving down to the next horizontal row, starting at the left with lithium (Li) which has 3 electrons, beryllium (Be) which has 4 and so on, across the chart to neon (Ne), which has all 8 of the available spaces of the second sphere occupied.

This system works well until reaching lanthanum (La, No. 57) where things become more complicated, because electrons are deposited on the next shell before the previous one is fully occupied. The periodic chart accommodates this anomaly by skipping from 57 to 72 in the main grid and setting down elsewhere the two groups numbered 58–71 and 90–103.

As an example, let's look at the element gold (Au, No. 79). Here the K, L, M and N shells are fully occupied. The next shell, (O) is left with its 14 places unoccupied while one electron is deposited on the P shell. It is this lone electron that is given up as a valence electron when forming ions (figure 1.2).

Even this peculiarity of empty shells occurs with enough regularity to form a system, as becomes increasingly clear by examining the physical characteristics of metals. These similarities allow the ele-

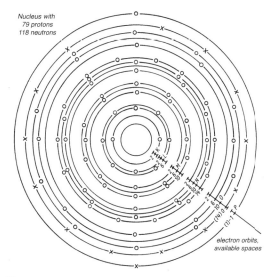

Figure 1.2
Electron disposition in the gold atom.

ments to be set one above the next in the chart to form a vertical column called a family.

The purpose of all this is to understand fundamental characteristics of metals and their relationships to each other. Some very interesting conclusions can be drawn from the periodic chart for the metals used by goldsmiths.

- It is apparent that those metals that are placed closely together usually alloy themselves with each other, while those that stand further apart are often incompatible. An example of the former is seen in copper and zinc, numbers 29 and 30, that combine easily to make brass. By contrast, vanadium (23) will not join easily with zinc (30).

- It is noteworthy that the components of the metals most familiar to goldsmiths – gold, silver and copper – stand over each other in a unified family. Neighboring them are the platinum group metals, the lightest next to silver, the densest next to gold.

- On the other side, positioned next to the precious metals, are the amalgam-forming mercury (Hg) and the additives cadmium (Cd) and zinc (Zn) that are used in making solders.

- Next to copper are the addition metals for brass and nickel silver, zinc (Zn) and nickel (Ni).
- The components of soft solders, tin (Sn) and lead (Pb), are placed above one another as related metals in the IV main group; they are so far removed from the precious metals gold (Au) and silver (Ag) that we can surmise (correctly) that there are not useful alloys.
- Even though copper (Cu) and tin (Sn) are just as widely separated, they form the bronze alloys; this apparent contradiction can be explained in that copper can absorb only a small proportion of tin. Alloys with more than 15% tin are unworkably brittle.
- The most important metals for improving steel are in the same Period (or horizontal row) as iron (Fe), and therefore have a certain relationship to each other. Molybdenum (Mo) and tungsten (W) take their place in the same family with chromium (Cr), and show certain similarities to it.
- On the left side of the Periodic Table with the "non-noble metals" are found the elements of bases, while the acid forming non-metals are on the right.

1.3
Internal Structures

1.3.1 ATOMIC AND CRYSTAL LATTICES

As many metalsmiths have seen firsthand, when the button on a casting is broken, a texture that is significantly different from the surface of the metal is revealed. While the cast piece is smooth and flat on the outside, the fracture surface is matte white, rough and grainy. This is a glimpse into the crystalline structure of which all metals are made.

Molecules of a metallic element are bound into structures called "crystals" or "grains" (figure 1.3). These are established along an ordered crystal structure, though they assemble into clusters that show an irregular outer shape. As metal cools and converts from liquid to solid, countless crystals form simultaneously. They interfere with each other, in the same way that the ripples caused by throwing a handful of pebbles into a pond soon collide with each other. In

the case of metals, the internal structure of a sample retains the accidental shape that this gives them. If we could look inside this kind of crystal, we would see a world measured in ten millionths of a millimeter, thousands of atoms ordered in regular rows, the rows stacked one on the other to form flat planes. These planes are in turn layered tightly upon each other to produce an orderly lattice structure.

Cohesion within the lattice is created by the fact that the metal atoms have given up the valence electrons of their outer shells. Technically this makes them ions, so we would properly refer to this as an ionic lattice structure. After giving up the valence electron, the positive charge of the protons predominate. The freed valence electrons of course stay in balance with the entire number of ions, but they no longer belong to a specific atom and instead move about as an "electron gas." The interaction of the negative charge of the electron and the positive charge of the proton ensures the cohesion of the entire structure. This is the principle of "metallic cohesion."

As metal solidifies from a molten state, crystals are formed independently of each other in random orientations. This means that although the geometry of the lattice is the same throughout the metal, the planes of the lattice structure in the individual crystals are positioned in completely different directions in individual crystals relative to each other.

The concept is relatively easy to picture on a two dimensional surface, but remember that this restructuring is happening "up" as well as "out." Because of the complexity of rendering this image, it is typical to simplify the crystal to a drawing such as figure 1.4, in which the unit cell is removed from its lattice. Ions are represented as spheres and the forces of cohesion are depicted as connecting lines.

The important metals for goldsmiths share a structure called the cubic face-centered lattice. The unit cell consists of a cube with three layered planes: the roof and floor surfaces each with four corner ions and one central ion. In between them lies a plane with the four central ions of the vertical wall surfaces. Gold, silver, platinum, iridium, palladium, copper, lead and gamma-iron, among others crystallize in this type of lattice structure.

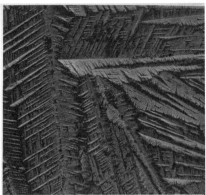

Figure 1.3
Clearly formed crystals (dendrites) upon the surface
of slowly cooled antimony.

Figure 1.5
Surface etching of grains in fine gold.

Figure 1.4
Basic unit cell.
a) cubic face-centered lattice
b) cubic body-centered lattice.

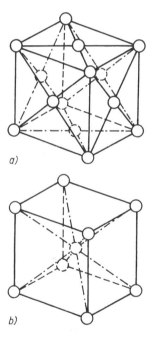

a)

b)

Even more densely packed are the ions in the cubic body-centered lattice: roof and floor surfaces of the cube each have four ions at the corners, in the lattice plane placed in between them one ion forms the center of the cube. Chromium, vanadium and alpha-iron, among others, crystallize in this type of lattice structure. There are also considerably more complicated crystal lattice systems such as the close-pack hexagonal (cadmium and zinc) and the tetragonal system, as seen in tin.

1.3.2 EXAMINATION OF THE STRUCTURE

A look at a fracture with the naked eye is enough to reveal the existence of crystals, but a meaningful investigation of them requires a microscopic examination of the crystal grain structure using a specialized microscope.

The piece being tested is sanded to a perfectly flat surface and polished to a high shine, so that no polishing scratches are visible, even with a microscope. This surface is then treated with an etchant to reveal the edges of each crystal. Even though all crystals of a pure metal have the same composition, they are attacked differently by the etchant because of their different orientations in the block of metal; if they were all ordered in the same direction they would be dissolved with equal intensity and the surface would remain smooth. The result of this process is called an etched grain surface (figure 1.5).

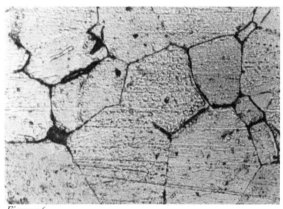

Figure 1.6
Grain boundary etching.

In grain boundary etching the etchant is made in such a way that the crystals themselves remain undamaged and only the thin easily soluble layer of grain boundary material is attacked. When a light source is beamed at an angle across this surface, minor differences in height show up as a fine-lined, spider web picture of the grain contours (figure 1.6).

The prepared test piece is placed into a metallurgical microscope, where a strong light source floods the surface and makes it possible to observe the object using a conventional eyepiece and lens. In general an enlargement of up to about 500 times is sufficient. The important information that can be derived from these images is detailed in the examples given in the following sections.

1.4
Divisions of Metals

There is no single encompassing way to group metals. Traditional groupings are based on practical requirements or measurable technical aspects such as melting point or tensile strength. Some examples of alternate groupings would include these:
- On the basis of melting point, metals might be classed as low, medium and high melting.
- On the basis of density, metals are light or dense.
- On the basis of use, metals are assembled into groups such as bearing metals, solders, semiconductor metals, spring metals and hard metals.

- For the gold and silversmith metals might be grouped according to the extent each is unaffected by the oxygen in the air, i.e. their ability to resist tarnish.
- On the basis of optical appearance the non-precious metals and their alloys can be categorized as:
  a) red and yellow metals (copper and its alloys)
  b) white metals (tin, zinc, bismuth, lead and their alloys)
  c) black metals (iron, steel, and nickel)

Because the last category is subjective, it should not be taken as completely accurate or always consistent. For instance we know today that the precious metals are not as resistant to oxidation as previously thought; the colored gold alloys are usually thought of first as precious metals, though on the basis of color they could just as accurately be placed with the colored alloys such as brass.

It is customary and correct to speak of "precious metal jewelry," but we should avoid the misleading term "real jewelry" as being complete nonsense. All metals can only be "real" metals and every piece of jewelry, regardless of the material of which it is made, can only be a "real" jewelry piece.

1.5
General Characteristics of Important Metals

GOLD

Gold has been known and valued since ancient times. It is the only elemental metal with a beautiful yellow color; it appears greenish translucent as gold leaf and can be polished to a highly reflective surface. Gold can be made so thin that a stack of 10,000 gold leaves is only 1 mm thick! The melting temperature is so high that it is only with some effort that pure gold can be melted by most jewelry torches. The ability of gold to conduct heat and electricity is lower than of silver and copper. Gold is almost completely resistant to air, water and acids, and can be dissolved only by a very strong acid called aqua regia. It is attacked by

Table 1.1
Characteristics of the important metals.

Metal	Symbol	Number	Relative Atomic Mass	Valence	Density in g/cm³	Melting Point in °C	Boiling Point in °C	Specific Heat in kJ/(kg·K)	Specific Melting Heat in kJ/kg	Heat Expansion in 10⁻⁶m/(m·K)	Heat Conductivity in W/(K·m)	Brinell Hardness in Bhn	Tensile Strength in N/mm²	Ductility in %
Gold	Au	79	196.97	1, 3	19.30	1063	2600	0.1310	67	14.30	311.5	18,5	131	40
Platinum	Pt	78	195.09	1, 2, 3, 4, 6	21.45	1774	4350	0.1331	113	8.99	73.7	56	132	41
Iridium	Ir	77	192.20	1, 2, 3, 4, 6	22.42	2454	4800	0.1294	117	6.80	59.3	179	491	6
Osmium	Os	76	190.20	2, 3, 4, 6, 8	22.48	2550	5500	0.1302	154	6.57	87.1	350	–	–
Palladium	Pd	46	106.40	2, 3, 4	12.03	1554	3387	0.2273	162	11.86	72.2	47	184	25
Rhodium	Rh	45	102.91	1, 2, 3, 4, 6	12.40	1960	4500	0.2474	217	8.3	149.9	127	410	9
Ruthenium	Ru	44	101.07	4	12.30	2450	2700	0.2315	193	9.1	105.1	220	378	5
Silver	Ag	47	107.87	1	10.53	960.5	2170	0.2332	104	19.17	418.7	26	137	60
Copper	Cu	29	63.54	1, 2, 3	8.96	1083	2350	0.3835	205	16.98	414.1	45	221	42
Mercury	Hg	80	200.59	1, 2	13.55	-38.84	357	0.1398	12	182	10.5	–	–	–
Zinc	Zn	30	65.37	2	7.13	419.5	907	0.3869	111	29.1	111.0	43	35	32
Cadmium	Cd	48	112.41	2	8.64	320.9	767	0.2315	57	30.0	92.1	16	63	55
Tin	Sn	50	118.69	2, 4	7.28	231.9	2360	0.2261	59	21.4	67.0	4	27	50
Lead	Pb	82	207.2	2, 4	11.34	327.4	1750	0.1251	24	29.1	35.1	4	13	31
Iron	Fe	26	55.85	2, 3, 6	7.86	1539	3000	0.4509	272	11.9	71.2	40	210	32
Titanium	Ti	22	47.90	2, 3, 4	4.49	1800	3262	0.5568	324	8.35	15.1	120	343	40
Aluminum	Al	13	26.98	3	2.70	660	2270	0.8959	385	23.86	230.3	17	45	40

free chlorine, potassium and sodium cyanides, bromium and some other chemicals, though this has little meaning for the goldsmith. Gold forms chemical compounds only with difficulty.

Gold is almost always alloyed with other metals to reduce the cost of a given weight, to increase tensile strength and to lower the melting point. By altering the additive ingredients, gold alloys may also be made in several colors. The standard colored gold alloys consist of gold, silver and copper. Cadmium or zinc are added to create solder; white gold is bleached by adding palladium and nickel.

PLATINUM

Platinum has been known since the middle of the 19th century but only since the beginning of the 20th century has it been used for making jewelry. It has a gray-white color similar to steel. Platinum is as soft and ductile as copper and takes a high polish. The melting point is so high that it can be melted only with an oxygen-fed flame or in an electric kiln. Like gold, platinum is essentially resistant to air, water and acids; like gold, it is only soluble in aqua regia. Platinum forms chemical compounds only with difficulty. Its ability to conduct heat and electricity is only half that of silver. Because platinum is very soft, it is typically alloyed with copper, palladium and sometimes iridium to increase hardness.

PLATINUM GROUP METALS (PLATINOIDS)

The following five metals are found together with platinum in Column VIII of the Periodic Table, and are similar in important chemical and physical characteristics. They are resistant to the effects of air, water and acid, and with the exception of palladium they are even resistant to aqua regia. Generally they are found together in nature. Palladium and rhodium were discovered in 1803, iridium and osmium in 1804; and ruthenium was first discovered in 1844.

Iridium is a silvery-white, brittle and very hard metal. Even when red hot, it can barely be deformed plastically. It may be worked in chip forming operations and it can be polished. It is rarely used in its pure form, but it is an important hardening agent in alloys; a small amount of iridium will significantly increase the hardness of platinum.

Osmium takes a special position in comparison to all the natural elements. It is very dense, and has extremely high melting and boiling temperatures. Osmium has such unusual hardness and brittleness that it cannot be worked in chip forming operations at all. Because of these unpleasant characteristics osmium is not used as a working material.

Palladium has a somewhat lighter color than platinum, takes a high polish, softens below the melting temperature and responds well to forging and welding. It is tougher than platinum but not quite as ductile or hard. Of all the platinum metals, palladium is the least noble, and therefore can be dissolved in sulfuric and nitric acids as well as aqua regia.

Because of its good workability, low melting point and relatively low price, palladium is the most commonly used of the platinum group metals. It plays an important role in electronic and dental applications. Palladium improves the characteristics of jewelers' platinum while brightening its color; palladium is also used to whiten white gold.

Rhodium is similar in color to platinum. It is normally completely resistant to attack by acids and acid mixtures but it can be dissolved in molten potassium hydrogen sulfate, $KHSO_4$, as well as in the alkaline cyanide solutions KCN and NaCN. It forges and rolls well at red heat. Because of its good optical characteristics and its high resistance to corrosion, it is used for electro-deposition (rhodium plating).

Ruthenium is so hard and brittle that it only appears as a gray white powder. When heated in air it forms black ruthenium dioxide, RuO_2, but it is resistant to other chemicals. Because of its unfavorable working characteristics, ruthenium is not used in the pure form, but is sometimes seen as an alloying ingredient for other platinum metals.

SILVER

Silver, which has been known since ancient times, has a pleasant white color and exceeds all other metals in its ability to conduct heat and electricity and in its reflectivity, polishability and shine. The thin silver oxide coating that forms in clean air has no practical significance, but sulfur in air causes the formation of a black silver sulfide layer. Silver is practically insoluble in water, but bactericidal silver ions are given off by the oxide layer. Because of this ability to kill germs, food vessels are sometimes silver plated. A more romantic manifestation is the historical trivia that Alexander the Great drank only from his silver helmet while on the march. Silver is easily dissolved in nitric acid and is attacked by the alkaline cyanides.

Because pure silver is too soft for most applications, it is almost always used in alloyed form. Tradition and centuries of experimentation have determined that the most suitable alloys contain an addition of 7.5% to 20% copper. Zinc and cadmium are added to create solders.

MERCURY

Mercury has also been known since ancient times. It is unlike any other metal in that it is fluid and gives off poisonous fumes at normal temperatures and must therefore be stored in a sealed container. Because mercury expands proportionally to temperature increases, it is used for thermometers. It is silvery-white and highly reflective; because of the high surface tension it rolls upon a solid surface as droplets. In the solid state, mercury is soft and ductile. It is easily dissolved in nitric acid and in aqua regia.

Historically mercury was known as quicksilver, quick as in "living." It forms amalgams with gold and silver and in this form it was important to the process of fire gilding. Though the process is not widely used today, in the past base metals were "quicked" with mercuric nitrate solution to reduce the electrochemical potential difference for subsequent electroplating.

COPPER

Copper, the only metal with a reddish color, was probably the first metal used by humankind. Copper can be easily polished, but gradually tarnishes in air. The first layer to form is a red oxide layer, followed by a black layer, created by the action of sulfur contained in air, and finally ending in the creation of a green patina caused by various sulfates and salts. Copper is soluble in nitric and hydrochloric acids and forms poisonous copper acetate with acetic acid. Only silver is a better conductor of heat and electricity than copper. The high melting point of copper makes it difficult to melt with a traditional natural gas flame. Copper is seldom used for jewelry but is often used for hollowware. It has great importance as an addition metal for precious metal alloys, for instance in sterling silver and karat golds.

TIN

Tin has a silver-white color and a high shine. It is very stable in air, but when heated it burns to form tin oxide, a white powder also known as "tin ash." It is attacked by acids. Tin is subject to a rather rare phenomenon called tin pest, which can cause old tin objects to disintegrate. The reason for this is still unexplained but is probably related to structural changes of the tetragonal β-tin and the cubic-tin that occurs below 180°C. Tin is very ductile, has a low tensile strength and melts at a low temperature.

The combination of tin with copper forms bronze, a metal so important it gave its name to an entire prehistoric epoch. Tin is alloyed with lead to make soft solders that are used in plumbing, electronics and several craft applications. Small amounts of tin can be absorbed in precious metal alloys, but larger tin contents cause brittleness.

LEAD

Lead, also known since ancient times, has a bluish-white color. It quickly forms dull gray insoluble coatings in air, water, sulfuric and nitric acids, but can be dissolved by hydrochloric acid. Lead is very soft and can be easily cut with a knife; its density lies significantly over the values of most other familiar metals.

Lead is contained in tin solders as an addition metal, and effects the lowering of the melting zone in niello. Small traces of lead can cause such brittleness in precious metals that they are rendered unusable. Because traces of lead stuck to precious metal alloys "eat" holes into them if heated to soldering temperatures, it is critical that even minute amounts of lead be removed from gold or silver alloys before they are heated. This is achieved first by scraping off as much as possible. If the metal is resistant to nitric acid, for example gold alloys over 18k (Au 750), the piece is boiled in a solution of 20% nitric acid. Gold alloys under 18k and silver-copper alloys such as sterling are treated in the following solution at a temperature of 60°C.

1 part 30% hydrogen peroxide (H_2O_2)
5 parts 20% acetic acid (CH_3-COOH)

ZINC

When zinc was first isolated in the 16th century, its primary use was as an addition to copper to make brass. Its bluish-white color does not last long because in air it is covered by a dull gray oxide. When heated in air, zinc forms a white powder called zinc oxide. Zinc is readily soluble in hydrochloric acid and is attacked by sodium hydroxide and liquid ammonia.

Zinc has a noticeably high coeffcient of expansion. At normal temperatures zinc is fairly brittle. Between 100°C - 150°C zinc can be plastically deformed, but at temperatures over 200°C it becomes so brittle it can be easily pulverized. Zinc is added to precious metal alloys to lower their melting points and to improve castability. In brass alloys, a greater proportion of zinc increases tensile strength and lightens the color of the metal.

CADMIUM

Cadmium, which was first discovered in 1817, has a silvery-white color but develops a dense gray oxide film in air and for this reason polish and luster do not last. It is similar in its chemical characteristics to zinc, but its combustion product, cadmium oxide, has a brown color in contrast to the white zinc oxide. Cadmium is soft and ductile.

Cadmium is used industrially as a corrosion-prevention coating for iron and steel. In colored gold alloys it improves the color of green gold. Cadmium can be used to lower the melting point of precious metal solders, but this is not recommended because of the serious health risk involved. Breathing fumes from melting cadmium can cause damage to the brain, nervous system, lungs and kidneys.

ALUMINUM

Aluminum was isolated in pure form in 1825, but it was not until the development of electric furnaces that mass production of aluminum became possible. Aluminum is silvery white, polishes well, and is air and water resistant because of an invisible, dense oxide layer that forms naturally. Aluminum dissolves easily in hydrochloric acid and sodium hydroxide. After silver and copper, it is the third most conductive metal of heat and electricity. It is sufficiently ductile to allow the creation of leaf; the foil version can be found in most kitchens. When a colored product is desired, the natural oxide layer is electrolytically thickened by anodizing to create a tough porous surface that can be dyed and sealed. This process not only opens the surface for coloring but also renders it more wear-resistant and nonconductive.

TITANIUM

Titanium, first isolated in 1825, has a flat gray color similar to steel. It takes a good polish and is resistant to air and water but has a high affinity for oxygen, hydrogen and nitrogen. The best means of dissolving it is in hydrofluoric acid, but titanium is also attacked by diluted hot hydrochloric acid; in nitric acid it covers itself with insoluble titanic acid, $TiO_2 \cdot H_2O$. In a very pure state it may be cold worked; otherwise it must be worked red hot.

Titanium is distinguished by an interesting combination of its metallic characteristics: high melting temperature and great tensile strength with relatively low density. In other words, it's tough and light, and has therefore found many applications in aircraft and rocket technology.

Titanium is used for jewelry because of the lovely effects that are produced by the clearly developed interference colors that can be achieved by exposing the metal to specific voltages of electricity. Another method, metal vapor deposition with titanium nitrite and titanium carbide, is becoming more important. In the jewelry industry this interest is spurred by the gold or black coatings and the resistance to abrasion that can be developed.

Working titanium

Because titanium behaves somewhat differently than the standard metals in the goldsmith's workshop some special attention to its working is in order here. When sawing, begin the cut with a very light stroke, and increase the pressure only when the blade has securely caught. The sawblade can be protected with a lubricating grease, but even with this precaution it will dull quickly. Titanium can be worked with standard files, but a light pressure is recommended. The file has a tendency to clog, loading itself with particles of titanium that will "smear" the workpiece. Because of this, the file must be cleaned frequently. When drilling, use sharp bits and a lubricant. You will notice that even quality bits will dull after a few holes are made. If a drill bit is broken off in the metal, it can be etched out with nitric acid. When using a rotating bur, cool the action with oil and work at a slow rotational speed (RPM). Titanium responds well to diamond and ceramic abrasive points.

Titanium can be plastically deformed, but it must be annealed often because it becomes hard quickly. When rolling, considerable pressure is required. To draw wire, anneal it first; the lubricant sticks better to the oxide layer. Instead of the usual drawing wax, oil or soap are recommended as lubricants. The metal toughens quickly so you can expect to anneal after about three passes through the drawplate. It's possible to hot forge titanium at temperatures between

650°–950°C, but the metal can also be worked cold. You will find that it is more amenable to stretching than compressing. Titanium cannot be soldered with either soft or hard solders; welding can only be done under a protective gas. SAFETY NOTE: there is a hazard of spontaneous combustion when titanium is heated at its surface, as for instance, when turning a sample on a lathe.

Because of the difficulty of welding, titanium is frequently joined with mechanical methods such as riveting or setting. Relatively low-cost spot welders (one brand is called Sparkie®) have made heat joins possible, particularly for attaching findings. It is generally impractical for the goldsmith to create a seam in the conventional sense. Titanium can be glued like any other metal if the connecting surface is large enough.

Titanium has established itself as a jewelry metal because of the beautiful colors that can be predictably achieved. When the metal is heated it shows the same colors associated with the tempering of steel, plus a few others. Unlike the fleeting effects on steel however, titanium colors are completely stable. When created by heat they are difficult to locate, but when the colors are achieved through the use of electricity, both the location and color can be precisely controlled.

The color phenomenon is caused by the development of an oxide layer, in which a certain part of the light is absorbed and only the remainder is reflected to be perceived by a viewer. As the temperature increases, the oxide layer becomes thicker and absorbs more light. There is a clear series of these colors, beginning with a bright yellow, which has a thin oxide layer (meaning that only a small amount of light is absorbed) and running through green, violet, bright blues to a dark blue. At this point, all colors except blue are being absorbed by the oxide film. If heat is continued, a second yellow color will be created at about 320° C.

Surface preparation
As mentioned, titanium is a tough, wear-resistant metal. To clean the surface in preparation for coloring, it is first sanded with various grits of abrasive paper. Standard abrasive compounds cannot be used

for polishing on the machine. The best shine seems to come with nickel oxide paste or with compounds intended for polishing steel.

To prepare the surface for color treatment, lightly etch the surface to create a matte texture. SAFETY NOTE: It is imperative to use great care when dealing with hydrofluoric acid. Because the skin will be attacked instantly upon exposure, rubber gloves and air-tight goggles are an absolute must.

METHOD I
To prepare the surface, dip the object in a 2% hydrofluoric acid solution, then rinse it well in running water. A commercially available proprietary enamel or glass etching paste will also achieve the desired matte surface and, because of its consistency, it is safer. To prevent spotting while the piece is waiting to be colored, leave it submerged in a standard pickle such as Sparex®.

METHOD 2
While wearing rubber gloves, splashproof goggles, a rubber apron, and using extremely effective ventilation, combine these ingredients:

> 20 parts concentrated nitric acid
> 20 parts concentrated hydrofluoric acid
> 20 parts lactic acid
> 40 parts distilled water

Only a plastic container may be used, and care should be taken that the environment is not too warm because hydrofluoric acid evaporates at 16°C (room temperature).

Dip the object into the solution with plastic tweezers, then immediately dip it, without rinsing, into concentrated nitric acid. To avoid grease spots, from this point on the titanium is no longer touched with the fingers.

Coloring process
A welding torch is particularly suited to achieving color effects on titanium because of its high temperature and focused flame. The torch can also be used

to melt into the metal, throwing the surface up into relief, thickening the edges and generally developing organic textures like those associated with reticulation. The opportunity for contrasting smooth and textured areas offers immediate and intriguing design possibilities. Only generalized colors and effects can be created with a torch. Because titanium is a poor conductor of heat, colors crawl slowly and it is difficult to achieve a specific uniform color on a large surface.

Because of the exactly defined relationship between the applied current and the thickness of the oxide layer that is created, titanium coloring is most precise with a process called electrolytic anodizing. In this technique, household electrical current is passed through a rectifier to reduce its voltage. An anodizing unit with a voltmeter can then be used to control the specific amounts of electrical current that are relayed to the titanium. This current will create the growth of a layer of oxidation of a specific thickness, which in turn translates to the perception of a specific color.

SAFETY NOTE: All connections and contacts outside the bath must be well insulated because a dangerously high current is used. Always wear rubber gloves and, because hydrogen gas is emitted in the process, ensure sufficient ventilation.

The piece being colored is submerged in a bath to evenly conduct the electrical current. This bath is called the electrolyte, and may be made of a wide range of liquids. A 10% solution of sodium sulfide is used commercially, but solutions as disparate as a weak liver of sulfur solution, sodium carbonate, ammonium sulfate, cyanide salt baths and Sparex® (sodium bisulfate) have also been used.

The workpiece is held with stainless steel clamps and attached to stainless steel cathodes with an insulated copper wire. Use a current density of 5 A/dm². As the current in the bath increases, thicker layers of oxide are formed. These in turn create the various color tones:

16v - yellow
22v - dark blue
27v - bright blue
58v - violet
70v - bluish-green

To create several colors on the same piece, the plate is first treated with the lowest voltage. The area on which this color is to be retained is then covered up (insulated) and the piece is taken to the next voltage. It is also possible to proceed in the reverse manner: first the highest voltage is used, then this region is covered up and all the remaining color everywhere else is removed by sandblasting. A lower voltage is applied to the metallic surface and a thinner oxide layer is formed, creating another color. To make specific areas metallically blank (white) use resists with sandblasting or cover the colored areas and etch selectively with hydrofluoric acid.

Special effects
The fact that colors are considerably more pronounced on an etched surface opens the possibility for a special effect. If the unprepared metal is covered with a resist and a pattern is scraped away then etched, the exposed metal will take the color in a vibrant hue, which will contrast with a duller color in the adjacent area. Use hydrofluoric acid to achieve this, and again, only when proper safety precautions have been followed meticulously. Another interesting effect is created by leaving the resist in place while the metal is electrolytically colored. In this way it is possible to decorate the colored surface with a gray design.

IRON
Iron, known since ancient times, has a bluish-white color, and can be polished to a reflective silvery surface. A characteristic indication of iron is its strong magnetism. Pure iron remains magnetic only temporarily, while carbon-containing iron (i.e. steel) retains magnetism permanently.

Iron rusts in moist air, and when heated forms a black layer of scale. It is more soluble in diluted acids than in concentrated solutions. Hardness and tensile strength of technically pure iron are similar to those of copper; chemically pure iron has even less strength. For these reasons it is very rare to find iron used in its pure form. Two examples are the iron cores of transformers and electromagnets.

Iron is the most widely used metallic material in the world, perhaps because of its alloying characteristics. Iron can absorb a wide variety of addition agents during the smelting process and responds well to a range of improvement agents. Such addition agents are silicon, manganese, chromium, molybdenum, vanadium, tungsten, cobalt and nickel. By far the most important additive to iron is carbon. Up to 6.67% carbon can be chemically bonded as iron carbide, Fe_3C; the carbon can also be dissolved in the structure as graphite.

Further information about the iron alloys are given later in this chapter in section 1.8.

1.6
Behavior of Various Metals in Air and Water

Gold, the most familiar precious metal, remains unchanged even when heated in air; in water it is just as passive.

Platinum and platinum group metals behave like gold in air and water. Platinum develops a bluc-violet oxide film between 400°C (752°F) and 850°C (1562°F) which dissolves upon further heating.

Silver reacts in the solid state with oxygen, forming a coating of silver oxide (Ag_2O) on the surface. Because this coating is only one molecule thick and therefore of no practical importance, we generally say that pure silver is resistant to oxygen in air. On the other hand, when there is hydrogen sulfide (H_2S) in the air, silver develops a dark coating of silver sulfide (Ag_2S). Silver is usually unaffected by water.

Mercury remains unchanged in dry air. When heated to 300°C it forms mercuric oxide (II) HgO, but it dissolves again at temperatures over 400°C. Because mercury is fluid at room temperature, it is markedly volatile and gives off highly toxic mercury vapor. It must be stored in sealed containers. Mercury is passive in water.

Copper is fairly stable in water and dry air; generally it develops a film of red copper (I) oxide Cu_2O that can be easily mistaken for the color of the metal itself. A dark deposit of copper (II) sulfide CuS is formed through the action of hydrogen sulfide in the air. Upon heating, black copper (II) oxide CuO develops which, together with the copper (I) oxide Cu_2O, forms a brittle, flaking scale on copper. In moist air, copper develops a dense coating of green patina of various copper salts. In earlier times patina was formed of

basic copper (II) carbonate $CuCO_3 \cdot Cu(OH)_2$

In our present atmosphere, we are also likely to find
basic copper (II) chloride $CuCl_2 \cdot 3 Cu(OH)_2$
basic copper (II) sulfate $CuSO_4 \cdot 3 Cu(OH)_2$

Under the influence of weathering, dirt and dust particles are also incorporated into the patina. This explains why a beautiful green patina might be found on the top of a church tower while a copper monument at the ground level develops a black-brown patina.

Tin, for all practical purposes, is not attacked by air and water. If it is burnt in a stream of air it produces a white powder, tin (IV) oxide SnO_2 (also known as tin ash) that is difficult to dissolve.

Lead develops a grayish-blue protective film of lead (I) oxide PbO quickly in air. This lead oxide also forms on the molten metal as so-called litharge (lead monoxide). In water, the metal will develop a thick coating of lead hydrogen carbonate $Pb(HCO_3)_2$ and lead sulfate $PbSO_4$.

Zinc is barely attacked by pure water. In air it forms a gray protective layer of basic zinc carbonate $2ZnCO_3 \cdot 3Zn(OH)_2$. When heated, zinc combusts to form zinc oxide (zinc ash) ZnO, a white powder that burns with a greenish light.

Metal	Acids and Their Salts							
	Nitric Acid HNO_3		Hydrochloric Acid HCl		Sulfuric Acid H_2SO_4		Aqua Regia 3 vol.-parts HCl 1 vol.-part HNO_3	
	salt	state	salt	state	salt	state	salt	state
Gold	-	-	-	-	-	-	$H[AuCl_4]$	-
Platinum	-	-	-	-	-	-	$H_2[PtCl_6]$	h
Palladium	$Pd(NO_3)_2$	h, c, v	-	-	$PdSO_4$	c, k	$H_2[PdCl_6]$	-
Silver	$AgNO_3$	-	-	-	Ag_2SO_4	h	-	-
Mercury	$Hg(NO_3)_2$	-	-	-	$HgSO_4$	h, c	$HgCl_2$	-
Copper	$Cu(NO_3)_2$	-	-	-	$CuSO_4$	h, c	-	-
Tin	H_2SnO_3	-	$SnCl_2$	-	-	-	-	-
Lead	$Pb(NO_3)_2$	v	-	-	$PbSO_4$	v	-	-
Zinc	-	-	$ZnCl_2$	v	$ZnSO_4$	v	-	-
Cadmium	$Cd(NO_3)_3$	-	$CdCl_2$	-	$CdSO_4$	-	-	-
Aluminum	$Al(NO_3)_3$	h	$AlCl_3$	-	$Al_2(SO_4)_3$	-	-	-
Iron	$Fe(NO_3)_3$	h,v	$FeCl_2$	v	$FeSO_4$	-	-	-

Table 1.2
Solubility in acid of the metals. Codes refer to solubility only in h = hot acid, c = concentrated acid, k = boiling acid, v = dilute acid.

Cadmium is similar in its behavior to zinc. It covers itself with an oxide film in air, and when heated it burns to form brown cadmium oxide, CdO.

Aluminum forms a thick protective film of aluminum oxide Al_2O_3 that renders it resistant to air and water.

Iron remains as a rule unchanged in dry air. Through the combined effects of moisture and oxygen in the air or in air-containing water (i.e. in normal environmental conditions) iron decomposes to create the well known crusty reddish brown rust whose chemical composition changes according to the conditions of formation. It is described more or less by the formula x FeO · y Fe_2O_3 · z H_2O. The porous structure of this coating promotes the continuation of the process until the entire block has decomposed into rust. When heated, iron forms a brittle black layer of iron (II, III) oxide is formed. This is iron oxide, Fe_3O_4 commonly called scale.

1.7
Behavior of Various Metals in Acid

Gold is impervious to even strong acids, but can be etched in aqua regia, a mixture of 3 parts hydrochloric acid and 1 part nitric acid. In this solution the gold is dissolved and forms tetrachlorogold (III) acid $H(AuCl_4)$.

Platinum is resistant to acids, but like gold it can be dissolved in aqua regia. In a hot mixture of acids, platinum dissolves to form hexachloroplatinic (IV) acid H_2PtCl_6.

Palladium dissolves well in aqua regia, forming hexachloropalladium (IV) acid H_2PdCl_6, which decomposes by evaporation to form palladium (II) chloride $PdCl_2$.

Mercury is easily dissolved in diluted nitric acid to form mercuric (II) nitrate $Hg(NO_3)_2$ and in hot concentrated sulfuric acid to form mercuric (II) sulfate

$HgSO_4$. It is insoluble in hydrochloric acid but is easily dissolved in aqua regia to form mercuric (II) chloride $HgCl_2$.

Silver is resistant to non-oxidizing acids such as hydrochloric and organic acids. It will dissolve in concentrated sulfuric acid to form silver sulfate Ag_2SO_4. Nitric acid is highly corrosive to silver (silver nitrate $AgNO_3$). Because of the resistance of gold to nitric acid, the two metals can be separated from each other with this "refining water."

Copper is not attacked by hydrochloric acid, but in nitric acid it is dissolved to form copper (II) nitrate $Cu(NO_3)_2$ accompanied by the formation of poisonous nitrous gases. In hot concentrated sulfuric acid, copper dissolves to form copper (II) sulfate $CuSO_4$. In acetic acid, copper forms verdigris, a mixture of copper acetates, such as $Cu(CH_3COO)_2 \cdot H_2O$ and $Cu(CH_3COO)_2 \cdot 5H_2O$.

Tin is transformed only slowly to tin (II) chloride $SnCl_2$ with hydrochloric acid; in sulfuric acid the transformation product is tin (II) sulfate $SnSO_4$. In boiling nitric acid, tin is oxidized to an insoluble white powder called stannous acid, H_2SnO_3.

Lead dissolves in diluted nitric acid to form lead nitrate, $Pb(NO_3)_2$. It is dissolved only slowly by diluted sulfuric acid, where it forms lead sulfate, $PbSO_4$. In hydrochloric acid only the lead (II) oxide PbO is attacked and transformed to lead (II) chloride, $PbCl_2$, which forms the highly toxic lead (II) acetate, $Pb(C_2H_3O_2)_2$.

Zinc dissolves easily in diluted hydrochloric acid to form zinc chloride, $ZnCl_2$. In diluted sulfuric acid it forms zinc sulfate, $ZnSO_4$.

Cadmium is easily dissolved in nitric acid to form $Cd(NO_3)_2$, but it is only slowly dissolved in sulfuric acid to form cadmium sulfate, $CdSO_4$. In hydrochloric acid it is transformed into $CdCl_2$.

Aluminum forms aluminum sulfate, $Al_2(SO_4)_3$ in sulfuric acid; in hydrochloric acid it forms aluminum chloride, $AlCl_3$ and in hot nitric acid it forms aluminum nitrate, $Al(NO_3)_3$.

Iron forms passive protective coatings in concentrated acids, but is easily soluble in diluted acids; in hydrochloric acid, iron forms iron chloride (II) $FeCl_2$. Iron in sulfuric acid will form iron (II) sulfate, $FeSO_4$ and in hot diluted nitric acid the transformation product is iron (III) nitrate, $Fe(NO_3)_3$.

1.8
Hardness of Various Metals

The science of materials testing creates quantifiable values for properties that determine the appropriateness of a metal to a specific task. The results of hardness and tensile strength testing are particularly useful because they offer comparisons between plastic deformability and the quality of the material when in use.

Hardness is generally understood as the resistance of a body to the pressure of another harder body that is pushed into it. In the Brinell DIN 50351 system, for instance, a hardened steel ball of diameter D is pressed into a test piece with a known pressure, F. The force continually climbs within 15 seconds and then is stabilized for 30 seconds at the maximum value. The result of this is an impression (or dimple) that has a measurable diameter, d (figures 1.8 and 1.9).

The size of the testing force is compared with the impression surface that is formed in the material. Note that it is not the depth that is measured but the diameter of the hemispherical depression. This yields the following formula:

$$Bhn = \frac{\text{testing force}}{\text{impression surface area}} = \frac{0.102 \cdot 2F}{\pi D (D - \sqrt{D^2 - d^2})}$$

Figure 1.8
Hardness testing machine. (Werkstoffprüfmaschinen, Leipzig)

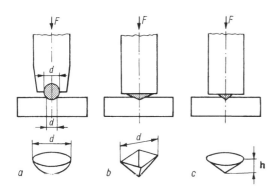

Figure 1.9
Hardness testing procedures.
a) Brinell hardness, b) Vickers hardness, c) Rockwell hardness.

F   – testing force in N *
D   – diameter of ball in mm
d   – hemispherical depression diameter in mm
Bhn – Brinell hardness number
 * Newton, a unit used to measure force.

To ensure the comparability of the measuring values, the impression size should be between .2 and .7 times the diameter of the sphere. In other words, if the material is so soft that a crater much larger than the sphere is created, the test results are no longer valid.

Precious and base metals are tested with a 5 mm ball. Two testing pressures are recommended: $F = 2450N$ for harder materials and $1225N$ for softer test pieces. (figure 1.10).

$$HV = \frac{\text{testing pressure}}{\text{surface impression}} = \frac{0.189\ F}{d^2}$$

By comparing the Brinell values, we can see how individual alloys behave when a tool intrudes into the workpiece, such as is the case in chiseling, forging, pressing and so on.

A different but similar testing procedure is called the Vickers test DIN 50133, in which a pyramid-shaped point with a tip angle of angle of 136° is used as the testing body and the testing force is compared with that from the measurement of the diagonal surface impression:

F   – testing force in N
d   – diagonal of the impression in mm
VH   – Vickers hardness unit

The usual testing force is 294 N with a load time of 10-15 seconds.

The Vickers test is especially useful for thin or unusually hard surfaces, such as electrolytic coatings.

A third method, the Rockwell hardness test, uses as a testing body a steel ball with a diameter of 1/16th of an inch, or a diamond cone with a point angle of 120°.

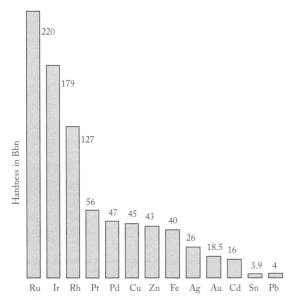

Figure 1.10
Brinell hardness of the most important metals.

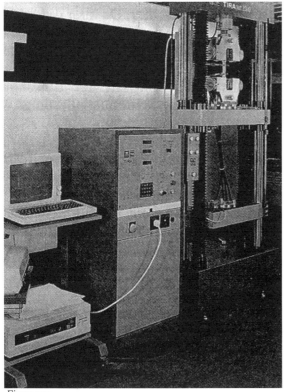

Figure 1.11
Universal testing machine TIRA test 2300 for draw, press and bending testing up to 100 kN testing load.

A measurement of the depth of penetration is taken, and from this the Rockwell hardness is directly determined: 1 RH = 2 μm.

Because it is simple and quick, this method is particularly well-suited to testing in a production situation.

1.9
Tensile Strength of Various Metals

Material to be used for making a setting must have as much ductility as possible so it can be pressed easily against a stone. Of course the hardness – the resistance to abrasion – can't be too low or the setting will wear away quickly. The material selected for a chain must have high tensile strength and considerable hardness to reduce wearing at the point where one link crosses another. At the same time, the links should be easy to bend while fabricating.

We could continue the list of examples in this manner. The results of tensile strength testing are helpful in clarifying the specific properties of materials. The values of hardness, ductility and tensile strength of the most important precious metal alloys are therefore plotted as curves and can be read from the diagrams.

If a metal has great tensile strength and a high elastic limit, it will be difficult to form the material permanently. Conversely (and positively in the case of jewelry) the piece will be difficult to bend out of shape or dent in use. If ductility is limited, the metal can only be stressed a little during rolling, drawing, forging, chasing, pressing, and bending. As a rule of thumb, a metal with possible elongation of at least 30% will lend itself to handworking. Even sawing and cutting require a plastic stress before the parts can be separated. The lower the tensile strength of a metal, the less force is required to part it. Fine gold sheet can be cut with paper scissors but sheet steel of the same thickness requires strong shears.

It's important that a ring, for instance, have sufficient tensile strength so the finished piece can't be bent or damaged when being worn. At the same time, ductility must be large enough to allow bending,

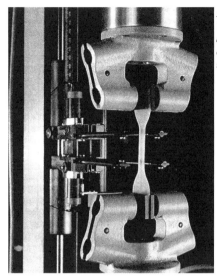

Figure 1.12
Testing rod clamped in place on ductility measuring tool.

hammering, and forming of the individual parts during making.

$$\sigma = \frac{F}{A_0}$$

σ – stress in N/mm^2 or MPa
F – testing force in N
A_0 – initial cross section in mm^2

Tensile strength tests give a clear representation of the changes that occur in a metal as it undergoes plastic deformation. The most popular machines in use currently are able to test for stretching, bending and compacting (figures 1.11 and 1.12).

$$\varepsilon = \frac{\Delta L \cdot 100}{L_0}$$

ε – ductility in %
ΔL – elongation in mm
L_0 – initial length in mm

1.9.1 CARRYING OUT THE TENSILE STRENGTH TEST
A standardized test rod is clamped in a tension machine and then stressed with a specific load, causing the rod to become longer and thinner. As the load increases, a rod narrows and forms a thin neck somewhere along its length, finally breaking in this spot (figure 1.13).

To evaluate the results, the testing force F is related to the initial cross section of the rod A_0.

The starting cross section of the rod is inserted into an equation, along with the load used. From this, the important concept of tension or stress can be derived. The ductility is ascertained from the relationship between the elongation and the original length of the rod.

Stress–ductility diagram
The elastic test procedes with increasing stress and the diagram is usually drawn up by the machine itself (figure 1.14). The load first affects the elastic elongation of the test rod; both values are in this elastic zone of the plastic deformation and are proportional in the

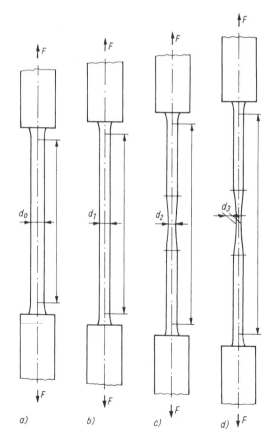

20

Figure 1.13
Ductility of a test rod.
a) original shape, b) uniform lengthening, c) the beginnings of necking-in, d) necking-in and fracture.

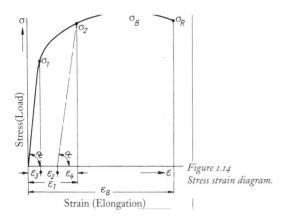

Figure 1.14
Stress strain diagram.

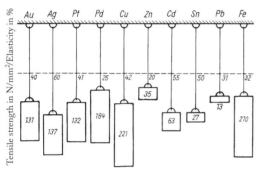

Figure 1.15
Elasticity and tensile strength of the most important metals.

sense of Hooke's law and the curve climbs in a straight line. When the load is released, the elongation goes back to the initial values on the same straight line.

This is related to the fact that individual crystals (grains) oriented in the original direction are still permanently deformed; while the entire block is only elastically deformed.

If the load values exceed σ (0.01) the actual plastic deformation of the test rod begins. The transition from the elastic to the plastic portion of the curve in practice follows smoothly, therefore the stress σ (0.02) is taken as the practical yield point, which effects a 0.2% elongation, during the plastic deformation the elongation increases faster than the load; the curve then runs flatter than in the elastic zone.

If the load is removed after plastic deformation has occurred, the plastic elongation is retained when the stress is removed.

If for example σ_2 is deloaded at a desired point; the curve does not fall vertically but instead returns to a line parallel to the straight line of the elastic deformation, so that at ε_2 the actual remaining elongation can be read off. If the elongation then is below the load ε_1 it goes back to ε_2 upon removal of the load.

If the same rod is then loaded again, the curve climbs on the straight line that it had descended on; that is from ε_2 to σ_2. This indicates that deformation of the elastic portion becomes even greater upon several repetitions.

When load is applied to a sample, the stresses are at first evenly distributed throughout the piece: the test rod is uniformly elongated. At some point, however, the rod will "neck in," becoming tapered.

$$\sigma_B = \frac{F_{max}}{A_0} \qquad\qquad \delta = \frac{L_B - L_0}{L_0} \cdot 100$$

Because this area is smallest, it is also the weakest. Additional force will be directed here, further reducing the diameter of the rod at this point and continuing to weaken it. Load is applied until the rod breaks, which it will do at the center of the narrowed section. The reading for the maximum elongation of the rod and its breaking strength σ_B is calculated at the failure load δ.

Practical evaluation
Both the measuring values σ_B and δ have great importance for the evaluation of a material.

σ_B	– tensile strength in N/mm²
F_{max}	– maximum testing force in N
A_0	– initial cross section in mm²
δ	– breaking strength in %
$L_B - L_0$	– elongation until failure in mm
L_0	– initial length in mm

Tensile strength σ_B forms the foundation of all constructive calculations of strength, but it also gives a useful picture of the ability of a material to withstand stress, shown as a comparative number; enlarged upon by the values of δ (figure 1.15). In the precious and base metals there is an approximate relationship between tensile strength and Brinell hardness.

$$\sigma_B \approx 4 \dots 5 \text{ Bhn}$$

The following influences can alter the tensile strength.
• Tensile strength usually increases with alloy formation.
• In deformed metal the tensile strength climbs at first, but then sinks sharply with the increasing degree of deformation when the limit of ductility is reached.
• Fine-grained structures offer higher tensile strength than coarse-grained ones.
• Tensile strength decreases with increasing temperature.

1.10
The Effect of Heat on Various Metals

The heat of a material is determined by the disordered individual movement of the unit cells within it. The most important measure for this internal energy is the temperature of the metal. If an amount of heat energy is added to metal, the temperature increases and the energy of the disordered movement of the atoms increases.

Increased movement causes thermal expansion in metals – as a metal heats up, it increases in size. The heat energy that is added to a metal is transferred from hotter to cooler regions because of the metal's heat conductivity, until a state of balance is achieved in the entire piece of metal.

Temperature is measured in °C; when the temperature changes the difference is expressed in K. For example, if a metal is heated from 10°C to 650°C when annealing, the difference is 640K. To determine the amount of heat required to raise the temperature of a sample a specific amount, use this formula.

$$Q = m \cdot c \cdot \Delta t$$

Q - amount of heat in kJ
m - mass in kg
c - specific heat in kJ/(kg · K)
Δt - temperature change in K

Example
What amount of heat is necessary to heat 25 grams of gold from 20°C to 1063°C?

$$Q_1 = 0.025 \text{ kg} \cdot 0.1310 \text{ kJ/(kg} \cdot \text{K)} \cdot 1043 \text{ K} = 3.42 \text{ kJ}$$

In order to liquefy the metal sample after reaching the melting temperature, (that is to dissolve the cohesion of the lattice structure), the additional energy of the melting heat is required. To continue with the previous example:

$$Q_2 = m \cdot q = 0.025 \text{ kg} \cdot 67 \text{ kJ/kg} = 1.68 \text{ kJ}$$

q - specific melting heat in kJ/kg

According to this calculation, to heat 25 grams of gold from room temperature to its melting point and then to liquefy it, it is necessary to have:

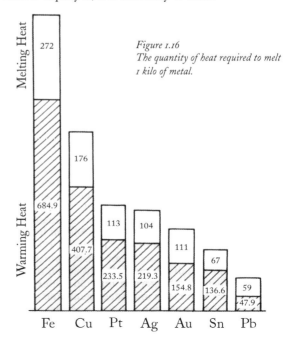

Figure 1.16
The quantity of heat required to melt 1 kilo of metal.

Q_1 = 3.42 kJ
Q_2 = 1.68 kJ
Q_{total} = 5.10 kJ

The heat required for melting is transferred to the metal from a torch or the elements of a kiln. Because it is impossible to direct all of this heat exclusively into the metal sample, a great part of the heat energy is inevitably lost. In practice this means that soldering surfaces, crucibles and the space around the operation is heated up along with the object. This means that more heat must be used to raise the temperature of the metal than is calculated in the formula.

The comparative values assembled in figure 1.16 give a good opportunity for comparison and show that significant differences can exist between metals. For example, melting copper requires about three times as much heat as is needed to melt gold, though both metals have almost the same melting temperature.

Heat expansion
All metals expand in all directions uniformly when heated, and shrink upon cooling. Because this phenomenon is particularly evident with wires and rods, measuring systems use linear expansion to describe the effect. The length-temperature coeffcient is used to express how much a rod of 1 meter lengthens if it is heated by 1K. The measured values are assembled for comparison in figure 1.17.

If we were to heat identical rods of zinc and platinum, and carefully measure their size, we would find that expansion in the zinc rod is more than three times that of the platinum rod. The remarkably low thermal expansion of platinum that this reveals can be useful information. For instance if you were to clad normal colored gold with white gold or platinum, the gold alloy will be elongated during soldering, while the thin sheet of platinum will remain almost unchanged. After both metals have been soldered together, the normal contraction of the colored gold will be prevented by the stability of the platinum, resulting in a warped object. A similar problem can

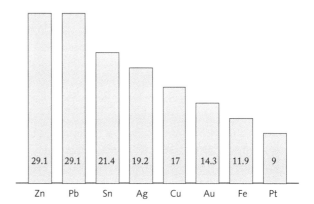

Figure 1.17
Heat expansion of the most important metals.

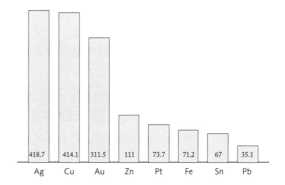

Figure 1.18
Heat conductivity of the most important metals.

occur when a silver object is bound with steel or iron binding wire. The binding wire indents the object during soldering and will distort the shape because the steel wire expands far less than the silver.

The thermal expansion of glass is minimal (α = 8.6 $\cdot$ 10^{-6} m/(m $\cdot$ K), as with platinum, so it is necessary to mix additional materials with enamel to raise its thermal expansion. By increasing the rate of expansion the enamel is better able to fuse with metals that are similarly expanded.

Heat conductivity
As shown in figure 1.18, the ability of a material to conduct heat is compared with the help of the coefficient of heat conductivity in W/(m $\cdot$ K).

Any goldsmith who has used bare hands to hold a silver wire while drawing a bead has been convinced of the high heat conductivity of silver. If equal lengths of silver and platinum wire are tested, you will find that the silver wire conducts six times as much heat as the platinum. Or to say it another way, to conduct equal amounts of heat, the silver wire would have to be 6 times as long as the platinum.

If a ring with a stone sensitive to heat has to be repaired, soldering must be so rapid that the stone can't heat up. Though such a soldering might be possible on a gold or platinum ring, it might prove impossible on an identical silver ring. So much heat will be conducted away that the joint is slow to reach soldering temperature. The ring as a whole will heat up to the point where the stone is threatened.

1.11
Reflectivity of Various Metals

All metals are understood to be opaque bodies that absorb a portion of the light that falls on their surface and reflect the rest. This is what determines their individual color, luster and brightness. The portion of the rays of various wavelengths that is reflected from various precious metals is diagrammed in figure 1.19. This chart assumes that the light falling on them is 100% of the visible spectrum.

Gold, the only colored precious metal, reflects less violet and blue than yellow and red. Hence, we see the color as a mix of yellow and red tones. Of all the metals, silver has the highest reflectivity, while the values for platinum metals lie significantly lower. Notice that the curve is similar with all the bluish-white metals.

If silver tarnishes, its reflectivity is greatly reduced because a considerable part of the light is absorbed in the silver sulfide coating. In the first thin film (which appears yellowish) the violet and blue rays are retained. As the thickness of the layer increases, the absorption is indicated by the corresponding arc and the layer appears brownish-yellow. If the coating gets even thicker, light falling on it is almost completely

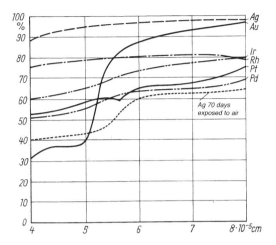

Figure 1.19
Reflectivity of the most important precious metals in the region of visible light.

absorbed and the silver object will appear black or bluish-black. This is of course the intended effect on a silver object that has been patinated with liver of sulfur.

Sometimes a silver object is plated with rhodium to protect it from tarnishing. In this case the transient but high reflectivity of silver is replaced by the somewhat lower but more stable reflectivity of rhodium.

1.12
Precious Metal Alloys

A mixture of two or more metals is called an alloy. These are usually made by melting together the component ingredients, but alloys can occur in exceptional circumstances through diffusion of solid, fluid or gaseous materials. These mixtures themselves in turn possess metallic characteristics.

Through careful selection of alloying components, characteristics of a pure metal can be significantly influenced and entirely new characteristics created. In the case of precious metals, the desire for creating new characteristics is combined with the intention of lowering their cost.

1.12.1 SOLUBILITY OF METALS

The following possibilities can occur when melting metals together.

Full insolubility

If there is no mutual solubility of the components in the fluid state, the metals form distinct boundary layers in the melt. These will lie upon each other according to their density. In this case the component metals would separate out from each other in the mold when cast. As you might guess, in this situation there is no possibility of making a usable alloy.

Complete solubility

This term describes the situation created when metals form a homogeneous melt in all desired mixture proportions, in which the initial materials can no longer be differentiated from each other. This case is by far the most common and the most important.

Limited solubility

In this instance, only a limited amount of the other metals present are absorbed in the melt of a metal; if these limits are exceeded the excess separates out in the melt as insoluble layers. The silver-nickel system can serve as an example of this. Up to 2% silver can be dissolved in nickel and in fluid silver up to 0.4% nickel can be absorbed. If the proportion of added metal is higher, both phases of the described proportions form two layers which are stacked one upon the other. In a 50% alloy for example, the melt consists of a nickel layer with 2% Ag and a silver layer with 0.4% Ni.

A prerequisite for a useful practical alloy is that a homogeneous single phase melt is formed, in which the components involved are completely dissolved. All practical alloys will fall into the category of mixtures that are completely soluble in the fluid state or those with limited solubility (such as the example of the Ag-Ni system mentioned above) when the specific alloy does not exceed the solubility limits for those metals.

1.12.2 BEHAVIOR IN THE SOLID STATE

The following structures can form during the crystallization of the homogeneous melt (figure 1.20).

Homogeneous mixed crystals

If the component metals form the same lattice structure and have about the same atomic sizes, full solubility can be retained even in the solid state. The crystal lattice is formed by the atoms of the component metals together; in all grains the alloy metals are distributed in the same proportion as in the entire alloy. The micrograph of an alloy of Au-Ag or Au-Cu is similar to that of a pure metal.

Heterogeneous mixed crystals

If the components are different in their structural composition, the components separate out during the solidification process and each lattice structure is only formed of one kind of atom. Individual grains will always consist of only one of the metals involved. This type of absolute insolubility in the solid state occurs only seldom in practice.

Limited mixed crystal formation

Although the components form a completely homogeneous melt in the fluid state, mixed crystals form during solidification in which one metal predominates. The crystal lattice of this metal incorporates a small number of the atoms of the other metals. The various kinds of grains may be easily seen on the micrograph. This type of alloy occurs fairly often and has great importance for goldsmiths. The Ag-Cu system is an example of this kind of alloy, and illustrates that characteristics of the alloy are significantly different from the pure metals.

Intermetallic compounds (metallides)

The atoms of the involved metals in the crystal lattice are incorporated in fixed proportional amounts, which are expressed with the aid of chemical symbols. Although these expressions, such as $AuCu$, Au_2Cu_3 appear to be chemical molecule formulas, they are used only to express the proportion of amounts with-

25

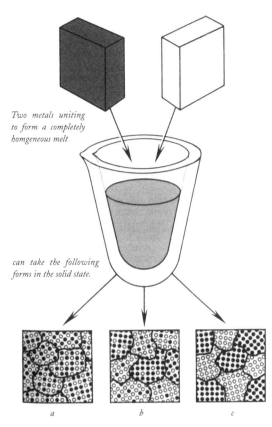

Two metals uniting to form a completely homgeneous melt

can take the following forms in the solid state.

a b c

Figure 1.20
Alloy formation from the homgeneous melt. a) homogeneous mixed crystals, b) limited crystal formation, c) heterogeneous crystal structure.

in metallic compounds. In a fixed proportion, the atoms of the lattice structure can be ordered in regular sequence so that, for example, the atoms of one metal occupy the cube's corners while the atoms of the other occupy the central positions.

Very complicated lattice structures can be formed which are significantly different from the pure metals, and whose components may be in such proportions as Cu_5Zn_8, and $Cu_{31}Sn_8$.

All metallides are hard and brittle and are barely or not at all plastically deformable.

1.12.3 BOUNDARY SYSTEM OF THE Au-Ag-Cu ALLOY
Au-Ag system

Phase diagrams provide a graphic representation of information about metals. These diagrams are extremely useful in understanding important fundamentals of metallurgy. The gold-silver (Au-Ag) diagram has a particularly simple curve, which makes it a good example with which to explain the principles of a phase diagram (figure 1.21).

In the coordinate system (or grid), temperatures are given on the vertical axis of the diagram in °C and the alloy concentrations are listed in parts per thousand on the horizontal axis. Specific transformation temperatures are empirically determined for various alloys of the system being defined, and then entered into the diagram and connected to each other by a line. Tests are made in a laboratory, and the resulting temperatures are entered into the grid.

In the case of pure metals the change of the state (passing from solid to liquid) occurs at a single temperature. With alloys there is an interval between the beginning and end of the solidification, designated as the liquidus and solidus temperatures.

The liquidus curve defines the limit of the fluid and the solidus curve that of the solid state of the alloy; between both curves is the transition state; the slushy state, in which the melt and mixed crystals (the fluid and the solid phase) exist simultaneously. In the phase diagram the metals in Zone I are molten, Zone II designates the semi-solid transition state, and in Zone III the alloy consists of solid mixed crystals.

The diagram is useful for understanding the process of solidification as well as for that of melting. The diagram illustrates:

- at what temperature a particular alloy solidifies
- the temperature necessary in order to liquefy it
- how it can be annealed
- whether it should be quenched

Following are some examples of information read from this.

1000 AU (0 AG)

In fine (pure) gold, the transition from solid to fluid occurs at 1063°C. At this temperature the metal stays in the slushy state only as long as is necessary to complete the transition from solid to fluid.

AU 900 (AG 100)

The diagram shows that this alloy of 10% silver displays an interval between the first sign of fluidness and the last bit of solid mass. The melting point has widened to a temperature interval, with a slushy transition state that lies between the solidus and liquidus values. At about 1058°C (1936°F) the first mixed crystals begin to precipitate out (the liquidus point). The mixed crystal formation is completed at 1048°C (1918°F), which is the solidus point.

AU 500 (AG 500)

In this alloy, in which both metals are mixed in equal proportions, the interval between the liquidus point of 1020°C (1868°F) and the solidus point of 1000°C 1832°F is even greater.

AU 250 (AG 750)

With increasing silver content, the difference between the liquidus and solidus points is again reduced (988...975°C) (1810-1787°F).

AU 0 (AG 1000)

At the extreme right hand margin, the diagram indicates that fine silver has a constant transformation temperature of 961°C, which is to say that it passes from a solid to a liquid without going through a slushy condition. As the phase diagram shows, all the possible liquidus points of the system lie on an arched convex curve while the solidus points form a curve that is arched toward the opposite, lower side. Both curves meet at the melting points of the original pure metals. Such a curve is typical for the formation of a homogeneous mixed crystal.

CHARACTERISTICS AND SIGNIFICANCE

Figure 1.21 graphs all the possible liquidus and solidus points between the melting points of pure gold and pure silver. The color changes with increasing silver content from the yellow of fine gold over to greenish and then to the white of silver. An especially clear green color develops between Au 600 and Au 700. The most intensive green-gold color is achieved with a 50% atomic proportion of Au and Ag, which occurs at Au 646.

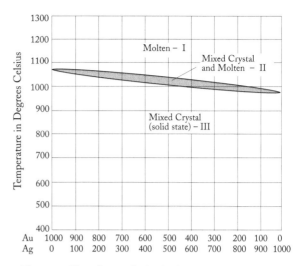

Figure 1.21 Phase diagram for the Au-Ag system.

Only those alloys whose gold content is somewhat under Au 523 can be destroyed by nitric acid. Alloys with a higher gold content are hardly attacked at all. They can be dissolved in aqua regia if the gold content is over Au 750, and the silver content is less than 25%. Alloys with a higher silver content become cloaked with an insoluble protective layer of silver chloride, AgCl, which prevents further attack. The tarnishing boundary lies at Au 377. Alloys with lower gold contents are blackened by sulfur and ammonia compounds contained in the atmosphere.

Alloys containing only gold and silver are rarely used in jewelry; there is usually some copper added. Even green gold, which contains little or no copper, contains other metals. The Au-Ag alloys are important as a boundary system of the ternary alloy Au-Ag-Cu, which will be described later.

Au-Cu system

The gold-copper system is similar to the gold-silver system just described in that it is made up of a homogeneous mix of two pure metals. The liquidus and solidus temperatures of all possible alloys lie under the melting points of the constituent metals: gold = 1063°C and copper = 1084°C. The minimum temperature or lowest melting point of 889°C is achieved at the concentration of Au 820, Cu 180. Both curves meet at this temperature, indicating that the liquidus and the solidus temperatures are the same – there is no slushy state.

Additionally the diagram reveals that in the solid state below 400°C, the intermetallic compounds of AuCu, Au_2Cu_3, and $AuCu_3$ can develop through the formation of superstructures. These can result in significant increases in hardness and tensile strength through slow cooling or by heat treating.

CHARACTERISTICS AND SIGNIFICANCE

The Au-Cu system includes the red gold alloys to which only pure copper has been added. When casting and soldering, it is important to remember the lowest temperature for the range between Au 850 and Au 700 (common jewelry alloys), which melt at about 900°C.

Note that the alloys between Au 500 and Au 750 (12k to 18k) lie in the zone of age hardening. If these alloys are to be worked after annealing or casting, age hardening must be prevented by quenching in water. If on the other hand the workpiece is to remain hard, it should be heat treated by soaking it at a low temperature after annealing.

Alloys under Au 650 are attacked by strong acids, particularly nitric acid, but alloys with higher proportions of fine gold resist attack. All alloys are soluble in aqua regia. Alloys under Au 508 have limited resistance to the atmosphere and tarnish visibly; they can be blackened with liver of sulfur. With the exception of a coining alloy of Au 900-Cu 100, gold-copper alloys are important primarily as a boundary system of the ternary (three-part) Au-Ag-Cu alloy system.

Ag-Cu system

Despite all attempts to bypass copper-bearing alloys, there are practically no better metals for jewelry and silversmithing work than those alloyed with copper such as sterling silver. Metal designation systems legally refer to the precious ingredients of an alloy, so Ag 900 means that of 1000 parts of an alloy, 900 parts are silver; the remaining 100 parts consist of the addition metal, normally copper.

The Ag-Cu alloys form a eutectic system, in which a mixture layer lies between both metals because only a limited number of the atoms of the one metal can be absorbed in the crystal lattice of other. A eutectic is a mixture of two or more materials which at a constant minimum temperature crystallize out together (Greek: eutektos: "easily meltable").

Even though silver and copper can be alloyed together in any desired proportion, the structure will always consist of only those kinds of crystal clearly visible in the metallograph:
• silver-rich α-mixed ("alpha-mixed") crystals with a maximum of 90 Cu.
• copper-rich β-mixed ("beta-mixed") crystals with a maximum of 80 Ag.

The liquidus curve runs in an almost straight line from the melting points of the pure metals (silver and copper) to the eutectic point, a mixture of 72% silver (Ag 720) and 28% copper (Cu 280) with a melting temperature of 779°C. The solidus curve also begins at the melting points of the pure metals and includes a horizontal section of the chart that touches the eutectic point, indicating that the alloy at this temperature passes immediately from solid to liquid.

When a molten alloy of silver and copper cools, formation of α-crystals begins at the liquidus temperature. When the temperature reaches 779°C the rest of the sample solidifies, blending the alpha and beta crystals. The temperature remains constant until the metal solidifies.

Note the difference between these points (figures 1.24 to 1.27):
   – eutectic (Ag 720)
   – hyper-eutectic (Ag 910-Ag 720)
   – hypo-eutectic (Ag 720-Ag 80)
   – non-eutectic (Ag 1000-Ag 910; Ag 80-Ag 0)

For a better understanding of a eutectic system, the process of cooling off will be explained using the accompanying diagrams.

AG 720

α-and β-mixed crystals precipitate simultaneously from the melt at a fixed temperature of 779°C. A fine grained structure, characteristic for the eutectic alloy, forms at this temperature. Hardness and tensile strength achieve their highest values in the Ag-Cu system in this mixture.

AG 800

In the non-eutectic alloy (temperature interval 820-779°C) the silver-rich α-mixed crystals precipitate out first. This reduces the silver content of the remaining sample. If the remaining alloy reaches a fine silver content of Ag 720 (the eutectic composition), the fine-grained eutectic α-primary crystals are surrounded by α- and β-mixed crystals.

AG 950

The alloy solidifies as a homogeneous structure of α-mixed crystals in the temperature range of 890-930°C. The copper content of these non-eutectoid alloys lies below the solubility limit of the α-mixed crystals (9% Cu). As the cooling proceeds, the crystal structure in the solid state prevents the solubility of the α-mixed crystals. The precipitation curve is cut at 700°C. As the temperature sinks further, copper from the α-mixed crystals precipitates out at the grain boundaries as alpha-mixed crystals. In practice this precipitation process is reduced by rapid cooling.

AG 500: The hypo-eutectic alloys have no practical importance for the goldsmith because of their yellowish color. Because the copper content lies over the eutectic value (temperature interval 779°C - 870°C), β-mixed crystals precipitate out first. If the fine content of the remaining sample reaches Ag 720, the copper-rich primary crystals form the eutectic structure.

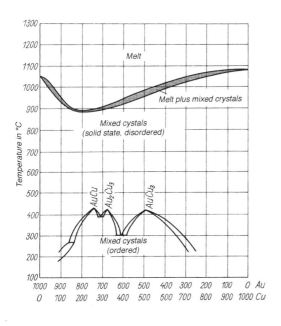

Figure 1.22
Phase diagram for the Au-Cu system.

Figure 1.23
Ag-Cu system.
a) phase diagram
b) diagram of the mechanical characteristics.

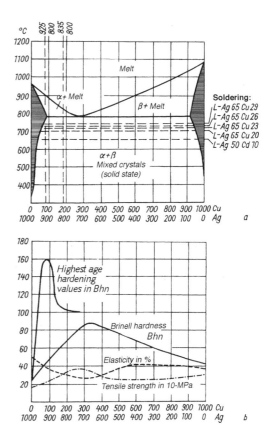

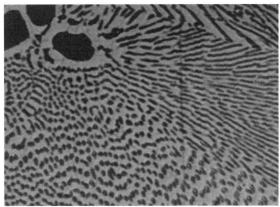

Figure 1.24
Ag 720 alloy. Eutectic structure; α-mixed crystals are bright, β-mixed crystals are dark. Magnification = 40.

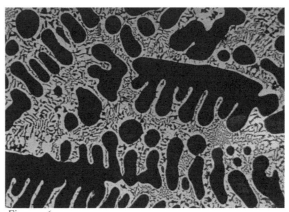

Figure 1.26
Ag 500 alloy. Hypo-eutectic structure; large β-primary crystals, surrounded by eutectic alloy. Magnification= 250.

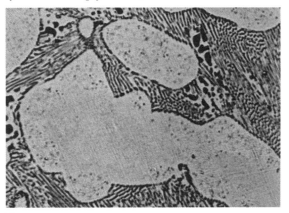

Figure 1.25
Ag 800 alloy. Hyper-eutectic structure; large α-primary crystals, surrounded by eutectic alloy. Magnification = 320.

Figure 1.27
Ag 950 alloy. Non-eutectic structure; only α-mixed crystals. Magnification = 400.

CHARACTERISTICS OF SILVER-COPPER ALLOYS

Only alloys with more than 72% silver are used in jewelry and silversmithing, so the following description will be confined to this region of the silver-copper diagram (table 1.3). As the proportion of copper increases, the natural white color of silver is tinted yellowish. At Ag 720 the resulting alloy has an unpleasant yellowish hue. If the copper content reaches 50% the alloy begins to look reddish; if the copper content climbs over two-thirds, the redness of the addition metal is very apparent.

As explained earlier, there are difficulties in melting fine silver because of a rapid increase in oxygen absorption that occurs as soon as a sample is molten.

This characteristic disappears when copper is introduced into the alloy because of the formation of copper oxides, which are resistant to high temperatures. Unfortunately as little as 1% of these oxides is enough to make the entire alloy hard and brittle, even fragile. When melting silver and silver alloys the exposure to oxygen must be minimized as far as possible.

The precipitation process in the crystal lattice causes significant increases in hardness. These are especially evident in the boundary zone between hypo- and hyper-eutectoid states, that is at Ag 920. To insure that this alloy will remain malleable after casting or annealing it must be quenched. Conversely,

Table 1.3
Silver alloys.

Designation	Composition in ¹⁰⁰⁰/₁₀₀₀			Melting Zone in °C	Density in g/cm³	Brinell Hardness in Bhn	Tensile Strength in MPa	Ductility in %
	Silver	Copper	Cadmium					
Ag 925	925	75	–	800...900	10.4	64...76	270...300	28
Ag 900	900	100	–	799...880	10.3	65...79	290...300	25
Ag 835	835	165	–	779...840	10.2	76...88	300...330	23
Ag 835 Cd	835	55	110	750...875	10.2	56...70	300...330	38
Ag 800	800	200	–	779...820	10.1	80...92	310...340	23
Ag 720	720	280	–	779...820	10.0	85...95	340...370	23

heat treating at low temperatures will increase the hardness of finished products.

Care must be used when soldering because all alloys of the eutectic zone begin to dissolve at 779°C. Note that phase diagrams always deal with an ideal picture in which the behavior of the pure metals and their alloys is subjected to laboratory-controlled slow cooling; there will likely be some divergence from this behavior as the alloys are used in practice. In the outer-eutectoid region, for instance, the solidus curve runs at lower temperatures in practice. This has the effect of causing the Ag 925 alloy to solidify like a eutectic alloy at 779°C. Sterling is therefore structurally endangered just as much as any other alloy when soldering. The "safe" solidus temperature over 800°C is not reached until the alloy achieves the proportion of Ag 950. This explains why the working temperature of silver solders cannot lie over 740°C regardless of whether the workpiece is made of Ag 500 or Ag 925. Only alloys over Ag 950 allow the use of higher melting solders.

By taking advantage of the singular characteristics of the melt interval of the Ag-Cu system, even high silver content alloys (e.g. over Ag 970)can be soldered with the eutectic Ag-Cu alloy (Ag 720).

Alloys with a high melting point are preferred for enameling because colored enamels must be fired at 750°C–800°C. Fine silver is best suited for this, but because of its malleability and low tensile strength, Ag 970 is generally used instead.

TARNISHING OF Ag-Cu ALLOYS

Silver has the best reflectivity of all metals. A polished silver surface reflects back almost all the light that falls upon it. Though most often associated with this high shine, sterling silver can also achieve a matte white surface through the application of a mild acid called a pickle. This process, known as "bringing up the silver" can be achieved on alloys as low as Ag 800.

Though silver alloys have this ability to take a shine or achieve a bright white, they nevertheless have one drawback: they tarnish.

Silver is almost completely resistant to oxygen but it combines with sulfur in the air to form silver sulfide Ag_2S. The copper in an alloy forms three distinct compounds:

copper (I) sulfide – Cu_2S (which is yellow)
copper (I) oxide – Cu_2O (which is red)
copper (II) oxide – CuO (which is black)

The amount of sulfur in the air has risen in recent decades because of the gases released by industry and automobiles, increasing the rate at which silver-copper alloys tarnish. It is safe to say that our ancestors were required to polish their silver plate less frequently than we are today!

The film of tarnish increases slowly. In the first thin sufide layer, only a portion of the light is absorbed, creating a situation in which the object appears yellowish, almost as if gold plated. With a growing layer of tarnish the surface takes on a brown cast that shifts to a dirty blue, bluish black and finally becomes a deep black. By this stage the once reflective silver has now lost its ability to bounce back the light that hits it – almost all light is absorbed by the tarnish layer. As the proportion of copper increases the speed of tarnishing also goes up. An Ag 800 alloy will tarnish much faster than sterling, Ag 925.

When sterling objects are in direct contact with skin the rate of tarnishing can increase dramatically because of sulfur often found in skin oils or cosmetics. Organic disturbances or illness can sometimes produce an increased secretion of sulfur which will be evidenced in rapid tarnishing of jewelry.

It is common for the black sulfide layer to rub off onto the skin where it is trapped in the pores, leaving a dark stain where a jewelry object has touched, for instance on a finger or wrist. This might leave a customer thinking they have been cheated with an inferior alloy. It is also possible that unusual tarnishing of silver jewelry is the result of chemicals encountered in a workplace. It is the duty of those of us in the field to explain these reactions to customers so as to retain the necessary relationship of trust.

Despite considerable efforts on the part of refiners to create a tarnish-free silver alloy, none has yet been found. The only solution for preventing tarnish, therefore, depends on excluding sulfur compounds from the surface, but so far no perfect solution has been found.

Rhodium Plating. A thin layer of rhodium applied through an electrolytic process protects the silver from tarnish but replaces its natural rich sheen with a hard, blue-white luster that resembles the chrome plating on a car; it is not nearly as attractive as the polish of sterling. While perhaps tolerable on simple jewelry (like inexpensive chains), the altered color of the shine is particularly apparent on flatware or hollowware. An additional drawback of rhodium plating is its tendency to turn blue-black when a piece needs to be repaired. The discolored surface cannot be polished so the piece must be replated.

Lacquering. A polished metal surface can be sealed from exposure to air with a transparent synthetic lacquer, preferably one that is baked on. In cases where no contact will be made with the piece – where the jewelry will not be worn nor the flatware used – this provides a reasonable alternative, the principle drawback being the sheen of the lacquer layer.

In cases where a piece is used or worn, those areas that are exposed to abrasion will soon shed their protective layer and start to tarnish. This makes a peculiar contrast to the still-coated areas, which of course remain shiny. Such a piece can be recognized instantly because of the unnatural quality of its patina. The solution is such cases is to soak the piece in a strong heated solution of baking soda to loosen the lacquer. The piece is then repolished and recoated.

Wax. In this traditional method, wax is combined with a solvent to create a thin paste that can be applied to a polished piece. It was developed in the trade to protect items from discoloring while in storage and is still useful in this context. Because of the thinness of the film, it rubs off quickly when an object is worn or used.

Periodic Cleaning. This is really the only acceptable way to keep silver alloys looking their best. In the case of objects in use, raised areas are constantly rubbed in the natural course of activity as tarnish accumulates in unreachable recesses. This has the effect of heightening the effect of whatever relief the piece contains.

In cases where a piece is not in regular use, for instance work on display in a shop or in a home, periodic cleaning will be necessary. With a mild proprietary dipping solution or a treated cloth, this is not a strenuous task, especially if it is attended to regularly.

Of particular concern is the care of historically important silver objects like those found in museums. Even with care, normal periodic cleaning removes trace amounts of the surface, which means that years of cleaning will reduce and eventually erase a pattern. The only solution would be to house the work in expensive air-tight cases that have been filled with inert gas.

1.12.4 PREFERRED ALLOYS

Over the course of time, certain alloys have been developed in which particularly good workability and optimal characteristics have been united.

Ag 970

Because of the low copper content, the characteristics are very close to fine silver. The color and tarnish resistance are the same, the alloy remains white when annealed, and at the most forms only an internal oxide zone.

Because of its high melting point, this alloy is particularly well suited for enameling. Transparent enamels especially, will yield their most brilliant hues. The alloy can be deformed up to 75% without annealing, so it is a good choice for sculptural forming and chasing work, delicate wire work and deep drawing. In use the soft alloy is easily bent out of shape and scratched, so where possible the work sequence is contrived to allow the object to retain whatever work hardening occurs during manufacture.

The hardness can be increased from 50 Bhn (Brinell hardness) to more than 100 Bhn by age hardening, though this possibility is still rarely used in the trade. This tendency must be considered when working this alloy. In order to repress it when annealing, the metal should be quenched immediately in order to retain its homogenous structure.

Ag 925

This is the English "sterling silver" or "standard silver." Due to its friendly working and wearing characteristics it is the preferred alloy for silver jewelry.

Color and tarnish resistance are similar to fine silver. The alloy is well suited to niello and low melting enamels. In order to prevent age hardening while annealing it should be quenched immediately. The alloy combines good formability while working with necessary stability in use. That is, it can be formed into objects relatively easily, but will hold its shape when finished.

The Ag 925 alloy has its greatest age hardening effect, from 60 Bhn in the annealed state, to 160 Bhn if the alloy is heated after annealing to about 300°C and allowed to cool slowly.

Ag 900

This alloy is still used in Germany and other parts of the world, but is not common in the United States. Though the proportion of silver is only slightly changed from the Ag 925 alloy, its properties are considerably altered. It no longer has a fine silver color but instead has to be achieved by repeated pickling after the work is finished. It tarnishes faster than the previously discussed alloys.

Ag 900 is equally well suited for casting, bending, soldering, forming and chasing. It is, however, too hard for fine filigree work and very deep sheet metal chasings. Ag 900 is not appropriate for enameling.

Ag 835

This alloy is frequently used for mass produced manufactured jewelry. Its main advantage is that its color and resistance to tarnishing is still almost that of Ag 900. However its mechanical forming and working is more difficult because its hardness and resistance to deformation is significantly greater. Even if there is evidence of age hardening effects, it is not as great as the change seen in the preceding alloy.

Ag 800

Solid, massive work and flatware is made from this alloy, whose principal advantage is its low cost. The most important drawback is its clearly recognizable yellowish color and its low stability in air. The silver content at the surface can be increased by "bringing up the fine silver" but not as much as with the richer alloys listed above.

Another disadvantage is that the high copper content results in the clearly detectable formation of poisonous copper salts in acidic foods. The best known examples are verdigris; copper acetate in vinegar. A comparison of the mechanical characteristics of this alloy with those of the Ag 925 alloy clearly shows how much less malleable the Ag 800 alloy is. If the alloy has to be strongly bent or stretched, regular annealing during the process is essential. Nevertheless the Ag 800 alloy casts better than alloys with a higher silver content. The liquidus temperature lies at 800°C (1472°F) so that a casting temperature of about 900°C (1650°F) is sufficient. This would be the temperature at which Ag 925 just begins to melt.

Denomination	Weight (g)	Fine Content (g)	Fine Content (in thousandths)
German Empire Gold Coins	**(1873 – 1916)**		
20 Mark	7.964	7.168	900
10 Mark	3.982	3.584	900
5 Mark	1.991	1.792	900
German Empire Silver Coins	**(1873 – 1916)**		
5 Mark	27.778	25.000	900
2 Mark	11.111	10.000	900
1 Mark	5.556	5.000	900
50 Pfennig	2.778	2.500	900
20 Pfennig	1.111	1.000	900
Silver Coins in Germany	**(1918 – 1945)**		
5 RM (large run)	25.000	12.500	500
3 RM and 3 M	15.000	7.500	500
2 RM (large run)	10.000	5.000	500
1 RM and 1 Mk	5.000	2.500	500
1 RM (small run)	13.890	12.500	900
1 RM (small run)	8.000	5.000	625
Silver Coins of the Federal Republic of Germany (since 1951)			
5 DM	11.200	7.000	625

Table 1.4
German precious metal coins since 1873.

Ag 720

This eutectic alloy is rarely used today because of its yellowish color, though it was seen in the 19th century when it was known as "12 lotiges" silver. The Ag-Cu system achieves its highest hardness and tensile strength with this eutectic alloy while is ductility is at a minimum. As this indicates, Ag 720 is difficult to form and is hard and springy in use. In some cases therefore, springs, pinstems or other strongly stressed parts might be made from it. Ag 720 is used as a soldering alloy for the hyper-eutectic alloys if enamel is to be applied.

Table 1.4 lists the metal content of various German coins.

1.12.5 THE EFFECTS OF ADDITIVES

If silver-copper alloys become ternary or multiple part alloys by further additions of metals, the charac-

teristics may be dramatically changed. Specific additions may be used to create desired conditions, as for instance when zinc or cadmium is added to create solder. It is also possible to create alloys that are for all practical purposes unusable through a random addition of ingredients.

Nickel

Nickel can be added to a Ag-Cu alloy in proportions up to 10 parts per thousand without noticeably affecting its color. The addition inhibits grain growth and consequently increases tensile strength. If the proportion of nickel goes as high as 25 parts per thousand the resulting alloy becomes hard, brittle and finally unusable because of the undissolved nickel portion.

Iron

Iron is not miscible with silver either in the fluid or the solid state. Small iron and steel particles therefore remain as brittle foreign bodies in the alloy. This explains the importance of thoroughly removing all traces of steel from filings before attempting to remelt silver alloys. If iron or steel particles are included in a melt they will show up as "comma silver" with characteristic comet trails left from polishing over a hard inclusion.

Lead

Alloys containing lead are brittle when warm (called "hot short") because the eutectic alloy formed when lead and silver combine (melting point: 304°C 580°F) is deposited naturally at the grain boundaries. This effect is so severe that even traces of lead can render a sample unusable. It is critical that any silver alloy that has come in contact with lead be scrubbed completely before being heated.

Tin

Small additions of tin reduce the melting point of the whole alloy. Fine silver can absorb up to 190 parts per thousand of tin and though this develops a heterogeneous structure, it is less susceptible to tarnishing than the Ag-Cu alloy. The addition of tin also creates a metal that is softer and more ductile. If the content of tin exceeds 90 parts per thousand, a brittle compound, Cu_4Sn, is formed. Because tin oxidizes readily, when this alloy is melted there is a tendency to form tin oxide, SnO_2 which is deposited at the grain boundaries and makes the alloy very brittle.

Aluminum

Up to 50 parts per thousand aluminum (4-5%) are soluble in the solid alloy. The color becomes even whiter than usual while hardness and rate of oxidation are increased. As with tin, the formation of silver alloys (in this case Ag_3Al) results in embrittlement. In addition, during melting and annealing the oxygen compound Al_2O_3 forms very easily and is deposited at the grain boundaries where it causes the alloy to break into pieces.

Zinc and Cadmium

Because both of these metals evaporate at low temperatures they are difficult to add to a silver-copper alloy. Both metals are used in the manufacture of alloys, though cadmium has recently been almost completely discontinued because of its health risks. Because these alloys are so important to metalsmiths they will be dealt with in some detail here.

Ag-Zn

Though as much as 200 parts per thousand of zinc can be absorbed by silver in its solid state, in practice the proportion of 140 parts per thousand should not be exceeded. These alloys are resistant to tarnish, polish easily, and are very ductile.

Ag-Cd

These alloys are also resistant to the atmosphere and may be easily worked. The solubility limit is quite high, falling at 300 parts per thousand. As mentioned previously, the positive characteristics of alloys containing cadmium are not sufficient to warrant its use. Mention of cadmium here is for historical and scientific accuracy but its use is not condoned.

Ag-Zn-Cd

The melting condition of this ternary system would make it useful as a solder, but its tensile strength is so low its practical applications would be very limited.

Ag-Cu-Zn

The addition of as little as a few parts per thousand added to a silver-copper alloy just before casting significantly increases the castability of the alloy. Because copper has the ability to absorb as much as 350 parts per thousand zinc, it is clear that this addition metal offers useful opportunities for solders. Even with this however, caution is advised – if the solubility limit is exceeded, the excess zinc alloys with the work material, eating holes into the metal.

For practical purposes, solder is made by first creating the eutectic alloy of copper and silver then adding zinc in proportions needed to achieve specific melting temperatures, generally at least 50K below the solidus

35

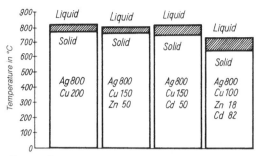

Figure 1.28
Reduction of the melt interval of Ag 800 by the addition of Zn and Cd.

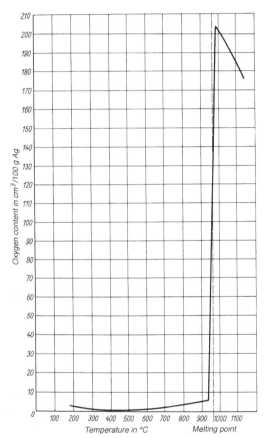

Figure 1.29
The relationship between temperature and oxygen solubility in fine silver (the change at the melting temperature is noteworthy).

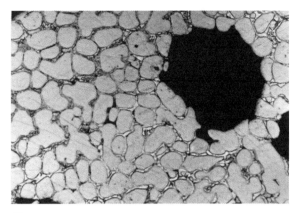

Figure 1.30
Ag 800 alloy.
Large gas bubbles in the structure. Magnification = 200

temperature of the work metal. The alloy is made more pliable and tarnish resistant through the addition of zinc.

Ag–Cu–Zn–Cd
Though no longer in use, this four-part solder was particularly useful where a combination of eutectic Ag-Cu was needed in conjunction with a low temperature. The radically low melting point of this alloy is made possible because the cadmium and zinc form a eutectic of their own.

Silicon
Silicon can be reduced from the quartz of the crucible material. Up to 15 parts per thousand can be bound as Ag-Si mixed crystals. As "hard silver" the alloy is even used for technical purposes. Larger proportions of silicon remain undissolved at the grain boundaries and the alloy becomes so brittle that it cannot be used. The grain enlargement can progress so far that heat cracking can occur.

Sulfur
Sulfur forms hard compounds such as Ag_2S and Cu_2S, which can be deposited between the grains as well as within them. The presence of sulfur can be traced to its inclusion in the raw materials being alloyed, sulfur-containing fuel and combustion gases, and residues (through sulfuric acid) from pickle or electrolytic copper.

Figure 1.31
Ag 800 alloy. "Bubbled silver."
a) bubble within the sheet after rolling and annealing
b) bubbles broken by further stressing
Magnification = 2

Phosphorous
Even small traces are enough to form the brittle intermetallic compounds Ag_2P or Cu_3P that deposit themselves as eutectic inclusions at the grain boundaries, These alloys become brittle, tarnish especially quickly and may be plated only with difficulty. Phosphorous is easily given up during the reducing melting of phosphor copper, if it is not completely used up for deoxidizing, or removing the copper oxide.

Oxygen
Silver can dissolve twenty times its own volume of oxygen above the melting point. That is to say that one liter of silver (10,500 grams) can absorb up to 20 liters of oxygen. A few degrees below the solidification point, however, the solubility of the volume of silver sinks by one half, and the oxygen is given up explosively – the metal "spits," figure 1.29. The oxygen, which can no longer leave the frozen cast pieces

is retained in the outer areas as gas bubbles. The hollow spaces reduce the tensile strength and limit the ductility of the metal. In addition, the metal can easily crack when rolled and drawn (figure 1.30). If the piece of metal is annealed during working, the gas expands and bubbles up to the softened surface to create "bubbled silver" (figure 1.31).

If the silver is alloyed with copper the absorbed oxygen is given up to the copper. This forms the copper (I) oxide compound which is also stable in the solid state. The compound can be seen especially clearly with low silver contents. The inclusions are finely divided and deposited between the grains and thereby reduce the formabiliy of the metal (figure 1.32). Cupric oxide, Cu_2O can appear in several different forms.

The CuO_2 parts are balled up together to form hard foreign bodies. During polishing of the surface they are not abraded and therefore project above the surface. Those that break out during working leave small holes behind. Because the metal surrounding the foreign body cannot be reached by the polishing tool, microscopic arcs are created. These characteristic blemishes give this fault its name: *"Comma"* Silver (figure 1.33).

Fire Scale refers to deep oxide stains that result from the oxidation of silver that occurs during annealing.

Sulfur is often contained in the gases used by a metalsmith's torches. It is absorbed by silver in the same way that oxygen is when the metal is melted. Like oxygen the sulfur gases can come out of solution during solidification and form "bubble silver." In addition, the compounds Cu_2S and Ag_2S can develop. These further weaken the cohesion of the cast piece when they are deposited along the grain boundaries.

1.12.6 THE TERNARY Au-Ag-Cu SYSTEM
While the melt diagram of the binary alloy can be depicted on a flat surface, the processes of the ternary system have to be understood as a three dimensional diagram shaped as a three-sided prism. The corners represent the pure metals, while the sides are made up

of binary (two-part) systems: Au-Ag, Au-Cu, Ag-Cu (figure 1.34).

The transformation curves, i.e. the temperatures of liquidus and solidus of each of the various possible combinations of the binary system, become transformation surfaces in the three dimensional diagram. It is clear that the characteristics of the binary boundary systems have effects on the ternary system so that the transformation surfaces connect directly to these curves. If, for example, some small percentage of gold is thrown into a silver-copper melt, the eutectic behavior of the silver-copper alloy remains the deciding factor for the three-part alloy. Only if the gold content is significantly larger does it alter the results as described by the diagram.

The liquidus curve of the boundary system becomes the liquidus plane, upon which are found all the liquidus points of the ternary alloys. Above this surface lies the fluid state, below this surface is the two-phase ("pasty" or "slushy") state. The melt at this moment is a balance of fluid and semi-solid material.

The shape of the surface may be compared with a landscape or cartographic map. From its deepest position (the eutectic point of the Ag-Cu system at 779°C) the alloy climbs gently upward, forming a "eutectic valley." This valley forms a flatish "floor" as it runs to the eutectic of the Au-Cu alloys, which are seen at 889°C.

From there the liquidus temperature climbs abruptly to the Ag-Au system, while a "flatish slope" draws closer to the copper corner.

The solidus surface is determined by the eutectic precipitation zone because this characteristic from the Ag-Cu system impacts the ternary system. This forms a eutectic precipitation structure of alpha- and beta-mixed crystals that retain only a limited proportion of gold. In the outer eutectic zone, homogeneous mixed crystals are formed as with the Ag-Cu system. The mixed crystals will contain gold atoms.

The eutectic zone stretches from the eutectic composition line of the Ag-Cu system with an almost hemispherical curve up to a gold content of Au 410 in the direction of the gold corner. A eutectic zone now develops from the eutectic composition line; that is, a

linear transformation curve of the binary edge diagram which is defined and enclosed by a concave and a convex curving surface. A cross section through this eutectic zone can be clearly recognized in the diagram for Au 333 (figure 1.44a). The explanation for this shape is that the eutectic structure does not form at a constant temperature as in the Ag-Cu system but rather develops during a temperature interval. Finally it should be observed that the eutectic zone of the ternary system climbs slightly from the Ag-Cu eutectic (779°C to point "K" 800°C).

Just as in the binary Ag-Cu system, the solidus curve climbs steeply from the eutectic to the melting points of the initial metals, the solidus curve also runs steeply from the eutectic area of the ternary system to both the Au-Ag and Au-Cu solidus curves. It climbs more slowly only toward the gold corner.

The precipitation zone in the solid state in the Ag-Cu system increases with sinking temperature and the precipitation curves run accordingly. An alloy formed with a homogeneous structure which, for example, consists of a alpha-mixed crystals upon ongoing cooling after the precipitation zone had been reached would no longer bond with all the copper particles involved with the mixed crystals so that they precipitate out as beta-mixed crystals, the homogeneous mixed crystal structure then becomes a two phase system.

There are also similar precipitation characteristics in the ternary system. The eutectic plane or surface spreads out below in the solid state to form a precipitation zone, which reaches deep into the ternary system as the temperature sinks. The precipitation zone widens out like a basement under the eutectic surface.

Concentrations, phase diagrams and vertical cross sections.

It is easy to see that such a complex three dimensional diagram is too complex for everyday use. As with any symbolic drawing, it is necessary to understand some conventions to make sense of a triangular phase diagram. The further you are from a corner, the less pure is the alloy. It follows, of course, that as you trace a line closer to a corner, the proportion of that alloy is

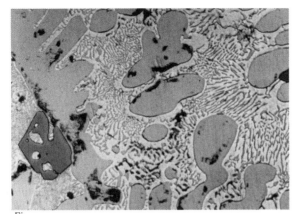

Figure 1.32
Ag 500 alloy. Primary and eutectic copper (I) oxide inclusions.
Magnification = 320

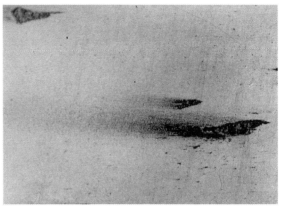

Figure 1.33
Ag 800 alloy. "Comma silver" with hard inclusions at the surface.
Magnification = 4

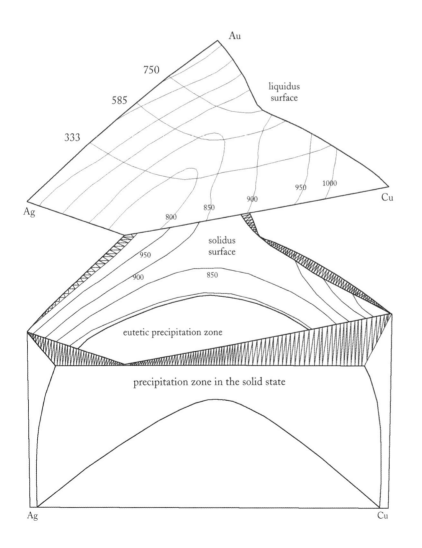

Figure 1.34
Ternary Au-Ag-Cu system depicted three dimensionally. The liquidus surface is raised so that the solidus surface with the eutectic precipitation zone is visible.

increased. The most important and decisive parts of the three dimensional diagram, namely the liquidus and solidus surfaces are commonly presented as concentration phase diagrams in which the relief of the three dimensional surface is depicted as a kind of topographic map. All points of the same temperature are connected to each other to create lines of the same temperature, called isotherms.

Figure 1.35 depicts how the liquidus surface is transferred. The isotherms are handled like geographic contour lines that connect points of the same height, to graphically convey the relief of the landscape upon the map. The closer together the contour lines lie, the steeper the mountainside. In the same way, isotherms express the relief of the temperature "surface" (figures 1.36 and 1.37).

Examples

The diagram has been sliced through on a vertical cross section to reveal the way the diagram displays the liquidus points as a surface. Three intersecting lines parallel to the side opposite from the gold corner represent the three most important jewelry alloys.

The figure shows that the gold content on the first cross section surface is Au 333 throughout the alloy, which is what allows it to be called Au 333 or 8k. The proportion of the addition metals (Ag and Cu in this case) is variable.

Two of the immediate advantages of the three-dimensional diagram are:

- It shows the behavior of all alloys with a certain thermal transformation characteristic from the concentrations phase diagram.
- The behavior of the alloys in all thermal transformations are depicted on the vertical section at a specific steady gold content.

Thermal characteristics

Because of the influence of the Ag-Cu system, the ternary system also forms α- and β-mixed crystals because of eutectic precipitation. Because the alloy has a gold content, there will also be a-mixed crystals that contain gold, silver and a little copper and β-

mixed crystals consisting of gold, copper and a little silver.

The composition of the mixed crystals changes with increasing gold content as can be seen on the overview (figure 1.39). Because gold may be mixed in any proportion with both addition metals, the quantity of dissolved copper in the α-mixed crystals and the silver dissolved in the β-mixed crystals diminishes with increasing gold content. Both types of crystal become increasingly similar in their composition with growing gold content, until finally with Au 420 both kinds of crystals have the same composition. The result of all this is that if the gold content lies over Au 420 only homogeneous mixed crystal structure will form from the melt.

The pure eutectic alloys with their minimum melting temperature and the typical fine-grained structure of α- and β-mixed crystals are depicted on the line between the eutectic point of the Ag-Cu system and point "K."

On both sides of this line over (hyper)-eutectic and under (hypo)-eutectic alloys form in the precipitation zone with the large primary crystals formed first and the fine-grained structure formed at the eutectic temperature. Alloys with the single phase, outer-eutectic mixed crystal structure are found outside of the eutectic precipitation zone on both sides.

The character of the Au 420 alloy outside the precipitation zone is always identical: homogeneous mixed crystal structures of only one kind of crystal. Because the precipitation zone enlarges in all directions in the solid state at temperatures below the eutectic zone, most of the outer-eutectic alloys are affected by precipitation during cooling. Below this boundary temperature, copper is precipitated out of the α-mixed crystals and silver separates out of the β-mixed crystals.

The ideal mixture can only be achieved at very high temperatures, or, conversely, over a long time at lower temperature. In practice, castings cool off so quickly that the diffusion is more or less prevented. At room temperature, the α-mixed crystals have more copper and the β-mixed crystals more silver than would be expected from looking at the phase diagram.

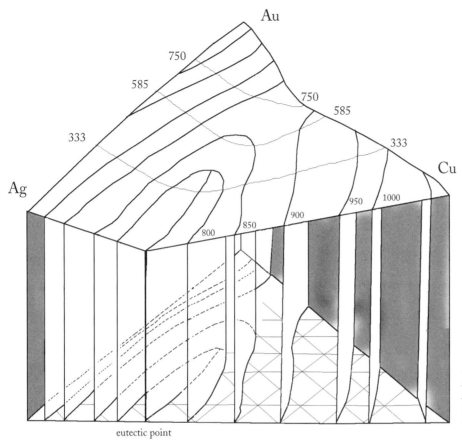

Figure 1.35
Au–Ag–Cu ternary system.
A projection of the three dimensional liquidus surface upon the two dimensional phase diagram

eutectic point

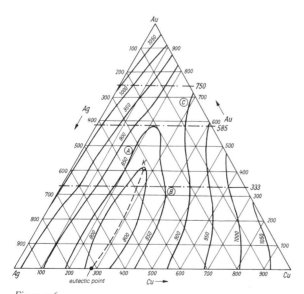

Figure 1.36
The Au-Ag-Cu ternary system.
Phase diagram of the liquidus surface.

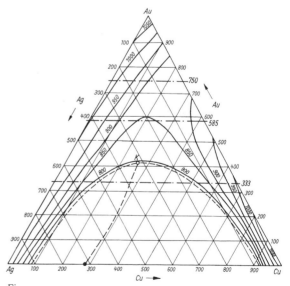

Figure 1.37
Au-Ag-Cu ternary ssystem.
Phase diagram of the solidus surface with the eutectic precipitation zone.

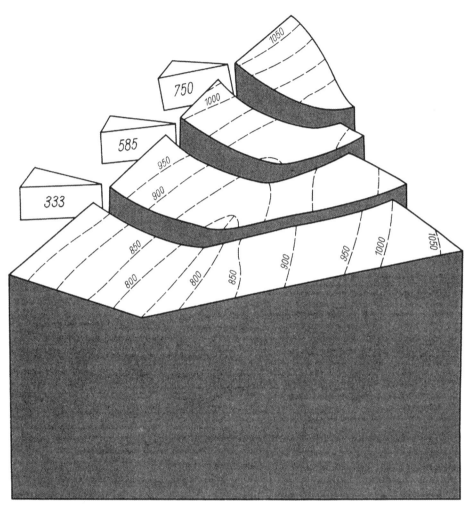

Figure 1.38
Au-Ag-Cu Ternary System.
Divisions of the vertical cross section at Au 333, Au 585, Au 750.

Mechanical characteristics

Because there is only one measurement of mechanical characteristics for each specific alloy, they can be depicted in the phase diagram with only one surface. The figure for Brinell hardness (figure 1.40) can serve as an example. The hardness values pile up to a mountain, whose peak lies near the medium colors at the Au 500 alloy. At the silver corner the mountain has its deepest foothills. Where it climbs slightly from the copper corner, there stretches to it from the Au-Ag system a "cliff" that reaches up to the peak. In the boundary systems the highest values are achieved with the eutectic Ag-Cu alloy (Ag 720) and the 750 red gold. By connecting the points of equal hardness we can create contour lines that can be transferred onto a phase diagram. From this the values can be read off in the same way as the shape of a mountain may be envisaged on a topographic map.

A comparison with the diagram for tensile strength (figure 1.41) reveals a very similar shape to the hardness diagram. Alloys of greater hardness have an accompanying high tensile strength or toughness.

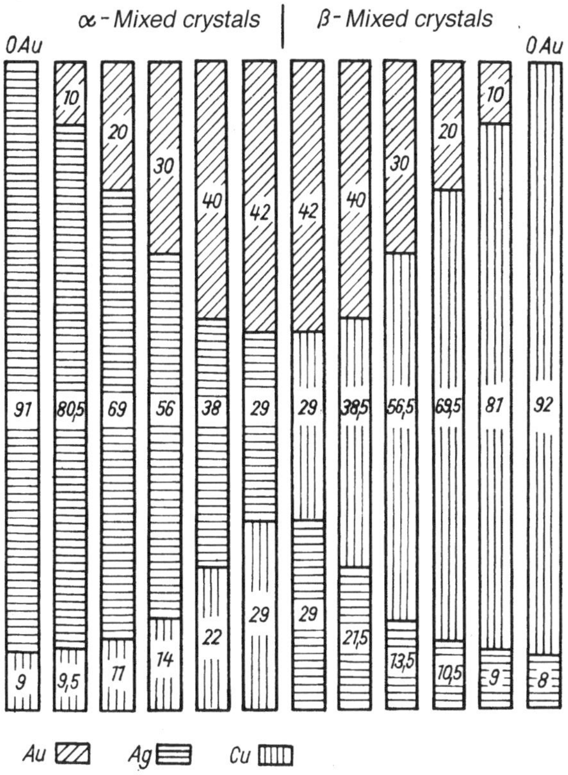

Figure 1.39
The approach of the concentration of α and β-mixed crystals with an increasing gold content.

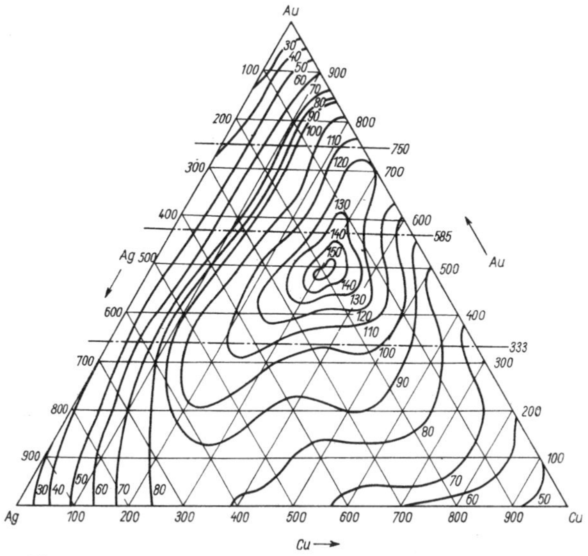

Figure 1.40
Au-Ag-Cu ternary system.
Phase diagram of Brinell hardness in Bhn.

When we examine ductility (figure 1.42) we find the relationships are exactly opposite, which makes sense because as a general rule alloys of great hardness usually show a low ductility. View this figure not as a mountain but as a crater. Ductility reaches its minimum value in the Au 400 alloy of medium color.

Chemical characteristics

The chemical resistance in the ternary system changes abruptly depending upon the proportion of gold atoms in the entire number of atoms, namely at 2/8ths, 3/8ths, 4/8ths gold atoms (figure 1.43) When calculating the units of mass one must remember that silver and copper have different relative atomic masses so that the limits of the resistance zones are different in pale and red alloys.

- Tarnishable (0/8...2/8, 0...25% gold atoms): The alloys of this zone are not only dissolved by acids but are even tarnished by the sulfur dioxide in the air and can be blackened in liver of sulfur.
- Soluble (3/8...2/8, 37.5...25% gold atoms): The alloy constituents are dissolved by strong acids leaving the gold as an insoluble residue behind.
- Attackable (4/8...3/8, 50...37.5% gold atoms): Strong acids attack the alloy constituents until the surface is enriched and becomes resistant to acids.
- Resistant (4/8...8/8, 50...100% gold atoms): These alloys are even resistant to strong mineral acids; they can only be dissolved in aqua regia.

Tarnishing in Au-Ag-Cu alloys

Fine gold remains unchanged by atmospheric influences so if a gold alloy tarnishes in the course of time it is because of the addition metals in the alloy. The limit of resistance of the ternary system lies at 25% gold atoms. This means that to create a gold alloy that will resist tarnishing, there should be at least 1 gold atom for every 3 atoms of alloy metals. The following boundary values for the remaining fine content figures are derived from an examination of the various atomic masses:

In practice this means that all alloys with less than 33% gold are in danger or tarnishing. Red gold alloys

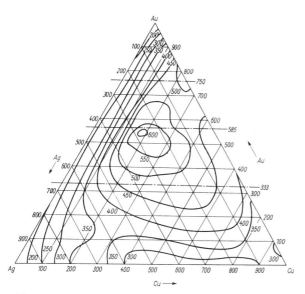

Figure 1.41
Au-Ag-Cu Ternary System.
Phase diagram of tensile strength (malleability) in MPa.

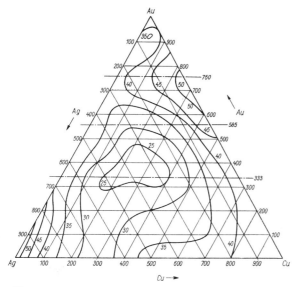

Figure 1.42
Au-Ag-Cu Ternary System.
Phase diagram of ductility in percentage.

44

tend to tarnish more than the paler ones, and can in fact still tarnish even if the atomic mass proportion of gold to copper is equal. When tarnishing does occur, the color change is not as blatant as with silver alloys – pale gold alloys become a dull greenish yellow, and red gold alloys become a dirty brown.

As with silver there is no practical way to prevent tarnishing on gold alloys. Of course it is possible to plate a layer of fine gold onto a surface, but this alters the color of the piece and is of course subject to wearing away. Lacquer coverings on gold have the same disadvantages as with the silver alloys mentioned above. And as was described with the silver alloys, it's possible to develop a discoloration of the skin with gold alloys. As mentioned with silver, this is no fault of the alloy but simply a result of unusual body chemistry or cosmetics. In some cases, gold jewelry is tarnished by contact with aggressive chemicals encountered on a job, for example by chemists, laboratory workers, photographers and hair dressers. If rings of different alloys are worn next to each other, an electrolytic salt can be formed by sweat that will facilitate the deposit of copper particles on the higher karat alloy. If the gold content is at or above Au 585 the alloy is for all practical purposes resistant to the air. As was the case with silver alloys, preferred gold alloys have been developed over time. Today the legally accepted designation in Europe is indicated in parts per thousand, while the United States will accept either this decimal or the conventional karat notation.

1.12.7 THE AU 333 ALLOYS
Melt Diagram

The melt diagram is given as a vertical cross section of the ternary alloy system (figure 1.44). To the left are the silver-rich pale gold alloys. Copper content increases to the right side of the diagram until a red gold with a pure copper content is reached at 667 thousandths parts pure copper.

	Au	Ag	Cu
Pale gold	377	623	–
Medium colors	440	280	280
Red gold	508	–	492

At 285 thousandths parts copper the alloy solidifies as a eutectic. Pale gold alloys between 120 and 285 parts per thousand copper form α-mixed crystals in the melt first. The rest of the melt solidifies during the transition though the eutectic zone as a simultaneous precipitation of α- and β-mixed crystals (figures 1.45 and 1.46).

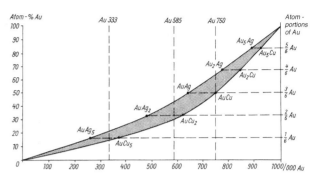

Figure 1.43 c)
Proportion of gold as a relationship of mass proportion and atomic quantity.

Characteristics

The reference of parts per thousand refers to mass, so even in an alloy made up of one third gold and two-thirds addition metals, the non-gold ingredients occupy more space because of their lower density. In the case of the Au 333 alloy for instance, every 2 gold atoms are surrounded by 9 silver and copper atoms!

This helps to explain the strongly non-precious character of the Au 333 alloy. When well polished, the color is significantly different from that of gold. The red alloys, that is the high copper content alloys in particular, are fairly unstable and tarnish easily in the air. All Au 333 alloys are easily soluble in nitric acid.

When making alloy choices, goldsmiths should remember to consider the characteristics of the metal in addition to the desired color. Sometimes the metal is blamed for deficiencies when in fact the problem was inherent in the alloy and could have been predicted. The overview of alloys shown in table 1.5 illustrate that the commonly preferred medium colored alloys are difficult to work. This is indicated by a high level of hardness and tensile strength and low ductility. These alloys have a low degree of deformability and require more frequent annealing than the pale or red alloys.

Through additions of nickel and zinc the mechanical characteristics can be improved so much that the alloy's ductility is doubled. However these nickel and zinc additions cause the solderability and castability to become even worse than they already are, which is

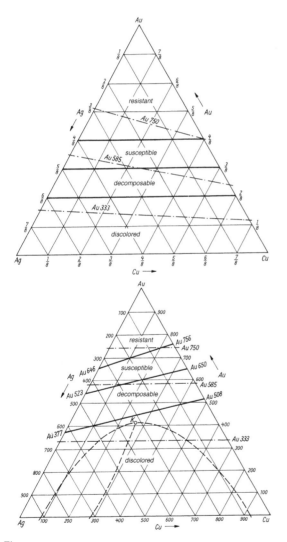

Figure 1.43
Au-Ag-Cu ternary system.
Phase diagram of chemical characteristics.
a) mixture relationships according to the quantities of atoms (%...%)
b) mixture relationships by mass proportion in thousandths parts.

45

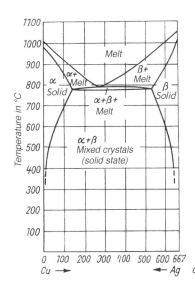

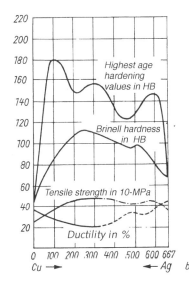

Figure 1.44
Au-Ag-Cu Ternary System.
Vertical cross section of Au 333
a) phase diagram
b) mechanical characteristics.

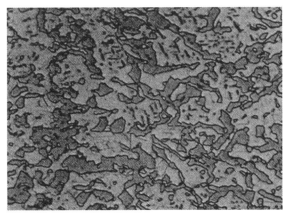

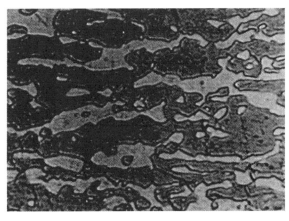

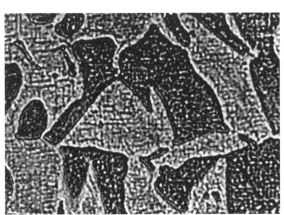

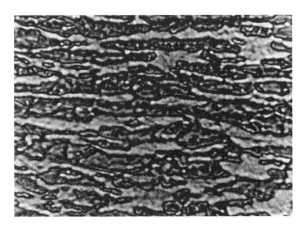

Figure 1.45
Au 333 alloy. Eutectic structure.
a) recrystalization structure after deformation and annealing. Magnification = 630
b) precipitation of the a- and β- mixed crystals by subsequent tempering. Magnification = 1600

poor anyway in the case of the Au 333 alloy. For all these reasons it is vital to know exactly what an alloy is to be used for in order to make the correct selection.

The Au 333 alloys need special care when soldering. As is true of all eutectic alloys, the lattice structure begins to fall apart as the melting point is reached, in this case just under 800°C. This causes the disturbing "orange peel surface" after which only a slight increase in temperature is needed for the piece to melt altogether. The melt diagram also reveals that not every alloy can be soldered with every solder. The solders described as "hard" have a working temperature of 790°C and are appropriate only for the hyper-eutectic alloys. Hypoeutectic alloys (those with less pure metal than the eutectic proportion) will require the "easy" solder, and even then care is recommended.

The Au 333 alloy is subject to age hardening if it is not quenched immediately after annealing. In alloys close to the eutectic, such as pale golds with approximately 100 parts per thousand copper, the Brinell hardness can be doubled by age hardening.

The principle advantage of the Au 333 alloy is its low cost, but this takes it's toll in terms of difficult workability, increased risk when soldering and of course its pale color. This alloy is a legal designation for gold in Germany, but in Great Britain the lowest alloy that can be marked as gold is 9 carat (Au 375). In the United States, the lowest permissible alloy that can be marked as gold is 10 karat (Au 416). These alloys contain around 40% gold, but really there are only 20% gold atoms mixed with silver and copper atoms. The richer alloys have noticable benefits in practical application.

- Color and shine of the alloys mentioned are the same, but the 9 and 10 karat alloys show better resistance to tarnishing and chemical corrosion.
- Because the melting zone of the light yellow Au-Ag alloys is around 1000°C (reddish alloys are around 800-900°C), soldering is less risky.
- Hardness and tensile strength are higher in the richer alloys so mechanical forming is easier and in fact resembles 14k (Au 585).

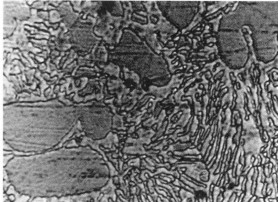

Figure 1.46
Au 333 Alloy. Hypo-eutectic (β-mixed crystal etched gray).
Magnification = 1600.
a) cast structure
b) recrystalization structure, rolled and annealed at 700°C
c) tempered after annealing (age-hardened for 4 hours at 400°C) precipitation processes in the mixed crystals.

The improvement in quality between 8k and 9 or 10k is significant and outweighs the slight cost difference.

1.12.8 AU 585 ALLOYS
Melt Diagram
Figure 1.47 shows that the alloys with this proportion of gold have a melt interval in which a structure of homogeneous mixed crystals is formed (figure 1.48). Notice the temperature differences between the pale and red gold alloys as well as between these alloys and those in the middle.

The middle alloys begin to enter a precipitation zone around 600°C. This occurs in the remaining alloys at a somewhat lower temperature. This zone forms an offshoot of the precipitation zone that in the ternary system stretches from the eutectic area to the gold corner. During precipitation the solubility inside the grains is reduced with the excess material precipitating out as a second kind of crystal or grain.

Characteristics
The Au 585 mix, also know as 14k, is perhaps the most important jewelry alloy. It is reasonably priced, has a pleasant color and high shine and is tough enough for practical use. All this is matched by reasonable defor-

47

mation, meaning it can be worked well. (table 1.6). Au 585 alloys are generally resistant to tarnish, and though the red alloys are soluble in acids, other versions of the alloy are very acid resistant. The yellow alloys offer the greatest resistance to working, but the addition of silver or copper, which makes the alloy red or green, also increases its ductility.

The Au 585 alloys solder better than the Au 333 mixtures because the average temperature difference between the solidus and liquidus points is about 40 K. The alloy casts well. The range of alloy has the ability (or disadvantage) of age hardening, particularly in the reddish alloys, because of the AuCu₃ lattice structure that forms when there is a large proportion of copper. To retain ductility in these alloys, quench them at about 650°C after annealing or casting. To encourage hardening, allow the object to cool slowly.

1.12.9 THE AU 750 ALLOYS
Melt Diagram
The relationship is clear and easy to understand (figure 1.49): the liquidus and solidus run from more than 1000° C on the silver side to less than 900°C on the copper side with an interval between them of about 20 K. While the "trough" of the ternary system is still intersected by Au 585 and Au 333, the vertical cross section of Au 750 lies outside this low area of the melt interval in the region of the steep rise in temperature of the liquidus and solidus plane. Only homogeneous mixed crystals are formed from the melt (figure 1.50).

Characteristics
The description of the Au 333 alloy above noted that the gold atom content is less than the stated parts per thousand would lead one to believe because of the density of the gold. The same principle is in effect here, but because this alloy is 75% gold, the result is reversed: 10 gold atoms for every 7 silver or copper atoms. Not surprisingly, this high proportion of gold in the entire alloy affects its characteristics significantly.

The bright gold color of the alloy is saturated and full, with high polishability. It remains unchanged in air (table 1.7). In its chemical behavior the alloy is

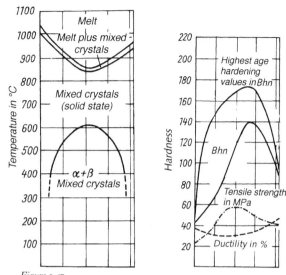

Figure 1.47
Au-Ag-Cu Ternary System. Vertical cross section of Au 585.
a) phase diagram,
b) mechanical characteristics.

almost the same as fine gold; it can only be attacked by aqua regia.

A comparison of the mechanical characteristics of Au 750 with the Au 585 alloy shows that the higher gold content metals are without exception easier to work. This is especially noticeable in the medium colors where hardness and toughness (i.e. tensile strength) increases with the copper content.

Uses
Anywhere fine chasing, forming of delicate wire work or similar methods which strongly stress the metal are used, a yellowish Au 750 alloy is recommended. The high tensile strength of the alloy guarantees that it will stand up to years of wear.

These values can be significantly increased by age hardening, especially in the reddish alloys. This is explained by the lattice structure AuCu of the Au-Cu binary boundary system. The Au 750 alloys are especially susceptible to age hardening because both formation possibilities are present. In the medium colored region the precipitation into α- and β-mixed crystals occurs. The reddish alloys lie in the zone of the AuCu₃ lattice superstructure. As this implies, it is important to quench the alloy after annealing if fur-

Color	Composition in Parts Per Thousand					Characteristics				
	silver	copper	zinc	tin	nickel	Melting Range in °C	Brinell Hardness in Bhn	Tensile Strength in N/mm²	Ductility in %	Density in g/cm³
pale yellow	534	133	-	-	-	870...790	100	440	28	11.0
yellow	445	222	-	-	-	820...800	110	470	24	10.9
medium yellow	333	334	-	-	-	825...800	115	480	25	10.9
orange	200	467	-	-	-	900...800	110	410	30	10.8
red	95	572	-	-	-	950...860	100	450	35	10.7
yellow	114	431	114	-	8	950...925	100	440	42	10.8
bright yellow	225	350	47	15	-	840...795	80	400	57	11.2

Table 1.5
Au 333 gold alloys.

Color	Composition in Parts Per Thousand					Characteristics				
	silver	copper	zinc	tin	nickel	Melting Range in °C	Brinell Hardness in Bhn	Tensile Strength in N/mm²	Ductility in %	Density in g/cm³
pale yellow	382.5	32.5	-	-	-	990...970	65	280	34	13.7
greenish yellow	310	35	-	70	-	810...800	105	450	46	13.7
yellow	280	135	-	-	-	870...830	130	510	32	16.6
medium yellow	188	227	-	-	-	850...810	130	540	36	15.5
medium yellow	110	184	71	-	50	880...830	120	470	35	13.5
orange	90	325	-	-	-	890...850	110	480	44	13.4
red	-	415	-	-	-	970...930	80	430	53	13.2

Table 1.6
Au 585 alloys.

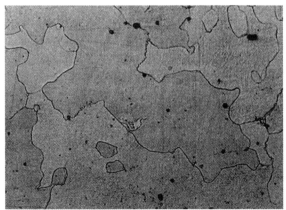

Figure 1.48
Au 585 alloy.
Annealed dead soft, homogenous structure. Magnification = 250

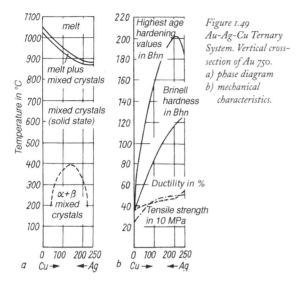

Figure 1.49
Au-Ag-Cu Ternary
System. Vertical cross-
section of Au 750.
a) phase diagram
b) mechanical
characteristics.

Figure 1.50
Au 750 alloy. Deformed and annealed recrystalization structure.
Magnification = 200

ther working is to be done. Soldering and casting present no particular difficulties with all Au 750 alloys. The alloy in which copper and silver are added in equal amounts (standard 18k yellow gold) is especially well suited to enameling.

In summary it can be said that appearance, workability and age hardening are so advantageous in the Au 750 alloy that it should be preferred at least in the making of one-of-a-kind pieces even if the higher gold content makes the material somewhat more expensive.

1.12.10 OTHER GOLD ALLOYS

Although gold coins are almost never used as currency, gold coins and commemorative medals are produced for investment and collectors. The following alloys would be the ones most likely selected for such medals.

- Au 986 (23.6 karat), the alloy of the most important European gold coin of former times, the ducat.
- Au 916.7 (22 karat), which was used as a coin alloy in Great Britain (the sovereign, guinea), Russia and Turkey.
- Au 900 (21.6 karat) was the preferred coining alloy from the previous century to the present, for example in German 5, 10, and 20 Mark coins minted between 1873 and 1914. Coins and medals of this

alloy can be found in Europe and the United States. For more information, readers are referred to specialized literature on numismatics.

Gold used in dental work requires a fine content of at least Au 750. In previous times the 20 karat (Au 833) was used because of its working and wearing characteristics, but this has been replaced today by a range of special dental alloys of gold and platinum group metals that are classified not according to the fine content but according to the intended purpose. Palladium can replace 2.5 times the amount of gold with the same wearing ability, and is therefore used in dental alloys, sometimes reducing the gold content of dental alloys below Au 750. Goldsmiths should be cautious when purchasing dental gold alloys because they might have properties that make them difficult to fabricate or finish.

In addition to the alloys used by jewelers today, several other alloys deserve mention for their historical significance. Though not in common usage, it is possible to find jewelry made in 9, 12, 15, and 16 karat. These are, respectively, Au 375, 500, 625, and 666.

There have always been attempts to bring low karat gold alloys such as the Austrian Quarter Gold (Au 250; 6 karat) into the trade because of its low cost, but the pale color and limited tarnish resistance have prevented them from becoming popularly accepted.

Alloy Color	Composition in $^{1000}/_{1000}$							
	Silver	Copper	Cadmium	Melting Region in °C	Density in g/cm³	Brinell Hardness in Bhn	Tensile Strength in N/mm²	Ductility in %
pale-yellowish green	250	–	–	1038...1030	15.9	32	186	36
bright yellowish green	214	36	–	1025...990	15.8	65	275	39
greenish yellow	167	83	–	970...940	15.6	97	363	42
bright yellow	125	125	–	895...885	15.4	120	471	45
reddish yellow	83	167	–	895...880	15.2	125	481	47
orange	–	250	–	900...890	14.8	135	520	52
green	167	–	83	1025...1000	15.5	58	412	45

Table 1.7
Au 750 alloys.

Nickel White Gold

White gold that contains palladium will be discussed in connection with the platinum group metals, but there is another type of white gold known as non-precious in which the principle whiting ingredient is nickel. The addition of as little as 135 parts per thousand of nickel (13.5%) are enough to remove the yellow color from a gold alloy.

In the Au-Ni system (figure 1.51) homogeneous mixed crystals form from the melt but precipitation begins to occur at 800°C. Copper mixes easily with nickel in any proportion. Silver absorbs only a small amount of nickel; alloys with higher nickel content become very brittle.

Because of this, non-precious white gold is alloyed from gold, nickel and copper without any silver to improve its castability. Zinc is sometimes added to reduce the melt interval. There are currently discussions in Europe and Japan to make the use of non-precious white gold illegal. Beyond the obvious advantage of lower cost, there are no advantages to the use of non-precious white gold. A drawback of this alloy is increased hardness and toughness, which are about twice as great as with precious white gold. In addition, the formation of a nickel oxide (NiO) makes casting difficult.

To avoid enlarged crystal growth, nickel white gold must be annealed frequently. The annealing temperature should lie between 600°C and 700°C. With every heating the object has to be covered in boric acid because the nickel oxide created is soluble in neither pickle nor other acids, which merely turn the surface yellowish. Mechanical abrasion is the only way to remove the nickel oxide once it forms. Nickel white gold must cool slowly after every annealing to prevent stress cracking. The alloy is particularly sensitive to sulfur because nickel forms sulfides easily. These concentrate themselves at the grain boundaries, weaken the cohesiveness of the structure and lead to heat embrittlement. Sulfur can be accidentally introduced into the studio from fuel gasses such as acetylene, charcoal soldering blocks and plaster investments.

Colored gold metalides

In some metals, gold forms superlattices in which atoms of both ingredients distribute themselves in a regular rhythm within the lattice structure of the mixed crystal. Some of these metalides have a striking color, such as the purple-violet amethyst gold, a metalide of $AuAl_2$, which represents a proportion of 78.5% Au and 21.5% Al.

Despite the high proportion of mass of the gold the light aluminum constitutes two-thirds of the number of atoms and therefore determines the metal's characteristics. The alloy is subject to corrosion, hard, and so brittle it can only be worked by mechanical abrasion, rather like a gemstone. All types of plastic deformation such as forging, rolling and drawing are impossible. Attempts have been made to introduce amethyst

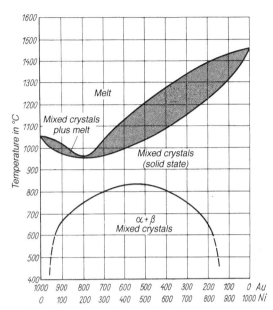

Figure 1.51
Phase diagram of the Au-Ni system.

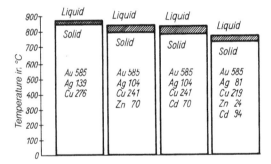

Figure 1.52
Reduction of the melt zone of Au 585 by the additions of Zn and Cd.

gold into jewelry design because of the color contrast it offers, but its dramatic restrictions have so far made this unsuccessful.

The same is true for the same reasons for other metalides of gold such as:

- violet gold and potassium KAu_2
- olive green gold and potassium KAu_4
- deep green gold and rubidium $RbAu_2$
- bright blue gold and indium $AuIn_2$

Attempts to improve the characteristics of the metallides by further addition metals have had no success, so the colored metallides remain a curiosity without practical value for the goldsmith.

I.12.II EFFECTS OF OTHER ADDITION MATERIALS
Zinc
The solubility of the metals of the ternary system for zinc is a maximum of:

- Au 40 parts per thousand of zinc
- Ag 200 parts per thousand of zinc
- Cu 400 parts per thousand of zinc

Fine gold mixes with zinc to form the brittle compound Au_3Zn at 50 parts zinc per thousand, but in practice this alloy is made impossible because of the solubility of the other components in the ternary alloy. A very slight addition of zinc to an alloy of gold, silver and copper acts as a reducing agent and improves the castablity of the metal. Zinc additions improve the yellow color of the pale gold alloys.

The addition of zinc to the 333 gold alloy increases its resistance to sulfur but this advantage is offset by an increased sensitivity to ammonia, which is found in soaps and cleaning solutions. Even the trace amounts of ammonia produced by the skin is enough to lead to stress corrosion that can cause the metal to crack and tear.

One of the most important uses of zinc is in the making of solder, where small additions are enough to lower the melt interval of the ternary alloy, as shown in figure 1.52.

Cadmium
The following discussion of cadmium is included for scientific and historical interest only. It has been proven to constitute a grave health hazard. Never use a solder containing cadmium.

Gold can absorb more than 200 parts per thousand of cadmium and silver can absorb over 300 parts per thousand of cadmium in the solid state. The color of Au-Ag green gold is made even more intense by cadmium additions. Cadmium is particularly effective in lowering the melting point of gold-silver-copper alloys; the combination of zinc and cadmium together creates a lowering that is more dramatic than either of the two white metals by themselves. Figure 1.52 illustrates the effective reduction in melt interval created by adding cadmium and zinc to an alloy conventional 14k alloy (Au 585), where the addition metals consist of one part silver and two parts gold.

The advantage of cadmium/zinc additions for solder is that a range of melting points can be created without diminishing the proportion or color of the gold. The solder is assayed at the same purity as the alloy, indicated by the term "plumb solders."

Tin

A gold-silver-copper alloy can safely absorb up to 40 parts per thousand of tin without significant damage. The embrittlement of gold alloys through contamination with tin solder is primarily effected by the lead contained in low melting solders. If the solubility limit of 40 thousandths parts of tin is exceeded, however, the formation of brittle tin compounds and tin oxides between the solidification structures is unavoidable.

Lead

Fractions of a percent of lead are sufficiently damaging to form the brittle compound Au_2Pb, which is deposited at grain boundaries, as illustrated in figure 1.53b. The alloy melts at a very low 418°C, and is too brittle to be worked, either hot or cold. Typical sources of lead contamination are soft solders or residue from a lead forming block. If a gold alloy has been exposed to lead, it must be thoroughly cleaned before heating to guard against contamination.

Iron

Because of their high melting point and easy oxidation, iron and steel particles become embedded in the structure of a gold-silver-copper alloy as inclusions as described with the silver alloy.

Aluminum

Ductility and tarnish resistance can be increased in low karat gold alloys by small additions of aluminum. However as soon as the low aluminum solubility of silver and copper is exceeded, brittle intermetallic compounds such as Au_4Al are formed and create an unworkable alloy. Remelting can create aluminum oxide (Al_2O_3), which further contaminates the metal.

Silicon

As described earlier, silicon can be reduced, or leached out from crucible material where it will contaminate gold by forming a low melting eutectic alloy (melting point 370°C).

Sulfur

Sulfur forms very few compounds with gold, but it reacts readily to the addition of metals like silver, copper, and lead, causing embrittlement (figure 1.54).

Phosphorus

Phosphorus, like sulfur, does not directly contaminate gold, but can have a negative effect on addition metals in an alloy, where it creates low melting brittle eutectic compounds. Phosophorus might be inadvertently introduced into a melt by its presence in under-refined natural gas or as a trace ingredient in addition metals (figure 1.55).

Gaseous materials

Gold itself doesn't easily react to oxygen but the addition metals react as described earlier. If hydrogen enters an oxygen-containing melt it bonds with the oxygen to form water vapor that is then trapped in voids in the metal and which can cause considerable damage during later working procedures. Other gases such as hydrocarbons, carbon monoxide, sulfur dioxides, etc. are trapped in the metal as gasses. During solidification they cause porosity which manifests itself as surface bubbles upon annealing.

1.12.12 PLATINUM AND PLATINUM GROUP METAL ALLOYS

Of the Platinum Group metals (platinoids), platinum is by far the most important for jewelry. Second in importance is palladium, which is used to whiten

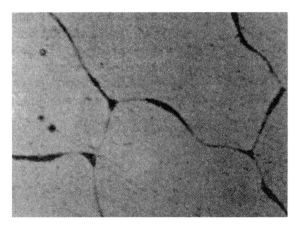

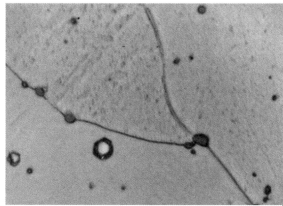

Figure 1.55
Au 585 alloy with 0.1% P. Phosfide precipitation at the grain boundaries and within the grains. Magnification = 630

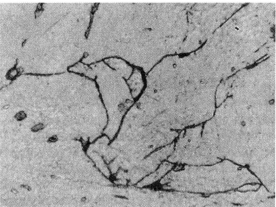

Figure 1.53
Au 720 alloy with 1% Pb. Precipitation of Au_2Pb at the grain boundaries. Magnification = 630
a) cast state
b) first microscopic cracking at the beginning of deformation.

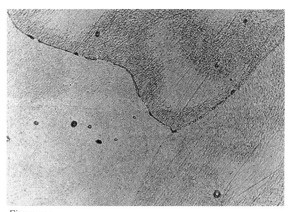

Figure 1.54
Au 585 alloy. Deposition of sulfur compounds at the grain boundaries. Magnification = 800

gold alloys and as a jewelry alloy in its own right. These metals are almost never used in their pure form; like gold, they are most common as alloys.

Jeweler's platinum

Even though platinum is more expensive than gold, alloys of platinum are not subject to international laws concerning composition and designation. Normally the alloys are stamped with the information of the chemical symbols and the platinum content in parts per thousand. "Pt 950," for instance, means the alloy contains 950 parts per thousand of platinum and 50 parts per thousand of addition metals. Unlike gold,

the characteristics of platinum are significantly changed by small amounts of additions (table 1.8).

Since its development about 100 years ago, jewelers have recognized the advantages of working in platinum alloys. Because of its neutral gray-white color, platinum is preferred as a setting for diamonds and colored stones. Its resistance to discoloring oxidation and high tensile strength make platinum alloys particularly well suited to delicate constructions and applications that depend on springiness, such as is the case with some stone settings.

The addition of alloy metals can lower melting point, increase the coefficient of heat expansion,

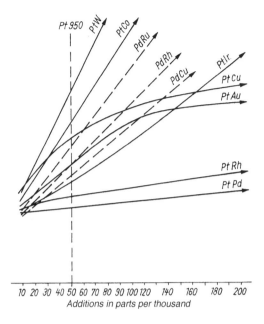

Pt 950
Pt W
Pt Co
Pd Ru
Pd Rh
Pd Cu
Pt Ir
Pt Cu
Pt Au
Pt Rh
Pt Pd

10 20 30 40 50 60 70 80 90 100 120   140   160   180   200
Additions in parts per thousand

Figure 1.56
Platinum and palladium, showing the increase of the Brinell hardness through alloy formation.

increase toughness, resistance to abrasion, hardness, ductility and tensile strength. Most of the platinum alloys used in jewelry-making use the following additions.

- When copper is alloyed with platinum, it forms a homogeneous mixed crystal system in which hardness and tensile strength are significantly increased by the presence of intermetallic compounds. This principle is used in the popular trade alloy Pt 960, which has shown itself to be a universally applicable alloy with good wearing characteristics.
- The addition of cobalt achieves similarly good mechanical characteristics while also improving castability.
- Because the hardness of platinum is scarcely changed by the addition of palladium, these alloys are well suited for setting and techniques that involve plastic deformation.
- The addition of iridium yields a significant increase in hardness and is especially useful in creating spring alloys. Hardness can be further increased by

the addition of other metals in combination with iridium.
- Another way to achieve extremely hard, springy alloys is through the addition of tungsten.
- Gold and rhodium are also used as addition metals, usually in alloys for technical or scientific applications.

Once perceived primarily as a carrier for diamonds, platinum alloys have recently gained popularity as a useful metal in a wide range of design applications. Working in platinum is no more difficult than working in gold or silver, but it requires understanding of its unique characteristics.

Select the most appropriate alloy for each purpose. Because of the danger of contamination from other metals, rolling and drawing should be followed by pickling in a warm 10% nitric acid solution, after which the jeweler's platinum can be annealed at 950-1000°C. After annealing, the metal can be quenched in water or allowed to cool in air. Avoid using clay crucible, charcoal blocks, and plaster-bearing materials when working with platinum – it will be embrittled by carbon, silicon and borates.

An oxygen-hydrogen flame is best suited for heating, but propane or natural gas with oxygen can also be used. Dark protective glasses should be worn to prevent eye strain from the high temperature flame. Because of its high carbon content, acetylene is not recommended for soldering platinum. Because of its high resistance to corrosion, fluxes are not needed when joining platinum. Both welding and soldering can be done on clean metal. No pickling is needed.

While solder is typically used for small sections, parts that are more than 0.8 mm thick are welded together by adding a small piece of the alloy to the joint area. This excess will create a clean dense join that allows enough extra metal to be later filed to shape. Fine gold can be melted onto platinum alloys without melting them.

Jeweler's platinum can be cast by the centrifugal casting procedure but special high temperature investment and crucibles are needed to withstand the melting point of the alloys, which are generally above

2000°C. Unless a high volume of casting is anticipated, it is common to have platinum alloys commercially cast by a company that specializes in it.

When sawing platinum alloys, lubricate sawblades with beeswax or a similar wax. Finishing should be done with fine abrasives and sandpapers in the range of 280-1000 grit. Conventional buffing compounds can be used for preliminary finishing. Final polish is most often achieved with an untreated wool buff.

Jeweler's palladium
While palladium is generally accepted as an addition for white gold, it has not gained wide popularity as a jewelry metal in its own right, despite many years of promotion by refiners. The reasons must lie more with tradition and custom than with the properties of the alloy, because palladium boasts many desirable attributes. It is cheaper than jewelers platinum and because of its lower density, only about half as much palladium as platinum is needed to make the same size object. Its color is even whiter than platinum and

its stability in air is equal. Palladium is slightly more workable but it has the same wearing characteristics as jewelers platinum.

Small amounts of addition metals (usually only about 50 parts per thousand) are sufficient to produce significant changes in the characteristics of palladium alloys. Rhodium and ruthenium are the most common additions, but copper, iridium and platinum are also added for some alloys. Table 1.8 shows some of the alloys currently in use.

Palladium white gold
Since the beginning of this century, metallurgists have sought a gold alloy with the color of the more expensive platinum. Mixtures of platinum and gold were unsuccessful, producing alloys that were too dark. In addition, the resulting alloys were heavy, costly and difficult to work. It was found that the addition of about 160 parts per thousand of palladium to a gold-silver alloy created a metal with all the desirable properties of gold at a lower cost. This is

Name	Composition in % by Weight			Density in g/cm³	Melting Region in °C	Brinell Hardness in Bhn	Tensile Strength in N/mm²	Ductility in %	Usage
	Platinum	Palladium	Remaining Metals						
Pt-Cu 960	96	0	4 copper	20.3	1745...1730	110	363	25	fabrication and setting work
Pt-Co 950	95	0	5 cobalt	20.2	1740...1730	130	-	-	centrifugal casting
Pt-Ir 800	80	0	20 iridium	21.7	1830...1815	190	-	-	fabrication work, chains, spring hardspring hard parts, more than 300 Bhn through
Pt-W 950	95	0	5 tungsten	20.9	1860...1840	155	-	-	plastic deformation
Pt-Pd 960	96	4	0	20.8	1760...1750	55	314	39	setting work
Pt-Pd 950	95	4.5	0.5 iridium	21.0	1760...1740	69	216	23	fabrication work
Pt-Au 950	95	0	5 gold	21.0	1740...1670	95	334	18	fabrication work
Pt-Rh 950	95	0	5 rhodium	20.7	1830...1810	70	235	44	fabrication work
Pt-Ir 950	95	0	5 iridium	21.5	1800...1780	80	226	40	spring hard parts
Pd-Cu	0	95	5 copper	11.8	1490...1470	85	275	21	fabrication and setting work
Pd-Ru	0	95	4.5 ruthenium 0.5 iridium	12.0	1570...1550	110	304	23	fabrication work
Pt-Rh 950	0	95	2 rhodium 3 ruthenium	12.0	1560...1540	95	314	23	fabrication work

Table 1.8
Platinum and palladium alloys

what we know today as "precious" white gold. Non-precious white golds based on nickel have described in a preceding chapter.

The somewhat higher price of precious white gold may be justified by the following advantages.

- The color is very close to that of jewelers platinum.
- Its color does not change when soldering and annealing.
- It can be easily worked in both chip forming and plastic forming operations.
- When setting, beads are easy to raise and yield a flawless bright cut.

To avoid heat fracture palladium white gold should not be soldered on charcoal soldering blocks.

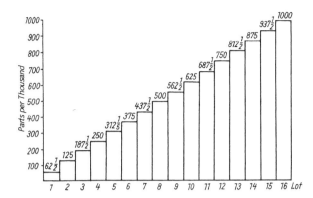

Figure 1.57
Fine silver content expressed in lot and parts per thousand.

1.12.13 ALLOY CALCULATIONS

Calculating of karat

Since 1888, stamping law in Germany has mandated the use of parts per thousand to express the amount of precious metal in an alloy, a nomenclature that continues in use in many countries. Before the introduction of the uniform metric measuring system the quality of the precious metals were expressed by several units as illustrated in table 1.9 and figures 1.57 and 1.58. These were based on the "Cologne Mark," which in the course of time was introduced in many German states.

The fine content definitions were derived from these units of measure, in which the quantity of the precious metal was taken as a basis for the "raw weight." In this way one might speak of "1 raw Mark." In the case of gold alloys, fine gold content was given in karat; silver alloys expressed fine silver content in Lot, a designation no longer in use.

An 18k alloy consists of 18 parts fine gold to 6 parts addition metals. This means a relationship of ¾ gold and ¼ additions, or 750 parts per thousand gold and 250 parts per thousand additions.

Silver alloys used a system in which the basic proportional unit was called a lot, and full measure (100% or 1 Mark) was indicated by 16. In other words, just as ²⁴⁄₂₄ equals pure gold, ¹⁶⁄₁₆ was the designation for

pure silver; the total amount can be divided into hypothetical units, either 1000 parts or 24 karats or 16 lots.

The mathematics of calculating purity are not as complicated as they might at first appear. Karat and lot represent fractions in which the denominator (the bottom term) is 24 for gold and 16 for silver. In this way, 18 karat gold may be written as ¹⁸⁄₂₄, which might be read as 18 divided by 24. This computation will yield the number 750, which is the parts per thousand designation.

A calculation system

Various methods have been developed for calculating precious metal alloys. The procedure shown here has the advantage that only a single proportions scheme is used, which insures that the amounts can be entered without any chance of mixing them up. Even those who make only occasional use of alloying calculations will find they can quickly recall this system.

The basic scheme states:

Parts per thousand   *Karat or lot*
total amt / fine content = total amt / fine content

This system will always express the amount of metal as a fraction of 1000, that is, as parts per thousand. The total amount in every case is 1000 parts per thousand, or 24 karats, or 16 lots. The mass of the metal will always be expressed in grams. The ingredients of precious metal calculations are the mass of a sample, the proportion of precious metal and the quantity of precious metal. If any two of these are known the other one can be calculated. Often the first step is to clearly identify what is known and what is to be determined.

Example 1
What is the fine content in parts per thousand of 13 lot silver?

$$1000 : x = 16 : 13$$

$$x = \frac{1000 \cdot 13}{16} = \underline{812.5 \text{ Ag}}$$

Example 2
How many lot are equal to Ag875?

$$1000 : 875 = 16 : x$$

$$x = \frac{875 \cdot 16}{1000} = \underline{14 \text{ lot silver}}$$

Example 3
Knowing that a ducat is 23.5 karat, how many parts per thousand are gold?

$$1000 : x = 24 : 23.5$$

$$x = \frac{1000 \cdot 23.5}{24} = \underline{979.2 \text{ parts per thousand}}$$

Example 4
How many karats is Au400?

$$1000 : 400 = 24 : x$$

$$x = \frac{400 \cdot 24}{1000} = \underline{9.6 \text{ karat}}$$

Example 5

	Fine Content	Total Mass	Fine Content Mass
a)	given	given	sought
b)	given	sought	given
c)	sought	given	given

5a)
25g of an Au 585 alloy should be made. How much gold is required?

$$1000 : 585 = 25 : x$$

$$x = \frac{585 \cdot 25}{1000} = \underline{14.63\text{g Au}}$$

5b)
How many grams of Au 333 can be made from 4.2 grams of gold?

$$1000 : 333 = x : 4.2$$

$$x = \frac{1000 \cdot 4.2}{333} = \underline{12.61 \text{ g Au } 333}$$

5c)
What is the proportion of gold produced when 6 grams of gold are melted together with 2 grams of copper and 1.5 grams of silver?

Total weight $= 6 + 2 + 1.5 = 9.5 \text{ g}$

$$1000 : x = 9.5 : 6$$

$$x = \frac{1000 \cdot 6}{9 \cdot 5} = \underline{631.6 \text{ parts per thousand}}$$

Mark	Ounce	Lot	Karat	Penny weight	Grain	Calculated in Grams
I	8	16	24	256	288	233.8
		I	1½	16	18	14.6
			I	10⅔	12	9.74

Table 1.9
Old weights and measures of precious metals.

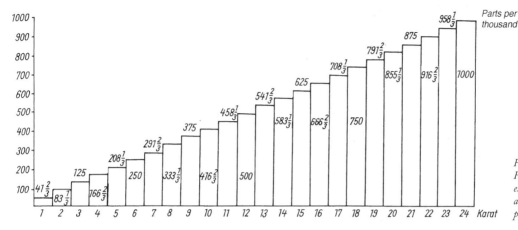

Figure 1.58
Fine gold content, expressed in karat and thousandths parts.

I.12.14 CHANGING AN ALLOY

It is sometimes necessary to remix an alloy of a different karat from materials on hand, either scraps or recycled jewelry brought in by a customer. In many cases it does not pay to remelt alloys in the goldsmiths workshop, and many benchworkers rely on experienced refiners to work their old material into sheet and wire of their specified alloy. Nevertheless, there are times when it becomes necessary to re-alloy gold in the studio, and it is for those times the following calculations are given. Further, it is important to the traditions of the field that the heritage of traditional knowledge of the ancient arts of goldsmithing not be lost.

Reducing the purity of alloys or alloying down
The mass of the fine gold remains constant in both the initial and final alloy; the difference between the two alloys is the result of the addition of other metals. In the calculations, the constant amount of fine gold can be given either as the weight of the initial alloy or that of the alloy desired (table 1.10, figure 1.59a).

Example 1
Starting with 9.2 grams of 14k gold (Au 585), how many grams of addition metals will be needed to create 8k (Au 333) and how much of that alloy will I have in the end?

When lowering an alloy, the calculation is based on the mass of the fine gold, so the first question is:

How much of the 9.2 grams of the sample is gold?
$$1000 : 585 = 9.2 : x$$

$$x = \frac{585 \cdot 9.2}{1000} = 5.38 \text{ g Au}$$

Because we're seeking the total quantity of gold to be used in the alloy the question then becomes: What is the total mass of the metal if 33.3% of it equals 5.38 grams of pure gold?

$$1000 : 333 = x : 5.38$$

$$x = \frac{1000 \cdot 5.38}{333} = 16.16 \text{ g Au}333$$

This is the total mass of the final alloy.

The amount of addition metals is calculated by subtracting the amount of gold (5.38 grams) from the total mass, or 16.16 - 9.20 = 6.96 grams of addition metals needed.

To put all this together: start with 9.20 grams of Au 585; add 6.96 grams of addition metals; and we get the final result:

16.16 grams of Au 333

Example 2
How much Au 750 will I need to start with to create 13.4 grams of Au 585? How much addition metal will I need to reduce the Au 750 (18k) to Au 585 (14k)?

59

The first step is to find out how much of the final alloy will be gold. We need 13.4 grams of gold that is 58.5% pure (i.e. Au 585). To determine this, use this equation.

$$1000 : 585 = 13.4 : x$$

$$x = \frac{585 \cdot 13.4}{1000} = 7.84\text{g Au } 750$$

Next, how much Au 750 will it take to provide that amount of gold? We can set up a ratio that says 1000 (total weight) is to 750 (% of gold) as x (total weight) is to 7.84. Because the phrase "is to" can be rendered as a fraction line, this can be written as

$$1000 : 750 = x : 7.84$$

$$x = \frac{1000 \cdot 7.84}{750} = 10.45 \text{ g Au } 750$$

In other words, this tells us that a sample of Au 750 weighing 10.45 grams contains the amount of pure gold we need to make the desired alloy. We weigh out 10.45 grams of Au 750.

To make up the desired final weight and alloy, we need to add metals equal to the difference between the Au 750 and the intended result. By subtracting 10.45 from 13.4 we arrive at a figure of 2.95 grams, which is the necessary addition metal to reduce the high karat sample to the lower karat.

$$
\begin{array}{r}
10.45 \text{ g Au } 750 \\
-\ 13.40 \text{ g Au } 585 \\
\hline
2.95 \text{ g addition metal}
\end{array}
$$

Raising the purity of alloys or alloying up

In this series of alloy calculations the initial alloy has the lower karat, while the desired result has a higher fine content. This is achieved, obviously, through the addition of fine gold. In these calculations the weight of the addition metals remains unchanged and is therefore used as a basis for the calculations.

Alloying Down	Alloying Up
The weight of the original alloy or the weight of the intended alloy can be assumed as known.	
Fine gold mass	*Addition mass*
remain unchanged	
The unknown entire weight is calculated	
Fine gold	*Addition metals*
upon the foundation of their constant masses.	
Basic formula	
$G : F = G : F$ (in $^{1000}/_{1000}$) (in g)	$G : Z = G : Z$ (in $^{1000}/_{1000}$) (in g)
The required mass of	
Addition metal	*Fine gold*
is determined as the difference between the entire weight and the	
Fine gold	*Addition metal*

Terms:
  G = entire mass
  F = fine gold weight
  Z = weight of the addition metals

Table 1.10
Lowering and raising alloys.

Example 1

How many grams of fine gold are needed to raise 7.7 grams of Au 333 (8k) to Au 585 (14k)? How much of that alloy will this yield?

The first step is to calculate how much of the 7.7 grams is addition metal, i.e. not gold. If 33.3% of the sample is gold, it is easy to see that 66.7% of the sample is not gold. To determine this amount, multiply .667 times the total weight of 7.7 grams:

$$1000 : 667 = 7.7 : x$$

$$x = \frac{667 \cdot 7.7}{1000} = 5.14 \text{ g addition metal}$$

As stated, the amount of addition metals will remain unchanged, so the question becomes: In a given sample of Au 585 in which the non-gold accounts for 5.14 grams, how much of the sample is gold? We know

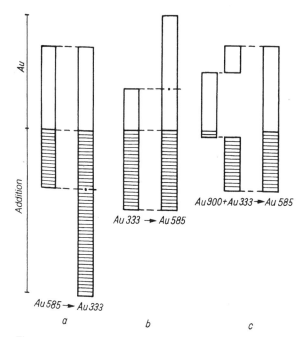

Au

$Addition$

$Au\,900+Au\,333 \rightarrow Au\,585$

$Au\,333 \rightarrow Au\,585$

$Au\,585 \rightarrow Au\,333$

a   *b*   *c*

Figure 1.59
Alloy calculation.
a) lowering an alloy
b) raising an alloy
c) alloying in between.

that Au 585 is 58.5% gold, and therefore 41.5% non-gold. If 41.5% of an alloy is 5.14 grams, how much of the alloy is gold?

$$1000 \ : \ 415 \ = \ x \ : \ 5.14$$

$$x \ = \ \frac{1000 \cdot 5.14}{415} \ = \ 12.39\text{g Au}585$$

This is the total mass of the new alloy. To discover the amount of fine gold needed to achieve this, we subtract the mass of the initial sample from the total mass. This is the amount of fine gold needed to raise the starting sample from Au 333 to Au 585.

$$12.39 \ - \ 7.70 \ = \ \underline{4.69 \text{ grams of pure gold}}$$

Example 2
If I want to make up 16.8 grams of Au 750 starting with some Au 585 (14k) I have on hand, how much of the lower alloy should I use, and how much additional fine gold will be needed?

The first step is to calculate how much of the desired alloy will be non-gold. We know that 750 parts per thousand of the 16.8 grams of this alloy are gold, and therefore that 25% is non-gold. This is an easy calculation.

$$1000 \ : \ 250 \ = \ 16.8 \ : \ x$$

$$x \ = \ \frac{250 \cdot 16.8}{1000} \ = \ 4.2 \text{ g addition metal}$$

I intend to start with Au 585, which has some non-gold, so the next question becomes: How much Au 585 (14k) is needed to provide 4.2 grams of non-gold? We know the non-gold accounts for 41.5% of Au 585, so we divide the known quantity (4.2 grams) by .415 (the non-gold proportion of the alloy)

$$1000 \ : \ 415 \ = \ x \ : \ 4.2$$

$$x \ = \ \frac{1000 \cdot 4.2}{415} \ = \ 10.12\text{g Au }585$$

This tells us to start with a little more than 10 grams of Au 585. Now we need to calculate how much fine gold to add to this amount to raise its purity to 750 parts per thousand. We subtract this portion from the total desired. The balance will be the amount of fine gold needed.

$$16.8 - 10.12 \ = \ \underline{6.68 \text{ grams of gold}}$$

Alloying between
In the situation described here, two alloys on hand are mixed without the addition of either gold or non-gold. The purity of the resulting alloy will obviously lie somewhere between the fineness of either of the starting samples. (figure 1.59c)

Example 1

Initial alloy:	*x* g Au 333
	y g Au 750
Desired alloy:	100 g Au 585

From samples of Au 333 (8k) and Au 750 (18k) you want to make 100 grams of Au 585. How much of each of the alloys should be mixed?

The calculation is complex because there are two variables; that is, the amount of the lower alloy needed will depend on the amount of the higher alloy being used, and vice versa. Until one quantity is fixed it is impossible to calculate the other.

a) Calculation procedure to be used: alloying between.

b)

Fine Content of Alloy Metal	Difference in Fine Content of the Desired Alloy	The Initial Alloys Proportion	Mass
Au 333	- 252	165 g Au 333	x g Au 333
Au 750	+ 165	252 g Au 585	y g Au 750
		417 g Au 585	100 g Au 585

c) The required amount of both the initial alloys is determined by their proportion to the entire weight of the desired alloy. To this end they are compared with the alloy proportion which is formed by the difference figures.

$$165 : x = 417 : 100$$

$$x = \frac{165 \cdot 100}{417} = 39.57 \text{ g Au } 333$$

$$252 : y = 417 : 100$$

$$y = \frac{252 \cdot 100}{417} = 60.43 \text{ g Au } 750$$

d) We melt together: 39.57 g Au 333
+ 60.43 g Au 750

We obtain: 100.00 g Au 585

Example 2

Initial alloy: x g Au 333
8.3 g Au 900
Desired alloy : y g Au 585

How much Au 333 is needed and what is the final mass of Au 585?

a) Calculation procedure to be used: alloying between.

b)

Fine Content of the Initial Alloy	Difference in Fine Content from Alloy	Proportion the Desired Alloy	Metal Mass
Au 333	- 252	315 g Au 333	x g Au 333
Au 900	+ 315	252 g Au 900	8.3 g Au 900
		567 g Au 585	y g Au 585

c) Comparison of the proportional mass with the actual masses.

$$252 : 8.3 = 567 : y$$

$$y = \frac{8.3 \cdot 567}{252} = 18.68 \text{ g Au } 585$$

$$315 : x = 252 : 8.3$$

$$x = \frac{315 \cdot 8.3}{252} = 10.38 \text{ g Au } 333$$

d) We melt together: 10.38 g Au 333
+ 8.30 g Au 900

We obtain: 18.68 g Au 585

Alloying with a specific color
Calculations so far have dealt only with proportions of gold and non-gold, but we know that by altering the amounts of copper and silver in a gold alloy it is possible to change the alloy's color. This section describes the calculations necessary to predict these changes. Because it is impossible to draw any material out of an alloy, we must start from the quantity of addition metals already in a sample. The calculations

explained in figures 1.60 and 1.61. help to clarify this process.

The first step is to calculate the individual masses of all components for the alloy whose mass is known. This can be either the initial sample or the desired alloy. In alloying down, the fine gold mass stays constant while the addition metals are adjusted. In alloying up on the other hand, the mass of one of the addition metals is constant, while the fine gold and the remaining addition metals are variable.

When alloying down, start with the addition metal whose proportion is reduced; if all addition metals are lowered, base calculations on that one whose difference between the old and the new addition content is the largest percentage (as determined by an educated guess).

As illustrated in the following examples, it is useful to set up a comparative overview of the composition

of the initial and desired alloy. A negative number indicates that the desired color cannot reasonably be made from the sample on hand.

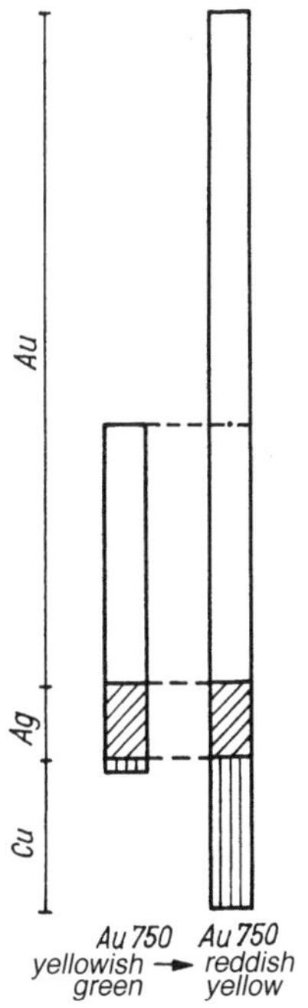

Example 1

Starting from an initial alloy of Au 585 orange-yellow gold in which 138 parts per thousand are silver and 277 parts per thousand are copper, create an orange-red alloy of Au 750 in which 36 parts per thousand are silver and 214 parts per thousand are copper. Because that's a mouthful, here is the same information presented as percentages.

Initial alloy:	12 grams of yellow gold
	58.5% gold
	13.8% silver
	27.7% copper
Desired alloy:	unknown quantity red gold
	75% gold
	3.6% silver
	21.4% copper

Because the karat (or purity) is being raised, there will be the addition of fine gold. In order to alter the color, the proportion of addition metals will be changed, in this case favoring copper to create a redder colored alloy.

The first step is to calculate the weights of each of the constituent metals. Because we know the relative quantity of each and also know the weight of the whole sample, this is an easy calculation. We are asking, respectively: How much is 58.5%, 13.8% and 27.7% of 12 grams?

$$12 \cdot .585 = 7.02 \text{ grams of gold}$$
$$12 \cdot .138 = 1.66 \text{ grams of silver}$$
$$12 \cdot .277 = 3.32 \text{ grams of copper}$$

The sum of the addition (non-gold) metals is 4.98 grams.

As described above (under alloying up), we begin calculation by assuming the quantity of the addition metals will remain constant. Because we are making the Au 750 alloy, we know that 25% will be non-gold.

Figure 1.60
Alloy calculation.
The change of color at the same fine content.

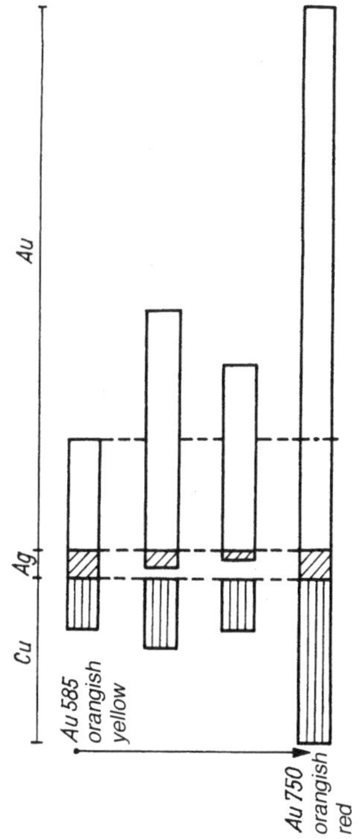

Au 750 yellowish green → Au 750 reddish yellow

Figure 1.61
Alloy calculation.
Alloying up with a change in color.

Au 585 orangish yellow

Au 750 orangish red

The question then is: If 25% of an alloy has a mass of 4.98 grams, what is the mass of the total alloy?

$$1000 \; : \; 250 \; = \; x \; : \; 4.98$$

$$x \; = \; \frac{1000 \cdot 4.98}{250} \; = \; 19.9 \text{ g Au585}$$

Now that we know the mass of the entire alloy and the percentages of the desired additions, it is simple multiplication to determine the specific amounts of those metals.

19.9 grams · .75 = 14.93 grams of gold
19.9 grams · .036 = 0.72 grams of silver
19.9 grams · .214 = 4.26 grams of copper

By showing the information in a chart it becomes clear that this alloy cannot be made from the alloys on hand, which contain too much silver. To achieve the high karat rich red color, it would be necessary to remove .94 grams of silver, a process that cannot be reasonably done in the studio.

	Entire Mass	Au	Ag	Cu
Initial Alloy	12.0	7.02	1.66	3.32
Difference	+ 7.9	+ 7.91	- 0.94	+ 0.94
Desired Alloy	19.9	14.93	0.72	4.26

Since that didn't work, we'll try calculating by using the starting proportion of copper as a fixed quantity. We know we want the amount of copper in the resulting alloy to represent 21.4% of the total, and we know that we start with 3.32 grams of it. The question becomes: What is the total mass of a sample when 3.32 grams equals 21.4%?

$$3.32 \text{ divided by } .214 \; = \; 15.5 \text{ grams}$$

Knowing this, we can determine how much of that total is gold: What is 75% of 15.5 grams?

$$15.5 \cdot .75 \; = \; 11.63 \text{ grams of gold}$$

We know that silver makes up 3.6% of the desired alloy, so again this is simple multiplication.

$$15.5 \cdot .036 \; = \; .56 \text{ grams of silver}$$

For easy comparison, we set these figures into a chart as before.

	Entire Mass	Au	Ag	Cu
Initial Alloy	12.0	7.02	1.66	3.32
Difference	+ 3.51	+ 4.61	- 1.10	0
Desired Alloy	15.51	11.63	0.56	3.32

Calculations that assume a constant amount of copper also fail to create a possible result, as indicated by the negative number in the silver column. Again, this alloy would require that some of the silver in the starting metal be removed, a practical impossibility.

Because starts with gold and copper both proved impossible, the only alternative is to start with silver as the fixed ingredient. What happens when I add no silver?

We know that silver is 3.6% of the desired alloy and that we start with 1.66 grams of it in the original alloy. Knowing this, what will be the total mass of an alloy in which 1.66 grams constitutes 3.6%?

$$1.66 \text{ divided by } .036 \; = \; 46.1 \text{ grams}$$

Knowing the total mass and the intended percentages of each of the constituents, it is easy enough to determine their masses. What is 75% of 46.1 grams? What is 21.4% of 46.1 grams?

Components of the desired alloy:
46.1 · .75 = 34.6 grams of gold
46.1 · .214 = 9.87 grams of copper

These figures are laid out as before.

	Entire Mass	Au	Ag	Cu
Initial Alloy	12.0	7.02	1.66	3.32
Difference	+ 34.1	+ 27.56	0.0	+ 6.55
Desired Alloy	46.1	34.58	1.66	9.87

Finally, we have created a situation without negative numbers, indicating that these proportions will yield the desired metal. We start with out original sample of 12 grams of Au 585, add 27.56 grams of gold and 6.55 grams of copper to create 46.1 grams of the red Au 750 alloy we wanted.

	Entire Mass	Au	Ag	Cu
Initial Alloy	29.26	24.37	2.43	2.46
Difference	12.39	0.0	+ 1.90	+ 10.49
Desired Alloy	41.65	24.37	4.33	12.95

Example 2
If I want to create 41.65 grams of Au 585 gold in which 104 grams are silver and 311 grams are copper, how much of the addition metals will I need to add?

Initial alloy: x g Au 833
                   with 83 g Ag and 84 g Cu
Desired alloy: 41.65 g Au 585
                   with 104 g Ag and 311 g Cu

Because we will be lowering the purity of the alloy, we use the formulas for alloying down, which specify that the gold content remains the same. The first step is to determine how much of the final alloy will be gold, silver and copper, respectively, or: What is 58.5% of 41.65 grams? What is 10.4%? What is 31.1%?

$41.65 \cdot .585 = 24.37$ grams of gold
$41.65 \cdot .104 = 4.33$ grams of silver
$41.65 \cdot .311 = 12.95$ grams of copper

Now to find the mass of the original alloy, knowing that the gold content, which makes up 83.3% of it weighs 24.37 grams.

When 24.37 is divided by .833 = 29.26 grams, the result is the total weight of the original sample. To determine the mass of the addition metals in the original sample, multiply their percentage by the total weight.

29.26 grams $\cdot .083 = 2.43$ grams of silver
29.26 grams $\cdot .084 = 2.46$ grams of copper

Because all the numbers are positive, we can proceed to melt the original sample of

29.26 grams Au 833
+ 1.90 grams silver
+ 10.49 grams copper

41.65 g Au 585

Changing color with a constant fine content
Suppose you have on hand gold of a certain color and karat and want the same karat but a different color. You can change the color by adding another metal, but you will also need to add fine gold to keep the karat constant. This calculation will follow the formula for alloying up.

Example
Starting with 24.9 grams of green Au 750, (214 parts per thousand silver, 36 parts per thousand copper) you want to make a red gold of the same purity that has 8.3% silver and 16.7% copper.

Initial alloy: 24.9 grams total mass consisting of
                 75% gold
                 21.4% silver
                 3.6% copper
Desired alloy: 75% gold
                 8.3% silver
                 16.7% copper

The first step is to determine the quantity of each metal in the initial alloy, or: What (respectively) is 75%, 21.4% and 3.6% of 24.9 grams?

$.75 \cdot 24.9 = 18.68$ grams gold
$.214 \cdot 24.9 = 5.33$ grams silver
$.036 \cdot 24.9 = .9$ grams copper

We will use silver as a constant, so knowing the quantity of the silver in the initial batch and its proportion

65

in the final alloy we can calculate the quantity of the desired alloy. That is, 5.33 grams equals 8.3% of what total?

$$5.32 \text{ grams divided by } .083 = 64.1 \text{ grams}$$

Determine how much of the new alloy will be gold or: What is 75% of 64.1 grams?

$$64.1 \cdot .75 = 48.08 \text{ grams}$$

Repeat the process for silver and copper by multiplying the total weight by the proportion of each constituent.

$$64.1 \cdot .083 = 5.32 \text{ grams}$$
$$64.1 \cdot .167 = 10.7 \text{ grams}$$

e) We melt together:

$$\begin{array}{r} 24.90 \text{ g Au 750} \\ + 29.40 \text{ g Au} \\ + 9.80 \text{ g Cu} \end{array}$$

We obtain: 64.10 grams of Au 750

	Entire Mass	Au	Ag	Cu
Initial Alloy	24.9	18.68	5.32	0.90
Difference	+ 39.3	+ 29.4	0.0	+ 9.80
Desired Alloy	64.1	48.08	5.32	10.70

1.13
Copper Alloys

Copper is added in limited amounts to precious metal alloys, but it forms the main component of many of the other popular alloys, which are collectively known as non-ferrous metals (table 1.11).

The following list shows the accepted descriptive prefixes used in the copper industry.

DIN	1787	ISO 1337	copper sheet and wire
DIN	1705	ISO 1338-1977	cast tin-bronze, bronze, red brass
DIN	1709	ISO 1338-1977	cast brass, special brass alloys
DIN	1714	ISO 1338-1977	cast complex-aluminum bronze.
DIN	1716	ISO 1338-1977	cast tin-lead-bronze
DIN	17660	ISO 426-1983	brass, special brasses
DIN	17662	ISO 427-1983	tin bronze
DIN	17663	ISO 430-1983	nickel silver
DIN	17664	ISO 429-1983	copper-nickel alloys
DIN	17665	ISO 428-1983	aluminum bronze

Brass is the result of alloying copper and zinc. Basic bronze is produced by alloying copper and tin, while many other bronzes are created by further additions of nickel, aluminum, silver, beryllium, manganese, and especially silicon. These are generally described with a descriptive term, such as "aluminum bronze." Standard brass can be whitened by the addition of nickel to create an alloy with the misleading name of nickel silver, which has no silver. It is also known as German silver.

When mixed with zinc, tin or aluminum, copper forms alpha-mixed crystals that are easily incorporated into the cubic face-centered lattice structure of copper. This contributes to the alloys' malleability. The saturation level of each of the additive metals is respectively, 39% for zinc, 14% for tin, and 9% for aluminum. Exceeding the proportion of the addition metal in the alloy forms complicated metallide structures that, with the exception of the β-mixed crystals, are so hard and brittle that such alloys cannot be forged.

Rather than try to explain the phase diagram of the difficult peritectic system, we will limit our investigation to the alloys with greatest application to practicing metalsmiths, shown here in figures 1.62 and 1.63.

Brass
If it proceeds from the diagram that the zone of the alpha-mixed crystals of 33% Zn at 902°C spreads out with 39% Zn at 454°C then in the practice an inter-

mediate state is "frozen in" with alloys of this zone. so that with a specific proportion of β-mixed crystals in the lattice is to be expected if the alloy contains more than 33% Zn.

Such alloys have a higher tensile strength, which can increase their wear resistance without their becoming brittle. When polishing these alloys, the β-mixed crystals are more difficult to remove and therefore create a minor surface relief that makes a high polish difficult to obtain. If the metal is etched, these crystals will be more easily corroded than the others and will leave a roughened surface. A higher proportion of β-crystals results in a less malleable alloy, though these metals will possess good forming characteristics when heated. Pure β-brass, (known as "turning brass") is formed in the continuous casting extrusion process.

The most common brass alloys for studio metalsmiths are those that contain no more than 30-35% zinc, known as alpha brasses. For sinking and stretching out vessels, for chasing and for decorative flatware of all kinds, #360 – an alloy of 30% zinc, 70% copper – is the most widely used. It combines malleability, toughness, and ease of supply with excellent polishability and coloring range. As the proportion of zinc decreases the red tones of the copper in the alloy become more noticeable. It would be expected, then, that a low zinc brass would more nearly approach the color of gold than a high zinc brass, and this is the case. The popular alloy sold under the trade name "NuGold" has roughly 88% copper. Conversely, as the zinc content increases, so does the hardness and tensile strength (or toughness) while the ductility decreases.

An alloy containing 10% zinc (sometimes known as tombak) is commonly preferred for jewelry work and as a substrate for plated goods. This alloy combines workability with a wide range of patina options, including a near gold color by dipping in pickle mixed with hydrogen peroxide. This alloy or a brass with even less zinc makes a suitable base for enameling work.

Of less interest to metalsmiths are the "Special Brasses" which generally do not work well under

hand methods. In these alloys, small additions of aluminum, iron, manganese, nickel, tin, lead or silicon are used to improve mechanical characteristics, chip-forming ability and resistance to corrosion.

Bronze

Since the time many centuries ago when this alloy gave its name to an epoch, bronze has proven itself as a useful casting alloy. Today it is widely used in art castings, but has proven itself valuable in technical applications as well. Though copper will absorb as much as 20% tin, the usual ceiling amount falls closer to 11%, an alloy traditionally known as Bell Metal. At lower proportions, specifically less than 6%, bronze will have a pure α-mixed crystal structure that renders it extremely malleable. As the proportion of tin increases, a eutectoid structure of α-mixed crystals and the brittle metallide Cu_3Sn is formed after a complicated transformation process.

Zinc-tin-bronze

This 3-part alloy produces an even thinner fluid melt, and is therefore recommended for delicate castings.

Nickel silver

In contrast to the copper alloys described above, when nickel is added to copper it forms a homogenous mixed crystal structure. Alloys with the ranges of 58-67% copper, 11-26% nickel, and 12-26% zinc consist of mixed crystals, which creates a metal well-suited to plastic forming. The most popular casting alloys will fall within the range of 45-50% copper, 10-16% nickel, with the balance being zinc. These mixtures have a heterogeneous structure of cubic face-centered lattices, alpha-mixed crystals, and cubic face-centered lattice $β_1$-mixed crystals.

Nickel silver lends itself to jewelry making because of its resistance to corrosion, favorable mechanical characteristics and relatively low cost. It can be easily gold and silver plated, and is preferred for pinstems and springs, even on precious jewelry, because of its great tensile strength.

The alloy was called "Pakfong" in China and has been used since the middle of the 18th century in

Material Type	Alloying Elements in %					Brinell Hardness in Bhn	Tensile Strength in N/mm²	Ductility in %	Usage
	Cu	Zn	Sn	Ni	Accompanying Metals				
CuZn 4	95...97	3...5	-	-	0.2	60	225	40	enameling work
CuZn 10	89...91	9...11	-	-	0.2	60	235	41	enameling work, fashion jewelry, doublee
CuZn 15	84...86	14...16	-	-	0.3	60	255	42	fashion jewelry
CuZn 20	78...81	19...22	-	-	0.3	65	265	43	fashion jewelry
CuZn 30	69...73	27...31	-	-	0.3	70	284	45	deep drawing work
CuZn 37	62...65	35..38	-	-	0.5	80	334	30	non-cutting cold forming
CuSn 4	95...97	-	3...5	-	0.3	70	314	48	non-cutting cold forming
CuSn 8	91...93	-	7...9	-	0.3	90	392	55	non-cutting cold forming
CuSn 12	87...89	-	11...13	-	0.3	105	314	15	casting alloy
CuSn 14	85...87	-	13...15	-	0.3	115	230	5	casting alloy
CuSn 4 Zn 3	93...94	2...7	3...5	-	0.2	110	420	60	tubes, springy parts, cast components
CuSn 6 Zn 6	86...90	5...7	5...7	-	0.2	100	400	50	tubes, springy parts, cast components
CuSn 10 Zn	87...89	1...3	8...11	-	0.2	90	294	10	tubes, springy parts, cast components
CuNi 12 Zn 24	61...63	24...28	-	11...13	0.2	80	350	40	deep drawing work, flatware
CuNi 18 Zn 20	60...64	23...17	-	17...19	0.2	85	380	36	deep drawing work, flatware
CuNi 25 Zn 15	58...62	12...18	-	24...26	0.2	95	400	32	deep drawing work, flatware

Table 1.11
Technically important copper alloys.

Europe as "white copper." Other names for nickel silver are German silver, Argentan, Alpacca, Alpaka, New silver, Christofle-metal, Alfenide.

1.14
Steel and Cast Iron

Iron and its principle alloy, steel, have for centuries been the most important metal of industry and technology. Steel is instantly apparent in goldsmithing tools, equipment and machinery. In addition, steel is sometimes used in the creation of jewelry, hollowware and flatware. Because of the large volume of specialized literature available on iron and steel, we will confine our discussion here to a short overview.

1.14.1 TYPES OF STEEL
Raw iron is refined from ore and poured into large crude ingots called "pigs." This material is then refined to create a wide range of alloys, some of which are listed in table 1.12. The great variety of steels means that there is probably an alloy designed for the specific need at hand, but it also requires greater care in selecting an appropriate type. When making chisels, punches or gravers, for instance, it is important to start with tool steels that will provide the desired wear resistance, hardness and flexibility. Here are a few of the hundreds of steels available.

Structural steel
Simple iron-carbon steels for machine parts that are not heavily stressed, usually named after the minimum tensile strength, such as St 34 or St 38.

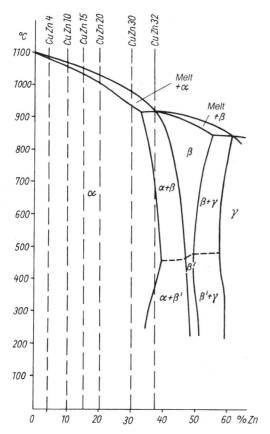

Figure 1.62
Cu-Zn phase diagram (cutaway view).

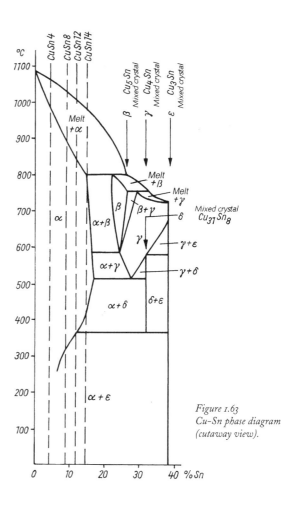

Figure 1.63
Cu-Sn phase diagram
(cutaway view).

Structural alloy steel
Alloyed with manganese, chromium, mobydenum; welds well, is used for steel and bridge construction.

Low alloyed steel
For conduit and pipe construction with a high heat tensile strength, alloyed with manganese, chromium-vanadium, chromium-molybdenum.

Heat treatable steel
Strength and toughness are increased by heat treatment. The carbon portion is 0.2-0.55%; manganese, silicon, chromium, molybdenum or nickel are added individually or in combination.

Carburized and nitrided steels
The surface is enriched with carbon or nitrogen during heat treatment. A particularly hard surface is obtained when hardened, while the core remains soft and ductile.

Spring steels
These alloys have a particularly highly elastic ability which is achieved by heat treatment and final cold forming. For high degrees of stress, 1% carbon and additions of silicon and manganese are used.

Tool steels
Alloys in this family can be hardened and tempered. Unalloyed tool steels contain between 0.35-1.7% car-

Raw Pig Iron: A product of the blast furnace. Contaminated by foreign elements.

0.3...5.0% C	Hardness and tensile strength are increased, ductility is reduced, melting temperature lowered.
0.3...2.5% Si	Graphite formation is fostered, castability is improved.
0.5...0.6% Mn	Formation of iron carbide is fostered, hardness and tensile strength are increased.
0.1...2.2 P	The melt becomes very fluid, the iron becomes hard and brittle.
0.03...0.1% S	The melt becomes thick and sluggish, the iron becomes hot-short.

White Pig Iron is formed by rapid cooling.	*Gray Pig Iron* is formed by slow cooling.
It is improved by Mn.	It is improved by Si.
C is bound up as Fe_3C.	The C is precipitated out as graphite crystals.
The fracture surface is white, hard, fibrous.	The fracture surface is gray, grainy.
It is the base material for steel .	It is the base material for cast iron.

Steel is forgable iron, from white pig iron, refined by remelting in a converter, a Siemens-Martin smelter or an electric smelter. Contains a maximum or 1.7% C.	*Cast iron* contains associated elements, is made from gray pig iron, is remelted in a cupola. It casts well, has the ability to fill molds well, is hard, brittle susceptible to blows. It contains 2.5-3.8% C.

Mild Steel	*Unalloyed Tool Steel*	*Alloyed Steel*	*Gray Cast Iron*	*Hard Cast Iron*
forgable, not hardenable, contains 0.05-0.35% C	hardenable, contains 0.35...1.7% C	is improved by associated element additions.	is slowly cooled cast iron and is brittle.	is rapidly cooled cast iron, tough and hard.

Table 1.12
The refining of raw iron.

Tempering Colors	Temperature in °C	Usage
pale yellow	210	measuring tools
straw yellow	220	tools for hard metals
yellow	230	chisels
dark yellow	240	burrs, reamers
yellowish brown	250	metal saws
brown-red	260	hammers, screw drivers
red	270	cutting and punching tools
violet	280	texturing and stone chisels
dark-blue	290	springs
deep blue	300	springs

Table 1.13
Tempering colors and temperatures.

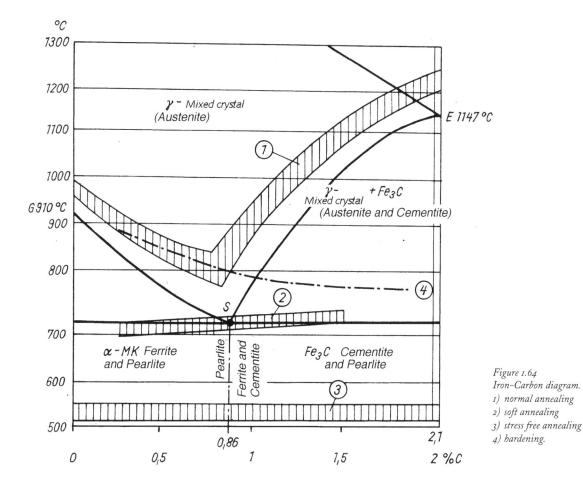

Figure 1.64
Iron-Carbon diagram.
1) normal annealing
2) soft annealing
3) stress free annealing
4) hardening.

bon and are the steels from which tools were traditionally made. Alloyed steels have been developed for cases where increased tolerances are needed. The quality of the material depends upon the degree of purity, the method of melting and the alloy additions.

Scale resistant and heat resistant steels
Additions of chromium, nickel and silicon render this steel durable even at temperatures up to 600°C.

Stainless and acid resistant steels
A thick oxide layer is formed by the addition of at least 12% chromium, which dependably protects the steel from corrosion. Tensile strength and ductility can be influenced by further additions of nickel, man-

ganese and molybdenum. Such steels are used for flatware, hollowware, and jewelry. Popular alloys include:

• 7Cr14 (0.07% C; 14% Cr; 0.6% Mn; 0.4% Si; balance Fe)
• 12CrNi188 (0.12% C; 18%Cr; 8% Ni; 0.4% Mn; 0.4% Si; balance Fe)

1.14.2 HEAT TREATMENT OF STEELS
Normal annealing
Recrystalization in the austenite region with slow cooling, in order to obtain a normal, fine-grained structure again after casting, forging, rolling and welding.

71

Annealed dead soft
After intensive cold deformation the structure is recrystalized by annealing over several hours.

Stress relieving annealing
Internal stresses in the structure are equalized by heat treatment at low temperatures.

Hardening and tempering
The steel is heated to the required temperature, then quenched in water, oil or brine, which forms a brittle structure called martensite, a needle-like crystal that gives the steel its toughness. Before the tool can be used, the brittleness must be relieved in a process called tempering.

In this step the martensite is partially decomposed by slow heating; hardness and brittleness are reduced as the temperature increases. Temperatures are traditionally read through the characteristic color changes of surface oxides, as indicated in table 1.13.

Structural steel
Steels with 0.25-0.6% carbon are tempered at 500-600°C, at which point the martensite is transformed into another crystalline phase (pearlite) which yields a tough steel.

1.14.3 ADVICE FOR WORKING STAINLESS STEEL
Because of their very low carbon content, stainless steels cannot be hardened by the quenching method just described. Their hardness can only be increased by cold deformation, (work hardening).

When heating stainless steels should not come in contact with carbon, which will produce carbonization that could negatively affect color, polishability and working characteristics.

Stainless steels can be cast centrifugally if the necessary heat is achieved. A special investment is required.

Stainless steels can be soldered with silver solder or white gold solder, using a good covering of a borax and boric acid mixture as a flux. Because the solder does not flow but works by capillary action, the seam must be as tight and narrow as possible. Stainless steels can be welded according to usual procedures.

1.14.4 IRON AND STEEL TYPE DESIGNATIONS
In table 1.14 various examples are assembled. Structural steel and simple cast iron are designated according to their minimal tensile strength. All other types of steel are named after the important addition agents; the symbol is given together with the number that designates quantity. With low alloyed steels this number is generated by multiplying the actual percentage content by the following factors:
  - C = factor 100
  - Cr, Co, Mn, Ni, Si, W = factor 4
  - Al, Cu, Ti, Mo, V = factor 10

With high alloyed steels the actual percentage proportion is given; "X" is placed before the steel name, for the carbon content the designation number is retained. A letter prefix is used to indicate the type of smelting used or other particular characteristics of a given steel, including advice regarding treatment and handling of stock materials.

Brand Designation	Smelting Method, pre treatment	Tensile Strength in N/mm²	Addition Materials in %		Delivery Forms of the Material
			C	Metals	
A St42 N	resistant to aging	412 (42 kp/mm²)	-	-	unalloyed mild steel, normalized.
T St38 G	Thomas-steel	373 (38 kp/mm²)	-	-	mild steel, annealed dead soft
MY C35 V70	Acid Siemens-Martin steel	-	0.35	-	unalloyed steel, hardened to 687 N/mm²
C100 W2 G	-	-	1.0	-	unalloyed tool steel, goods class 2, annealed dead soft
EB 13 CrV53 V	basic electric furnace steel	-	0.13	(⁵⁄₄=)1.25 Cr; (³⁄₁₀=)0.3 V	low alloyed steel, hardened
X10 CrNi 18.8 V	-	-	0.10	18% Cr; 8% Ni	high alloyed steel, hardened
GGL-20	-	196 (20 kp/mm²)	-	-	unalloyed pig iron (gray cast iron), lamellar with graphite
GS-E 25 CrMo56	electric furnace steel	-	0.25	(⁵⁄₄=)1.25 Cr; (⁶⁄₁₀=)0.6 Mo	low alloyed cast steel

Table 1.14
Iron and steel types.

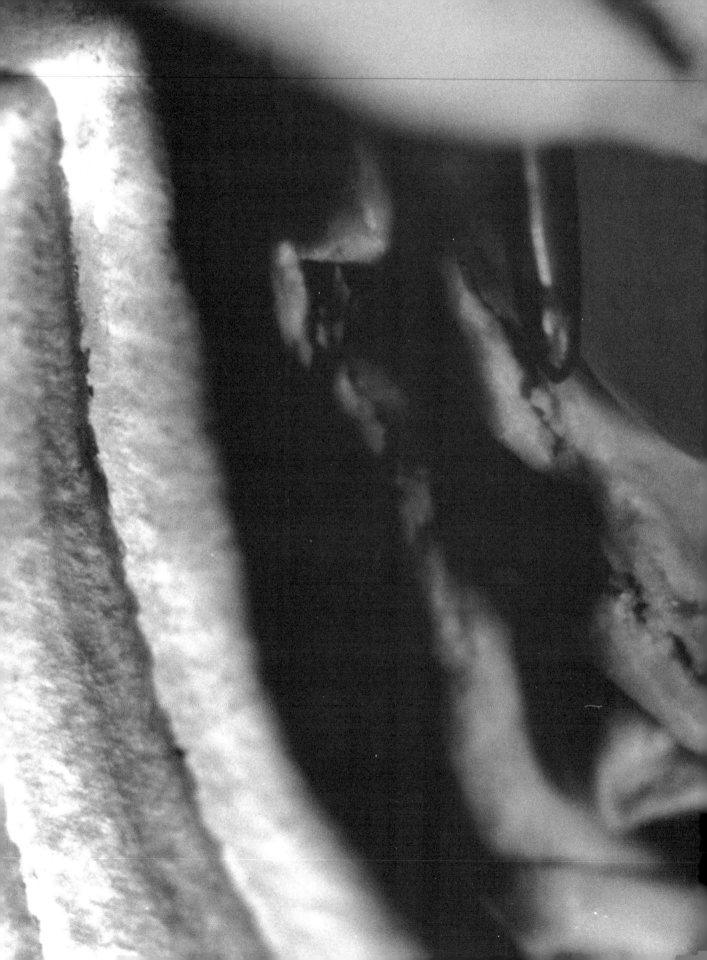

CHAPTER TWO

Other Materials

This chapter describes materials that, along with gemstones, have become familiar resources for goldsmiths. Unlike gemstones, these materials can be worked in the studio, generally with tools already on hand. In this regard these non-metals are distinguished from gems, ceramic and porcelain, for which specialized literature is recommended.

2.1
Ivory

The threatened extinction of elephants by ivory hunters has led in recent years to an international agreement banning the trade and working of ivory worldwide. Law abiding citizens in any country that has signed this agreement (which includes Germany and the US) will therefore no longer work ivory nor offer it for sale.

Fossilized mammoth ivory, which has recently become more widely available, may be worked though this is a limited resource and the ethics of the activity may be questioned. In the future the working of bone (typically beef bones) will probably be of increasing importance.

The following pages describe the process of working ivory, partly because it is important that a professional goldsmith understand the historical traditions of the field, and largely because these methods apply equally to bone.

Elephant tusk
Technically speaking, this material is the only true ivory, but in common usage the word is used for other similar materials. Elephant tusks show a pattern of arched crossing lines when viewed in cross section. Starting at the larger end, a tusk is hollow, generally for a third to a half of the total length. The point is solid and contains a core of nerve fibers.

The pushing tusks of the West African elephant are 2-3 meters long, 15-16 cm thick and weigh from 45-80 kg. They are pale shades of yellow, green, and red. Tusks of East African elephants display a characteristic dull milk white. The light yellow-white color is so characteristic it has been taken up in normal speech as the color designation "ivory."

Tusks of the Asiatic elephant are only 1-1.5 meters long with a weight of 20-30 kg. They have a finer grain and are softer, with a pure white color, but unfortunately they yellow very easily. This probably explains why even though the Asiatic elephant tusk is easier to work, in Europe the African is found more frequently.

Ivory can be identified by the distinguishing pattern of arching lines that criss-cross to create a grid made of curved parallel lines. This is true of all tusk material, and will never be seen in bones of any species. Though the pattern is more visible from certain orientations than others, it can be found in all but the smallest samples.

Material	Density in g/cm³	Color	Structure	Strength
Elephant Tusk	1.7 ... 1.83	yellowish white, also greenish white, reddish white	typical graining	elastic, low brittleness
Mammoth Tusk	APPROX 3.0	yellowish white	fossil, fine hairline cracks	hard, brittle
Walrus Tusk	1.95	greenish to yellowish white	similar to elephant tusk	elastic, low brittleness
Hippopotamus Tusk	1.9	white	dense	hard
Narwhal Tusk	1.95	pure white	fine grain	brittle
Sperm Whale Tooth	1.9	yellowish white	fine grain	carves well
Bone (beef)	–	yellowish white	smooth to finely striped	soft, elastic
Plastic	1.0 ... 1.3	white to yellowish	smooth, dense	soft, elastic

Table 2.1
Types of ivory.

Mammoth tusk

Mammoths, predecessors of today's elephant, dropped countless tusks eons ago that have become fossilized through long-term exposure to minerals. These can still be found in pieces as large as 5 meters long, and are worked as a legal alternative to elephant ivory. This material is harder, denser and heavier than normal elephant ivory and is often criss crossed by fine brownish-green hairline cracks.

Walrus tusk

After working, this material is similar to elephant tusk but in the natural state samples are easily distinguished because they are often ribbed on the outside, glass hard and dark. The tusks are 60-70 cm long with a weight of 2-3 kg, and reveal a greenish-yellow material inside. Walrus tusks are rarely seen as a working material today, but they may be seen in older work.

Hippopotamus tusks

The cutting and eye teeth are 40-60 cm long and weigh from 4-5 kg. They offer a hard, white material that does yellows only slightly over time. These are teeth rather than tusks, though the terms are often interchanged.

Narwhal tusk

This costly ivory comes from the screw-like spiral, hollow tusk of an Arctic whale. The tusk, which can be up to 3 meters long, is harder and more brittle than elephant tusk, pure white with fine texture. It reveals delicate, concentric circles in cross section.

Sperm whale tooth

Again these are technically teeth, not tusks, but because of their exotic origin they are often considered in a category similar to ivory. Most teeth are about 12 cm long and 6 cm thick and appear as a yellowish-white material that is easily carved. Whale teeth are most commonly found in the northern hemisphere, and can be studied in museums related to 19th century whaling.

Bone

Almost any bone can be used in the creation of jewelry, but the most commonly used come from cattle. Sections that are particularly dense and fibrous are selected, degreased, dried and worked in a similar manner to ivory.

Imitations

Recent years have seen several convincing plastics that imitate ivory, including a dense material referred to as ivory Micarta. Besides their ecological advantages, these materials are easy to carve or decorate because of their fully homogeneous structure.

2.1.1 WORKING OF IVORIES

Of all the types of ivory, real elephant tusk is still preferred, though for the ecological and ethical reasons mentioned earlier, its use cannot be condoned. The particular loveliness of ivory is the result of its delicate translucent color and arching grain. Cut lengthwise a net-like texture of diamond shaped elements becomes clear. Cut in cross section, the pattern is revealed as full ellipses.

Ivory carving can be traced back to the Stone Age, and (unfortunately) is still done today to create reliefs and fully dimensional sculptures. Traditionally, goldsmiths joined specialists in ivory carving to create objects in this unique material. Objects that combined gold and ivory were popular even with the ancient Greeks under the term "Chryselefantin."

As in wood carving, it's important to observe the grain direction. The material can split and fail to yield a smooth surface when carving takes place at a right angle to the grain. Another concern when working ivory is to avoid localized overheating that can result from drilling or carving with burs. Beyond the unpleasant smell of burnt bone, over-heating will cause the ivory to yellow, or even turn brown. To prevent this from happening, cool the ivory frequently in water and use power equipment only at slow speeds.

Ivory is worked according the following basic techniques. The rough shape is sawn out of the tusk with a circular saw, bandsaw, or a jewelers saw. It's also possible to rough out a form with a chisel, but unlike

Figure 2.1
Ivory boxes, turned. Wilfried Weisse, Erfurt.

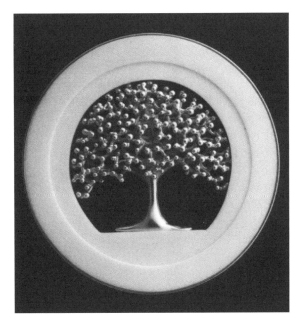

Figure 2.2
Ivory brooch, turned, centrifugally cast silver. Rainer Schumann, Dresden.

Figure 2.3
Ivory pendant, carved. Gudrun Höpner, Dresden.

wood, only small chips should be cut away with each stroke. From here burrs, rasps and large files are used to further advance the form, then details are worked in with small burrs set into the handpiece of a flexible shaft machine. Gravers and scrapers can also be used at this stage and are especially useful when the ivory or bone is being turned on a lathe.

It's also possible to mechanically deform ivory if it is boiled in water for 20 minutes. The structure is softened so much by this that it's possible to slowly and carefully bend the ivory in any desired manner if possible while still holding it submerged in hot water. Once a new shape is established, the position should be fixed until the ivory has completely cooled back to room temperature, or it will probably revert back to its original position.

Though literature from ancient times offer descriptions of a process of peeling ivory to create thin sheets that could be ironed into flat panels, I have been unable to achieve these results. This process is possible with cow horn, however, so the confusion might be the result of an early mistranslation.

The finished ivory shape is polished with pumice powder and water; using toothbrushes, linen rags, wooden sticks, cloth buffs or felt wheels at the polishing machine – or simply the end of a finger. Because ivory is very soft, a delicate touch is required when polishing sharp edges and flat surfaces. The familiar cutting and polishing media normally used in working metals such as tripoli or rouge should not be used at any time, because their colored residues will become trapped in the pores and cracks, permanently staining the work.

Final polishing is followed by gently simmering the work in a solution of equal parts of water and mild detergent, accompanied by a soft brushing. This treatment is also useful to clean old ivory. To brighten lightly yellowed ivory, soak the piece for up to 4 days in water to which some hydrogen peroxide has been added. Bleach is reserved for cases of extreme yellowing, and should be used in a cold water solution, or a slightly warmed mixture that includes about 10% hydrogen peroxide. Work may be allowed to soak for up to 10 hours, but should then be rinsed by soaking in clean water for at least twice that long. The effect of the bleaching agent must be continually checked during the treatment because of the danger that the fluoroapatite $Ca_5F(PO_4)_3$ contained in the ivory can be dissolved out by a bath that is too warm, too concentrated, or allowed to soak for too long. Such an over treatment will clean the ivory to a bright white, but it will also become porous and matte, so the actual loveliness of the ivory is lost. If this should occur, the ivory may be polished again, then daubed with pure olive oil which will be drawn into the pores to rejuvenate the luster.

There are numerous recipes for coloring ivory, which are mostly based on the fact that the material is etched with natural, namely animal or plant dye stuffs. Synthetic dyes have not proven themselves of value, because they usually are not sufficiently durable. The ivory's ability to absorb dyes is increased if it is soaked first in a warm, greatly diluted salt, potassium nitrate or nitric acid solution, after which it must be thoroughly rinsed in water. To turn ivory a warm brown color, soak it in a cup of strong black tea.

Figure 2.4
Brooches. Bone, filed and polished, centrifugally cast silver. Barbara Hesse, College of Applied Art, Heiligendamm.

Figure 2.5
Cameo pendant engraved in bone.

2.1.2 WORKING WITH BONE

Finished products of bone can look similar to ivory, but because of fundamental differences in the structures of the materials, there are some differences in their working. The bones of cattle that have a tubular shape (i.e. leg bones rather than ribs) are preferred and can be obtained from butchers in sizes up to 6 cm in diameter, 30 cm long with a wall thickness of about 1.5 cm. The bones of older cattle are preferred because of their especially dense, tight structure.

First all gristle, fat and flesh has to be completely removed. Even after that, they still have to boiled for several hours, first in a strong detergent, such as Tide® or a similar product. The bones are then rinsed in clear water which is changed numerous times, then allowed to dry naturally.

At any time during this process the pieces are roughly cut with a circular saw, coping saw or similar tool to create pieces of a convenient working size. During boiling it will become apparent that a layer of about a millimeter and a half is dissolved away. Additional material must be removed with a scraper.

When the material is thus made ready it is worked into shape with garnet abrasives. Steel tools quickly become dull when used on bone, so files are used only when there is no other way to achieve a particular form. The bone dust created by sanding and grinding will be deposited in the pores of the skin and breathed into the mucus membranes and lungs. Because of the health hazard posed by this dust, a respirator should be worn when working bone and all mechanical apparatus such as polishing machines must have an exhaust system.

Because dark abrasive media intrude into the pores of the bone, dark-colored abrasives such as garnet are avoided at the final stages. As an abrasive paper fills with bone dust it has a milder effect and the cutting action turns into a polishing one. To speed the process, abrasive papers can be glued onto wooden disks that are mounted onto the polishing machine, though be warned that this kind of fast action will create an unpleasant odor. By following the usual progression from coarse through increasingly finer papers, a silky luster is achieved.

The bones may be drilled and shaped with flexible shaft burrs, with diamond and ceramic abrasive tools preferred over metal burs. Bone may also be engraved, but because the structure is more fibrous than ivory, cuts made at right angles to the fibers are often irregular and frayed.

The silky luster obtained with polishing paper is a popular finish, but to achieve a higher shine, use titanium oxide or zinc oxide mixed to a paste with solvent alcohol. The paste is applied with the finger or soft leather and rubbed until it falls off as a dry powder. Bones can be dyed with wood acids and fabric dyes, but because of fat residues and structural differences the color may be unevenly absorbed leaving the surface spotty and clouded.

2.2
Mother of Pearl

"Mother of Pearl" is formed from the inside of the shell of oysters, certain types of sea snails and Nautilus shells. Thick shelled shellfish that are especially preferred for their mother of pearl deliver almost unusable pearls, the pearl-bearing mollusks being typically thin shelled.

A mollusk shell consists of three layers:

- The outer layer contains primarily the dark protein material conchiolin.
- The middle layer is formed of tiny triagonal calcium carbonate prisms which stand vertically upon the outer shell.
- The inner mother of pearl layer consists of tiny platelets of rhombic calcium carbonate, which are layered upon each other like roofing tiles and glued together by conchiolin.

Mother of pearl as a component of the protective shells of mollusks, is always found in the shape of concave plates, at largest perhaps 30 cm in diameter, but usually only 10-20 cm long and a few millimeters thick. Even though calcium carbonate (the basic component) is fairly soft, mother of pearl has the necessary hardness and toughness for use as a gem because of the special ordering and the adhesion of the components with conchiolin.

The particular beauty of mother of pearl comes from its optical characteristics, the result of absorption, refraction and reflection of light in the extremely thin crystal and conchiolin layers. Taken together, all this is described as sheen. The varied appearance of mother of pearl is determined by the type of mussel or snail in which it formed, its place of origin and the density of the material of which it is made. The basic colors of mother of pearl tend toward pink, bluish, greenish, or pale yellow. It is also possible to find mother of pearl as colorless or slightly translucent, which is considered especially valuable. In certain snails, mother of pearl can be as dense as porcelain and definitely colored, such as green, brown, pink.

The well known shell cameos are carved from the housing of the helmet snail which has clearly differentiated white and brown layers.

2.2.1 WORKING METHODS

While horn, tortoise shell and ivory may be bent when sufficiently hot, this is not possible with mother of pearl. This means that work is always restricted to a curved sheet. When small units are cut from the shell, the curvature is hardly noticeable, as for instance in common shirt buttons made of mother of pearl. If the original material was thick enough, it is even possible to grind flat pieces that have no trace of the original curve. This is typically the case when mother of pearl is used for inlay, as when pieces of various hue and value are assembled to create a pattern or composition.

Mother of pearl is most commonly worked with abrasives, but artists who are used to working with metal, which is considerably more resistant, should be advised to use a light touch. Mother of pearl can be cut with a jewelers saw, using coarser or finer blades depending on the thickness of the piece being cut. The material is shaped with the same files, drills, burs, gravers and scrapers used to work metal. Despite the apparent softness of mother of pearl, continued use will dull steel tools, so diamond, corundum, silicon carbide abrasives and carbide steel tools are recommended if extended work is anticipated. Fine abrasive papers and pumice are used for final finishing once the form has been achieved. Mother of pearl is polished with cloth or felt buffs charged with a fine polishing compound such as Viennese (also called French) Chalk.

Spotty or damaged mother of pearl products can be bleached after polishing by soaking the object in a solution of 30-50% hydrogen peroxide for 5-10 hours. This is followed by washing with soap and water, after which the piece is boiled in clean water for at least 20 minutes. This last rinsing is an important step that removes all traces of bleach from the shell which might otherwise stain the clothing of a person wearing the jewelry.

After bleaching, the mother of pearl is given one more treatment, this one a mild acid treatment to improve color and loosen the surface structure for final polishing. Dip the work in a hot 2% hydrochloric acid solution for 20-60 seconds. Of course standard safety precautions mandate the use of rubber gloves, goggles and protective clothing whenever acid is being handled.

Mother of pearl can be colored to enlarge its already wide range of effects. The first step in the coloring process is to prepare the surface by etching it lightly in a mixture of one liter of ammonium hydroxide with 80 grams of silver nitrate. To achieve a darker color, add 30-40 grams of copper sulfate. The length of time required to create a color can vary from 6 to 36 hours. When the desired color is achieved, the shell is rinsed thoroughly in running water. To add additional color, set the mother of pearl in a coloring bath with 3-5 grams per liter of aniline dye until the desired color is obtained.

Use standard epoxy to glue mother of pearl sections into metalwork after it has been thoroughly degreased. To clean dirtied objects that contain mother or pearl, use a soft brush and soapy water.

2.3
Tortoise Shell

As was mentioned above in the case of elephant ivory, this material is derived from an endangered species and its use is not condoned. In certain areas it may be illegal. The following description of the working properties of this material is provided as a foundation for the traditions of goldsmithing and for those cases where the concerned professional may have occasion to work on an older piece.

The highest quality tortoise shell is obtained from the sea turtle, principally the hawksbill, whose armored shell consists of plates of bone layered into the leather skin of the animal and covered on the outside with horn plates. The 13 main plates of the back armor sometimes achieve sizes of about 20 x 30 cm by 3-7 mm thick and each weighing about 250 g. The 13 belly plates are less valuable, because they only produce a yellowish "blonde" tortoise shell with a dark pattern.

In contrast the plates of the back armor have a flaming yellow, reddish or reddish-brown pattern on a dark greenish to black-brownish ground. Especially valuable is the black yellow speckled East Indian tortoise shell and the wide flamed Chinese material. On the other hand the Egyptian tortoise shell with small reddish-brown spots is of only limited value. Tortoise shell consists of pure protein, a structural protein that also appears in hair, hoofs, horn and feathers.

2.3.1 WORKING METHODS

Tortoise shell can be flattened by heating it in linseed oil, boiling water or over steam, then pressing it between steel plates until it has cooled to room temperature. Larger plates of shell can be made by "welding" pieces together. To do this the parts to be joined are first beveled to increase their contact areas. The degreased pieces are softened in boiling water and then pressed together in a vise so that they meld together to form a homogeneous mass. Naturally some practice is necessary to discover the precise conditions required for welding.

Subtractive forming is undertaken just as in metal and with the same tools. Care must be used, especially when using power tools, that the tortoise shell does not become so hot it burns. While small holes can be drilled, it is more efficient to create them by piercing with a hot needle. Finishing is accomplished with fine abrasive paper and pumice powder.

To create a high polish, mix a paste of tin oxide and any light oil and apply it with a cloth or piece of leather. Another polishing compound for tortoise shell is the traditional furniture polish made of 1 part shellac added to 14 parts by weight 96% alcohol. The polish is rubbed in with leather or a soft rag.

2.4
Horn

Though the term is sometimes used to describe a particular shape ("horn of plenty") and sometimes incorrectly applied to antler ("stag horn") the following section refers specifically to horns in their true sense.

Figure 2.6
Brooch and bracelets. Silver with horn additions.
Waltraud Behrendt, Arnstadt.

Figure 2.7
Neckpiece. Silver, middle part made of filed and polished horn.
Rolf Lindner, Erfurt.

Figure 2.8
Bracelet. The linked units are filed and polished horn; the connections are gold. Rolf Lindner, Erfur. (Museum des Kunsthandwerks Leipzig)

The substance is similar to tortoise shell, in that it is a flake-like, layered protein material. "Buffalo horn" is the most valuable type of animal horn. It originally was obtained from Bison and Aurochs, and later from American bison. Antelope, gazelles and gnu (wildebeest) are especially valued because of their fine grain. Today the horns of cattle ("steer horns") are usually used, but those of sheep and goats are also used.

The cattle horn used most often today can vary according to the type and place of origin. Horn is often sandy colored, but there are white, gray, brown and black varieties. Some horn is uniform in color, but most appears as striped or speckled; it can be opaque to transparent.

Because horns grow over tapered bone nubs on the skull of the animal, each horn has a hollow interior, leaving only the pointed tip as a solid mass. This is generally cut off when working to allow the rest of the horn to be flattened and rendered as sheet material.

Standard tools are used for subtractive forming and as indicated above, it is again important to avoid generating heat, which will scar or discolor the horn. As with tortoise shell, a section of horn is generally cut off and sliced along its axis, softened in hot water and stretched out to form flat sheets. As was the case with tortoise shell, the pieces must remain pressed between steel plates until completely cooled to room temperature.

Finishing is also accomplished in the manner described above for tortoise shell. Small marks are removed with fine abrasive papers, followed by a paste made of pumice and oil. Horn can be polished with compounds usually used on metal with conventional polishing equipment, or with the shellac-alcohol solution mentioned previously.

In earlier times, familiar functional objects such as shoe horns and combs were made from horn, but today these are made more efficiently of plastic. In jewelry design, horn combines well with metal and other materials and is still seen in buttons, belt buckles and other fashion articles (figures 2.6 to 2.8).

2.5
Wood

Equipment and tools made from wood were always important to goldsmiths, but in this section we are considering the use of wood as a material for direct use in jewelry and hollowware. Wood is ideally suited for many applications because of its ease of subtractive shaping and relatively low cost.

2.5.1 WOOD GRAIN

Because of the way it grows, wood has a fibrous structure (determined by growing conditions), consisting of cells radially oriented around the central axis of the trunk. During the spring growing season these are light colored and soft; they turn dark and hard in the dormant or slow-growth winter months. The results of this rhythm are the well known annual rings that give each piece of wood its unique finger print. Inside the trunk lies the darker colored dead wooden core, called heartwood, surrounded by the light colored, soft sapwood.

The characteristics of a cut sample of wood are primarily the result of the direction of the grain and the orientation of the sample to the way it was cut. If a piece is cut at right angles to the axis of the trunk (end grain wood) the resulting material is more homogenous and denser than a sample cut parallel to the axis of the trunk, which will show the grain more clearly. The mechanical toughness is significantly greater in the direction of the fibers than at right angles to it.

2.5.2 PRECIOUS WOODS

Metalsmiths work primarily with dense exotic hardwoods, but there are many instances in which more familiar woods such as maple, apple or pear are ideally suited because of their color and grain. Small scraps of precious woods are often available inexpensively from woodworking businesses.

It unfortunately becomes necessary once again to mention the ecological damage that has been the result of careless harvesting of hardwoods from rain forests in the southern hemisphere. Because of international concern, recent legislation has sought to control the sale of certain rare hardwoods. These are still available as a controlled, replanted crop from reputable dealers. Concerned goldsmiths will want to research proper channels for obtaining this material.

Ebony

True ebony is remarkably dense, heavy, hard and brittle. The heartwood is black, dark gray or dark brown, in some pieces showing a bluish striation. The light sapwood is not usually used. The best quality is that of the bluish-black Madagascar ebony. Macassar ebony is clearly grained; black stripes on a reddish-brown ground. Because of its dense structure, ebony may be turned, carved, filed and finished to a bright polish. It has no easy cleavage. Because of the appealing contrast of this dark material with the light color of silver, it has long been a popular material for jewelry, hollowware handles, and knife handles. Because of its relatively high price, ebony is sometimes replaced by less valuable woods that have been chemically colored with stains.

Mahogany

Classic mahogany comes from Cuba and other Caribbean islands, but because the groves there are so badly decimated, it is rare to find first quality product from those sources. Most of the mahogany we see today comes from Central America or from West and Central Africa, which produces a striped variety.

Regardless of their origin, all mahoganies share the rich reddish-brown color, which darkens in the course of time, with clearly evident patterns that may be described as spotted, fiery, wavy, stippled and grained. Because the long fibers of this wood are oriented in the direction of growth, mahogany resists splitting and planing. It retains its shape when drying does not warp – and rarely splits. Fine grained mahogany lends itself well to subtractive work and has a long tradition of use in jewelry and hollowware. It combines well with gold due to the richness of its color.

Rosewood

This familiar and diverse species can be identified by its dark reddish-brown color, its extreme hardness and the characteristic scent of violets that can be detected when the wood is filed or sanded. Most samples are marked with deep black bands in more or less parallel stripes. Rosewood is hard, heavy, dense and responsive to traditional carving with chisels or rasps. It resists splitting and will quickly dull steel tools. In final finishing stages, oils can leech from the wood to render the surface unpleasantly matte. To prevent this, dissolve the dyed oils with alcohol before polishing. Rosewood is often used for jewelry and hollowware in combination with precious metals.

Cedar

As early as the 3rd century BC, cedars from Lebanon were cut as construction lumber, especially for ship building. Now many species of cedars are protected by law and are therefore not available any more in Europe. Contemporary "cigar box cedar" is probably a variety of juniper that has a similar aromatic scent. This "cedar wood" is somewhat lighter than mahogany, has a beautiful grain and does not darken with time. It carves well, is easily worked subtractively, splits easily, scarcely changes shape while drying and rarely cracks.

2.5.3 VEINED WOODS

In addition to characteristics shared by all wood within a species of tree, individual samples display naturally occurring growth patterns or mutations that can make parts of even common wood exceptional. Arched, intricate, wavy, or patterned sections are often formed at the junction of roots, limbs or as the result of injury to the tree while it was growing. Decoratively grained areas may be found in virtually any wood, but are most familiar in box wood, yew, ash, veined birch, walnut, olive, elm, black poplar, and sugar maple.

Since ancient times, grained woods have been used for decorative purposes. Turned decorative containers were much loved in the Renaissance and the Baroque periods and continue their popularity even today, when dense, heavily-grained woods are preferred for turning. Because of their complicated grain patterns and resultant dense structure, these woods typically carve and turn well and take a high polish.

2.6
Plastics

Editor's Note: The field of polymer chemistry is vast and changing constantly. The following information is presented as general background only. Students seeking more detailed information are encouraged to pursue specific literature.

It hardly needs noting that we are surrounded each day with synthetic materials. The pervasive way this material has affected every aspect of modern life leaves us with the assumption that the field continues to grow and improve and will play an even greater role in our lives in the future.

There is an abundance of specialized literature about plastics and how to work with them, so we need not go into great detail here. But because plastics are playing an increasingly important role in the field of jewelry design, both in one-of-a-kind pieces and in the fashion industry, a brief description is appropriate here.

For our lay purposes we can define plastics as a man-made substance characterized by large molecules. These are derived by transforming either natural or synthetic raw materials. Though we use the word inclusively, it is helpful to narrow the definitions according to their technical uses:
  – plastics
  – elastics (rubber-like elastics)
  – synthetic fibers
  – fluid plastics (glues, lacquers, resins)

Today the range of plastics is so vast and varied that a casual survey can only point out large distinctions. Readers with particular interests in plastics are encouraged to pursue specialized literature, with the hope that the following overview will make subsequent research more meaningful.

Plastics consist of organic macromolecules, some obtained by modification of large-molecule natural materials (cellulose, casein plastics), and others produced completely synthetically from low molecular materials. Plastics fall into two general categories: One family are called thermoplastics – they are moldable when warm then become solid when cooled.

Because thermoplastics can go through this transition indefinately, they can be used over and over.

The other group are called thermosetting plastics because they emit heat when they go from a liquid or paste to a solid. These plastics remain solid even when reheated; examples are epoxies and phenolics.

2.6.1 SYNTHESIS PROCEDURES
Addition Polymerization
(examples: polyethylene, polystyrenes & acrylic)
A precondition of this process is the presence of multiple carbon compounds in the monomer initial molecule. When these compounds are activated by catalysts, the molecules are made inordinately reactive. They open neighboring molecules and combine with them to form a macromolecule; this is the start of the reaction.

Because the macromolecule that is formed still has open valences, further ethylene molecules can attach themselves, like beads on a string. In this way the macromolecule can continually grow (the growth reaction) until all reactive initial molecules have been incorporated (the end reaction).

If "A" is the monomer initial molecule, the reaction principle for the polymerization is:

$$A + A + A + A \ldots \rightarrow \text{ macromolecule}$$

Polycondensation
The macromolecule is formed from two different kinds of initial molecules (for example "resin" and "hardener"), whereby low molecular materials – usually water – are freed.

The initial materials "A" and "B" react in the following manner:

$$A + B \rightarrow \text{ macromolecule} + \text{water}$$
$$\text{resin} \quad \text{hardener}$$

In typical polycondensation, monomers not only combine themselves linearly in the macromolecule but also form "bridges" between the macromolecules. This mechanism forms the interconnections of the structure and makes this an ideal adhesive.

Polyaddition

In this case, macromolecules are formed by the unification of various kinds of initial molecules, but without the formation of further materials:

$$A \; + \; B \; \rightarrow \; \text{macromolecule}$$
$$\text{resin} \quad \text{hardener}$$

2.6.2 PLASTIC MATERIALS

Polystyrene

Polystyrene is a typical thermoplastic. It naturally occurs as a glass-clear material but may be colored with dyes. It has a hard, shiny surface, is resistant to acids and is barely attacked by solvents. Polystyrene is widely used in injection molding procedures, and is commonly used to produce inexpensive articles such as souvenirs, toys and some kinds of fashion jewelry.

In manufacture, the granulated plastic mass goes from a supply funnel through a hydraulically powered nozzle. The mass is pushed forward in an electrically heated injection cylinder until the necessary fluidity is achieved at 190-250°C. In this state the plastic mass is injected through a nozzle into the mold. In mass production, an injection machine is programmed so the procedure progresses in an precisely determined sequence:

- Closing of the two part injection mold.
- Lifting stroke of the cylinder.
- Forward movement of the plastic mass in the injection cylinder.
- Injection into the casting mold.
- Cooling of the plastic mass in the mold.
- Opening of the mold.
- Ejection of the molded piece.
- Closing of the two part injection mold.

Because polystyrene is dissolved by organic solvents or benzene, pieces can be chemically welded by applying a solvent. Small amounts of a solvent are applied to each surface, which are then pressed together forming a permanent, almost invisible joint.

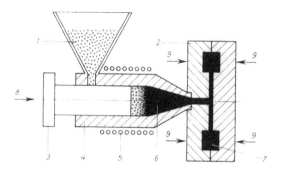

Figure 2.9
How an injection casting machine for plastics works.
1) granulated plastic
2) two part mold
3) pressure ram
4) housing
5) heater
6) softened thermoplastic
7) cast piece
8) force of pressure
9) pressure holding mold onto injector.

Polystyrene remains stable in shape at temperatures of about 100°C. It is possible to work polystyrene subtractively, but even the modest heat of a hand operated jewelers saw will generate enough friction heat to soften the chips to the point where they spontaneously weld. This can be prevented only by cooling the sawing action with water or a blast of pressurized air.

The main disadvantage of polystyrene is its limited ability to resist bending when a force is laid against it. This problem was addressed by layering elastic molecules into the structure as the polystyrene molecule is being generated (polymerized). A special development is a polymerization of:

- acrylonitrile (for chemical resistance)
- butadiene (elasticity)
- styrene (hardness, thermoplastic characteristics)

These ABS plastics are characterized by particularly useful working characteristics; it is especially noteworthy that this plastic can even be electrolytically covered with metal.

Polyethylene (PE)

Polyethylene polymers are divided into categories according to their density. The low density material is the familiar PE-LD (0.915-0.939 g/cm³), while the higher density, or more rigid material is technically described as PE-HD (0.940-0.965 g/cm³). Both have practical importance.

It is useful to compare two popular families of plastic – polyethylene and polystyrene. Both are thermoplastics. Polyethylene is milky translucent, but can be colored as an opaque material in glowing colors. It has a great ability to retain its shape and excellent resistance to breakage, and is highly resistant to heat and chemicals. A piece of polyethylene can be bent back and forth hundreds of times without breaking.

Polyethylene is well suited to injection molding, except for its high shrinkage factor during cooling. This falls between 1-3%, which is considerably higher than the shrinkage rate for polystyrene. Polyethylene can be deep drawn into suitable shapes by vacuum forming and with sufficient cooling and sharp tools, subtractive shaping is also possible.

Polyethylcnc has a slick, "slippery" surface; it is resistant to water, chemicals and organic solvents, which makes it difficult to glue, weld or print on. For this reason parts made of polyethylene are typically joined together mechanically, for example using tabs.

Polymethylmethacylate (piacryl, plexiglas, acrylic, pimma)

This is another member of the thermoplastic polymer family, but it is significantly different from the plastics described above because of its transparency, which is rated at 92%. Polymethylmethacrylate can be colored without affecting its transparency, and is resistant against weather, non-oxidizing acids, bases, mineral oils and greases.

Plastics in this family are well suited for subtractive chip forming operations. They can be easily worked with coarse files and saws, and can be drilled, turned, and carved with burs. Pieces can be easily welded or glued. When heated to temperatures between 120°-170°C, polymethylmethmethacrylate can be stretched and deep drawn as a soft ductile mass. In order to retain shape, the piece must be held in position during cooling.

Polymethylacrylate is often purchased as sheet, rod or bar stock, but it can be obtained in liquid form as its monomer initial material, known as hardener and catalyst. These can be cast, and may be colored with pigments or synthetic dyes during the process. Further additives or filler materials such as brick dust or metal powders can create a wide range of effects. A rubber mold may be made from an original model, then filled with polymethylacrylate. It is allowed to harden, when the item can be removed and finished.

Unsaturated polyester resins (UP)

"Esters" are compounds that form from organic acids and alcohol through aqueous disassociation. Linear macromolecules grow through polycondensation leaving free valences, that are "unsaturated." In this resinous state, ductile fluid masses form. This unsaturated resin can be dissolved in styrene which polymerizes with the addition of catalysts. The double bonds of the free valences of the resin molecules dissociate, causing the polyester molecules to be joined together by bridges of polystyrene. In this way, the casting resin forms a hard interconnected mass called a thermosetting plastic.

This ability to be cast, combined with the transparent nature of the material and its ability to accept a wide range of additives, give polyester resins tremendous potential. Polyester resins are clear as glass, resistant to light, resistant against water, weak acids and organic solvents. They may be colored in a wide variety of hues. Polyester resins may be easily worked subtractively by conventional grinding, filing and sanding. In addition, resin can be poured into molds and can have materials embedded into it. A commercial example of the use of this is the synthetic amber that can be made by casting an appropriately colored resin into a cabochon-shaped mold. In some cases natural amber is embedded in the plastic to create a material that is part synthetic and part genuine.

Another use of this resin in jewelry is to pour it directly onto a metal surface to fill up depressions or cloissons created by wire strips. To improve adhesion,

Figure 2.10
Brooch and earring. Chased, granulated silver, modeled, painted plastic. Gabriele Putz, Magdeburg.

Figure 2.11
Neckpiece. Modeled plastic, silver, leather. Gerhild Freese, Berlin. (Staatl. Museen zu Berlin, Kunstgewerbemuseum)

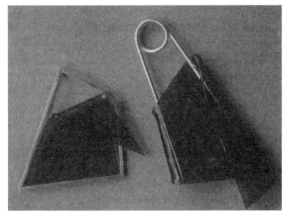

Figure 2.12
Pins. Piacry, thermally shaped, silver. Annette Pergande, College of Applied Art, Heiligendamm.

the metal surface is first cleaned and roughed. In some cases it might also be useful to build a temporary wall of paper or tape around the object so it can be over-filled to allow for shrinkage as the plastic cures. After it has hardened, the resin is ground down, refined and polished.

By using less than the recommended proportion of hardener, the amount of shrinkage can be reduced – though the resin will take longer to cure. In general the properties of the material itself will not be affected, though the surfaces exposed to air may not harden but will remain sticky. To prevent this, seal the surface from air with a sheet of kitchen foil or plastic wrap that can be easily cut away during finishing. Colored transparent resins can be layered in ways that have traditionally been used for vitreous enamels, for instance by layering colors to create a rich effect, or by decorating a surface that is then covered with a transparent colored enamel.

Yet another use of resins is their application to bond glass fiber mats that have been soaked with the polymer. These materials, familiar to some from boat building or auto repair, are remarkably light but have a high tensile strength. Because of their strength and ease of use, polymer resins have found wide use as adhesives, most notably as the family called epoxies.

Epoxy resins
The starting material for these resins are the two organic compounds epichorhydrin and bisphenol A which can combine with each other in such a way that the epichlorhydrin contains a ring of oxygen atoms that disassociates and so makes possible the bonding with the OH radical at the free end of the bisphenol A molecule.

In the presence of alkalis, hydrochloric acid may be disassociated from this new molecule, creating a new reactive epoxy ring that can react with the OH radical to form another bisphenol A molecule. In this way the structure grows to form an epoxy macromolecule. The mass that is developed forms the fluid resin. The solidification begins with the addition of the hardener through the meshing of the macromolecules into a thermoplastic. This dissociates the oxygen ring at the end of the epoxy resin molecule which causes the following reaction to occur:

Dian and Epichlorhydrin

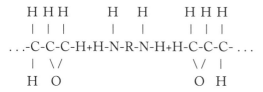

| End of an epoxy resin molecule | Amine (hardener) | End of an epoxy resin molecule |

Portion of an epoxy resin molecule after hardening:

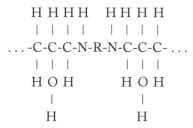

The hardening of the epoxy resin proceeds as a polyaddition, uninhibited by the creation of secondary materials such as water, gases, and acids. If set free these would need to spread out during the reaction. Because of this these casting resins solidify without bubbles, forming homogenous sheets of adhesive that will harden consistently and with great strength.

Epoxy resins are naturally transparent with a light yellowish-brown tone; they can be colored easily. They are resistant to even aggressive organic and inorganic materials and because they undergo almost no shrinkage while hardening they are well suited as a casting resin. When casting it is best to vacuum the mix to remove bubbles created in the mixing process.

The photos in this chapter illustrate jewelry pieces that convincingly demonstrate how non-metallic materials can enrich jewelry deign. By taking advantage of traditional materials worked in unusual ways and new technological possibilities, modern goldsmiths continue to enlarge their field of opportunity.

CHAPTER THREE

Studio Chemistry

3.1
Acids and Bases

The importance of safety precautions cannot be over stressed: the following chapter is presented as background information valuable to professional metalsmiths. Anyone pursuing direct work with Aqua Regia or the acids mentioned in this chapter is advised to seek the help of trained specialists familiar with these strong chemicals. Acids should not be handled or even uncapped except in the presence of proper protective clothing and equipment.

When diluting acids, always add the acid to the water – never the reverse. In this way the denser fluid mingles with the water, distributing the heat that is inevitably produced.

Table 3.1
Acids and bases.

Acids		Bases	
The molecule consists of			
HCl (H$^+$ Cl$^-$) H$_2$SO$_4$ (2H$^+$ SO$_4{}^{2-}$)		NaOH (Na$^+$ $^-$OH) NH$_4$ OH (NH$_4{}^+$ $^-$OH)	
Hydrogen is the chemically active component.	The acid radical is a nonmetal or non-metallic oxide.	Metal or ammonia group	Hydroxide ion is the chemically active component.
The number of			
H$^+$ ions the acid radical	is the valence of	$^-$OH ions the metal	
In water solution dissociation results in freely mobile, electrically positively charged			
hydrogen ions	and negatively charged	metal or ammonia ions	
acid radical ions H$_2$SO$_4$ → 2H$^+$ + SO$_4{}^{2-}$		hydroxide ions NaOH → Na$^+$ + OH$^-$	
The strength of the acids and the bases is expressed by their degree of disassociation in an aqueous solution.			
The name is formed from			
the characteristic central atom of the acid radical with addition of the "acid" (sulfuric acid, for instance). The lower degree of oxidation is expressed by adding "ous." The higher degree is expressed by adding "per" (sulfurous acid, perchloric acid). "Ortho" and "meta" is used for water of hydration (orthoboric acid).		the specific metal (or ammonia) with the addition "hydroxide" (sodium hydroxide). The aqueous solution is called a "base."	
Blue litmus paper turns red (pH < 7), tastes sour. Metals are dissolved to become salts.		Red litmus paper turns blue (pH > 7), feels slippery. Fats are emulsified and saponified.	
Neutralization: When an acid reacts with a base, water and a salt form and the solution becomes neutral (pH = 7). H$_2$SO$_4$ + 2KOH → K$_2$SO$_4$ + 2H$_2$O			

Name	Formula		Valence of the acid radical	Salt
	Hydrogen	Acid Radical		
cyanic acid (prussic acid)	H^+	CN^-	I	cyanide
boric acid (orthoboric acid)	$3H^+$	BO^{3-}	III	borate
metaboric acid	H	BO_2^-	I	metaborate
tetraboric acid	$2H^+$	$B_4O_7{}^{2-}$	II	tetraborate
chromic acid	$2H^+$	$CrO_4{}^{2-}$	II	chromate
dichromic acid	$2H^+$	$Cr_2O_7{}^{2-}$	II	dichromate
hydrofluoric acid	H	F	I	fluoride
silicic acid	$2H^+$	$SiO_3{}^{2-}$	II	silicate
carbonic acid	$2H^+$	$CO_3{}^{2-}$	II	carbonate
phosphoric acid	$3H^+$	$PO_4{}^{3-}$	III	phosphate
nitric acid	H	$NO_3{}^-$	I	nitrate
hydrocloric acid	H	Cl^-	I	choride
sulfuric acid	$2H^+$	SO_4	II	sulfate
hydrogen sulfide	$2H^+$	S^{2-}	II	sulfide
gold tetrachloric acid	H	$[AuCl_4]^-$	I	chloroaurate

Table 3.2
Important acids.

Boric acid, H_3BO_3

Boric acid is a very weak acid that crystallizes in the form of small white, translucent flakes. It is generally sold as a white powder and is easily soluble in hot water. The salts, called borates, include a compound called borax, which is used in flux. When heated, water that is chemically bound to the boric acid is driven out. At roughly 70°C, metaboric acid, which has a melting point of 160°C is created. With continued heating to 500°C, boric oxide appears.

$$H_3BO_3 \rightarrow HBO_2 + H_2O$$
orthoboric acid   metaboric acid   water

$$2HBO_2 \rightarrow B_2O_3 + H_2O$$
metaboric acids   boric oxide   water

At 577°C this material begins to form a fibrous cloak over an object that is highly resistant to penetration by oxygen. Therefore, boric acid is used during soldering to help prevent the development of firescale at temperatures up to 900°C. If a metal object is covered with this film during annealing, the metal oxides present are transformed into metaborates, as in the following example:

$$B_2O_3 + CuO \rightarrow Cu(BO_2)_2 + \text{other}$$
boric oxide   copper (II)   copper   products
oxide   metaborate

It is important to note, however, that at these temperatures the metaborates that have been dissolved in the boric oxide are deposited upon the metal surface as a thick resilient layer of slag that will prevent the access of newly active boric oxide material. This greatly reduces the effectiveness of later additions of boric acid to a piece being heated. Because of this, it is better to have an excess of boric acid at the outset of heating rather than to have too little.

When the temperature is increased to over 900°C, the boric oxide becomes fluid enough to act as a flux. At this point the boric acid is a clear slippery fluid that facilitates the flow of solder. If allowed to cool slowly to room temperature, the boric acid coating will withstand immersion in water. It can be easily dissolved in standard jeweler's pickle, and will also dissolve in boiling water.

Nitric acid, HNO₃

- Pure (100%)   Density 1.52.g/ml
- Red smoking (98%)   Density 1.50 g/ml
- Concentrated (69.2%) Density 1.41 g/
  called reagent grade
- Diluted (25.5%)   Density 1.15 g/ml
  called commercial grade

This very strong acid is a colorless oily liquid in its pure state, but upon exposure to light it forms nitrous oxide NO_2 which has a sharp odor and pale yellow-to-brown color, both attributes that are commonly used to distinguish this acid. Nitric acid blends easily with water, achieving its most constant mixture at 69.2%. The boiling point of reagent grade nitric acid is 121.8°C.

Nitric acid is a strong oxidizer: organic materials (like skin!) will be stained yellow and dissolved. Great care must be used whenever handling this acid or in the presence of its vapors. Metals are first oxidized and dissolved to form nitrates.

With copper the following reaction occurs:

$$3Cu \quad + \quad 2HNO_3 \qquad \rightarrow$$
copper   nitric acid

$$3CuO \quad + \quad H_2O \quad + \quad 2NO$$
copper (II) oxide   water   nitric oxide

The two acid molecules used for oxidation are converted to water and nitric oxide. The nitric oxide immediately oxidizes in air becoming $(NO_2)_2$ which dimerizes as a reddish-brown poisonous vapor. The metal oxide is now converted to a salt:

$$3CuO \quad + \quad 6HNO_3 \qquad \rightarrow$$
copper (II) oxide   nitric acid

$$3Cu(NO_3)_2 \quad + \quad 3H_2O$$
cupric nitrate   water

Six further nitric acid molecules are used up in salt formation through which even more water is freed. These two reactions may be merged into the following summary equation:

$$3Cu \quad + \quad 8HNO_3 \qquad \rightarrow$$
$$3Cu(NO_3)_2 \quad + \quad 4H_2O \quad + \quad 2NO$$

The reaction with silver follows a similar course, again releasing water and the poisonous gas nitric oxide while creating a salt called silver nitrate:

$$6Ag \quad + \quad 2HNO_3 \quad \rightarrow$$
$$3Ag_2O_3 \quad + \quad H_2O \quad + \quad 2NO$$

$$3Ag_2O \quad + \quad 6HNO_3 \quad \rightarrow$$
$$6AgNO_3 \quad + \quad 3H_2O$$

$$6Ag \quad + \quad 8HNO_3 \quad \rightarrow$$
$$6AgNO_3 \quad + \quad 4H_2O \quad + \quad 2NO$$

Certain base metals such as aluminum, chromium and iron are soluble only in diluted nitric acid because an impenetrable oxide film is formed in the concentrated acid. Gold and platinum are not attacked by nitric acid which explains why it has traditionally been used to purify those metals. A 50% nitric acid solution (refining water) can be used to separate gold from silver.

Typical studio uses of nitric acid are for etching, to dissolve various metals, for pickling and bright dipping, for gold testing and for making Aqua Regia. A variant of this acid, nitrous acid , HNO_2 is only available in diluted solutions; its salts are termed nitrites.

Hydrochloric acid, HCl

Hydrogen chloride gas is a colorless gas with a stinging smell, strongly hygroscopic (i.e. it easily absorbs water from the air). Dissolved in water it produces hydrochloric acid.

- Fuming (40%)   Density 1.198 g/ml
- Concentrated (24-36%) Density 1.12-1.18 g/ml
- Dilute (12.5%)   Density 1.06 g/ml

When diluted hydrochloric acid is heated, some of its water evaporates, leaving the acid more concentrated. At the boiling point of the acid (111°C), dangerous hydrogen chloride gas is released. A constant mixture is achieved at the proportions of roughly 20% HCl and 80% water.

Hydrochloric acid is a strongly smelling, strongly etching aqueous solution of hydrogen chloride gas that mandates extreme caution. As raw hydrochloric acid the solution is colored yellow by contamination with iron (II)-chloride.

Many non-precious metals are dissolved to form chlorides, as for instance:

$$Zn \quad + \quad 2HCl \quad \rightarrow$$
zinc \qquad hydrochloric acid

$$ZnCl_2 \quad + \quad H_2$$
zinc chloride \quad hydrogen gas

In the case of some metals, action of the acid creates a chloride film that covers the metal and inhibits further reaction. This is the case with silver, which forms a greasy insoluble skin as illustrated in the following reaction:

$$2HCl \quad + \quad 2Ag \quad \rightarrow \quad 2AgCl \quad + \quad H_2$$

Because of this, silver is practically insoluble in hydrochloric acid.

Aqua Regia

Though not technically an acid but a mixture of two acids, this compound deserves to be included in this section because of its extreme potency and its traditional association with goldsmithing.

Aqua Regia is produced by mixing together 3 volumes of hydrochloric acid with 1 volume of nitric acid. Because the mixture decomposes when stored for more than a few days, it must be freshly prepared before each use. Its purpose is limited to dissolving the "kings" of metals – gold and platinum. The chemical reaction can be demonstrated using gold as an example. First of all the nitric acid oxidizes the hydrochloric acid.

$$HNO_3 \quad + \quad 3HCl \quad \rightarrow$$
nitric acid \qquad hydrochloric acid

$$NOCl \quad + \quad Cl_2 \quad + \quad 2H_2O$$
nitrosylchloride \quad chlorine gas \quad water

Through this reaction the two active agents nitrosylchloride and chlorine are formed. The first, nitrosylchloride, O = N-Cl, can be understood as an acidic chloride of nitrous acid, while the other active component, chlorine ions, at their moment of their release work upon the gold ions and are therefore significantly more aggressive than chlorine gas Cl_2.

$$Au \quad + \quad NOCl \quad + \quad Cl_2 \quad \rightarrow$$
gold \quad nitrosylchloride \qquad chlorine gas

$$AuCl_3 \quad + \quad NO$$
gold chloride \quad nitric oxide

The gold (III) chloride combines immediately with a further molecule of HCl to form a complex acid:

$$AuCl_3 \quad + \quad HCl \quad \rightarrow \quad H[AuCl_4]$$

This chlorine gold acid combines with four molecules of water to form bright yellow crystals. In the trade these are commonly referred to as "gold chloride." When mixed with additional water this compound dissolves to make a fluid of the same color.

$$H[AuCl_4] \cdot 4H_2O$$

The reaction on platinum works in a similar way. The end product, chloroplatinic acid, is formed and crystallizes out with six molecules of water.

$$H_2[PtCl_6] \cdot 6H_2O$$

Sulfuric acid, H_2SO_4

- Pure (100%) \qquad Density 1.85 g/ml
- Concentrated (98.3%) \quad Density 1.84 g/ml
- Raw (9-98%) \qquad Density about 1.84 g/ml
- Dilute (about 10%) \quad Density 1.06-1.11 g/ml

All metals except gold and platinum can be dissolved in hot concentrated sulfuric acid to form sulfates. In its pure state sulfuric acid is an oily, colorless fluid with a high density. Fuming sulfuric acid contains excessive sulfur trioxide SO_3 and is therefore particularly active.

Sulfuric acid is strongly hygroscopic and can remove even chemically bonded water from many materials, carbonizing organic materials in the process. This makes it particularly dangerous! Sulfuric acid can be diluted to any proportion with water.

The reaction of metals in sulfuric acid may be seen in the following:

$$Zn + H_2SO_4 \rightarrow ZnSO_4 + H_2$$

Even metals that are high on the electromotive scale can be dissolved by prior oxidation in a similar manner to nitric acid as with the example of copper.

$$\underset{\text{copper}}{Cu} + \underset{\text{sulfuric acid}}{H_2SO_4} \rightarrow$$

$$\underset{\text{copper (II) oxide}}{CuO} + \underset{\text{sulfur dioxide}}{SO_2} + \underset{\text{water}}{H_2O}$$

This is possible because the sulfuric acid is converted during the oxidation of the metal into sulfurous acid, which immediately disassociates to form sulfur dioxide and water. The copper oxide is dissolved as well, in the same way the black layer of copper (II) oxide that forms during annealing is dissolved in pickle.

$$\underset{\text{copper oxide}}{CuO} + \underset{\text{sulfuric acid}}{H_2SO_4} \rightarrow$$

$$\underset{\text{copper sulfate}}{CuSO_4} + \underset{\text{water}}{H_2O}$$

The entire reaction is then

$$Cu + 2H_2SO_4 \rightarrow$$
$$CuSO_4 + SO_2 + 2H_2O$$

The red copper (I) oxide is first converted to copper (II) oxide in the sulfuric acid and is then dissolved away in the manner just described.

$$\underset{\text{copper (I) oxide}}{Cu_2O} + \underset{\text{sulfuric acid}}{H_2SO_4} \rightarrow$$

$$\underset{\text{copper (II) oxide}}{2CuO} + \underset{\text{sulfur dioxide}}{SO_2} + \underset{\text{water}}{H_2O}$$

Formation of the oxides that are necessary for this dissolving is possible only in concentrated acid. When cold sulfuric acid is diluted to less than 20% it will dissolve only base metals such as iron, zinc, and aluminum, leaving copper and silver unattacked. This effect can be useful for those cases when a section of base metal needs to be removed from a precious one, for instance to remove a broken drill bit from a sterling object, or to etch away an aluminum core set into a precious tube as a support for bending.

In the goldsmith's studio, sulfuric acid is used for pickles, in gold testing, as an additive in bright dip, to dissolve various metals as just described and in acid copper plating.

Sodium hydroxide, NaOH
Sodium hydroxide forms white, translucent, brittle, crystalline flakes that are strongly hygroscopic, and like all bases, it feels slippery between the fingers. This is a signature of a base, the slipperiness being caused by dissolved skin cells. When dissolved in water, sodium hydroxide forms a strong base that is used as a powerful cleaning and degreasing solution. This solution has the ability to emulsify fatty materials and mineral oils. When fats are mixed with sodium hydroxide they are converted to glycerin and fatty acid salts which create soap. Potassium hydroxide, KOH, reacts identically to sodium hydroxide and can be used for the same practical purposes.

Ammonium hydroxide, NH₄OH
If the colorless, sharply smelling ammonia gas NH_3 is passed through water, both components interact to create reaction products that immediately dissociate in the solution as shown here:

$$NH_3 + H_2O \leftrightarrows NH_4^+ + OH^-$$

The ammonium hydroxide NH_4OH thus formed consists of the dissociated positively charged ammonium ions NH_4^+ and the hydroxide ions OH^-. The base only exists in this form; a direct chemical combination of both materials does not exist. Upon heating, the reaction runs in reverse and the base again

Chemical name of the base	Common name	Name of the "lye" solution	Formula		Valence
			Base portion	Hydroxide group	
ammonium chloride	sal ammoniac	sal ammoniac	NH_4^+	^-OH	I
calcium hydroxide	slaked lime	chalk water	Ca^{2+}	$(^-(OH)_2$	II
potassium hydroxide	etching lye	potash	K^+	^-OH	I
sodium hydroxide	etching lye		Na^+	^-OH	I

Table 3.3
Important bases.

forms ammonia gas and water. As a weak base, ammonium hydroxide works in a similar manner to that described with sodium hydroxide as a cleaning and degreasing agent.

3.2
The Nomenclature of Salts

In a salt the acidic hydrogen is replaced by a metal, the salt consisting then of a metal and an acid radical. In a double salt, two different salts are combined in such a way that though they are stable as a solid, they disassociate in an aqueous solution as if both salts were dissolved separately. Alum disassociates in such a manner:

$$KAl(SO_4)_2 \rightarrow K^+ + Al^{3+} + 2 SO_4^{2-}$$

A complex salt on the other hand is a compound of a higher order in which a salt with completely new characteristics is formed. This new salt doesn't break up into its individual components in an aqueous solution but instead forms complex ions such as potassium gold cyanide:

$$K[Au(CN)_2] \rightarrow K^+ + [Au(CN)_2]^-$$

Table 3.4 lists the names of salts and their relationship to various acids and metals. It's possible to determine the oxygen content of an acid by interpreting the suffixes as shown:

-ide = with oxygen free acids
-ate = with acids with a normal oxygen content
-ite = with acids with limited oxygen content
hypo. . . ite = with hypo-oxygen content acids
per. . . ate = with high oxygen content acids
(peracids)

3.3
Dealing with Toxic Chemicals

Strict and specific rules governing the sale, storage and use of strong chemicals have been devised to protect people and our environment. Goldsmiths must take responsibility to learn the appropriate ordinances of their area and should take steps to ensure compliance. The following general advice is presented to provide broad background information.

Toxins are defined as dangerous chemical materials that can cause temporary or permanent health damage or death to living organisms.

Highly toxic chemicals
   – mercury compounds
   – hydrocyanic acids and their salts (ingredients of electroplating baths)
   – nitric acid (including fumes)
   – hydrochloric acid (including dilute solutions)
   – sulfuric acid (including dilute solutions)
   – ammonia solutions
   – potassium hydroxide (potash lye)
   – sodium hydroxide (sodium lye)
   – soluble copper and silver compounds
   – methanol (methyl hydrate or solvent alcohol)

Packaging for these toxins must be designed in such a way that shaking, spilling or evaporation is impossible. The container must be clearly different from containers for food or drink. The proper chemical name of the contents, the name of the supplier, and maker must be given on the packing as well as codes that indicate the nature of the danger posed by the contents. Where applicable, the word "poison" must be clearly displayed.

Table 3.4
Important salts.

Chemical Name	Other Name	Formula		Usage
		Metal	Acid Radical	
sodium tetraborate	borax	$2Na^+$	$B_4O_7{}^{2-}$	flux
calcium carbonate		Ca^{2+}	$CO_3{}^{2-}$	polishing compound
potassium carbonate	potash	$2K^+$	$CO_3{}^{2-}$	flux and in electroplating
sodium carbonate		$2Na^+$	$CO_3{}^{2-}$	flux and in electroplating
sodium hydrogen carbonate	bicarbonate of soda	Na^+	HCO_3^-	cleaning and degreasing
copper (II) carbonate	malachite, patina	Cu^{2+} Cu^{2+}	$CO_3{}^{2-}$ $(^-(OH)_2$	medium eutectic soldering material
zinc carbonate	"white rust"	Zn^{2+}	$CO_3{}^{2-}$	natural protective layer on zinc
ammonium chloride	sal ammoniac	$NH_4{}^+$	Cl^-	flux
gold (II) chloride	gold chloride	Au^{3+}	$3Cl^-$	flux and in electroplating
potassium chloride		K^+	Cl^-	electroplating
sodium chloride		Na^+	Cl^-	flux, refining medium
mercuric (II) chloride	mercury sublimate	Hg	$2Cl^-$	etchant for steel
silver chloride	chloride of silver	Ag^+	Cl	electroplating and refining
zinc chloride	soldering water	Zn^{2+}	$2Cl^-$	flux
tin (II) chloride	tin salt	Sn^{2+}	$2Cl^{2--}$	analytical work
potassium dichromate		$2K^+$	$Cr_2O_7{}^{2-}$	etchant for silver
sodium dichromate		$2Na^+$	$Cr_2O_7{}^{2-}$	silver streak testing
silver dichromate		$2Ag^+$	$Cr_2O_7{}^{2-}$	silver streak testing
gold (I) cyanide		Au^+	CN^-	electroplating
sodium gold cyanide		Na^+	$Au(CN)_2{}^-$	electroplating
silver cyanide		Ag^+	CN^-	electroplating
sodium silver cyanide		Na^+	$Ag(CN)_2^-$	electroplating
potassium silver cyanide		K^+	$Ag(CN)_2^-$	electroplating
calcium fluoride	fluorspar	Ca^{2+}	$2F^-$	etchant for glass, flux
ammonium nitrate		$NH_4{}^+$	NO_3^-	metal coloration
potassium nitrate		K^+	NO_3^-	flux
cupric nitrate		Cu^{2+}	$(NO_3)_2$	flux
sodium nitrate		Na^+	NO_3^-	flux
mercuric (III-) nitrate		Hg^{2+}	$(NO_3)_2$	quicking
silver nitrate		Ag^+	NO_3^-	electroplating
disodium hydrogen phosphate		$2Na^+$	HPO_3	electroplating
calcium sulfate		Ca^{2+}	$SO_4{}^{2-}$	this is plaster
copper sulfate		Cu^{2+}	$SO_4{}^{2-}$	electroplating

To prevent dangerous inappropriate use of toxins they must be kept separate from other materials and stored safely to prevent unauthorized access. A special toxic materials room is required when large amounts of toxic materials are being stored on site. Normally only small amounts of toxins come into the goldsmith's shop and in those cases a stable, lockable cupboard labeled "Poison" is considered sufficient.

Toxic materials that are used for working purposes may only be dispensed to employees or their agents who must be over 18 years old, have passed their toxic materials examinations or have at least once a year be instructed in how to handle toxic materials.

Dispose of toxic materials only through legally provided channels and according to the specific instructions provided by the handling company. Keep track of the receipt and disposal of all toxic materials in a logbook, attaching receipts as documentation. These should be kept on record for at least 10 years.

Rules for dealing with toxic materials
- Even those with years of experience must remain vigilant and cautious when working with toxins.
- Never bring toxic materials in contact with a body or clothing.
- Always wear rubber gloves.
- If toxic fumes are present, work must be done under a chemical fume hood.
- When toxic materials are no longer needed they should be returned immediately to their locked storage.
- In every regard steps must be taken to insure that misuse is impossible.

Handling Metals

4.1
Weighing, Measuring and Fitting

Science, technology and economies are being internationalized to an increasingly large degree, emphasizing the need for a universal system of measurement. The international system of unit measure (Systeme International d'Unites or SI for short) has been created by representatives from many countries and was adopted for scientific measurement in the US in February 1964. It is also legally binding in Germany.

The nomenclature of SI units starts with a basic unit of weight, length, volume or time and extends outward with consistent use of prefixes that indicate the mathematical extension being described, always on a "base ten" system. For example the basic unit of length is a meter. A milli-meter is $\frac{1}{1000}$ of this. A centi-meter is $\frac{1}{100}$ and a kilo-meter is 1000 of them. These prefixes can be applied to grams (weight) and litres (volume) with the same meanings. The precision of such mathematical relationships makes it relatively straightforward to convert one unit to another.

A great number of historically developed idiosyncratic units of measurement have been replaced by SI unit measures. In daily experience, traditional units of measure cling tenaciously to life as witnessed in the US by the glacial progress of the general culture to think in metric units.

Obviously this book will rely on SI units of measure, both for their accuracy and for their international acceptance. Measurements that are particularly important for the goldsmith are assembled in tables in the Appendix.

4.1.1 THE SCALES

Though the terms are commonly used interchangeably, there is a difference between "mass" and "weight." Mass represents the actual size of the substance of an object regardless of external conditions, while weight, or to be precise, "weight force," depends on the force with which the object is being drawn toward the earth. The relationship between mass and weight can be illustrated in this formula:

$$F_G = m \cdot g$$

F_G – weight force in kgm = N
m – mass in kg
g – gravitational pull in m/s²

Because the force of gravity on our planet is greatest at the poles, the same mass appears heavier there than at the equator (g = 9.788 m/s²). The 45th parallel, (which marks Germany and much of the US) is about equidistant from the pole and equator so these forces tend to balance out with a constant gravitational pull of 9.806 m/s². This means that in our everyday life, mass and weight are apparently identi

cal; perhaps this is the reason the terms are not clearly differentiated in normal speech and the amount of a substance is termed the "weight."

In general practice we put a sample on a balance scale and determine the heaviness as equal to the substance. The sample is compared to the calibrated weights, both of which are being attracted to the center of the earth at the same rate:

$$F_{G1} = F_{G2}$$
$$m_1 \cdot g = m_2 \cdot g$$

F_{G1} – weight force of the goods in N
m_1 – mass of the goods in kg
F_{G2} – weight force of the weights in N
m_2 – mass of the weights in kg
g – gravitational pull in m/s²

Technically speaking, "This ring weighs 5.6 grams" is a false statement. To be correct we should say: "This ring has a mass of 5.6 grams." To express the weight rather than the mass, the correct phrase would be: "This ring has a weight force of 54.936 mN."

The traditional goldsmiths scale is an ancient

Table 4.1 Important units of measurement.

Size	Symbol Used in Formula	SI-Unit	Further, Derived Units	Discontinued Units
length	l	m	= 100 cm = 10,000 mm 1 cm = 10 mm	
weight	m	kg	= 1000 g 1 g = 1000 mg 1 k (metric carat) = 0.2 g	
density	ρ	kg/m³	= 10⁻³ g/cm³	
force	F	N		p, kp, Mp (1 kp = 9.81 N)
tensile strength	σ_B	N/m²	= 1 N/m² 1 MPa = 1 N/mm² 10⁶ N/m²	kp/mm² (1 kp/mm² = 9.81 N/mm²)
Brinell hardness	Bhn	–	Bhn (the nunber value is that of the final unit in kp/mm²)	kp/mm²
time	t	s	1 h = 60 min = 3600 s	
temperature	T	K	°C	
difference in temperature	ΔT	K	(also °C when using Celsius temperatures)	

device that still belongs to the basic equipment of most goldsmithing workshops. It works according to the principle of the lever balance, setting one weight against another for comparison (figure 4.1)

The balance beam of the scale rests on a knife edge fulcrum that is cradled in a socket. This point is exactly centered on a beam that is equipped with pans of equal weight on each end. It is of course vital that the beam and pans be able to move freely. The center point of the beam is equipped with a pointer and a fixed mark that indicates when the beam is precisely horizontal.

Weights of 1 gram and heavier to be used in a balance are typically made of brass. The milligram weights are little aluminum plates. If these were in brass they would be so small as to be easily lost. Even the aluminum plates must be handled with tweezers.

After hundreds of years of use, the balance has recently been usurped by a new generation of gold weighing equipment known the electronic precision balance. The goods to be weighed are placed onto the pan of the scale, and the exact mass is immediately visible on a digital readout. The time honored practice of placing weights and waiting for the beam to stop swinging has been replaced by this efficient device, which saves considerable time compared with the older procedure.

The only disadvantage of the modern electronic scale is that it is considerably more expensive than the standard balance. It is therefore wise to consider the needs and resources of a shop before determining which kind of measuring equipment is needed. Because of their cost, electronic scales are generally seen only in shops that make frequent use of weight measurement.

4.1.2 MEASURING LENGTH

An experienced goldsmith is often able to judge to correct thickness for a particular application intuitively, but it is good practice to use precise measurements whenever possible. As important as it is to be able to judge by "feel," it's unwise to avoid proper technique from a sense of pride. It's difficult, for instance, to

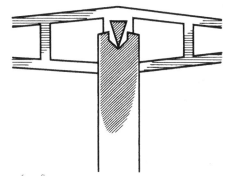

Figure 4.1
The pivot of the balance beam with wedge and groove.

Figure 4.2
Sartorius Portable electronic scale. (Firma Sartorius GmbH, Göttingen)

Sartorius Model No.	Weighing Capacity in g	Reads in g to:
PT 120	121	0.01
PT 600	610	0.1
PT 1200	1200	0.1
PT 6	6100	1

Table 4.2
Scale range and precision.

judge the optimal relationship of deformation to annealing when rolling simply by feel. With careful measurement, such information can be determined quickly and with confidence.

A steel ruler is the simplest measuring instrument for determining length. A useful version in a goldsmith's studio is a flexible ruler that allows accurate length measurements along curves. The ruler should be positioned so that there are no shadows or angle distortions between the lines on the rule and the surface being measured. Even so, accuracy with a ruler is commonly considered to be about 1 millimeter.

A sliding caliper is generally less precise than a proper vernier, but is quick and therefore handy for general use. As an added advantage, a sliding calipers can often be used to check for rightness of an angle as well.

Inner and outer dimensions can be more exactly determined by using a vernier calipers. A vernier scale (invented by French mathematician Pierre Vernier in the 17th century) is a secondary scale attached to a larger measuring instrument that indicates fractional units of those being indicated on the primary scale.

The principle of the vernier device, as illustrated here in a metric ruler, is that a 9 millimeter length is divided into ten sections. This means each division is 0.9 mm long; or 0.1 mm shorter than the division markings on the beam rule. The tenths of a millimeter are read off at the spot where a division mark of the vernier scale lines up perfectly with one of the main millimeter marks on the beam rule.

Example

Figure 4.3 shows a close-up view of a vernier scale when an object is being measured. Because the 0 mark is closest to 25, we know that is the approximate size of the object. Because it doesn't line up exactly, we can also determine that it is not exactly 25 mm. To determine how much bigger it is, we count the lines on the lower scale, starting from the left, until we find the one that lines up perfectly with a line from the upper scale. In the example, this is line #4, which tells us the precise measurement is 25.4 mm.

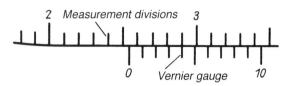

Figure 4.3
Vernier scale of the Vernier caliper.

Figure 4.4
Precision measuring devices.

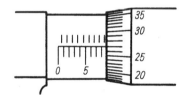

Figure 4.5
Detail of micrometer reading. See next page for explanation.

Some calipers are combined with a dial so measurements can read directly from a circular scale. In the most modern calipers measurement is shown by an electronic digital display.

The degree gauge (also called a spring gauge) is primarily used for measuring the thickness of sheet metal and the diameter of rods and tubes. The tool is cheap and easy to use. As the arms are pressed together a gap is created at the mouth of the tool. The distance across this gap is indicated by a pointer and measured increments along the arc-shaped scale. This is generally divided into millimeters (sometimes by tenths) but is also available in douziemes and inches. The resulting measurement is somewhat casual but often sufficient for the studio benchworker.

The tool traditionally accepted as the standard for precise measurement of thickness is the micrometer, shown in figure 4.4. Like the degree gauge, it is most commonly used to measure thickness, but in this case the gap between measuring plates is achieved by turning a threaded spindle. The threading of the spindle is carefully engineered so that a complete rotation of the outer cylinder enlarges the gap 0.5 mm. The hub is divided into half millimeters; the thimble has 50 division marks which each represent 0.01 mm. Micrometers are also manufactured that measure thousandths of an inch.

Example
The first or most general measure is read off the central cylinder. In the example shown (figure 4.5) here the last visible mark is 8.5, the 8 coming from the lower register and the .5 being indicated by the small marks just above. The scale on the outer sleeve indicates 27 as lining up with the primary line on the spindle. These two numbers are taken together to determine the exact measure:

8.5 mm + 0.27 mm = 8.77 mm

A dial gauge converts this system into a device that is both easier to read and more comfortable to use. In this tool a probe is pushed against the object to be measured, and the resultant thickness is transferred to a dial so measurements can be read from a circular dial scale to a precision of 0.01 mm.

The most advanced thickness measuring tool is a digital electronic micrometer. As with the dial gauge, the object is set into a U-shaped opening and touched with a probe. An evaluation is effected by a microprocessor with a digital display to a precision of 0.001 mm. The results can be stored and the zero setting can be set in any position, making the instrument particularly helpful for comparative measurements.

4.1.3 CHECKING ACCURACY

Fitting tools are used to check the geometric accuracy of shapes, as for instance in determining if parts are at a right angle or if a corner is truly square. Normally checking and fitting tools have no measurement markings.

A straight edge is the simplest form of fitting tool and is generally used to determine if a line or edge is perfectly straight. The slightly rounded edge (reminiscent of the blade of a butter knife) is held vertically along an edge, then held up to a light source. The appearance of a crack of light reveals areas that are out of true. The piece is then filed or sanded and rechecked until the straight edge lies perfectly along it.

A simple square is a precisely made "L" of a resilient material that is used to determine whether parts join at a perfect right angle, (figure 4.6). It can be used either inside or outside a corner. A variation is the try square, (try in the old-fashioned sense of "test") in which one length of the "L" is thicker than the other. This creates a stop that makes it faster to set one piece against another. In one style of try square, a butt plate is attached to a simple square.

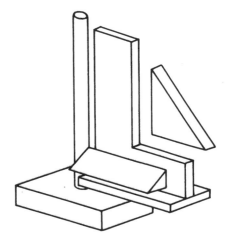

Figure 4.6
Ways that one can use the try square.

A goldsmith has frequent occasion to use dividers, the familiar compass-like tool that consists of two legs held in tension with a spring and controlled by a threaded rod that opens or closes the gap between the tips. These are used to scribe out circles, but are also used to compare sizes from one object to another, as when measuring a stone against a setting bur. They are also useful in scribing a line parallel to a given edge, and for "holding" a measurement.

4.1.4 DENSITY

Density, or the relationship of mass to volume, is one of the most important characteristics of materials. It is contained in the formula

$$\rho = \frac{m}{V}$$

ρ = density
m = mass
V = volume

If we are handed equal sized cubes of aluminum and steel, our first observation is their difference in density. An important device for identifying gemstones is the measurement of their density, which can quickly and accurately expose an imitation. There is a story that Archimedes used the hydrostatic weighing method of water displacement to expose a goldsmith who claimed that a crown was made of fine gold when in fact it was made of alloyed material.

The density of an alloy can be calculated if the densities and amounts of the constituent metals are known. Density values of the frequently used metals and alloys are given in the Appendix.

- For each component the mass, understood as 1 gram, is inserted into the formula as shown below.
- The densities of any given metal can be looked up in a chart and also set into the formula.
- Resolve the equation to determine the density of the alloy, a statement of the relationship between the entire mass (1 g) and the entire volume.

Example 1
What's the density of an alloy of 33.3% gold (Au 333) and 66.7% copper (Cu 667)?

$$V = \frac{m_1}{\rho_1} + \frac{m_2}{\rho_2} = (\frac{0.333}{19.3} + \frac{0.667}{8.96}) \text{ cm}^3$$
$$= 0.0917 \text{ cm}^3$$

$$\rho = \frac{m}{V} = \frac{1 \text{ g}}{0.0917} = 10.91 \text{ g/cm}^3$$

Example 2
What is the density of a 14k alloy of 58% gold (Au 585), 28% silver (Ag 280) and 13.5% copper (Cu 135)? From these figures it is possible to calculate the mass of plate and wire by using the following formulas.
- mass of square wire = $a^2 \cdot l \cdot \rho$
- mass of round wire = $r^2 \cdot \pi \cdot l \cdot \rho$
- mass of sheet = $a \cdot b \cdot s \cdot \rho$

$$V = \frac{m_1}{\rho_1} + \frac{m_2}{\rho_2} + \frac{m_3}{\rho_3} = (\frac{0.585}{19.3} + \frac{0.280}{10.39} + \frac{0.135}{8.96}) \text{cm}^3$$
$$- 0.0723 \text{ cm}^3$$

$$\rho = \frac{m}{V_{\text{ges}}} = \frac{1 \text{ g}}{0.0723 \text{ cm}^3} = 13.83 \text{ g/cm}^3$$

Example 3
What is the mass, respectively, of a round wire that is 1.5 mm in diameter and 25 cm long in 8k (Au 333) and 14k (Au 585)?

The tables are consulted to determine the density of each alloy: Au 333(ρ = 10.8 g/cm³), and Au 585 (ρ = 13.5 g/cm³). These are then plugged into the formula and worked as shown.

$$m = r^2 \cdot \pi \cdot l \cdot \rho$$

Au 333 = $0.075^2 \cdot 3.14 \cdot 25 \cdot 10.8$ = 4.77 grams
Au 585 = $0.075^2 \cdot 3.14 \cdot 25 \cdot 13.5$ = 5.96 grams

Example 4

What is the mass of a strip of 22k (Au 900) sheet that is 1.5 x 2 mm in cross section and 20 cm long (ρ = 15.4 g/cm³)?

$$m = a \cdot b \cdot s \cdot \rho = 1.5 \cdot 20 \cdot 0.2 \cdot 15.4 = \underline{61.8 \text{ grams}}$$

Of course sometimes it's useful to ask the question the other way around: How thick a sheet, (or how long a wire) can I make from material on hand? Use the following formulas to determine the length or thickness of wires that could be made with a given quantity of material.

A = area of the cross section

– length of square or round wire: $\quad l = \dfrac{m}{A \cdot \rho}$

– thickness of square wire:

$$a = \sqrt{\dfrac{m}{l \cdot \rho}}$$

– thickness of round wire, ($d = 2\, r$):

$$d = 2 \sqrt{\dfrac{m}{\pi \cdot l \cdot \rho}}$$

– length or width of a sheet:

$$a = \dfrac{m}{b \cdot s \cdot \rho}$$

– thickness of a sheet:

$$s = \dfrac{m}{a \cdot b \cdot \rho}$$

Example 1

How thick will a 3 g round wire be if is it 12 cm long and made from 14k (Au 585)? (The density of the gold alloy, from the chart, is 13.5 cubic grams).

$$d = 2 \sqrt{\dfrac{m}{\pi \cdot l \cdot \rho}} = 2 \sqrt{\dfrac{3}{3.14 \cdot 12 \cdot 13.5}} = 0.154 \text{ cm}$$
$$= \underline{1.54 \text{ mm}}$$

Example 2

How long will a round wire of 1 mm diameter be if it is made of 8k gold (Au 333)? (The density of the gold alloy, from the chart, is 10.8 g/cm³).

$$l = \dfrac{m}{r^2 \cdot \pi \cdot \rho} = \dfrac{7}{0.05^2 \cdot 3.14 \cdot 10.8} \text{ cm} = \underline{82.57 \text{ cm}}$$

Example 3

If I need a strip of 22k gold (Au 900) that is 15 mm wide and 18 cm long, and if I have 10 grams of metal, how thick can it be? (The density of the gold alloy, from the chart, is 10.3 g/cm³).

$$s = \dfrac{m}{a \cdot b \cdot \rho} = \dfrac{10}{1.5 \cdot 18 \cdot 10.3} = .036 \text{ cm}$$
$$= \underline{0.36 \text{ mm}}$$

Following the logic of the preceding examples, it is possible to determine mathematically the mass of any metal object as long its shape can be expressed in geometric terms.

Example 4

How much metal will be needed to make a smooth wedding band of 8k gold (Au 333) that is 2 mm by 4 mm in cross section and forms a ring with a 20 mm inside diameter?

$$m = (R^2 - r^2)\, \pi \cdot h \cdot \rho = (1.2^2 - 1^2) \cdot 3.14 \cdot 0.4 \cdot 10.8$$
$$= \underline{5.97 \text{ grams}}$$

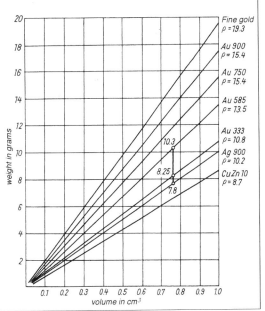

Figure 4.7
The relationship between mass and volume in some important alloys.

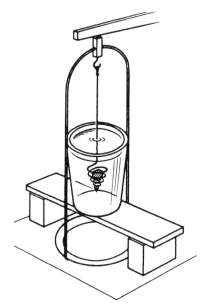

Figure 4.8
Gold balance, rebuilt as a hydrostatic balance.

Example 5
How thick could the ring be if only 4 grams of Au 333 are available?

$$m = (R^2 - r^2)\, \pi \cdot h \cdot \rho$$
$$4 = [(1 + x)^2 - 1^2] \cdot 3.14 \cdot 0.4 \cdot 10.8$$
$$x^2 + 2x - 0.295 = 0$$
$$x = 0.14 \text{ cm} = 1.4 \text{ mm}$$

Of course in most cases it will be difficult or impossible to reduce a design to simple geometric forms, so these calculations will of necessity be approximations. Even in light of this qualification, it is often useful to know in advance how much material will be needed, or whether metal being supplied by a client will be sufficient for the job.

Another practical aspect of determining density is revealed through an understanding that objects of the same size and shape have the same volume. This means that there is a mathematical relationship between an object made of, say, silver and the same object made in gold. Here is the formula that converts the density of a piece of jewelry made in one material to the same piece made in another.

$$V_1 = \frac{m_1}{\rho_1} \qquad V_2 = \frac{m_2}{\rho_2}$$

As explained above, it is common practice to consider mass and volume as equal, so it is possible to interchange the values:

$$\frac{m_1}{\rho_1} = \frac{m_2}{\rho_2}$$

Example 6
If the mass of a 22k (Au 900) (ρ = 10.2 g/cm3) ring is 7.8 grams, what is the mass of the same ring made in
a) 8k (Au 333) (ρ_1 = 10.8 g/cm3) and
b) 14k (Au 585) (ρ_2 = 13.5 g/cm3)?
The density values are listed in figure 4.7.

Calculations use the proportion relationship between mass and density:

a) $\quad 7.8 : 15.4 \quad = m_2 : 10.8$
$\qquad\qquad m_1 \quad = \underline{5.7\text{g Au } 333}$

b) $\quad 7.8 : 15.4 \quad = m_3 : 13.5$
$\qquad\qquad m_2 \quad = \underline{10.32 \text{ g Au } 585}$

Determination of density by weighing

The hydrostatic balance (figure 4.8), is a familiar tool to gemologists, who use it to determine the density of samples. It is a trustworthy and uncomplicated instrument used to determine specific gravity. It is just as easy to use this tool to determine the density of jewelry objects, and from this, to determine the proportion of fine gold in the alloy.

Obviously the sample being tested must consist of a single metal and cannot have any gemstones or other materials. Density testing can be useful not only as a corroboration for the touchstone streak test but also for the low karat zone, where the touchstone test is no longer useful.

According to the Archimedes principle, the difference between the actual mass and the apparent loss of mass in water is the same mass as that of the displaced water. Because one gram of water has a volume of one cubic centimeter, this amount is the same as the volume of the test object.

$$|V| = |m - m'|$$

The equation is:

$$\rho = \frac{m}{m - m'} \cdot \rho_W$$

or

$$|\rho| = \left| \frac{m}{m - m'} \right|$$

m   = mass of the test object in air in g
m′ = apparent mass in water in g
ρ = density of the test object in g
ρ_W = density of the water = 1 g/cm³

The procedure itself is very simple. First determine the weight of an object in the normal manner. Then make a "bridge" over the weighing pan in such a way that a glass beaker with water in it can be placed over the weighing pan without affecting its mobility, as shown in figure 4.8. Suspend the object by the thinnest wire possible so as to limit its effect on the calculations.

The wire is attached to the balance beam above the beaker so the object can move freely under the water and the mass of the submerged object is recorded. These values can be inserted into the formula to determine the density of the object. Armed with this information, it will be possible to calculate the relative proportion of a given alloy in a sample by comparing this information with the density values given in charts.

4.2
Testing Precious Metals and Their Alloys

Metals commonly used in the metalsmith's studio can be divided into two groups. Colored metals would include pure gold, most gold alloys, copper, and non-precious alloys such as brass or bronze. The category of white metals includes fine silver, silver alloys, white golds, platinum, platinum group metals and their alloys; white non-precious metals such as tin, lead or cadmium and their alloys.

The purpose of precious metal testing is to deter-

Testing Acid	Composition	density g/ml
gold testing acid (Au 333)	20 ml concentrated nitric acid	1.41
	20 ml water	
gold testing acid (Au 585)	40 ml concentrated nitric acid	1.41
gold testing acid (Au 750)	40 ml concentrated nitric acid	1.41
	1 ml concentrated hydrocloric acid	1.198
	15 ml water	
silver testing acid	3 g potassium dichromate	11.84
	3 ml concentrated sulfuric acid	
	32 ml water	
platinum testing acid	18 ml concentrated nitric acid	1.41
	24 ml concentrated hydrocloric acid	1.198
	6 ml water	

Table 4.3
Testing acids.

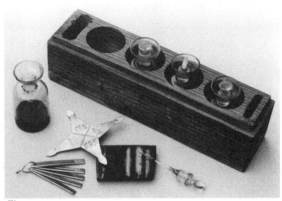

Figure 4.9
Equipment for precious metal testing: testing acids, testing stone, testing needles, testing star.

mine, first, whether a given sample is precious or base, and, second, to determine what proportion of an alloy is precious. Sophisticated equipment is used in a precious metal laboratory to determine content and purity values with great precision, but our attention here is given to methods a working goldsmith can use in the studio to determine metal content to a practical degree of accuracy.

4.2.1 TOUCHSTONE TESTING

It is important from the outset to carefully consider the concentration of acids used for testing. Testing acids available from commercial suppliers as pre-mixed preparations are preferred because acid solutions mixed in the studio are subject to inaccuracies that will effect the veracity of the results (table 4.3). The proper bottle for storing acid is equipped with a ground glass stopper that fits snugly into the neck of the small clear glass bottle that contains the acid. The stopper is often fitted with a thin applicator rod that is used to apply acid to a sample. (figure 4.9).

The testing stone
Black Lydian slate has proven itself to be the best material for a testing stone because it possesses all the characteristics required of a good testing stone: it is uniformly matte black, has a homogenous, non-porous structure and is harder than the metals being tested. And it is resistant to acids, which means it won't disappear after a few uses. Despite many years of attempts, it has not yet proven possible to develop

an artificial material with these ideal characteristics.

After a few uses the stone will retain streaks from previous experiments, making further use difficult. To remove these, rub the surface with charcoal and water. The cleaned and dried stone is then very thinly rubbed with a fine oil to keep its surface smooth and tractable.

Testing needles
Testing needles are simply samples of gold alloys of known value attached to larger pieces of an inexpensive metal to make them easier to handle. In practice, a typical size for a needle is in about 6 centimeters long, and they are generally made of brass. These are often linked onto a ring for ease in storage. An alternate style uses a star made of brass in which each tip is coated with a different alloy.

The range of alloy samples needed will depend on the kind of work that comes to the shop and the degree of accuracy required. With a small range of testing needles, for instance, it might be possible to determine a given sample as being "better than 10k but less pure than 18k." By using a more complete metals test kit, the alloy could be determined to a closer tolerance.

It's possible to make testing needles in the studio as long as you are certain of the alloys being used to make the needles or stars. And of course it's possible to replace the needles with actual jewelry objects or bits of sheet and wire stock of a known karat.

Reaction on Streak	Possible Alloy	Further Evidence
Dissolves without residue	a) gold alloy less than Au 300 b) silver-copper alloy with less than Ag 500 c) base metal alloy	a) gold test with Au 333 testing acid b) test for silver
Brown color to the streak, a brown residue	gold alloy with less than Au 500	quantitative test
No attack	gold alloy with more than Au 500	quantitative test

Table 4.4
Streak test with Au 585. Behavior of testing acid.

4.2.2 COLORED METALS AND ALLOYS

The first step is to determine whether the alloy in question contains any gold at all. To do this, select an unobtrusive spot on the object and use a file or scraper to remove any plating that might be on the piece. Using the glass stopper or a small plastic rod, apply a drop of nitric acid to the scratch and observe the reaction. If there is no apparent change, the piece is probably solid gold. A green streak on an otherwise unaffected surface indicates a gold plated object made of base metal. If the entire area subjected to acid turns green, the piece consists entirely of base metal.

To determine the relative proportion of gold in an alloy, rub the exposed area (where any possible plating has been removed) along a touchstone to create a streak roughly 5 mm wide and 20 mm long. Dab this golden streak with concentrated nitric acid (the Au 585 testing acid) and after waiting about 5 seconds, check the reaction against the table shown here. Where exposed to nitric acid, gold is not attacked, but silver is converted to gray-colored silver nitrate $AgNO_3$ and copper reacts to become to greenish copper nitrate $Cu(NO_3)_2$.

Because this test is effective only on alloys that contain over 50% gold, the test must be repeated on another place in the streak with diluted nitric acid (the Au 333 testing acid). This is particularly indicated when the first test colored the streak brown or dissolved it altogether. The results of this exposure to the milder acid are then compared with the information in table 4.5.

If the gold content is less than 50% (Au 500) the additional metals that make up the alloy are dissolved while the undissolved gold is left behind as a brown residue. If the alloy doesn't contain any gold, the components are completely converted to nitrates, a reaction that is usually accompanied by active bubbling of the acid. Because copper is almost always a significant component of colored alloys, the remaining solution usually takes on the blue-green color of cupric nitrate. The Au 333 testing acid is so diluted that alloys containing less than 30% gold remain unattacked by the acid. The touchstone test can reveal alloy values from pure gold (Au 1000) down to Au

Table 4.5
Streak test with Au 333. Behavior of testing acid.

Reaction on Streak	Possible Alloy	Further Evidence
dissolves without residue	a) gold alloys less than Au 160 b) silver-copper alloy with less than Ag 500 c) base metal alloy	a) reagent glass test b) test for silver
brown coloring of the streak, brownish residue	gold alloy with Au 160 to Au 300	quantitative test
no attack	gold alloy with more than Au 300	quantitative test

160; below this proportion of gold, reaction vessel testing must be used.

This test is used if an alloy has reacted like a non-precious alloy in the streak test (creates a green or blue green reaction) and yet is still suspected of having a small gold content.

The test depends upon the solubility of the addition metals and the stability of gold in warmed, concentrated nitric acid. A piece of the questionable alloy weighing about a half a gram is dissolved in heated nitric acid in an active ventilation device. Non-precious metals and silver are converted to nitrates, but any gold that may be present is deposited as a dark brown powder on the bottom of the vessel. This is then separated from the solution by filtration, washed with distilled water and dried out on filter paper. If the powder takes on a metallic shine when rubbed with a steel burnisher, there is probably some gold in the residue.

Quantitative gold test
The tests just described are qualitative: they determine whether or not there is gold present in an alloy. The approximate quantity or proportion of gold must be determined next. The first step uses the touchstone method to approximate the purity of an alloy, which makes the next step a little easier.

The sample being tested is again rubbed onto a touchstone as before. On the basis of the reaction to the test acids it should be possible to make an educated guess about the possible purity or karat of the sample. Using test needles or pieces of gold or jewelry of a known alloy, make a streak parallel to the sample streak. Paint a swath of testing acid at right angles across the two streaks and carefully observe the reaction of the metals to the acid. If they behave differently, select another testing needle to create another streak, again near to and parallel with the original streak of the piece being tested. Continue in this way, always subjecting both a known and an unknown streak to the same exposure of the same acid. When the reaction of the two streaks is identical you will have determined the karat of the sample. With sufficient experience it is possible to obtain results with a tolerance of 50 parts per thousand, or 5%.

The touchstone test is restricted to alloys that are between Au 200 and Au 800; alloys that are more pure than 80% or less pure than 20% cannot be accurately measured through this method and will require assay (technical analysis) for accuracy.

The following examples should help to better understand the procedure.

Example 1

The qualitative test indicates a gold alloy with between 160-300 parts per thousand gold. A streak is made on the stone with each of Au 333, Au 250 and Au 200 needles, together with the questionable alloy. The Au 333 testing acid is spread at right angles over the streaks. It is immediately apparent that the Au 200 streak is attacked and changes color while the Au 333 streak remains unchanged. The streak made by the sample shows a brown color, as does the Au 250 streak. From this information it is reasonable to conclude that sample has about the same fine gold content as the last testing needle, and is about 25% pure.

Example 2

The qualitative test produced a result of more than 500 parts per thousand gold content. Streaks are made on the stone with known samples of Au 585, Au

666 and Au 750 alongside a streak made by the alloy being tested. The four lines are then daubed with the Au 750 testing acid. In this case, the Au 585 streak will be attacked first, then a few seconds later the Au 666 streak will begin to discolor. The Au 750 streak will remain unchanged. Because the sample alloy remains unchanged, it is safe to conclude that its fine gold content is around 750 parts per thousand or higher. To obtain a more precise analysis it is necessary to have the sample assayed.

Testing for fine gold

As mentioned above, if early tests or intuition leads to the suspicion that a sample is composed of pure gold, an alternate test must be used to confirm purity. The first step is to melt a small amount of the unknown sample without any flux. If the metal is pure it will reveal a sea green color during melting and even after cooling it will remain untarnished. If the surface of the melted and cooled ball has a brown film, this indicates the presence of impurities. If the sample passes this early test, it is successively subjected to the following tests:

- About one gram of thinly rolled out test material is dissolved in about 6 ml of Aqua Regia. The solution is brought to a boil. There should not be any yellow-white silver chloride flakes present.
- The solution is diluted with 20-30 ml distilled water.
- 5 grams of hydrazine hydrochloride N_2H_5Cl is added and the is solution stirred. All the gold pre cipitates out as a brown sediment on the bottom of the vessel until the remaining solution is as clear as water.
- Some of the clear liquid is removed and combined with ammonia (ammonium hydroxide). If the solution turns blue, this indicates the presence of copper. If flakes form, this indicates the presence of lead, though this might also suggest that bismuth, iron, or aluminum may be present.
- If the sample being tested has withstood the test this far by neither discoloring the solution or precipitating as flakes, a couple drops of

ammonium sulfide are added to the liquid. If there is still no precipitation, the sample is almost certainly pure gold.

4.2.3 WHITE METALS AND ALLOYS

First the sample in question is treated like the colored alloys in the qualitative test, rubbed on the touchstone and tested with the Au 585 acid. The following possibilities arise from this.

Silver and silver alloys

In practice an experienced eye will usually be able to determine by color and luster whether a piece is made of silver, a base white metal such as nickel silver, or a precious white alloy such as white gold or platinum. If this can be determined by eye, it's usual to proceed directly to the qualitative test described below.

STREAK TEST WITH RED SILVER TESTING ACID

As before, the work being tested is scratched in a location where the minor scar will be least noticeable. A drop of silver testing acid is placed on the scratch and the reaction is carefully observed. If the piece being tested is a silver-copper alloy, both metals are dissolved by the sulfuric acid and converted to sulfates. With exposure to potassium dichromate, the silver sulfate is converted to silver dichromate, which has a characteristic blood red color. The test for silver, then, is that an alloy containing silver will turn the brownish red testing acid a strong blood red.

$$K_2Cr_2O_7 \quad + \quad Ag_2SO_4 \quad \rightarrow$$
potassium dichromate   silver sulfate
brownish red
$$Ag_2Cr_2O_7 \quad + \quad K_2SO_4$$
silver dichromate   potassium sulfate
blood red

This test is not effective for alloys containing less than 25% silver, though it's worth noting that such alloys have such a yellow color and are so easily tarnished that they are very unlikely to be encountered as jewelry or flatware. Nevertheless, such alloys are sometimes used for technical products, so it is useful

to understand the test tube reaction test described below, which can be used to assess low-silver alloys.

STREAK TEST WITH NITRIC ACID & SODIUM CHLORIDE

This is an alternate test to the one just described and has the advantage of using nitric acid, the same acid used in gold testing. The sample is rubbed on a touchstone to create a streak, which is dabbed with concentrated nitric acid. Both the silver and the non-precious metals present are converted to nitrates. When sodium chloride (table salt) is added, the silver nitrate is converted to silver chloride, which has a characteristic milky color.

$$AgNO_3 \quad + \quad NaCl \quad \rightarrow$$
silver nitrate   sodium chloride
$$AgCl \quad + \quad NaNO_3$$
silver chloride   sodium nitrate

The proof for silver is the appearance of a milky or cloudy liquid. If the solution remains clear the alloy contains either a small quantity of silver or no silver.

REACTION IN A TEST TUBE

This test is used to confirm or deny the presence of silver when its content is below 25%. The procedure is based on the same chemical reaction that occurs in the streak test just described, but because of its larger scale, the reaction is more clearly visible in the following method.

While observing all necessary safety procedures, dissolve about a quarter gram of the questioned alloy in a clear reaction vessel with nitric acid. This is then diluted with distilled water, as usual adding the acid to the water rather than the reverse. A small amount of table salt is stirred into the solution; if silver is present it will form silver chloride, which as noted has a milky color. If the solution remains clear, it contains no silver. To confirm a positive test, add a small amount of ammonia, which should cause the cloudiness to disappear.

QUANTITATIVE TEST

It is also possible to test for silver content of an alloy by purely visual analysis. Though this is not strictly scientific, it is possible for an experienced observer with good color sense to determine content to within 30 parts per thousand, or 3%.

The touchstone is used as a neutral palette on which to gauge a variety of streaks. Scrape the questioned object along the stone to create a silver-colored line, then use bits of metal or objects of known composition to create streaks of a similar size running parallel to the sample. Examine the stripes in good light, seeking to find a color match between the unknown piece and a known sample.

This method fails if the unknown sample contains zinc or cadmium, which will brighten the streak. In such cases more sophisticated testing methods must be used to determine silver content.

FINE SILVER TESTING

This test is similar to the reaction in a test tube. A small amount of silver (1 g) is dissolved in 5 ml of nitric acid. The formation of a dark sediment indicates the presence of gold in the alloy. To this add 20 to 30 ml of ammonia until a piece of litmus paper turns blue.

If a dark sediment forms, it contains gold. If neutralization has been reached, a temporary precipitation of silver oxide forms; it is dissolved by the addition of further ammonia. The formation of further precipitate indicates the presence of lead, bismuth, iron or aluminum. If the solution turns blue, it contains copper. Only cadmium and zinc remain undetected with this method.

Platinum, platinum alloys and white gold

The first step is to determine whether the metal in question has platinum content, is a variety of white gold, or an acid-resistant non-precious alloy. Any of these would be indicated by resistance to the Au 585 testing acid (concentrated nitric acid).

STREAK TEST

The metal streak on the touchstone is first dabbed with Au 750 acid. If it is attacked, the alloy is almost certainly a white gold, probably with a content of less than 660 parts per thousand. If the streak is unaffect-

ed, it is then tested with platinum testing acid. Platinum can be dissolved by hot Aqua Regia but is resistant to the same acid at room temperature. Gold, however, will be attacked by Aqua Regia even at room temperature, so action by unheated acid will reveal an alloy as containing gold. A few non-precious alloys (such as certain steels) also remain undissolved in room temperature Aqua Regia, but these can usually be separated out by their appearance.

Reaction on Streak	Possible Alloy	Further Evidence
Dissolution without residue and without the acid being colored yellow.	a) silver alloy b) platinum-silver alloy c) base alloy	silver test
Attack or dissolution with yellowish coloring of the acid.	a) palladium b) palladium-alloy	laboratory analysis
No dissolution, some reddish coloring	White gold with less than Au 500.	laboratory analysis
Attack with brown color and residue.	White gold with less than Au 500 (a high percentage of base white metal and silver).	silver test
No attack, the streak is unchanged.	a) platinum b) platinum alloy c) white gold alloy with more than Au 500 d) base alloy	platinum test

Table 4.6
Streak test with AU 333 testing acid with white alloys.

Reaction on Streak	Possible Alloy	Further Evidence
More or less rapid dissolution	white gold	laboratory analysis
No attack	a) platinum b) platinum alloy with more than Pt 800 c) base alloy	laboratory analysis

Table 4.7
Streak test using platinum differentiating acid with white alloys.

REACTION IN A TEST TUBE
Extreme safety precautions are required for conducting this test. About half a gram of the alloy in question is boiled in diluted nitric acid (1:1). Silver, nickel and other non-precious metals are dissolved; palladium, gold and platinum remain behind. The metal being tested is then placed in room temperature Aqua Regia. White gold will be cloaked in a dark surface film. Palladium will be indicated by the acid solution itself becoming darkly colored. Platinum will remain unaffected by the strong acid.

To complete the test, the Aqua Regia is heated. Platinum will dissolve, turning the solution a brownish red. The volume of the solution is reduced by further heating; if the solution contains platinum, a brownish red precipitate of $(NH_4)_2[PtCl_6]$ is formed upon the addition of sal ammoniac.

QUANTITATIVE PLATINUM TEST
Truly precise analysis of platinum alloys can only be accomplished in a precious metals testing laboratory; the similarity between metals in the platinum group can easily lead to errors. The variable solubility and dissolution rates of the platinum metals in heated Aqua Regia can however provide a general sense of the composition of platinum-bearing alloys.

As described in gold testing, comparison streaks of an unknown sample and known alloys are rubbed on a small piece of unglazed porcelain plate. Working under a fume hood, a small quantity of Aqua Regia is heated to about 70°C. The streaked ceramic plate is dipped into the hot acid and observed closely to dis-

tinguish a similar reaction between the unknown metal and a streak made by a proven sample. Metals that exhibit similar response to the hot acid are probably very close in composition.

4.3
Refining

The principle of this ancient, valued procedure is described here because of its historical interest, and with the thought that young people coming into the field should be aware of the basic procedures of the trade, even though they may not pursue them. In the case of precious metal refining, it is generally more efficient to send scrap to a reputable refiner where sophisticated equipment and years of experience will insure accuracy. In addition, the procedures described below use dangerous acids that mandate industrial quality ventilation and safety precautions, which makes the decision to send out refining chores even more compelling.

4.3.1 THE PRINCIPLE OF "QUARTER REFINING"
The method described below is appropriate for refining batches of clean scrap metal such as cut off pieces, sprues and filings. Polishing residue and floor sweeps require a radically different approach because such scraps are likely to contain a wide assortment of miscellaneous materials.

Preparing the metal
- Large pieces of foreign materials are picked out and iron or steel particles are removed with a magnet.
- Any combustible materials such as wood, paper, pitch, wax, grease, etc. are burned away through a gentle annealing.
- Any non-precious metal impurities such as lead or tin (from soft solders), zinc, iron, aluminum, or other metals are dissolved in hot concentrated hydrochloric acid. The scraps are set into a safe vessel and covered with a generous amount of acid and remain there until bubbles no longer rise from the scraps. This step is especially important if tin is present, because even a minute amount will contaminate precious metal.

Preparation of the Initial Materials
Burning off (removing flammable materials)
Magnet use (remove iron particles)
Boiling in hydrocloric acid (Sn, Pb, Zn, Fe,
Al are dissolved to become chlorides).
Alloy down to Au 250 at the highest, roll it
out thinly.

Dissolve in Nitric Acid
(Ag, Cu, Zn are dissolved to form nitrates)

Transform the Precipitate into Gold	**Transform the Solution into Silver Precipitate it with NaCl**
dissolve in Aqua Regia (Au to $H[AuCl_4]$); reduce to Au with $FeSO_4$; Melt the gold.	($AgNO_3$ becomes $AgCl$); reduce to Ag with Zn and dilute H_2SO_4; Melt the silver.

Table 4.8
The working procedure when quarter refining.

- The solution is poured off and the metal is washed.
- The scraps are then melted together. This process relies on the ability of acids to attack base metals and in the process isolate gold. Because metals become resistant to acid when combined with gold, it is vital that the scrap contain no more than 25% gold (Au 250). If the scrap is of a higher gold content it is first necessary to add base metals so as to "dilute" the alloy down to a point where it will be susceptible to acids. This is known as "quartering" the scrap, and explains the name of the process.
- The scrap is melted together, stirred well with a quartz or carbon rod and poured into water so as to create small spherical pieces called shot. In the case of smaller amounts of scrap, the material is melted to a blob on a charcoal block, quenched and rolled out to become as thin as possible. This thin sheet is then cut into small pieces. In both cases the intention is to create finely divided material with a maximum surface area for attack by the purifying acid of the next step.

Dissolution in nitric acid
- Use extreme safety precautions
- The prepared metal is placed in an appropriate container and covered with slightly diluted nitric acid. In this bath, non-precious metals and silver are converted to nitrates, while gold falls out as a sediment.
- The nitrate-containing solution is poured off and the residue is treated again with nitric acid, this time slightly heated to accelerate its corrosive action. This repeats the action of the first step. When no further dissolving appears to be taking place, this solution can be poured off and added to the previous acid for subsequent reclaiming of the silver present.
- The residue is washed with distilled water and caught in a paper filter.

Dissolution in Aqua Regia
- The residue is next dissolved in Aqua Regia, which dissolves impurities and of course the gold itself. It is important that the previous step has removed any

silver present in the scrap. If more than 5% silver were remaining at this step, the metal would become cloaked with silver chloride, which is impervious to acid.

- Excess Aqua Regia is removed from the solution through evaporation in the draft of a fume hood until it is as thick as syrup.

Reduction of the gold

- Metallic gold is precipitated from the solution of salts that was formed by the Aqua Regia by adding iron (II)sulfate solution. When the addition of further iron (II)sulfate solution produces no more precipitation the reduction is complete.
- The solution is allowed to sit for a minimum of two hours, after which time it should have settled. The liquid is decanted to leave behind a residue that contains fine gold. This is thoroughly rinsed, then dried.
- The fine gold is melted into an ingot, which can be tested for purity as described earlier.

Reduction of the silver

- To reclaim silver from the solution that was set aside after the first step in the gold reclamation process, table salt is added to provoke the formation of silver chloride. This is added and stirred until all precipitation of silver chloride has stopped.
- After allowing the curd-like precipitate to settle out, the solution is stirred, which will cause the precipitate to ball up. The remaining solution can be discarded (safely!) because the recovery of the copper it contains does not pay for itself.
- The residue is rinsed until the runoff washing water no longer registers acidic with litmus paper.
- The sediment is next mixed with dilute sulfuric acid and zinc is added to a point of saturation. This will precipitate silver according to the following equation.

$$2\ AgCl\ +\ Zn\ +\ H_2SO_4\ \rightarrow$$
$$ZnSO_4\ +\ 2\ HCl\ +\ 2\ Ag$$

- The liquid is poured off and the residue is melted to create an ingot. It may be tested for purity as described earlier.

4.3.2 TREATMENT AT THE REFINERY

The higher the proportion of precious metals in a container of material sent for refining, the simpler the treatment at the refinery. This affects the length of treatment time and therefore the cost of refining. For this reason it is best to remove from scraps any foreign materials such as pitch, plaster, wood, etc. The pile of scraps is stirred with a magnet to remove iron and steel particles, then it is burned to remove organic materials such as paper, wax and sawdust. It is not necessary to melt the remaining sweeps together.

Because they are handled differently by a refiner, it is best to package large clean pieces of scrap separate from filings, which in turn are kept separate from sweepings. The more clearly these categories can be defined, the easier it will be for a refiner to process. The job is made easier still if you can be clear about what metals a given batch of scrap is likely to contain; this is especially true where platinum metals are involved.

Scrap

This category includes sheet and wire scrap that result from fabrication, trimmings from castings such as sprues, and unwanted objects such as might be received from a customer or bought for weight value. As far as possible the scraps should be sorted according to fineness or purity of each alloy. The scrap should be weighed and placed in a rigid container such as a cardboard box or steel can. Plastic bags are not recommended because they can be torn by the sharp edges of scrap pieces. The container should be labeled with the total weight and, if possible, with the name or alloy of the scrap, such as "46 ounces, Ag 925 (sterling)" or "320 grams scrap, primarily Au 333."

Filings

The term filings includes not only the powder that is the result of using a file, but the chips, curls and particles that result from drilling, turning and grinding. Residue from abrasive papers (retrieved by burning) are also included in this category.

Filings are weighed and collected into a plastic bag that is then packed into a rigid box that can be well sealed with tape. It is labeled, for instance, as "216 grams of Au 585 filings (free from platinum metals)" or "326 grams Ag 925 filings."

Sweeps or lemel

All dust and residue swept from the work bench or retrieved from the sweeps drawer or bench skin are called sweeps or lemel. These are kept separate from floor sweepings or residue collected from scratch-brushing and polishing, which have considerably less valuable. Bench sweeps are cleaned with a magnet then packed and labeled in the same manner as filings.

Scrap containing platinum

The recovery of platinum and platinum group metals is exceptionally difficult and expensive, particularly if the individual platinum group metals have to be separated from each other. Because of this, scrap that contains platinum should always be carefully separated from other scraps and labeled accordingly, such as "11.8 grams scrap with about 90% platinum content." Even in the case of sweeps the approximate platinum content should be stated, for instance, "19.4g mixed filings (Au, Ag and about 20% Pt and Pd)."

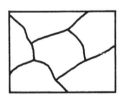 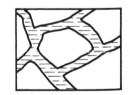

Figure 4.10 Dissolution of the grains when melting.

Electrolytic residues

When the electrolytic baths used in plating become unusable, the metal contents are precipitated out chemically and sent to a refiner for recovery. Rhodium plating baths are concentrated by evaporation and the concentrated solution is sent to a refiner to recover the metal.

4.4
Melting

4.4.1 THE MELTING PROCESS

Melting is obviously an everyday event for a goldsmith, who frequently combines scraps from a previous piece to create a raw material for a new piece. The technical definition of melting is the transition from the solid to a fluid state by the addition of sufficient heat. The complex processes that take place at a microscopic level are to this day not fully researched, and are described here in a general way sufficient for a practicing goldsmith.

The crystal lattice that constitutes a metal is not a frozen and immobile structure even at room temperature. Rather, it is a dynamic system in which metal ions are surrounded by orbiting electrons, which within certain limits are in constant motion. The mutual attraction of the electrons and other atomic particles holds them together.

A temperature increase of about 15°C causes the motion to double, which allows the atomic bonds to loosen. The structure softens because the atomic cohesion decreases as the spaces between atoms grows. This is apparent to the naked eye as slumping when an unsupported flat sheet of metal is annealed. This increase in distance between atoms is also revealed by the expansion of metal when it is heated.

When the melting temperature is reached, some atoms develop a greater energy of movement than their mutual atomic attraction so atoms are freed from the lattice structure. In other words, the atoms are more inclined to move apart than to be held together, so they give up their lattice structure and become fluid. The lattice structure does not suddenly collapse; the melting process is a condition of advancing breakdown of structure. Because the surface of a piece of metal is the first area to reach melting temperature, the dissolution of the lattice structure begins there. The core has not yet reached temperatures high enough to transform from solid to fluid. A parallel process can be identified in microscopic dimensions, where the relatively loosely bound outer atoms in the grain boundary area are freed first. Only bit by bit does the dissolution of the crystal proceed from the outside toward the core of the crystal (figure 4.10).

This process of dissolution of the crystal is called the Frenkel Effect, a description of the peculiar move-and-replace action of atoms as a metal nears the melting temperature. The crystalline order decays progressively as a considerable number of atoms lose their place in the lattice structure and force themselves between the regularly ordered neighboring atoms. This creates holes in the lattice structure in one area and "overcrowded" lattice in another area. If atoms were rigid forms like a bricks in a wall, it would be impossible for newly dislocated atoms to squeeze into the already complete lattice. In reality however, the electron shells of the atoms are deformable and it appears that by a limited displacement (or shifting) of

the neighboring atoms, additional atoms can be forcibly incorporated into the crystal lattice structure.

Additional molten material is formed between the shrinking grains, creating a material in which the solid grains move about like ice cubes in a body of water. The metal can be observed as having a semi-solid paste-like consistency. As mentioned, this process starts at the surface and proceeds throughout the mass until the metal sheet or block is reduced from a solid to a liquid. At this point there is nothing recognizable of the original metal pieces – they have been reduced to a homogenous molten blob.

Throughout the melting process, heat energy from the torch is used to destroy the lattice structure and increase the frequency of the vibrations of subatomic particles. In pure metals, the temperature needed to do this remains constant until the entire block is completely fluid. In alloys, the temperature normally rises slightly during the destruction of the lattice structure. Eutectic alloys exhibit properties similar to pure metals. A phase diagram is a graphic representation of the relationship between time and temperature in the melting process. By linking the points that describe the melting points of various proportions of

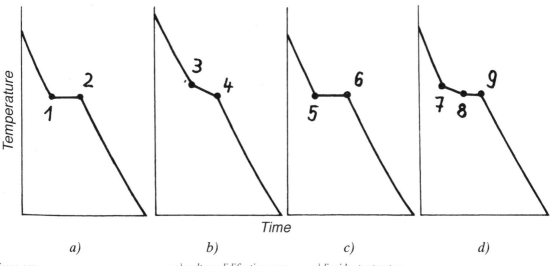

Figure 4.11
Basic kinds of melting curves.
a) pure metal
b) standard alloy
c) eutectic alloy,
d) hyper or hypo eutectic alloy

1-2) melt or solidification curve
3) liquidus temperature
4) solidus temperature
5) liquidus temperature
6) solidus temperature
5-6) eutectic temperature

7) liquidus temperature
7-8) formation of the primary crystal
8-9) formation of the eutectic structure
9) solidus temperature

an alloy, a typical melting curve emerges (figure 4.11).

The amount of heat required to change the whole state varies with each metal because it is dependent on the specific heat and the melting heat of the metal concerned (compare with table 1.16).

4.4.2 EQUIPMENT AND ACCESSORIES

The traditional method for melting metal remained unchanged from ancient times to the middle of the last century. A crucible was placed in the middle of a charcoal fire, which was blown to red heat through the use of a bellows. This was difficult, tiring and even risky because a crucible could easily break and spill the precious metal into the ashes.

In more recent times this method of melting has been replaced by the use of natural gas, or by bottle gases such as acetylene, propane or Mapp gas. These have brought a fundamental change to the melting procedure.

Melting with natural gas

The modern goldsmithing studio typically uses an open gas flame for melting what are usually small amounts of metal. Torches fueled by natural gas, propane, or acetylene are often boosted with compressed air drawn from an electric compressor to create temperatures that melt several ounces of metal efficiently. For metals with a high melting point such as platinum, pure oxygen must be mixed with the fuel to generate the high temperatures required.

Where it is available, natural gas (also known as town gas or city gas) is convenient. The plumbing must be laid by a certified tradesman, but once installed the flow is constant and the only ongoing expense is the fuel itself. Where natural gas is unavailable or costly to install, portable tanks are used instead. These obviously save the cost of installation, but require regulators, and must themselves be leased or purchased.

The torch used for melting is similar to that used for soldering except that it is larger in size. In order to heat a bulky charge of scrap, it is necessary that the flame be large and broad enough to encompass the entire mass.

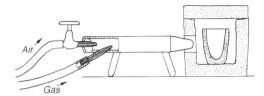

Figure 4.12
Melting furnace with its attached burner.

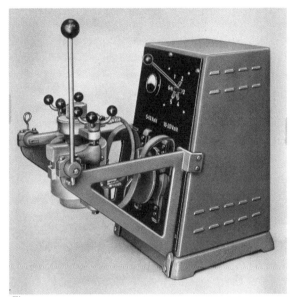

Figure 4.13
Electric induction crucible kiln. (Firma Arno Lindner, Munich)

A little practice is needed to achieve the correct mix of fuel and air. The proper flame is a balance in which there is sufficient air to fully oxidize all the fuel present, but nothing more. If there is too little oxygen, unburned fuel particles risk contaminating the metal and the flame is producing less than its potential temperature. This is called a reducing flame. If on the other hand there is too much oxygen, the oxygen molecules that are not captured by the flame are free to attack the metal, creating oxides that will appear as a skin on the metal and are a possible contaminate. This is called an oxidizing flame, and should be avoided.

The most efficient way to melt relatively small quantities of metal (say from 50g to 150g) is with the use of an improvised muffle kiln that will contain the

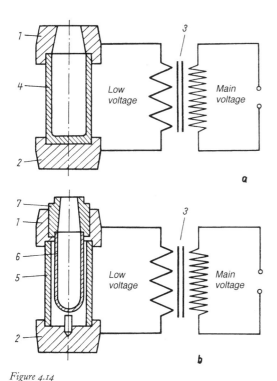

Figure 4.14
Operational diagram of the induction melting crucible transformer.
a) graphite heating element (up to 1300°C)
b) graphite-ceramic heating system (to 1600°C)

1) upper and, 2) lower carbon contact, 3) transformer, 4) graphite
crucible, 5) carbon tube, 6) ceramic curcible, 7) pouring spout.

heat of a torch. These can be made as needed from fire brick and consist simply of a small enclosure with a hole on one side to allow for entrance of a torch. It is best if the interior corners of the kiln can be fitted with small bits of brick to convert the interior shape from a rectangle to something more like a cylinder. That is, the corners are softened so the torch flame is swirled around the interior of the kiln – this produces a more uniform heating.

A graphite or ceramic crucible is set into the kiln and loaded (or "charged") with the scrap metal to be melted. Some flux is generally added to the metal at the outset, and more will be added after the metal becomes molten. A firebrick cover is placed over the enclosure and the torch is lit in the usual manner, using a mix of fuel and air that creates a soft "bushy" flame. This system has the advantage of creating surprisingly high temperatures in a short time with a sparing use of fuel.

Melting with an electric kiln
Melting with electrical energy has the following advantages:
- even heating
- controllable and regulated temperature
- no influence on the melt by impurities from fuel and fuel residues in the melt
- a significantly shorter melting time
- significantly higher melting temperatures than with gas heating

A small electric kiln such as is sold for enameling can be used for melting metals as long as it reaches the necessary temperatures. Because the crucible set into a kiln chamber is radiantly heated by the hot air in the kiln, the coils of the kiln must produce heat in excess of the melting temperatures to be sufficient to heat a crucible. That is, some of the heat energy created by the kiln is "wasted" by heating the air.

Several companies offer an induction melting furnace like the one shown in figure 4.13. These are described by the size of the crucible they accommodate, and are typically available with manual dials or automatic devices to control temperature. They are available in very large sizes for industrial use, but even a small unit will be a welcome addition to a small workshop.

As shown in figure 4.14, induction devices rely on a graphite crucible clamped between carbon contacts. In this way the crucible itself becomes the field of electrical resistance. Electrical energy is transformed to low tension which creates tremendous heat. Graphite crucibles can be used only for temperatures up to 1300°C. For temperatures up to 1600°C, induction melting furnaces use ceramic crucibles that are embedded in a graphite tube which serves as the electrical resistance.

Alloys that contain copper should be stirred with a carbon rod during the melting process to ensure that ingredients are thoroughly mixed. To stir white gold alloys, a neutral quartz rod is used, but in this case care must be taken against the radiant heat that is projected out the back end of the rod, which acts like fiber optic cable in transferring radiant energy. When melting silver alloys, a steel rod is preferred.

Melting crucibles and dishes

GRAPHITE CRUCIBLES

These practical and common crucibles are made of a mixture of clay and graphite. They must be stored in a dry place and should not be allowed to freeze. Like most crucibles, they are supplied in a raw state, and must be annealed by slow heating and lined with borax to make them ready for use. Though they are expensive they last a very long time if handled carefully (figure 4.15).

HESSIAN CLAY CRUCIBLE

These coarser ceramic crucibles are made of clay that contains no iron or chalk, mixed with quartz and brickdust to retard shrinking and cracking caused by thermal shock. Though they do not need to be annealed, they will last longer and give better service if they are glazed with borax before the first use. Metal residues that remain after use must be removed by melting them out; attempts to chip them out might break the crucible.

DISH CRUCIBLES

These ceramic and silica crucibles are available as shallow round dishes or rectangular vessels designed to fit into specific casting machines. They are made of the same materials as the Hessian clay crucibles and require the same pretreatment with borax to line the melting trough with a glassy protective skin. In some styles a half lid is provided to focus the melting flame and protect the melt from excess oxidation.

THE USE OF CRUCIBLES

A separate well-marked crucible should be used for each specific alloy being melted. The first step in melting is to heat the empty crucible until it is red hot. Metal to be melted is then added until the crucible is about half full. The advantage of preheating is that this shortens the length of time the metal must be exposed to the torch, and therefore significantly reduces the possibility of oxidation. In larger melts, a piece of charcoal is sometimes placed directly on the metal to act as a lid, which in this case would also have a reducing (purifying) effect.

Crucibles are best lifted from a kiln with wide tongs

Figure 4.15
Melting crucibles: Hessian clay crucible, graphite crucible, melting ladle, graphite tube, melting dish with lid.

that encircle the body of the vessel. Grasping the lip of the crucible with narrow tongs is not recommended because of the risk of snapping off a piece of the crucible.

When a crucible is no longer fit for use, it can be sent to a refiner along with floor sweepings to reclaim whatever metal remains lodged in the pores.

Reducing fluxes

SODIUM TETRABORATE (BORAX) $Na_2B_4O_7$

Borax is the most universally used flux for precious metals, and is important both in melting and soldering. Borax forms a protective glaze on the walls of a crucible, protects molten metal against the invasion of oxygen, and dissolves oxides that are present.

Borax is a salt that forms large, transparent colorless monoclinic crystals as the decahydrate $Na_2B_4O_7 \cdot 10\ H_2O$. This becomes cloudy when exposed to air. So-called "jewelers borax" crystallizes as hexagonal crystals with five molecules of hydrated water $Na_2B_4O_7 \cdot 5\ H_2O$ from the aqueous borax solution. If this form of borax is heated slowly up to 741°C, the hydrated water is driven off and the solid becomes anhydrous borax, which does not "puff up" upon heating. This loose powder is not well suited to use as a casting flux because it is a light powder that is easily blown away by the gas flame.

The traditional cone borax used by jewelers around the world as a flux gives up most of its water between

350-400°C. This is what causes the undesirable "puffing up" stage that threatens to scatter small pieces of solder. Upon further heating the borax decomposes into sodium metaborate and boron trioxide. In the molten state both melt into each other:

$$Na_2B_4O_7 \rightarrow 2\,NaBO_2 + B_2O_3$$

borax · · · · · · sodium metaborate · · · · boron trioxide

Undesirable metal oxides are transformed into metaborates by the boron trioxide. The sodium metaborate mixes easily with the newly formed borates in the borax melt and effects their transport from the metal-flux boundary region so there are always fresh active boron trioxide particles in the working area.

While boric acid forms only a thin protective layer on metal at temperatures below 900°C, borax has the advantage of greater oxygen absorbing ability. Also, it starts sooner, becoming active at about 700°C.

SODIUM CARBONATE (SODA) Na₂CO₃

This sodium salt of carbonic acid forms large clear crystals as a hydrated soda with 10 molecules of water. Calcined (anhydrous or water-free soda) is available in the trade as a white powder. It is used in goldsmithing as a flux. It melts at 860°C, converting metal oxides present in the melt into carbonates, which come off as a slag. During this process the flame color changes to yellow as a result of the sodium.

$$Na_2CO_3 + CuO \rightarrow$$

sodium carbonate · · · · copper (II) oxide

$$CuCO_3 + Na_2O$$

copper carbonate · · · · sodium oxide

POTASSIUM CARBONATE (POTASH) K₂CO₃

Potash is strikingly similar to soda in appearance and application. It melts at 897°C; the flame takes on a violet color as the potassium is freed during melting.

Flux mixtures

Many goldsmiths use fluxes carelessly, sometimes trusting to unscientific formulas or substituting

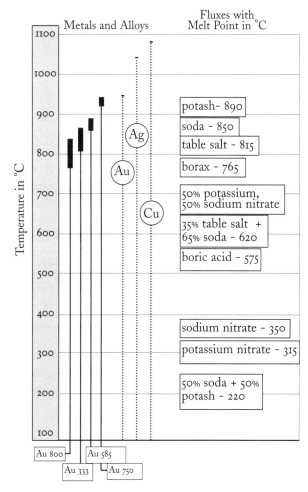

Table 4.9
Melting zone of some metals and alloys for comparison. Thick sections in alloy lines indicate solidus / liquidus range.

ingredients that are close at hand for those specifically called for in a recipe. It is important to remember that the elements of a flux are included either to increase the purifying action of the flux or to change the melting point of one of the ingredients. Understanding the chemistry involved can make the selection and use of fluxes easier.

For instance some recipes call for a mixture of boric acid and soda, but these combine to form borax, so it's more efficient and cheaper to start with borax in the first place.

$$H_2B_4O_7 \quad + \quad Na_2CO_3 \quad \rightarrow$$
tetraboric acid   sodium carbonate

$$Na_2B_4O_7 \quad + \quad H_2O \quad + \quad CO_2$$
borax   water   carbon dioxide

Table 4.9 diagrams the melting point of several metals and fluxes, and reveals that borax has a relatively high melting point, becoming active only 50° below the melting point of the eutectic silver copper alloy. This means the metal will become heavily oxidized before a flux of pure borax can spread out and form a protective glaze. Other common fluxes such as potassium carbonate (potash), sodium carbonate (soda) or sodium chloride (salt) have even higher working temperatures.

The table further shows that the melting temperature of flux mixtures can be significantly reduced by mixing them. Potash and soda melt at 690°C, table salt and soda have an even lower melting temperature of 620°C. By adding these ingredients to borax, the working temperature of the three part mixture will be significantly lower than pure borax, and therefore much more useful as a protective flux. Further, by increasing the sodium and potassium metaborate content, the slag formed by boron trioxide can be transported away faster than is the case with borax alone.

$$K_2CO_3 \quad + \quad Na_2B_4O_7 \quad \rightarrow$$
potassium   borax
carbonate

$$2\,KBO_2 \quad + \quad 2\,NaBO_2 \quad + \quad CO_2$$
potassium   sodium   carbon
metaborate   tetraborate   dioxide

By understanding this dynamic, it is possible to achieve the advantages of a borax-based flux even for metal alloys whose low melting points would seem to make this impossible. The following recipe provides a happy meeting of protective glazing, slag formation and low melting point:

2 parts soda, 2 parts potash, 1 part borax

or, for especially low melting alloys:

1 part salt, 2 parts potash, 1 part borax

Many suppliers of chemicals to the trade offer fluxes under various proprietary names whose tested and scientifically-based compositions are consistently reliable.

Oxidizing fluxes

POTASSIUM NITRATE – SALTPETER KNO_3

The potassium salt of nitric acid forms colorless crystals that are stable in air. Saltpeter is used for oxidizing melting (driving off base metals) because after it melts at 339°C it is able to oxidize non-precious metals. The potassium nitrate changes to potassium nitrite, losing an oxygen atom, which is then available for oxidation.

$$KNO_3 \quad + \quad Pb \quad \rightarrow$$
potassium nitrate   lead

$$KNO_2 \quad + \quad PbO$$
potassium nitrite   lead oxide

SODIUM NITRATE $NaNO_3$

This is very similar to potassium nitrate but has the disadvantage of being very hygroscopic. As a flux, it works like the related potassium nitrate and becomes molten at the slightly lower temperature of 316°C. The melting point can be reduced even further by melting together equal parts sodium and potassium nitrate, which has a melting point of 218°C.

4.4.3 MELTING
GOLD, SILVER AND THEIR ALLOYS

Fine gold

Metal in the form of granules or clean bits of scrap can be melted without any special preparation or additions. This is not the case with the brown powdery gold dust that is recovered during the refining process. To remove impurities, this dust is mixed with saltpeter and borax and just enough water to create a thick paste. This is pressed into a crucible, where it is slowly heated until the melting point of the pure metal is reached and it appears as a blob of solid metal. If the dry powder is simply sprinkled into a crucible and heated, voids will be created in the melt, and the gases that form there might leave the gold fragile and brittle. An additional difficulty is that the gold powder is at risk of being blown out of the crucible by the force of the torch flame.

Fine silver

Just as with fine gold, granulates or clean scraps of pure silver may be melted without any additions. This is not possible, however, when melting silver obtained as a product of silver refining as described previously. If this powder were melted with oxidizing fluxes, a significant portion of the metal would be lost by becoming bound up with the slag. To avoid this, silver is reduced to solid metal by heating it slowly with a soda flux, which prevents oxidation and has the further benefit of assisting in the removal of chlorine, which is often found in recovered silver.

Alloys from pure metal

It is vitally important to start with pure metals when creating or modifying alloys. Even trace amounts of impurities in the addition, or non-precious metals that go into an alloy can cause serious structural flaws in a metal. For this reason the use of recycled metal from old brass objects, copper coins or copper from the electronics industry is not recommended.

In general, borax added during melting is sufficient flux when making new alloys. In order to avoid unnecessary oxygen absorption, the following protective covering mixture may also be added to the melt:

3 parts wood charcoal (clean, not a prepared soldering charcoal block)
2 parts sugar
1 part ammonium chloride

The high volume of carbon in this mix will create a purifying reduction zone over the surface of the melt.

SILVER-COPPER

Whenever copper is involved, it is especially important to guard against oxidation. Start by rolling pure clean copper into thin strips, then paint these with boric acid and heat them to form a protective glaze on the metal surface. If the copper was delivered to the crucible as thick chunks these large pieces will almost certainly oxidize before they are totally melted, creating copper spots in the cast ingot that easily oxidize and lead to damage during working.

Fine silver is set into a crucible and melted until fluid, then the prepared copper is added gradually, a bit at a time. Because of its greater specific heat, copper requires a greater quantity of heat to melt than silver. If too much copper is added at one time to the pool of molten metal, the entire melt might fuse into a block that is difficult to melt.

GOLD-SLVER-COPPER

The first step in making this three part alloy is to set the two precious metals into a crucible and heat them at the same time. This method requires less heat because the melting point of a silver-gold alloy is lower than the melting point of fine gold. When the precious metals are fluid, add copper that has been prepared with boric acid as described above. As usual, oxidation is minimized by using a soft, bushy, reducing flame.

Various multiple material alloys

In addition to work metals such as karat gold and sterling silver, a goldsmith is frequently called upon to create other alloys such as colored golds or solders. Special needs might arise, especially when combining metals with low melting points.

It is a common misunderstanding that metals should be added in descending order of melting point; that is, start with the highest melting metal and work down. It is better practice to start by melting the precious metals, then add the base metals to the melt. Metals with a very low melting point should be added in the form of a preliminary alloy to prevent their oxidation and evaporation. Zinc, for instance, is introduced into an alloy in the form of brass. If zinc were simply sprinkled into an already molten puddle, an uncontrolled portion would burn off as vapors, which destroys the accuracy of measurement and is also a health hazard.

If for some reason this is impossible and it becomes necessary to add pure zinc, start by first melting the precious metals together in an open dish crucible, using borax as a flux as usual. When the metals have become fluid and thoroughly mingled, remove the torch and allow the lump to cool until it just freezes. Pry the lump up slightly and shove the zinc under it; the residual heat of the button will probably be enough to melt the zinc, which will immediately be drawn into the alloy. The entire lump may then be remelted in order to homogenize.

In the same way that the melting point of some metals is raised to facilitate alloying as just described, there are other situations in which a high melting point, such as for copper or gold, can be lowered by preliminary alloying.

An alternate method of handling low melting alloys is to create a relatively air-tight packet by carefully preparing the ingredients prior to melting. For instance, when making a silver-copper zinc (Ag-Cu-Zn) solder alloy, the component metals are rolled out to the thinnest possible strips. These are then stacked and wrapped in fine silver foil in the same way a parcel is wrapped for mailing. This "package" is then hammered as tightly together as possible and set into a crucible for melting. The interior of the packet will melt first, leaving the fine silver wrapping intact as a shield against oxidation until the final stages of melting when it is drawn into the alloy. To completely homogenize the alloy, it should be rolled out, cleaned and remelted twice.

4.4.4 RE-MELTING ALLOYS

When working with perfectly clean scrap, granules, or otherwise compact clean material, all that is needed is to work in a clean crucible and coat the melt with a little borax. It is always good practice to heat only as long as necessary to complete the melt; do not overheat or prolong heating.

It sometimes happens that alloys are unworkable because of impurities or incorrect proportions. When correcting such errors, it is first necessary to understand what created (or might have created) the problem. Even if it is not possible to determine the exact cause, it helps to have a suspicion. In some cases a problem might be the result of incorrect handling of the material, for instance when a sheet has cracked during rolling because of insufficient annealing. In a case like this, simple remelting with the use of conventional flux is sufficient. In other cases the root of a problem might be traced to impurities formed while alloying.

Reducing re-melting

This method of purifying an alloy through remelting is used when a goldsmith suspects impurities caused by oxygen or other gases that have become dissolved in the metal, either in their pure form or as metallic compounds.

Oxygen is the most common trouble maker in this regard, and is most often seen as the red copper (I) oxide Cu_2O. This compound is stable at high temperatures and can only be dissolved in the fluid state by a reducing flux as described here.

- In most cases an alloy can be purified by adding the flux previously mentioned; a mixture of 2 parts soda, 2 parts potash, 1 part borax. This is stirred into the fluid melt, which is then gently poured into an ingot mold. Because this is the safest method, it should always be tried first.

- The removal of larger amounts of oxidation is achieved with the addition of 0.5% cadmium, which is extremely dangerous to breathe. As in previous sections, this is included here in the interest of scientific and historical accuracy, but this process is not recommended for the conventional studio. Cadmium should only be melted in situations in which industrial quality air removal systems are in proper use.

As described above, cadmium is added by slipping a small charge under a still hot button in a shallow dish crucible. When the cadmium is taken into the alloy, it bonds with metal oxides there, pulling the oxygen atom away to form cadmium oxide, which evaporates. Any remaining cadmium residues do not affect the alloy.

• For damaged alloys in which large quantities of oxides must be removed, phosphorous in the form of phosphorus copper can be used as a purifying agent. This is more complicated, because if too much is added to a melt the unused remnants can damage the alloy. For this reason only the smallest possible doses are used, and even then they are added bit by bit. Typically, an addition of only 2% phosphorus copper is sufficient, and this contains only 2% phosphorous. This is added as described before, by sliding the small portion of phosphorous copper under a just-hardened lump in a crucible.

Metal oxides are dissolved according the following sequence:

$$5\ Cu_2O\ +\ 2\ P\quad\rightarrow\quad P_2O_5\ +\ 10\ Cu\qquad(1)$$

$$Cu_2O\ +\ P_2O_5\quad\rightarrow\quad 2\ CuPO_3\qquad\qquad(2)$$

$$10\ CuPO_3\ +\ 2\ P\ \rightarrow\ 6\ P_2O_5\ +\ 10\ Cu\qquad(3)$$

The first phase of the reduction, illustrated in the first line above (1), shows that gaseous phosphorus pentoxide is formed. The reaction then proceeds as diagrammed in line (2) where a reduction of the Cu_2O content causes the formation of copper metaphosphate $CuPO_3$. As shown in line (3) this is only partly redissolved and casts off the balance as slag. The P_2O_5 fumes generated act as a protective gas envelope over the surface of the melt and the metal stream when pouring.

Unfortunately this useful reducing agent has the drawback that even small amounts (0.001% is sufficient) of phosphorus residues can cause significant damage to the whole alloy. Brittle compounds such as Ag_2P, Cu_3P, Ni_3P are formed. These lower the workability of the metal and create low melting eutectic alloys.

Oxidizing melting
In cases where an alloy has been damaged by the presence of non-precious foreign metals such as lead, tin, zinc or aluminum, the alloy is remelted with an oxidizing agent. This forces the undesirable metal to form oxides that can be carried off in the slag or refuse material that accompanies the molten flux.

The alloy is weighed and set into a ceramic crucible; a graphite crucible could burn through. The crucible is filled about a third full with metal, and heated until the charge is molten. Working under a fume hood, an amount of saltpeter equal to the weight of the metal is poured onto the melt and heated until the mass stops bubbling. The activity of the saltpeter is indicated by a green color in the flame.

The molten material is then poured onto a steel plate to cool and broken with a hammer to release the small pieces of gold. These are picked out, boiled in nitric acid, washed and dried. Each lump of gold should be hammered out as thin as possible and checked for gray fracture surfaces. If these appear, the process should be repeated. This pure material is now ready to be alloyed with copper and silver as described earlier, to make up a karat gold. This of course involves remelting, which if done properly provides another occasion for purifying the metal.

Melting filings
If filings are to be reclaimed by remelting the following conditions must be fulfilled:

– they must be from an alloy of specific fine gold content
– there cannot be any foreign metals mixed in with the filings
– filings must be free of abrasive and polishing residues
– filings must not have any significant residues of non-metallic impurities

Iron remnants are removed from a batch of filings by trawling repeatedly with a strong magnet. The filings are then spread on a sheet of steel and annealed to burn off any combustible debris.

If the filings are not particularly contaminated, they are set onto a square of tissue paper along with a spoonful of the flux mentioned earlier (2 parts soda, 2 parts potash, 1 part borax). The paper is wound up in

127

a twist to keep the light particles of metal and flux from being blown out of the crucible by force of the torch flame. When the metal is molten and has been properly stirred, it is cast into an ingot mold or onto a charcoal block.

If there is reason to suspect damaging impurities in the filings, they are mixed instead with a larger quantity of saltpeter to create the oxidizing melt just described. Again the ingredients are bound up in a twist of thin paper to keep them in the crucible. The button created by this process is pried from the crucible as soon as it is solid, pickled and remelted using a standard reduction melting.

4.4.5 MELTING OF PLATINUM AND WHITE GOLD
Studios that do only a little work in platinum and white gold are usually best advised to send their scrap to a refiner for reclamation. Not only do these metals require higher heat (and therefore specialized equipment) in refining, but they are particularly sensitive to impurities and can frustrate a person not familiar with their refining characteristics. On the other hand, businesses that work with platinum or white gold regularly will probably find that a small platinum melting system can pay for itself.

Standard graphite crucibles cannot be used when melting platinum because at its high melting point the carbon in them is dissolved and can be absorbed by the metal, creating porosity. Because high temperatures generally accelerate chemical reactions, even a ceramic crucible can cause problems; the aluminum, silicon and cadmium contained in the clay can be reduced out and can mix with platinum to form brittle compounds. This tendency is addressed by lining the crucible with "burnt chalk," CaO. Covering or fluxes are not normally used, though boric acid is sometimes added to white gold.

These metals are best melted in an electric induction melting kiln. When using an oxy-acetylene flame, there is the potential to contaminate the metal with fuel gases if the balance of the torch is not delicately handled. Once they are molten, platinum or white gold are poured into ingot molds just like any other gold alloy.

4.5
Casting

The term castability does not simply describe a single characteristic of a metal, but rather encompasses several complex aspects of the physical properties of a metal as they influence its ability to be poured when molten into a mold. The four principal factors are surface tension, viscosity, vapor pressure, and casting temperature.

Surface tension
This property determines the shape of the stream of a metal as it is poured, its ability to fill a mold and the speed with which the molten metal spreads out in the mold.

The atoms in the interior of a molten mass can balance out each other's energy, but the atoms in the exterior region have an excess of energy. They attempt to equalize or reduce this excess amount by reducing their surface area. Of all possible geometric shapes, the sphere has the smallest surface area. This explains, for example, why spilled mercury immediately draws itself into spheres.

In almost all metals, temperature and surface tension are in an inverse relationship. As temperature increases, surface tension decreases. The melt looses shape. Copper is an exception: its already large surface tension is increased as increasing heat is applied. Table 4.10 compares some values for common studio metals.

Surface tension can be significantly reduced by alloying, or through the addition of nonmetal materials. The extremely high value of copper can be reduced almost by half through the addition of 50% tin. For this reason it is traditional to add small quantities of zinc or cadmium to precious metal alloys just before casting.

Viscosity
Like surface tension, viscosity influences the ability of a metal to fill a mold. The ability of a molten metal to send off gases and its ability to be dissolved in flux are also related to its viscosity.

Viscosity, or "stickiness" or "runny-ness" is caused by internal friction and deformation resistance. Temperature and viscosity are related inversely. As the temperature rises, internal friction declines. The viscosities of several metals at their melting points is given in table 4.11.

Viscosity is also important in fluxes. The viscosity of a molten flux must be many times higher than that of the alloy being melted so it remains behind in the crucible when the fluid melt is cast.

Vapor pressure
The vapor pressure of a metal at its boiling temperature reaches the atmospheric pressure before it is transformed to a gaseous state. To a limited extent metals evaporate even below this temperature. A particularly clear example of this is mercury, which because of its high vapor pressure volatizes noticeably even at room temperature, though its boiling point is not reached until 327°C. A similar situation exists with zinc, which evaporates as soon as it passes its melting point. This explains why a zinc-bearing alloy such as brass cannot be held at its melting point too long without significantly reducing the proportion of zinc left in the alloy.

Casting temperature
Though this seems obvious, it is important to know if the melting equipment at hand is sufficient to reach the melting point of metals to be cast. Clearly the melting temperature and the amount of excess heat necessary for casting must be within the working capabilities of the heat source. When working with sterling (Ag 925) which has a liquidus temperature of 900°C, heating equipment must be capable of reaching 1000°C, that is, the ability to reach temperatures at least 100 K (Kelvin) in excess of melting points. For an 80% silver alloy (Ag 800) a torch or kiln that reaches 920°C will be sufficient, again achieving the 100 degree margin since the melting point of Ag 800 is 820°C. Most conventional fuel torches produce heat in the 1100°C range.

Metal	Surface Tension in mN/m	Temperature in °C
copper	1103	1131
zinc	750	600
tin	510	500
lead	400	500

Table 4.10
Surface tension of xome metals.

Metal	Viscosity in Pa
copper	0.35
zinc	0.34
lead	0.27
cadmium	0.23
tin	0.19

Table 4.11
Viscosity of pure metals at the melting temperature.

4.5.1 THE CASTING PROCEDURE

The first step, of course, is to heat the casting metal (the charge) until it is completely melted. This can often be determined visually, but it's a good habit to confirm the melt by stirring the mass with a quartz rod. If any chunks of semi-hard material are encountered, continue heating and check again. In order to fill a mold completely, the metal must remain fluid until it has penetrated every detail of the mold. Because the metal is loosing heat as it enters the mold (it is, of course, no longer exposed to a flame at this point) the metal must be heated above its liquidus point so that it can drop a little in temperature and still remain liquid. The degree to which the metal must be over-heated depends upon the character of the metal, the length of the pour from crucible to mold, and the shape of the mold.

When the metal has reached the correct temperature, the coating of flux is drawn aside with a rod and the metal is poured into the mold in a steady, thin stream. The length of the pouring stream should be as short as possible so the metal is not unnecessarily cooled off on its way into the mold and absorbs as little atmospheric gas as possible from the air. To shield the metal from oxygen, a piece of burning wood can be held close to the pour; the flame uses the oxygen from the surrounding environment, thereby preventing it from joining with the molten metal to form oxides. A similar effect can be achieved by pouring through the flame of a Bunsen burner or similar small natural gas torch. After filling the mold completely, the metal should solidify as quickly as possible. That is to say, the ideal pouring temperature is hot enough to insure the metal is completely fluid for as long as necessary to fill the mold, but no hotter.

4.5.2 THE SOLIDIFICATION PROCESS

The solidification process is the reverse of the melting process. In a gaseous phase, metal particles can for the most part free themselves from each other and move about in space but in the fluid molten state, a mutual attraction between metal ions and free electrons restrains the metal as a somewhat cohesive unit, typically a puddle whose shape is determined by the vessel in which the fluid is contained. When the supply of heat stops, the mobility of the atoms or the metal ions in the metal is reduced and the solidification process begins.

Seed formation

Solidification starts when the temperature of a molten metal sinks below the solidification temperature. When the conditions for attraction between molecules are more favorable than the conditions for movement (that is, when the temperature falls below a certain point), molecules attract each other and order themselves to make a unit cell. The atomic properties of each metal predispose it to organize according to a particular pattern, which is known as a lattice structure. The first crystal to form is called the seed crystal, and provides the orientation of the lattice for all adjacent crystals.

CRYSTAL GROWTH

As the molten mass cools and molecules slow down they layer themselves along the seed crystal if they have come near enough for mutual attraction to occur. As the newly layered atoms conform to the unit cell system, a three dimensional crystal lattice with regularly ordered lattice planes develops. This is called a crystal or grain (figure 4.16).

Crystal structure

The actual process of crystal formation is considerably more complicated than this simplified description conveys. As a sample of metal solidifies, thousands of seed crystals form simultaneously, with adjacent atoms falling into position in the lattice structure at speeds that cannot be imagined. And though this is diagrammed two dimensionally, it is of course happening in real space. Not only are new seed crystals developing throughout the melt, but there are probably seed crystals from the previous structure that did not fully dissolve when the metal was molten. And as some molecules join onto existing seeds, others solidify independently and continue to make new seed crystals.

Solidification heat

The vibration energy given up from ions in the crystals formed first is transformed into heat again, so the metal lattice structure heats up again, even if no additional external heat is being supplied. That is, the process of solidification generates heat. Or, to make it more confusing, as things cool down, they heat up. In practice this heat is so minuscule it is of only theoretical importance.

If heat is supplied uniformly as a quantity of molten metal cools, the crystals grow in all directions equally. If however heat is supplied in a preferred direction, crystals develop linearly and take the shape of stalk-like shapes with extensions that resemble twigs and needles from a fir tree. These are called dendrites (figure 4.17).

Grain formation count and the speed of crystallization

Grain formation count and the rate at which a metal forms crystals are important phenomena that are independent of each other and different for each metal. Grain formation count refers to the number of grains formed in a solidifying melt in a given time. The speed of crystallization expresses how quickly a mass is converted from random (fluid) to ordered (solid) structure. Neither characteristic can be changed, but both can be influenced by external conditions to achieve specific results.

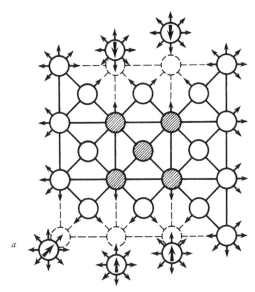

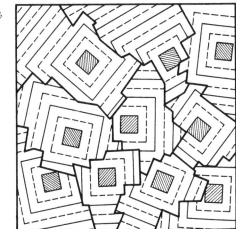

Figure 4.16
Grain growth and crystal structure.
a) crystal growth through deposition of atoms from the melt, b) formation of the crystal structure by the meeting of the growing crystals.

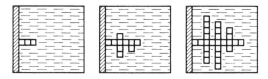

Figure 4.17
The formation of a dendrite by the regular growth of the crystal.

The typical intention is to achieve as fine a grain structure as possible because this generally produces a metal with the best working properties. This is achieved by the formation of many grains simultaneously; they grow close together and quickly collide with each other, limiting the size of individual grains. To increase the grain formation count and the speed of crystallization, the metal is heated only as much as necessary and then cooled as rapidly as possible, within certain limits related to stress.

Figure 4.18 illustrates two characteristic grain growth patterns. In the first example, tiny grains are formed around the perimeter of the ingot mold where the metal cools first. This is followed immediately by the formation of dendritic grains that are oriented toward the center of the ingot mold. The second illustration demonstrates the effect of an overall cooling rate, in which evenly distributed larger grains are formed.

4.5.3 SHRINKAGE IN VOLUME
In some applications, shrinkage is critical and therefore deserves careful description here. Even when fluid, a mass of molten metal shrinks as its temperature decreases. As the mass solidifies, there is a sudden reduction in the volume which can be very significant in some metals. And even after a metal has solidified a certain amount of shrinkage in volume can still take place.

When metal ions are heated to above their melting points each atom vibrates dramatically, taking up a lot of space like a dancer spinning erratically with outstretched arms. As a metal cools it is drawn into a well-organized lattice structure. This well packed material takes up less room, so we can say the metal mass shrinks. As the object cools further, the spaces between atoms are reduced, so there is a small reduction in volume at this point as well. This is the reverse of the familiar well known phenomenon of the expansion of metals as they are heated. The most significant shrinkage is that which takes place in the first phase of solidification, as crystals fall into regular patterns.

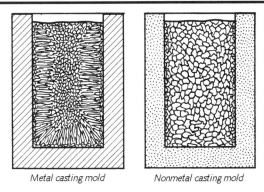

Figure 4.18
Different internal structures resulting from differing mold materials.

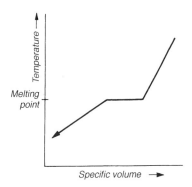

Figure 4.19
The volume change of a metal in relationship to the temperature.

Table 4.12
Volume reduction in pure metals upon freezing.

Metal	Volume Reduction in %
gold	5.03
silver	5.0
copper	4.25
lead	3.38
zinc	4.7
cadmium	4.72
tin	2.9

Rounded edges

Knowing that a cast object will shrink as it solidifies, it comes as no surprise that corners and sharp edges are likely to become rounded as a piece pulls away from the walls of a mold. This problem is less pronounced in centrifugal and vacuum casting, where the process exerts a continuous pressure on the solidifying metal as it cools. In other casting methods, the use of a large button is recommended to maintain pressure on the material. In objects with critical measurements the model should be made slightly oversize so as to allow for this inevitable shrinkage.

Shrinkage cavity formation (porosity)

The transition from randomly-oriented to lattice-oriented crystals that occurs as a metal solidifies can create voids or cavities in an otherwise solid sheet. These are sometimes large enough to be seen with the naked eye and sometimes microscopic; either way they weaken a metal and make a bright finish impossible.

Crystal formation normally begins at the walls of a mold as they conduct heat away and cool the metal. This just-solid metal takes up less room than it did a split second before, so the molten metal can be said to shrink away from it, creeping inward, toward the interior. This is seen in the characteristic funnel shape cavity that occurs in an ingot: the sides are solidified because of the relative cooling effect of the mold, and the top is cooled because of its exposure to air (figure 4.20a). This funnel shaped cavity is exposed to atmosphere and is therefore likely to oxidize.

New crystals form against this first level and grow inward toward the center of the molten mass. After the entire perimeter of the shape has solidified, further shrinkage will create voids and result in a porous structure. As the millions of crystals fall into a tightly packed crystal lattice, each grain is pulled this way or that to find alignment with existing grains. The result is the creation of many small cavities of various sizes (figure 4.20b). If there is molten metal in the area, it will be drawn into these cavities and will form dense metal. Shrinkage cavity formation cannot be completely avoided, but there are methods to limit the damage as much as possible.

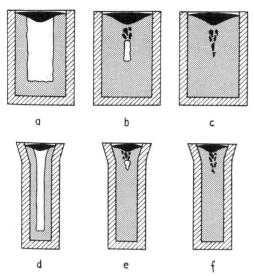

Figure 4.20
Void formation in a cast piece.
(white: molten; gray: solidified metal; black: void)
a to c) voids in workpiece, d to f) void in the button of the casting,
a and d) outer void, b and e) inner voids, c and f) inner and outer void

- Use a slow casting speed and heat the metal only enough to make it molten. In this way the metal that first enters the mold will start to solidify immediately, while additional molten metal is still being delivered to the casting.
- Use a mold that allows for a generous button at the gate, and be sure to use sufficient metal to fill this area. If this is the largest metal mass, it will be the last to cool. This means it can supply molten metal to fill the voids in the adjacent areas as they solidify.
- In order for the button to supply excess material, the sprue that connects the piece with the button must remain fluid. To prevent early solidification of the sprue it should be thicker than the thickest section of the model.
- Additional shrinkage reservoirs should be added to a model to accommodate those areas that are thick enough to cool slowly but because of the shape of the piece are at a distance from the button. These lumps are designed to remain fluid for a split second after the object itself hardens so they can

supply additional metal as needed to fill shrinkage voids. If they play their role well, these reservoirs will have porosity when examined closely.

4.5.4 CASTING STRESSES

When a cast piece cannot shrink unhindered, the solidifying mass will be affected by stresses that cause the piece to either crack or distort. As determined by their origin and characteristics, these are either internal or external stresses.

External casting stress
If a mold material is unable to contract as a solidifying metal shrinks, the push and pull will result in an external stress. This usually occurs in metal molds. The ring diagrammed in figure 4.21a is cast around a steel mandrel; it wants to shrink together while solidifying, but is prevented from doing this by the steel core. When the shrinking metal can no longer fit around the unyielding core, it cracks, as shown in the lower left. The H-shaped cast piece wants to shrink together in the direction of the arrows because the thick end beams produce the greatest stress. The thin connecting bridge, being the weakest area, yields to the pull of shrinkage and cracks (figure 4.21b).

Internal casting stress
Internal stresses are caused by different cooling rates of sections within a single object. Areas with larger cross sections will cool (and therefore shrink) slower than thin areas. When thin sections have solidified into their final shapes and dimensions, thicker areas are just starting to shrink. The illustration of a wheel in figure 4.21c illustrates what can happen. The outer ring and spokes will solidify first and resist the pull of the thicker hub as it cools and shrinks. Because there is no give in the already solid spokes, they will be cracked as the interior section pulls against them.

In the similar shape shown in figure 4.21d, the wheel has a smaller hub and thicker circumference, which will be the last area to solidify. The shrinking outer ring will pull against the already solid spokes, perhaps causing them to crack. If they are strong enough to resist the pressure, the stress of the outer

133

ring can only be accommodated by tearing along the circumference. Even in cases where visible cracking does not occur, tensions are nevertheless created in such castings that might show up in later use.

Layered stresses
This special kind of internal stress appears in thick ingots or sheet-like cast pieces that cool in progressive layers from outer to inner sections. Again the push and pull of soft areas against those that are already rigid will cause the metal to tear (figure 4.21f). Accelerated cooling often causes layered stresses; they can be usually be avoided by cooling an ingot slowly.

4.5.5 GRAVITY POUR CASTING

When molten metal is poured from a crucible into a prepared mold, the physical laws of gravity and hydrodynamics determine the way the metal flows into the mold. We can divide this process into three closely linked phases: entering the mold, flowing through it, and filling out the mold.

The fluid metal enters the mold with the force of gravity

$$v = \sqrt{2 \cdot g \cdot h_1}$$

and by this achieves the kinetic energy.

$$E_k = \frac{m}{2} \cdot v^2 = m \cdot g \cdot h_1$$

g – acceleration of fall in m/s²
h_1 – height of pouring stream in m
v – speed of fall in m/s
m – mass of the melt in kg
E_k – kinetic energy in J

Example
With what kinetic energy does the charge of molten metal (m = 100g) hit the mold from a height h_1 (15 cm)?

$$E_k = m \cdot g \cdot h_1 = 0.1 \cdot 9.81 \cdot 0.15 J = \underline{0.147\,J}$$

As this shows, the force with which molten metal fills a mold is dependent upon the height of the fall and the weight of the melt. As long as the metal is fluid, a hydrostatic pressure is in effect that facilitates filling as it presses against the walls of the mold:

$$p = h_2 \cdot g \cdot \rho \cdot 10^3$$

h_2 – full height of the mold in m
ρ – density of the cast material in g/cm³
p – hydrostatic pressure in Pa

This pressure is dependent only on the density of the material and of the height of poured mass, in this case the distance from the floor of the mold to the top of the button. It doesn't matter how wide the pouring gate or button is; hydrostatic pressure is affected only by height. Because hydrostatic pressure pushes out in all directions equally, the molten mass presses not just on the floor of the mold, but upon the walls as well. The amount of this pressure is the same throughout the mold, even near the pouring gate.

Example
What is the hydrostatic pressure within a mold if a melt of silver ρ = 10.3 g/cm³) is poured from a height of h_2 (10 cm) ?

$$p = h_2 \cdot g \cdot \rho \cdot 10^3$$
$$= 0.1 \cdot 9.81 \cdot 10.3 \cdot 10^3 Pa$$
$$= \underline{1.01 \cdot 10^4\,Pa}$$

When small amounts of material are being cast, hydrostatic pressure is not significant. In the case of larger castings such as bells however, the mold is set into a hole in the ground and tightly packed in stamped earth to withstand the load.

Sheet and wire ingot molds
Various kinds of molds for making wire and sheet are sold by suppliers. Molds for making slabs (the thick plate that will be rolled down to produce sheet) are often designed so various widths can be cast. Figure 4.22 shows a combination sheet and wire mold that

has this feature as well as the ability to cast short rods that can be rolled into wire.

To make an ingot mold, simply bend a piece of square wire into the contour of the intended shape, as illustrated in figure 4.22. This is set between two sheets of steel that have been hammered or ground slightly to create a pouring funnel. Position the assembly in a vise or secure it with a C-clamp.

Regardless of the type of mold, it is prepared before each use by wiping the interior surfaces clean, then coating them with either a layer of soot (from a candle flame) or a thin film of oil. If oil is used, be careful to avoid excess, which will burn and in the process create waste products that will compromise the ingot. Traditional methods have lately been replaced by a silicone, which can be sprayed into the mold before each use. This is available from suppliers of casting equipment.

Casting molds should be set in a tray or shallow dish that contains a layer of sand. This will insulate any spills that might occur and will make retrieval of the metal easier. When working with large quantities it is helpful to set the mold at a slight angle. In this way spilled metal will slide down the outside of the mold rather than hit the tray with a splash.

Iron and steel molds, especially those with a bulky mass, must be preheated before pouring or the ingot will cool too quickly, typically solidifying before the pour is even complete. Use either a torch or kiln to heat the prepared mold until it is too hot to be held. Molds of aluminum have the advantage of being heated by the heat of the casting metal itself.

Wedding ring mold

The traditional ring mold illustrated in figure 4.24 is useful for small shops that make a lot of bands. This expandable steel mold with a half profile of a wedding band carved into each side can be purchased from a supplier of jewelry equipment. This is fitted with a springy piece of steel that acts as a core; note that it must be rebent from time to time so that it fits tightly against the mold.

As a general practice it is better to cast a ring blank too small rather than too large. A small ring can be forged to increase its size; this hammering process has

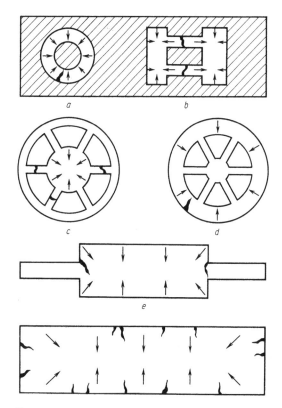

Figure 4.21
The formation of casting stresses.
a) & b) outer cast stresses, c) to e) internal cast stresses,
f) stresses upon a sheet.

the advantage of compressing the internal structure and thereby strengthening the piece. As with an ingot mold, this mold is oiled or sooted and warmed until too hot to touch. It is set into a dish of sand in preparation for casting. The metal is melted as described earlier and poured into the mold in a smooth steady motion. Care is taken to avoid splashing or throwing the metal too abruptly.

The cast metal will solidify first where it is cooled by contact with the mold; that is, on the side walls of the wedding ring and on the outer surface of the casting button. Shrinkage is compensated by the excess metal of the sprue and button, which will remain fluid a split second longer than the shank of the ring. If this were not the case and the button cooled first, the inevitable shrinkage of the casting as it solidifies will create voids, resulting in porous metal.

Figure 4.22
Combined sheet and wire ingot mold.

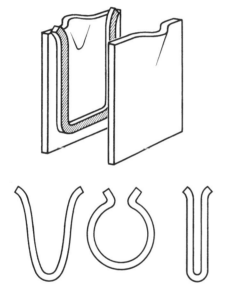

Figure 4.23
Home-made ingot molds with various inserts.

Figure 4.24
Wedding ring mold in the open position.

Table 4.13
Possible errors when using a wedding ring mold.

Symptom	Reason	Remedy
casting mold not filled out	metal is too cold, the mold too cold or too hot, gas or air cannot escape	higher melting temperature heat the mold until hot to the hand
porous casting	channel be-tween the casting button and ring too narrow,	soot the mold instead of oiling it, enlarge the air passages enlarge the cast-ing channel
voids upon the insides of the ring under the casting button	melt is too cold	use a higher cast-ing temperature, heat the mold until hot to the hand

Waste molds

In addition to making sheet and wire, it is possible to create simple molds for casting findings, components or entire pieces of jewelry. These molds are typically one-use affairs that must be broken apart to retrieve the casting. For this reason they are categorized as waste molds.

The ancient methods described in this section have largely been superseded by centrifugal casting, which will be discussed later. These techniques are included here, however, because they still offer useful alternatives for a small shop. Because the cost of equipment is low, these traditional gravity methods can be useful in a shop that otherwise cannot justify the cost of centrifugal equipment. In addition, these direct methods are useful to create a "blank" for subsequent carving or shaping in that a large form can be given a starting shape quicker and with less waste than by carving such a shape from heavy stock. And finally, these methods should remain in the repertoire of goldsmithing because of the pleasure of the process itself.

4.5.6 CUTTLEFISH CASTING

Cuttlefish casting is a quick and fairly accurate casting method. Its applications are limited only by the thickness and overall dimensions of the shell. It is difficult to achieve fine details on the surface of the casting, but this is offset by the richly complex texture that is a natural by-product of this method.

The back plate or cuttlebone of the ordinary squid (genus: sepia) serves as the mold material. The elliptical shell is a bright white, porous material that can be easily indented by pressing a model into it. One side of this material is covered with a thin, hard crust that resembles plastic. Cuttlefish bones for casting can be purchased through jewelry suppliers and pet stores, where they are sold for use in birdcages.

The process of preparing a two-part mold will be described by using a ring as an example.

Model

The model must be made of something solid enough to withstand being firmly pressed into the cuttlefish. Plastic or metal models are ideal. Wood or hard wax models will work if they don't have delicate sections. Traditionally a model might have been made from lead, which is easily hammered and bent into shape. Remember to avoid direct contact with skin when using this potentially dangerous metal. Depending on the shape being made, it is sometimes possible to start with an existing ring and simply modify it to meet the particular needs at hand.

The model is given shape with hammers, files and any other tool necessary. It should be made a little tight (a quarter size too small) to allow for the material that will be removed as the casting is finished. If the model needs to be strengthened in specific places, two part metal epoxy can be added as needed and filed to shape after it has hardened.

It is critical that the model have no undercuts so it can be lifted cleanly out after being pressed into the cuttlefish. Removal will be easier if the inside of the band is slightly rounded rather than being perfectly flat.

The casting mold

Select a medium-size shell and cut it in half lengthwise. Flatten the face of the soft side of both of these pieces by rubbing them on coarse sandpaper or against each other. Because this makes considerable dust, it is best to perform this operation over a waste basket. The goal is to create surfaces that are smooth, broad and flat enough that no light is visible between the two pieces when they are held firmly together.

Position the model in the thickest part of the cuttlefish. The model is set onto one side in its proper location along with several small registration keys of steel or brass sheet. The other half of the shell is set in alignment on top of this and the two shells are brought together with a firm even pressure until the two sanded faces make full contact. Be certain the mold is thick enough in the area around the model to provide strength in the mold. The internal registration keys can be augmented by making a couple saw cuts or drawing bold lines with a marker when the two halves are together.

The mold halves are separated and the model removed, using tweezers if this seems prudent. It is important that the mold not be damaged during this process. A funnel-shaped sprue is cut into each side of the mold. This must be wide enough to insure that it will be the last part of the casting to cool; that is, it should be thicker than the thickest part of the ring. Small vents are cut from the model leading upward to allow for the exhaust of air and combustion gases as the molten metal enters the mold.

The finished mold is cleaned with a soft, dry brush, and the parts are reassembled, using the registration angle keys and saw cuts for alignment. The parts are then tied together with binding wire and the mold is dried by being set into a warm spot such as under a lamp. It is now ready for casting.

Some more complicated objects will require molds of three or even more pieces. The following example describes the casting of a ring with a hollow bezel, as illustrated in figure 4.25.

Model for three-part mold

A model like this can be carved from plastic, either sawn from a thick block, or built up by adding epoxy to a plastic ring cut from a length of tubing. Alternately, the model could have been carved from plaster or lead. To make a "blank" of the latter material, bend up a quick ring in sheet brass, considerably wider than the model will need to be. Then use a strip of the same brass to make a silhouette of the intended form, somewhat like a cookie cutter shape. Press these a little way into a charcoal block, then pour molten lead into the form thus created. After it has cooled this form can be reduced to the correct shape with files. Wear rubber gloves to protect your skin from exposure to lead while working. An advantage of a lead model is that the shank can be sawn through at the back and the size adjusted by simply opening out the ring.

The mold

As described above, a large cuttlefish bone is cut, this time into three pieces. These are again sanded and rubbed until each has a surface that is smooth and perfectly planar. It is important that these surfaces fit

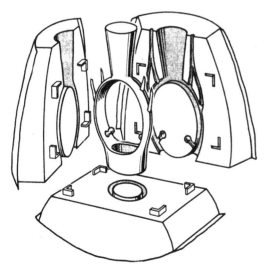

Figure 4.25
Three part cuttlefish mold with the rough casting opened up.

tightly against each other or the molten metal will spill out the cracks. The ring model is set onto one panel of the mold so its top element (the hollow bezel) extends above the mold. Registration pins are laid into position and the other half is set onto the model and the two units are pressed together until they meet. The halves of the mold are separated and the model is carefully removed. The pieces are put back together, using the registration pins to insure accurate placement, and the top surface is trued up with sandpaper or a file.

The mold is reopened and the model is set back into place. The head of the ring, which projects out of the mold is pressed vertically into the third piece of cuttlefish, again being certain that the pieces are brought together so tightly that no gaps remain between them. The location of this piece is registered either with saw cuts or bold ink lines, or both. The model is then removed, a pouring gate and air vents are cut as described above, and the interior of the mold is blown clean of any dust. The mold is reassembled and tied securely with binding wire. The assembled mold is shown in figure 4.26.

Casting

In order to promote solid metal free of porosity, a large button is suggested for cuttlefish casting. This will be the result of carving a large gate and remembering to use sufficient metal to fill it. In order to improve the castability of the metal, it's a good idea to add a small amount (about 0.5%) zinc just before pouring the metal. This will lower its melting point, make it less viscous, and decrease the surface tension of the molten mass. All of these factors will allow the casting to fill more completely and pick up detail better. The metal should be poured into the mold at the lowest possible temperature; if it's too hot the mold will be prematurely burnt up. This can cause a loss of detail in the mold and might also make the cast porous. To prevent this, pour the metal just as a skin starts to form on the charge in the crucible.

Figure 4.26
Closed three part cuttlefish mold, prepared for casting.

4.5.7 SAND CASTING

Though sand casting has been largely replaced by centrifugal casting in recent decades, for hundreds of years it was the most popular of all casting methods. It still plays an important role in the production of large metal forms, and can offer the advantages of low cost, quick results and ease of duplication to those goldsmiths who take the time to master it. Though sometimes thought of as coarse, sandcasting can yield results that are as fine and true to detail as any other casting method.

Mold frames or mold bottle
There are many variations possible, but the most common mold frames for small scale work are made of steel or aluminum and consist of a pair of almost identical rectangular frames; boxes with neither a top nor a bottom. Each has an opening cut in one of the narrow sides, usually enlarged by a flange that creates a funnel when the frame halves are put together. The only difference between the parts is that one unit, called the cope, has registration pins projecting out from it, while the other half, the drag, has tabs to receive those pins. These hold the frame together and make it possible to line up the sections perfectly.

Preparation of the sand
Dry molding sand is passed through a fine sieve into a bowl and slowly moistened with water, kneading aggressively to insure even distribution of the moisture. The sand is worked until it is pliable and easy to shape. The consistency is correct when a lump squeezed in the hand retains its shape even when it is tossed into the air and caught.

Preparation of the mold
The octagonal chased brooch illustrated in figure 4.27 will be used here to describe the process of sand casting. The drag (the mold half without the pegs) is placed on a piece of plate glass with its inner edge facing down. The model is set onto the glass in the lower third of the frame and both model and frame are dusted with parting powder. Traditionally this is a yellowish, fine-grained powder derived from plants of the Lycopodiaceen group. Talcum or cornstarch can be substituted. Whatever the powder, a tablespoon or so is placed in the center of a small patch of linen or cotton fabric, whose corners are then pulled up and bound with a cord. The idea is to make a bulb of the powder that will shed a fine dust when it is shaken or tapped against an object.

The prepared sand is sprinkled over the model and into the frame until it is perhaps a centimeter thick. This is then pressed down with the fingers, starting gingerly but progressing until it is compacted under considerable pressure. The degree to which the sand is pressed against the model will affect the detail achieved in the casting. More pressure will yield a better result.

The frame is filled to overflowing with more sand, which is again pressed into place, starting gently but continuing until it is packed under great pressure. Use a block of wood as a ram to pound the sand against the model, continuing to add sand as necessary to insure that the mold is filled to its top edge. This ramming explains why it is important for the model to be made of a sturdy material. The top surface is made level in a process called "striking off" by running a piece of wood or a steel bar along the top of the mold.

A second piece of wood, glass or Plexiglas is set on top of this piece of the mold frame and held in place while the whole unit is flipped over. The top piece of glass (the one that was originally on the bottom) is removed and the other half of the mold frame is lowered carefully into position, aligning the pins to

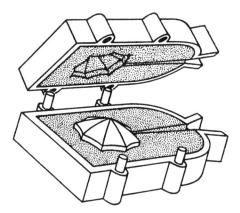

Figure 4.27
Mold frame for sand casting.

Figure 4.28
Pendant, gold plated silver. Sand cast, then worked with engraving tools and chisels. (Lajos Bartha. Budapest, Hungary).

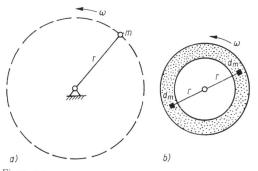

Figure 4.29
Physical basic principle of circular movement.
a) rotation of a point of mass upon a circular path, b) rotation of a ring shaped "solid body."

insure an accurate fit. The exposed surface of sand is dusted with parting compound. As before, sand is sprinkled into the frame and packed, starting lightly but ending with a ramming stroke from a block of wood. Enough sand is added to be certain the mold is completely filled, then it is struck off to make a smooth flat surface.

The mold halves are then separated by gently lifting off the top half. The model itself is pulled from the sand with tweezers, taking pains that the sand is disturbed as little as possible. A casting gate or sprue is cut into both halves of the sand, using a blade or needle to scoop sand out, starting at the model area and moving to the open section of the mold wall. One advantage of starting at the model is the lower chance of spilling sand into the model cavity. The passage thus carved is smoothed and strengthened by brushing it with a fine paintbrush dampened with water. This will improve the flow of the liquid metal and prevent loose sand particles from being torn off and carried along with it.

The casting gate should be as long as possible to allow the weight of the metal trapped there to exert its push against the casting as it cools. This increases the likelihood of creating a dense casting, which is desirable. Because the porosity of the sand allows whatever air is in the cavity to escape in advance of the in-rushing metal, vents are not usually necessary for jewelry scale objects. As a last step before casting, the mold is checked carefully to be certain that no

loose sand has fallen into the cavity, and that the gate offers a wide smooth entrance for the pour. One section of the frame is then lifted carefully, inverted and slowly lowered into position on its mate. Flat boards are placed on either side of the mold to hold the sand in place. These are clamped to secure them, but not so tightly that the sand is collapsed.

Preparing to cast
The mold is slowly dried by indirect heating, for example in an oven. If the drying goes too rapidly the mold can crack. To determine whether all of the water contained in the mold has been driven off, hold

a mirror close to the pouring gate. A telltale mist on the glass will indicate the presence of moisture, indicating the mold is not yet ready for casting. If no moisture remains in the sand, the mold can be heated with an open flame until it is hot enough for casting. The metal is heated to a temperature about 150°C over the liquidus temperature and poured into the hot mold (figure 4.28).

4.5.8 CENTRIFUGAL CASTING

The principle difference between this method and the traditional gravity pour is that the molten metal is flung into the mold with much greater acceleration through the use of centrifugal force. In centrifugal casting, the mold moves in a circular path about a center of rotation. From a physical viewpoint the mold represents a mass point (figure 4.29m) which circles at the distance (r) about the center with a angular momentum (w).

The kinetic energy of the action can be calculated with this formula (converting to consistent units where needed)

$$E_k = \frac{m}{2} \cdot r^2 \cdot \omega^2$$

m - mass of the melt in kg
r - distance from the point of rotation in m
ω - angular speed in s^{-1}
E_k - kinetic energy in J

The normal acceleration is produced by the movement of rotation.

$$a_n = \omega^2 \cdot r$$

a_n = normal acceleration in m/s^2
n = revolutions per minute in min^{-1}

and because $\omega = \frac{\pi n}{30}$ we get $a_n = r \left(\frac{\pi n}{30} \right)^2$

Example
What kinetic energy ensues if a melt of 100g silver is slung into the mold in a casting machine with n = 300 min^{-1} (r = 25 cm)?

$$E_k = \frac{m}{2} \cdot r^2 \cdot \left(\frac{\pi n}{30} \right)^2$$

$$= \frac{0.1}{2} \cdot 0.25^2 \left(\frac{3.14 \cdot 3 \cdot 10^2}{3 \cdot 10} \right)^2 J$$

$$= \underline{3.08 \ J}$$

thereby the normal acceleration is:

$$a_n = r \left(\frac{\pi n}{30} \right)^2 = 0.25 \left(\frac{3.14 \cdot 3 \cdot 10^2}{3 \cdot 10} \right)^2$$

$$= \underline{246.49 \ m/s^2}$$

From the example calculated the following interesting comparison values emerge:

- gravity pour
  a = 9.81 m/s^2
- centrifugal casting
  a_n = 246 m/s^2; about 25 times larger
- rotating ingot mold casting
  a_n = 986 m/s^2; about 100 times larger

While the term centrifugal casting accurately describes the method by which molten metal is introduced into the mold, the more consistent nomenclature will describe this as a lost wax, waste mold process. This method has been used to create jewelry for over 2000 years. Until recent times, however, the process was used to create one-of-kind objects, with each casting model worked up more or less from scratch. When the dental industry starting using lost wax investment casting in the 1920s, industrial research and development led to the creation of procedures and equipment that rendered this ancient process more useful for production.

The principle areas of investigation were in the creation of rubber molds to make multiple wax models that had all the detail of originals, stronger and more versatile investment, and casting machines large enough for the production scale quantities of metal.

In recent years this technology has advanced to the point where large machines spin several flasks simultaneously in a vacuum vessel filled with protective gas. This guarantees a top quality casting with absolutely consistent results. At the same time, parallel development and education was underway to make centrifugal investment casting simple and inexpensive enough for small studios. It is now commonplace for a jewelry designer to create his or her own model and make a mold as needed in the studio. It can be burned out and cast within the same day as the creation of the model, and worked entirely under a single craftsman's hands.

Among the advantages of industrial lost wax casting are the fact that even shapes with undercuts can be accurately reproduced, castings are denser because of the force with which metal is forced into a mold, shrinkage is reduced for the same reason, and in the case of tree casting, where a single button will suffice for as many as 50 units, less metal is needed.

Equipment

The equipment needed in any shop will depend on the way the studio uses casting. A studio working in mostly small runs or one-of-a-kind castings will have different needs than one that produces identical units by the hundreds. Here are some general guidelines.

- For making wax original models
  various kinds of wax
  modeling tools
  flasks
  investment
  a small centrifugal casting machine or hand sling

- For making single-use metal models
  mold frames
  plasticine
  silicon rubber
  Vaseline or separating media
  injection wax
  investment
  a small centrifugal casting machine or hand sling

- For production runs from metal models
  mold frames
  plasticine
  silicon rubber or vulcanizing rubber
  vulcanizing machine

Vaseline
injection wax
wax injector
flasks with rubber sprue bases and sprue formers
electrically heated hot wax tool
investment
vacuum investing platform
burnout kiln
centrifugal casting machine

TYPES OF WAX

Modeling or kneadable waxes are commercially available in various hardnesses and degrees of plasticity (figure 4.30). These highly plastic materials are available as rectangular, square or round rods cut to short lengths and on spools that have the advantage of limiting waste. Manufacturers create a range of softness in their modeling waxes and generally indicate this by color, though these are unique to each source.

A valuable alternative to modeling waxes are the so-called hard waxes, which can be worked subtractively like soft wood through the use of drills, chisels, burs and files. This wax is sold in the form of large blocks, sheets of various thickness, solid bars, rods and tubes. Again there are several hardnesses or degrees of brittleness from which to choose, and here again this is revealed through the color added to each wax. Generally the softest wax is blue, followed by green, which is a midrange. The toughest wax is often a deep purple color, but note that because each manufacturer creates its own color scheme, experimentation is recommended.

TOOLS FOR MODELING WAXES
  – a small sharp knife
  – scalpel shapes and rounded tools
  – modeling tools of various shapes
  – scraping and pressing tools improvised from
    metal, wood and plastic as needed
  – an electric wax pen

The last item on the list can be made in the studio by combining an electric soldering iron with a rheostat (light dimmer). The result will allow control of the pen temperature, which is important to achieve a range of uses. The tip that comes with the soldering iron can be supplemented by other shapes made in the studio from copper wire bent into loops of a convenient size. These can function as smoothing spatulas, knives, ball points, and toothed spatulas.

TOOLS FOR HARD WAXES
– spiral sawblades, or coarse jewelry blades such as are used for cutting wood or plastic
– rasps and coarse files
– scrapers

Models of soft wax
Modeling wax is plastically formable and can be shaped in the fingers. As the temperature of the wax increases, as is the case for instance when handling it, it becomes increasingly soft and susceptible to damage. Placing a model in a refrigerator or a dish of cold water periodically as it is being worked will restore its rigidity.

Modeling wax is available in sheets of various thicknesses, usually calibrated in the same system as precious metals. These can be cut with a sharp knife such as a scalpel, and bent or folded easily. As just mentioned, it might be necessary to stiffen the wax in a cold water bath while working, but alternately it is sometimes necessary to soften the wax to achieve a desired effect. The model can be passed quickly through a flame or heated with a hair dryer, which is the less risky option. Most wax workers keep a small alcohol lamp or a gas flame at hand to heat the tools used to join the wax. Hot tools can also be used to cut

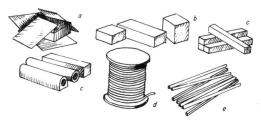

Figure 4.30
Modeling wax.
a) sheets of kneadable wax, b) hard wax block, c) wax rods, d) wax wires in rolls, e) shaped rods in different cross sections in hard wax.

through sheet wax, though it will usually be necessary to blow slightly at the puddle created by a hot needle to displace the wax. Even with this there is a characteristic thickening of the edges around the piercing, which distinguishes this result from a sawn version.

In the same way, edges of a wax sheet can be melted to create the effect of an upset edge. Wax can also be dripped onto a surface to create an interesting effect, either directly from a melting wire or through a small ladle with a hole made for the purpose. In these cases wax is dripped onto a sheet of wax that serves as a base. Be careful not to allow the wax to build up so thickly that the final casting in metal is awkwardly heavy.

Textures can be carved or scratched in with various tools, which will leave slightly softer marks if they are slightly heated before touching the wax. Numerous possibilities can be discovered by the designer with a little imagination.

When constructing a wax model from several parts, the units are welded together with a heated knife or needle tool. To accomplish this, arrange the units so they touch and pass a hot tool through the joint, pressing the pieces together gently as the wax cools.

Modeling wax is also commercially available in the form of wire, again usually calibrated to match the familiar sizes of precious metal wire. These can be pressed onto a sheet of wax or melted into its surface. In addition, wax wires can be assembled to create open, airy designs with the wax wire in a similar manner to metal wires. The wax wires are easy to bend and fuse together and can be quickly fused with the touch of a hot needle. To stabilize a wire form while under construction, build on a metal or wooden form that has been lightly oiled to allow for release of the finished model. An alternate method starts with a core carved from a lump of hardened investment that corresponds to the interior shape of the piece being created. In this case the investment becomes part of the mold when the model is invested, and breaks away with the rest of the investment after casting.

It's worth noting that a creative designer will go further than simply recreating in wax wires the same shapes that could be as easily made in metal wire.

143

Instead, a good design will take advantage of the unique properties of wax models, for instance the irregular cross-section and enlarged joins that are so easy in wax but quite uncharacteristic of metal fabrication.

Because wax sheet and wire so closely mimics the familiar shapes of metal, there is an advantage in abandoning the pre-formed material in favor of wax that is pinched into irregular sheets and rolled into wires of varying cross section. Working this way brings the metalsmith directly into the world of fully sculptural forms, and automatically opens the door to forms that could not be made by fabrication in metal.

Models can be formed on a flat surface as appropriate, or on a dowel or ring mandrel in the case of rings. Modeling wax is first pressed onto the form to create the general shape, then given detail with modeling tools to create shapes and refine the texture.

Hard wax models
In cases where cross section varies, it is unquestionably easier to create a form in wax than to carve the shape directly in metal. The process is faster, easier and has the added advantage of not wasting precious materials. The process is made particularly easy by starting with commercial tubes of wax in which the finger hole is already made. A piece of such a tube can be sawn off with a coarse saw, then shaped with rasps and files. The piece is given its final surface finish with scrapers and sandpaper and is ready to be cast.

Some people prefer to start from a solid block of wax and drill or saw the finger hole as needed. This can be trued up by sliding the wax form onto a heated steel mandrel. From here the shape is cut with a spiral blade and given its desired shape with rasps or coarse files. If stones are to be set in the casting, the seats can be carved out with small chisels or rotary burs, remembering that the casting will shrink slightly from the model.

Investing the wax model
When the model is encased in an investment mold, the path of entry for the molten metal, called the gate (or sprue) is formed by attaching a wax wire or strip to the model. This should be slightly thicker than the thickest section of the model. Ideally, sprues are attached in a way that satisfies these three factors:
- The model lies in the direction of flow. In the same way the veins of a leaf all point in a direction away from the stem, so all the sections of a model should point away from the entry point of the sprue.
- The sprue is attached onto the thickest part of the model. This will reduce the risk of porosity and insure the most direct path into the mold.
- The attachment point should allow the casting to be cleaned up as easily as possible.

If necessary, more than one sprue can be attached to satisfy all these requirements. Proper design of a form to be cast will take into account the best cross sections for casting. For example, if the main sprue is attached to the shank it must be thick enough to permit the required amount of metal to flow into the head of the ring before the shank freezes.

As a rule, the distance between casting button and cast piece should be as small as possible to facilitate the speedy entrance of the metal into the mold. Where this is not practical, a small ball of wax is positioned on the sprue near the model to serve as a reservoir. This provides a cast mass larger than the thickest part of the casting when the button cannot provide that benefit.

As a first step in preparing the mold, it is common practice to dip the wax model into methylated spirits or a proprietary wetting agent to degrease it. The model is generally attached to its rubber sprue former or base for this, though this is not critical. If it hasn't been done by now, the next step is to attach the main sprue to a base that makes a water-tight seal with a flask of an appropriate size. There should be a distance of about 10 mm between the model and the walls of the flask and 15 mm from the model to the top of the mold.

The jewelry industry has developed several all purpose investments modeled after those used in the dental trade. These are mixed with distilled water according to the manufacturer's instructions and well stirred in a rubber bowl. It is important to minimize the creation of air bubbles in the mix, which should be of a smooth creamy consistency. Once mixed, the investment bowl is tapped to agitate the air bubbles to the surface where they will pop.

In the hard core method, the model is painted with a layer of investment. The creamy investment is laid on thickly in broad strokes to avoid trapping air in undercuts and textured areas. Once covered, dry investment powder is sprinkled onto the form to thicken the layer just applied and hasten its curing. After a couple minutes the process is repeated until a layer about 5 mm thick covers the entire model.

The flask is then filled with investment, pouring down the side of the flask to avoid creating bubbles. If an pierced flask is being used, it is wound in paper or tape to avoid the investment from flowing out the holes.

This uncomplicated investment procedure is sufficient for the occasional single piece. If there are still air bubbles in the investment, "warts" appear on the cast model which require additional finishing work. This is inconvenient but not usually an impossible situation. If a vacuum bell and a vibrator are available a more aggressive method is used to remove bubbles, as described below.

Drying and burning out

When it is certain the investment in the flask has cured, usually about 20 minutes, the base is pulled off and the flask set into a warm spot that will hasten drying. During this stage and especially in the burnout that follows, the mold is positioned with its opening down so that so that the wax can flow out.

When the mold is dry (a minimum of a couple hours, but preferably overnight) the flask is set onto a mesh in a small kiln and heated to a temperature sufficient to burn off the wax and vaporize any residue it might leave behind. It is critical that this heating be done slowly to protect the mold, which can be broken if moisture inside turns to steam and expands. Burnout is complete when the interior of the mold glows bright red.

Casting

The table hand centrifuge (figure 4.32) is recommended for beginners and those who cast only rarely.

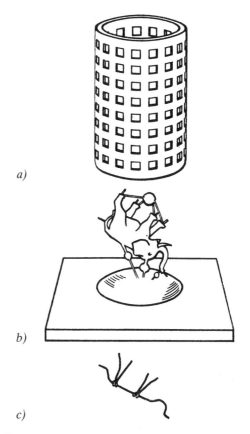

Figure 4.31
Prepared single model with its flask.
a) flask, b) model with shrinkage reservoirs, c) wire armature.

The construction is simple enough that an enterprising metalsmith can easily make the machine in the studio. Small flasks can be placed directly in one of the two pans; larger flasks need a counterweight.

The still-hot mold is placed on one of the pans directly from the burnout oven and heated again with a torch to keep it hot. If a crucible is being used to melt the metal, it is placed on a fire brick close at hand and brought up to the melting point, as revealed by swirling the crucible to insure its fluidity. If the gate area of the mold is being used for a crucible, the metal is simply set into this reservoir and heated until it is fluid. In both cases flux is added at the beginning and midway through the melting process.

When the metal is thoroughly melted, the casting is thrown by pulling the rope vigorously. This rotates the pipe and balance arm and of course the pans fly

145

up to compensate for the centrifugal force. While exciting, this process is also a little dangerous, and workers should be wearing leather aprons, heavy gloves and eye protection before attempting this. Even better, the entire centrifugal machine should be surrounded by a sheet metal wall at least 15 cms (6") taller than the machine to catch any metal that might spill. The pull cord can be fed through a hole in this screen.

After some practice it is possible to obtain equally good results with a hand sling (figure 4.33) but the danger of casting errors is significantly greater. To use the sling, set the burned out flask into the center of the pan and melt the casting charge in the button reservoir until it is fully fluid. Start the sling moving with a gentle but deliberate motion, then accelerate it to a full powerful swing with the arm fully extended. Continue swinging for several rotations, which will force the metal into the flask with great force. It is important to keep the torch on the metal until the very moment of the swing to insure that the metal remains molten.

After about 3 minutes, the hot flask is dipped into cold water to separate the cast piece from the remains of the investment. Because the steam that escapes in this process is laden with silica, it is very important to wear a respirator when quenching. The main sprue is cut off and the cast piece is ready to be smoothed and polished. Figure 4.34 illustrates several examples of work cast in this manner.

Metal models for mass production
A single cast piece that began as a wax model can also be used to make a rubber mold that can in turn yield a series of wax models for production. The stages of this process are illustrated in figure 4.35. This process, or variations on it, are widely used in the jewelry industry because they allow all the advantages of wax carving at a relatively low cost per unit. Wax models make possible effects that are difficult or perhaps impossible to achieve directly in metal. From a design standpoint it is worth noting that while making a mold of a fabricated object denies the inherent qualities of both metal and casting, starting with a wax

model remains true to the material (wax) while expanding the potential of a familiar media (metal).

When carving an original model, remember that both rubber molds and castings involve shrinkage. Compensate for this by making the original larger and thicker by about 5-10%.

One kind of rubber mold cures at room temperature or low heat, and for this almost any material makes a suitable model; not only metal but plastic, wood and plaster, for instance. In the case of the more resilient vulcanized rubber molds, models must be made of a material that can withstand temperatures of over 150°C and considerable pressure. Because the process releases sulfur it is best if the model is plated with gold or rhodium.

The beauty of mold making is that every nuance and detail will be reproduced. But it's valuable to remember that the reproduction can never be better than the original! Just as every positive element will be reproduced, so too will every irregularity. Each model must be finished and cleaned up with great care. Every messy solder joint will be molded and show up on each reproduction with perfect precision! The model should be brought to a high polish if the finished piece is to shine. Likewise, any matte or decorative texture is carved deeply into the original model.

Bezels and prong settings can be bought commercially or made at the bench and soldered onto the model before making the rubber mold. Remember to allow for shrinkage by making the setting a little loose. It's also wise to allow a little extra material for the clean up and finishing that will be necessary on most castings.

The advantages of rubber molds are particularly clear in the case of repeating segments, such as bracelet units, earrings and cuff links, where molds relieve the goldsmith of the tedious work of careful matching of parts.

Though casting is commonly associated with massive or sculptural forms, it displays great results with wire and pierced units as well. Even a twisted wire, as might be used decoratively around a bezel, can be reproduced in a rubber mold with great detail. It's

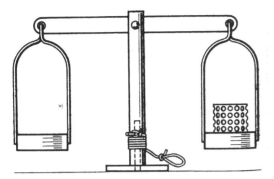

Figure 4.32
Simple table centrifuge with the flask in position.

Figure 4.33
Hand sling caster.

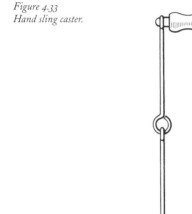

(a

(b

(c

important in a case like this to wind the wire tightly and to insure a complete solder flow so the mold rubber doesn't crawl into the small spaces between the coils.

It is difficult and sometimes impossible to create a usable rubber mold around enclosed pieces or those with a strongly conical shape, such as an enclosed bead or a basket setting. These pieces are best fabricated entire, then cut in half with a clean line. Molds can be made of the two halves that are cast as indi-

147

Figure 4.34
Unique pieces modeled from wax.
a) brooches, silver (Fachschule für Ang. Kunst Heiligendamm),
b) brooch, gold (Rainer Schumann, Dresden), c) brooch, silver and slate (Rainer Schumann, Dresden).

vidual units and then soldered together. If possible, the addition of registration pegs and matching holes in the original pieces will facilitate the assembly.

It is best to consider factors of clean up and finishing from the earliest phases of design. In this way decisions can be made about where to locate sprues, findings and textures in such a way that can have significant impact on the commercial viability of a piece. It might be found, for example, that it takes less time to cast a piece in sections that can be later joined than to cast a single unit that is difficult to clean up.

Vulcanized rubber mold

This process, in which raw rubber is molded around a model and vulcanized through heat and pressure, produces flexible rubber molds of great precision and strength. Because of the initial cost of the equipment, this process is less appropriate for small shops than for large industrial applications. For the small studios the easier procedure with silicone rubber is recommended.

The vulcanizing process uses a stout metal frame, usually aluminum, within which the mold is formed. This is packed half full with sheets of raw rubber that have been cut to fit into the frame. The metal model is laid on this stack, then another similar layer of raw rubber sheets is set on top in such a way that the model is trapped between the mold materials. A metal sprue wire previously soldered onto the model should reach to the outside of the mold. Hollow spaces in the model, such as the inner hollow of the head of a ring, are filled with snippets of rubber. The frame is covered on each side with a steel plate and heated (vulcanized) at 150°C for about 20-40 minutes in a vulcanizing press (figure 4.36a).

After cooling, the now solid block of rubber is carefully sliced down its center line with a scalpel or similar fine blade. It is desirable (and somewhat inevitable) that this cut be irregular, because this will help in registering the parts of the mold. An alternate method, particularly appropriate when molding flat objects such as coins or flat pendants, is to dust a layer of talcum powder on the original model and the first layer of rubber sheets. In this way the interface

between the mold halves is not permitted to fuse, so the mold sections can be pulled apart without resorting to a blade. In this case at least two small domes are set into the mold as registration pins.

Rubber molds of silicone rubber

Mold frames for this process do not need to withstand the heat or pressure of the vulcanizing process and can therefore be made by simply bending up a strip of sheet metal. The model is pressed into a flat pad of plasticine to half its depth, and a couple ball bearings are added as registration pins. The model and plasticine is covered with Vaseline or a proprietary spray as a release agent.

Rubber and polymer are mixed together according to the instructions to make a castable liquid. After stirring the ingredients thoroughly, air is removed from the gooey mixture in a vacuum or vibrating machine, first while in its bowl and then again after it has been poured around the model. Silicone rubber mixtures are available that produce rubber molds of different hardnesses.

After it hardens (from a couple hours to overnight, depending on the product) the plasticine and steel balls are removed, the surface of the mold half is coated again with Vaseline and a second batch of mold compound is mixed up to be poured on top of the first mold half. The second mold half will have registration bumps where the steel balls were so that so that after removing the model they can be fit back together correctly.

A simple method of making a mold for a ring starts with a brass tube that fits snugly into the finger hole of the ring. This is soldered onto a plate of brass and a larger tube is made to become the outside wall of the mold. The ring model is positioned on the smaller tube and mold compound is poured into over the model in the space between the core tube and the larger unit. After hardening, the rubber mass is withdrawn from the mold and cut with a blade held at a right angle to the ring shank. The mold is then separated, the model removed and the mold halves reassembled Of course the inner brass tube must stay in the rubber mold during later wax injection.

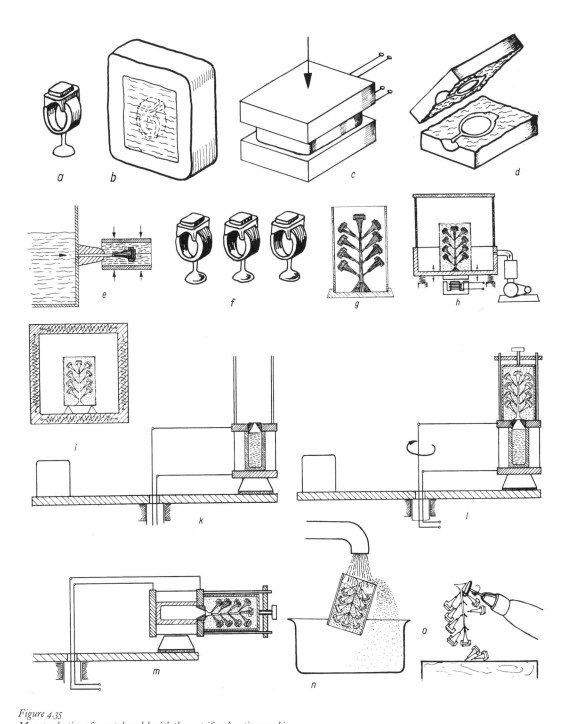

Figure 4.35
Mass production of a metal model with the centrifugal casting machine.
a) metal model, b) model embedded in raw rubber, c) vulcanizing press treatment, d) separated rubber mold, e) wax injected into the rubber mold, f) wax model, g) wax tree in the flask, h) flask, i) melting the wax out and pre-heating of the flask in the electric kiln, k) melting the metal, l) flask mounted onto the melting crucible, casting machine rotated, m) casting the metal into the spinning flask, n) removing the finished cast tree from the flask, o) cutting off the finished pieces.

149

The ideal injection wax should:
- cool as quickly as possible
- shrink as little as possible
- possess a certain elasticity
- burn out without any residue

Prepare a rubber mold by powdering it lightly with talcum or corn starch or, alternatively, spraying a thin film of silicone parting agent. Either will allow the wax model to be easily removed from the mold. In commercial studios, a wax injector, such as the one shown in figure 4.36b is used to inject molten wax into the rubber mold. The device consists of an electrically heated water bath that melts a reservoir of wax that can be forcibly injected into a mold. The rubber mold is held tightly between two aluminum sheets and held onto the nozzle of the wax injector. After allowing a few seconds for the wax to harden, the elastic mold can be peeled back to safely remove the model.

In a small studio that cannot justify the expense of an injector, a hypodermic syringe is recommended for filling the rubber mold. Another alternative is to use the hand centrifuge, described above for sling casting, to force molten wax into a mold. In this process, the mold is set into the dish of the sling an secured there with sand or sawdust. Molten wax is poured into the mold with the aid of a funnel and the apparatus is quickly swung in a large arcing circle.

Investing a wax tree
In large volume situations, sprues of the individual wax models are welded to a "trunk" of a large central wax sprue often by using an electrically heated hot wax tool, though it can also be done with a heated knife. The models must have a minimum distance of 2 mm between them and 5 mm from the wall of the flask so that the investment does not crack. The individual pieces are positioned in an ascending spiral around the central sprue so they fill out one after the other. It's important that each model be tilted slightly in the direction of the flow; that is "pointed downstream." The trunk of the tree is carefully attached to the center of the dome of a rubber sprue base, also called a sprue former.

a

b

Figure 4.36
Additional equipment for centrifugal casting.
a) vulcanizing press,
b) wax injector. (Firma Arno Linder, Munich)

Investment is mixed thoroughly with a stirring tool, then vacuumed under the bell jar to remove air bubbles. The proof of this step is that the creamy investment is visually reduced in size by the elimination of air bubbles. The entire tree is dipped into methylated spirits or a specially formulated wetting agent, then the flask is fitted onto the rubber sprue base to make a water tight seal. A collar of thin plastic is wound around the flask in order to compensate for temporary swelling in volume during vacuuming. This is removed after the investment has set.

The vacuumed investment is poured into the flask in such a way that it flows along the flask wall next to the models and fills around the tree from the bottom up. The flask is then set under the bell jar and vacuumed one more time to remove any remaining bubbles. The flask is set aside in a protected place until the investment sets, which usually takes about 20 minutes.

Once dry, the flask is set into a kiln with the sprue opening facing down, and in such a way that was can drip out the opening. The flask is heated to 700°C in temperature increments of 100°C per hour and is then ready for casting.

Ideally there should be about 7 hours between investing and casting, preferably not more. The final temperature of the flask should be between 550° and 700°C, but the actual casting temperature can be lower, in which case the flask is allowed to cool down before casting. The proper casting temperature is 50°C above half the melting point of the alloy.

DETERMINING THE AMOUNT OF METAL NEEDED

The amount of metal required can easily be determined by a comparison with the density of the metal to be cast to the density of the model. Because the density of wax is very close to 1, the mathematics for determining the amount of material needed for a casting is a simple process. The weight of a wax model is multiplied by the specific gravity of the material to be cast, a figure that can be found in the Appendix. For instance, if a model for a ring weighs 2 pennyweight and will be cast in sterling (specific gravity 10.41) the equation is:

2 x 10.41 = 20.82 pennyweights (or 1.04 ounces)

The formal description of this relationship is:

$$V_W = V_M$$
$$m_W : \rho_W = m_M : \rho_M$$

because $\rho_W = 1$ g/cm³ produces

$$m_M = \rho_M \cdot m_W$$

V_W — volume of the wax
m_W — mass of the wax
V_M — volume of the metal
m_M — mass of the metal
ρ_M — density of the metal
ρ_W — density of the wax

Equipment

CRUCIBLE CENTRIFUGE

This piece of equipment is well suited to small production studios and has gained great popularity because of its low cost, simple operation and dependability. It can be used equally well for small single item flasks or larger tree-sprued flasks. The size of the various models is generally given according to the weight of gold alloy that can be cast; 250 grams is a popular size.

In the case of the hand centrifuge described above, centrifugal force is created when a rope is pulled, in a motion not unlike starting a lawn mower motor. In this case the force is supplied by a heavy spring in the canister-shaped base of the device. The machine is wound up to put the spring under tension, then temporarily held into position with a locking pin.

The metal is usually melted with a torch in a crucible that is cradled on the arm of the casting machine, though it is possible to melt the metal with an induction kiln and pour it into the crucible when needed. When the metal is molten, well fluxed and in a ceramic reservoir tight against the flask, the pin is released, causing the arm to swing suddenly in a quick and even rotation, which forces the fluid metal into the cavities of the mold.

CENTRIFUGAL CASTING MACHINE

When selecting a casting machine, keep in mind that careful manufacturing and top quality materials will be justified by a machine that will deliver consistently sound castings for many years, often in fact, decades of use. Figure 4.38a shows a high quality centrifugal casting machine.

In the Hellberg kiln, a graphite tube serves as a resistance heater that transfers the heat onto the actual ceramic crucible; in this way temperatures of up to 1600°C are possible. The melt can also be heated directly in the graphite crucible but only to 1300°C. The electrical and mechanical controls and operating equipment are installed in the machine's housing, while the melting and casting equipment is installed on a rotating metal disc.

The crucible is first preheated in the vertical position, then filled with metal which is soon melted. During this process the preheated flask is locked in place with the clamping mechanism. The rotating disc is rapidly set in motion with an electric motor, during which the electric current for melting is still turned on, insuring that the melt remains fluid. When the proper RPM is achieved, a release is used and the melting and casting equipment is braked hydraulically into the horizontal casting position. This automatically shuts off the current.

With the centrifugal casting equipment described previously, the mold begins to fill up as the crucible and flask start to move, meaning that by the time the apparatus reaches full velocity the casting procedure itself is already over. The advantage of this machine is that the maximum centrifugal force is achieved before the metal is set loose. This has proven a successful process for all alloys of gold, silver, brass, bronze and nickel silver.

VACUUM CASTING EQUIPMENT

Unlike the previously described methods, which *throw* molten metal into a mold, this process uses a vacuum to *draw* the metal into the mold. Models are invested following the same procedure as for centrifugal casting, both in the case of large trees of multiples or for a few separate models. The flask, howev-

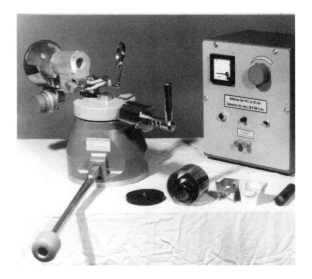

Figure 4.37
Table centrifugal casting machine. (Firma Manfred Heinze, Leipzig)

er, is different, and has holes along the walls and a flange around the top as shown in figure 4.39.

The vacuum pump serves a double function, first removing air bubbles from the investment, then in drawing the molten metal into the mold in a process formally known as vacuum assist casting. The vacuum device usually also contains a vibrator so that both the bowl of investment and the filled flask can be jiggled as well as vacuumed to assist in the removal of bubbles. The flask is burned out in the usual manner and then set into the appropriate port on the vacuum caster so that a seal is made around the flange.

The metal is melted in the flask opening with the gas torch. Meanwhile the neighboring vacuum bell is evacuated. When the flask receptacle chamber is connected to the vacuum bell with a foot switch a sudden negative pressure is formed and the air is drawn out of the porous investment and from the hollow cavity in the mold so that the melt sitting over it is suddenly sucked into the mold and the cavity is filled up. One of the advantages of this procedure is that the flask remains in one place so the risks and stresses associated with rotation are avoided.

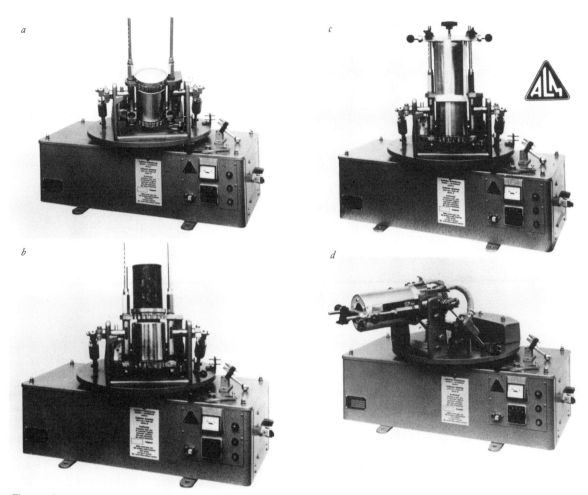

Figure 4.38
Electric melting and centrifugal casting machine. a) without flask, b) flask set into position on top, c) flask connected tightly to the melting crucible, d) casting position when spinning. (Firma Arno Lindner, Munich)

4.5.9 SPIN CASTING WITH A METAL MOLD

Figure 4.40 shows a device used to cast seamless plain wedding bands. To use this rotational mold, an exactly measured quantity of metal is melted in a crucible and poured into the opening at the top as the steel cylinder is rotated mechanically. The result is that the metal is deposited evenly around the walls of the mold. If the intended ring is to have a bevel or be half round, these shapes can be turned in the form after casting, or machined into the mold itself. Such a mold can be made by a machinist without great difficulty or cost.

The casting gate (1) is screwed in the lid of the upper piece of pipe (2). This pipe (3) is set loosely onto the solid bolt (5). Spacer rings (4, 5) are slid onto the bolt to determine the area left between the top of the bolt and the outer sleeve, which of course represents the width of the band being cast. An outer rim with holes ensures a smooth running of the mold.

The power to rotate the mold can be provided by a small motor with a high RPM, like those found in coffee grinders. Motors with roller bearings are preferred over those with friction bearings for this application. In order to keep the hands free for pouring and to allow for different RPMs, a foot rheostat like those used for sewing machines is a recommended.

4.6
Rolling and Drawing

4.6.1 THE NATURE OF DEFORMATION

The phenomenon of deformation of a metallic material is a complex collection of many processes happening simultaneously. In order to describe it, we will consider these as discreet actions, but keep in mind that in fact they are all happening at the same time and influencing each other. Our study here must be confined to relatively basic information:

• What occurs inside a single crystal?
• How is the crystal structure altered?
• In which ways is the entire piece of metal deformed?

Fundamentally what occurs in individual crystals and in the lattice structure is the same for all stresses. The changes on a larger scale, in the whole sample, for example, are dependent on the method of deformation being used. Forging is different from drawing, and bending is not the same as riveting. Because the effects of stress at the crystal and grain level are the same, one example will suffice for all forms of deformation. We'll use rolling to illustrate the process.

Elastic deformation
Elastic deformation was already described in the discussion of the stress-ductility diagram (figure 1.14). Any plastic deformation causes an elastic deformation in the whole block of metal as well as in each individual grain. Elastic deformation, you will recall, describes the effect of a metal returning to it's original shape when a load (or force) is removed. Even in this case, however, close examination will reveal that a few of the grains have begun to deform mechanically, meaning the stress has altered them to the point where they don't "snap back." The reverse situation is also true: even when a sample has been stressed to the point it has mechanically deformed, a few crystals can be found that have only been stressed elastically.

Figure 4.41 shows a simplified view of the changes within a grain during elastic stress. Imagine the atoms

Figure 4.39
Vacuum casting equipment. (Firma P.P. Schula, Lübeck)

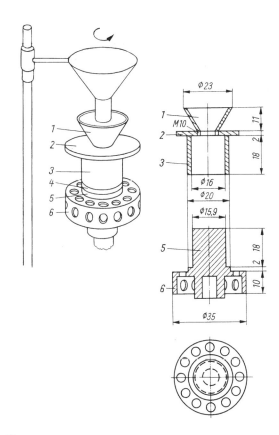

Figure 4.40
Flask for centrifugal casting for wedding rings.
1) casting funnel, 2) tube cover, 3) upper tube piece, 4) in between rig,
5) solid rod, 6) lock.

as spheres joined by elastic bands. As illustrated in 4.41b, the space between atoms is reduced in the direction of pressure while the lattice structure is widened at right angles to it. If the pressure strikes the lattice structure from an oblique angle, as in 4.41c, the rectangle becomes a rhombus, where again the spaces between atoms decrease in the direction of the stress and increase at a right angle to it. In other words, the metal is squeezed downward and outward.

If in fact each atom was linked to its neighbor by a rubber band, if the stress were removed, the lattice would return to its original symmetrical structure. This is the definition of elastic deformation.

Plastic deformation

Plastic deformation results when stress is so great the form is permanently altered. Plastic deformation is always preceded by elastic deformation. That is, metals will first move elastically, retaining the ability to spring back. If the load exceeds the elastic limit, the distances between the atoms do not grow any further, but the entire atomic lattice shifts along preferential slip planes These planes are especially dense with atoms. In cubic metals these planes are diagonal.

To describe the phenomenon using the rubber band model, we could say that when the bands can stretch no further, they are torn off from all atoms of the slip plane, the atomic "spheres" jolt along by one slip stage. Here the rubber bands are re-attached, re-forming the mutual bonds of the atoms (figure 4.41d). This establishes the structure as it existed before, but with the crystals now in new locations. The outward shape of the grain has been changed, but the atoms within the crystal lattice are again ordered according their crystal system.

A gold grain, for example, is still organized according to the cubic face-centered lattice structure, even after rolling. The more slip planes available in a grain and the greater degree that the atoms shift on these planes, the more the grain changes from its original shape. If it is drawn out in one direction, as for instance when wire is pulled through a drawplate, it becomes narrower in the dimension at right angles to it as the result of numerous slip planes, as illustrated in Figure 4.41e. Such a shift of the lattice structure is only possible if the load is oriented in the direction of the preferred slip planes. A stress in a different direction is resisted by the grain because only a small portion of the force can be used for deformation. It is possible that the force available is only enough for an elastic displacement of the lattice structure (4.41b).

The lattice structure's resistance to deformation

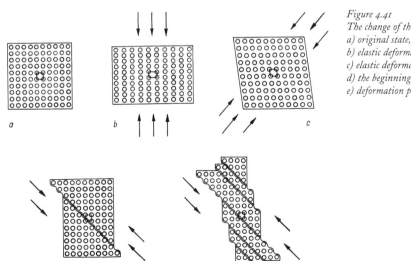

Figure 4.41
The change of the lattice structure with deformation.
a) original state,
b) elastic deformation with vertical force applied,
c) elastic deformation with diagonal force applied,
d) the beginning of plastic deformation upon a slip plane,
e) deformation proceeding upon further slip planes.

increases with the degree of deformation: the more the structure is changed and the stronger the force being applied, the greater the amount of force required to continue the deformation.

Effects in the grain structure

In the description of the solidification process it was noted that a piece of metal is not an orderly crystal but instead consists of a multitude of small crystals (grains) which are randomly oriented. Because of this it makes no difference which direction the load is applied. Only those grains that are by chance oriented in the optimal deformation direction will give way and be plastically deformed. It's true that a single grain has an ideal orientation for deformation, but because grains are randomly oriented in a sample a multi-crystal piece of metal is equally plastic in all directions.

When a grain lying in the direction of deformation stretches, it immediately affects neighboring crystals because it is bonded to them. They are first elastically stressed, then they shift their positions through plastic deformation: the structure "flows." If the deformation continues along a single direction, grains become increasingly elongated, eventually creating a structure made up entirely of long thread-like grains running in the same direction. This is a typical structure for metals that have been drawn or rolled. In plastic deformation, then, the originally randomly oriented sample develops a ordered grain structure according to the direction of working.

As the process continues, increased force is necessary not only to push the grains along their slip planes, but to push other grains out of their way (figure 4.42). Additional brittle grain boundary material is precipitated between the grains, stiffening the structure. This can inhibit deformation or even make it completely impossible. The grains are eventually stretched to the limits of their formability. If the stress continues, the forces of cohesion holding the sample together are exceeded, and the structure begins to tear.

For most metals, increased deformation increases

hardness, tensile strength and maximum elongation and decreases ductility. That is, as you work harden metal, it gets tougher, longer, less malleable, and more brittle. Figure 4.43 charts these mechanical characteristics for copper. While actual values will vary for other metals and alloys, the tendencies and graphed curves are similar.

4.6.2 ROLLING

Rolling can be thought of as a local (or isolated) deformation process during which thickness is decreased, length increased, and width remains unchanged. The sample is pressed and advanced through the rollers because friction pulls it into place as the rollers are turned. In order to understand the microscopic effects of metal passing between moving surfaces, we should first describe what happens when metal is squeezed between two unmoving surfaces.

Forging between fixed surfaces

Stress is delivered, in these cases, at a right angle to the surface of a sample. This would be the case, for instance during forging, forming, chasing, and stamping. As shown in figure 4.44, the metal does not distribute the stress uniformly, but reacts differently throughout different zones, some of which are affected much more than others.

- Contact between the tool and the surface of the sample produces such a great deal of friction that the metal cannot spread sideways from there. The lack of movement here extends inward to grains in close contact, limiting deformation in Zone I. This is equally true of the hammer (on top) and the anvil (on the bottom).
- The block of metal at right angles to the direction of load is bulged out by the external pressure and therefore the perpendicular force cannot affect the structure in Zone III.
- The structural changes are concentrated in Zone II which lies between the other zones, areas that are not affected by the deformation.

Forging between moving surfaces

This information can now be carried over to the rolling process. As in forging, the rollers create friction at the point of contact with the sample, minimizing the ability of the metal to move at that point. The tendency for greatest deformation to take place in the interior sections can be seen in the flow illustrated in figure 4.45.

Because the metal is constantly being brought into increased stress as it passes through the rollers, the situation differs from the impact of an unmoving force as described above. The area of greatest deformation lies on line FF, just behind the location of the smallest gap between the rollers. This results in the metal at the surface being pushed backwards forming a back flow. The metal in the area of the back flow moves slower and in the forward slip area faster than the peripheral rotation speed of the rolls; only the metal of the flow divide moves for the most part at the same speed as the rolls.

In addition, the pressure of the rolls is not as equally distributed over the entire cross section of metal as might be assumed from the simplified diagram. Instead, the outer areas of the metal are more strongly deformed than the center of the piece of metal. It can even happen that the area in the center is almost entirely unaffected, as illustrated in figure 4.46. It is sometimes possible to observe this phenomenon with the naked eye by observing a leading edge of metal sheet that has been rolled. It becomes clear from these explanations that the structure of the metal is subjected to high stress and deformation during rolling, and must therefore be of faultless quality if it is to withstand the process. Or to say it another way, if you have an ingot that suffers from deficiencies like pits and cracks, putting it through the rollers with the intention of correcting these flaws is ill advised. The stress of rolling will only make them worse.

Equipment

The rolling mill shown in figure 4.47 is especially designed for the small workshop. The rolling mill frame consists of four round pillars which connect the upper and lower end plates together. The bearings in

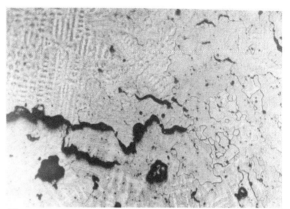

Figure 4.42
Alloy of Au 585. Large-grained sructure, seen cracking during early forming. V=125

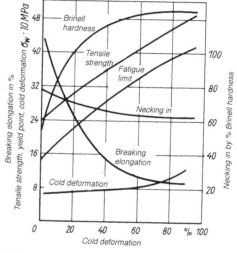

Figure 4.43
Changes in the properties of metal during transformation (example: copper).

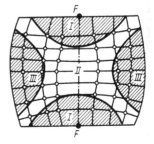

Figure 4.44
Conic flow.

which the roller's arbors rotate can travel vertically on the polished guide columns. The rolls are 45 mm in diameter and 90 mm wide. The upper pair of rollers can handle sheet from 0.01 mm to 5 mm thick. The grooved lower rollers are used to roll out square wire from 1 mm to 5 mm. The rolling mill is operated with a hand crank, a reduction gear making the work as easy as possible. The gap between the sheet rolls is adjusted with the large wheel mounted on the top of the machine; the wire rolls are regulated with two knurled knobs out of sight beneath.

The material being worked should emerge with a smooth, almost polished surface from a good rolling mill. This requires rolls of high quality steel that even after long use retain an undamaged polish. All the other parts of a rolling mill have to withstand great stresses and should therefore be made of first class materials too.

Whether a hand-operated rolling mill is sufficient for regular use or whether it pays to have an electric rolling mill depends on the size of the business and its production program. Large production companies would not be able to manage without them. The rolling mill shown can be converted to a powered machine by mounting an electric motor into the base and constructing an appropriate power train for it.

A variation on a rolling mill called a beading machine is used by sheet metal workers to form sheet stock. With the proper attachments, this machine can be used by goldsmiths to bend up hollow bracelet forms and similar shapes. In this case, a strip of the appropriate width is fed between rollers that curve the metal into a loop as they alter its cross section, creating a compound curve. All that remains is to solder on an inside piece, or deck, to create a bracelet.

Care of the rolling mill
- Do not roll any hard and brittle materials like steel or oxidized metal.
- Remove borax residues before rolling stock through the mill.
- Dry material well before rolling it.
- Use all parts of the rolls evenly so they do not wear down in the middle.

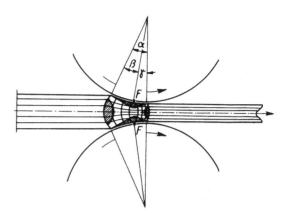

Figure 4.45
The rolling process with the the zone of flow.

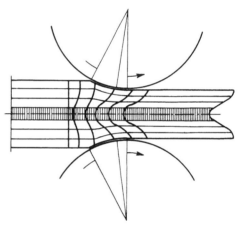

Figure 4.46
The rolling process with a thick block of metal. The core zone is not affected by the pressure of rolling.

If minor repolishing is needed, cut a piece of fine abrasive paper the same width as the rollers and fold it, abrasive out, over a wooden dowel that is also cut to the same width as the rollers. Tighten the rollers until they make contact with the rolls and turn the crank, holding onto the paper. Avoid using a coarse abrasive, which risks making the problem worse rather than better.

Preparing an ingot
Before being rolled into sheet, a cast ingot must be prepared by systematic, heavy forging. This will break up the crystals, which, after annealing, will be in the best condition for rolling. Only after the metal has

Figure 4.47
A combination sheet and wire roll. (Firma
Eugen Dinkel, Hockdorf)
left) driven by a hand crank,
right) driven by an electric motor.

been thoroughly compressed and prepared with annealings should it be rolled to its intended thickness. Though this appears to be an additional step, don't shy away from preliminary forging. It will significantly improve the quality of the sheet and wire being made.

ROLLING A SHEET

Before rolling, check to insure that both the ingot and the rollers are free of debris. Even a small piece of grit on either surface will create flaws that can be time consuming to remove. Start by opening the gap between the rollers so the ingot passes easily between them, then narrow the gap until the rollers make light contact with the ingot. Pass the metal through the mill once without any pressure to be certain the surface is uniformly flat. Remove the ingot from the mill and bring the rollers a little closer together. Compress the metal only a little with each pass, rather than attempt a dramatic reduction all at once. Use both hands and when necessary the entire force of the body to turn the handle.

It doesn't matter whether the piece is flipped upside down for the next pass. It can also be rolled back and forth without harm, but it should not change its direction of rolling without being annealed first. That is, do not rotate the work 90° unless you anneal it first. If a square sheet has to be rolled it must first be stretched long in one direction, annealed and then lengthened at right angles to the previously worked direction.

Once you begin a rolling action, continue with a smooth even stroke until the piece has passed through the mill. Stopping in the middle or cranking with a jerky motion will result in horizontal marks, or steps, on the sheet. Attempts to speed up the process by making large thickness changes between passes will result in hard work, stress on the mill, and lines that are the result of strained, irregular rolling speed. It's faster in the long run to progress efficiently in small increments.

Many mills allow the two sides of the rollers to be adjusted separately, which allows the rollers to be taken out of parallel if desired. In this way it is possible to roll a strip so it takes on a curve. Remember to set the mill back to parallel when you are done!

It goes without saying that metal must be annealed periodically as it is reduced in the rolling mill.

159

Annealing too soon is a waste of time, while annealing too late risks damaging the metal through stress cracks. Though tempting, it is not recommended to judge the proper annealing sequence by feel; thick ingots are tough to roll even when annealed, and thin sheet might not feel work hardened even when it is due for annealing. Instead, use a micrometer to test the reduction, and anneal as needed. In the case of sterling, sheets should be annealed when they have been reduced by half. A 5 mm sample, for instance, should be annealed when it measures 2.5 mm, and again when it is half of that, 1.25 (figure 4.48).

ROLLING WIRE

The process of reducing rod-shaped ingots to wire is similar to the sheet process just described, because the forces of rolling are almost identical. As before, the rod should be forged with a hammer and annealed to prepare the crystal structure for rolling. When this is done, the rod is inserted into a large groove in the wire rolling mill and given a light pass to insure a flat surface. The rolls are then brought closer together (or the rod is moved to the next smaller groove) and it is rolled through. The piece is then rotated 90° and passed through the same hole. In the case of wire, the mill exerts stress not from just two directions, but from six because of the shape of the grooves.

Table 4.15
Troubleshooting problems in rolling.

Symptom	Cause	Remedy
The sheet is warped.	Irregular roller pressure; Center is worn.	Anneal and planish the part of the metal that has not been stretched enough. The rollers should be turned down to dress them.
The sheet is warped.	The direction of rolling was changed without annealing.	Anneal and planish the part of the metal that has not been stretched enough.
The sheet curves to one side.	The rolls have more pressure on one side: The rolls are worn on one side or the regulating screws are tightened unequally.	Equalize the screw positions. Have the rolls turned down to dress them.
The metal cracks on the edges.	An unsuitable ingot mold. The material has been stressed beyond it's breaking point. The material has impurities in it. There has been large grain formation caused by too-frequent annealing.	Open the cracks out broadly with a saw and anneal. Re-finish the ingot mold. Re-melt and purify the metal.
The sheet is heavily cracked, brittle, or has mosaic-like crack formation.	Either the metal has impurities or has exceeded the breaking strength, or has developedlarge grain formation.	Re-melt and purify the metal or send it to a refiner.

Annealing is required as above. The rod is passed through the mill until it approaches the desired size. For certain cross sections, the piece is then further reduced in a drawplate.

4.6.3 DRAWING

The principle of this procedure consists of reducing the thickness of a pointed, tapered wire by drawing it through a conical opening in a tool made of a hard material. The wire will simultaneously take the shape of the hole. Drawing is different from rolling in that the pressure of drawing it not transmitted through the turning action of the mill, but instead depends on force directed locally at the area of compression. This means the amount of possible drawing force is limited by the tensile strength of the material, a fact that is particularly evident when drawing thin wires.

Metal thickness is reduced by its passage through the draw cone. The steeper the cone, the greater the reduction; which of course means increased resistance and stress. The ideal shape of the cone and percentage of reduction are engineered into the design of a proper drawplate. By moving systematically through adjacent holes, the stress is minimized. Because of

friction on its outer surface, metal on the outside of a rod is most affected by the drawplate, with the inner core remaining almost unchanged.

Tools

The most important tool in the drawing process is without doubt the drawplate. This consists of a plate of high grade steel into which similar shaped holes have been placed whose size is evenly reduced from one hole to another. Figure 4.49 shows how such a drawplate hole is made. The change in thickness occurs in the drawing cone while the cross section is shaped near the front, or smaller end, of the hole. The most common drawplates have round holes, and are used to reduce the size of round wire. Specialty shapes include rectangular, square, triangular, and knife-shaped drawplates. It is also possible to have unique shapes made up by an industrial die-maker.

The quality of the wire produced depends upon the condition of the drawplate. Only when the holes are absolutely smooth can a perfect wire be produced. The treatment and handling of drawplates begins with their storage. A quick way to damage a drawplate is to toss it casually into a drawer. A container

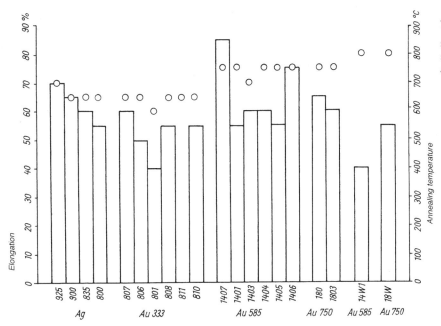

Figure 4.48
The allowable elongation when rolling and the necessary recrystalization temperatures for the important precious metal alloys.

in which the drawplates can be placed always pays for itself. Don't use a drawplate for any purpose other than drawing wire and making tubing. Despite their simple appearance, drawplates are sophisticated precision instruments and require at least nominal care.

To use a drawplate, place it between two protective plates of copper or another soft metal in a vise, positioning it so the holes to be used are reasonably close to the jaws. File a taper on the wire, feed it into the first hole where it is restricted, and grasp it firmly in drawtongs. These are sturdy pliers with handles long enough to allow them to be held with both hands. The flat jaws are sharply textured so that the wire does not slip out even with a strong pull (figure 4.50).

Wires over 2 mm thick will require the use of a drawbench, a device that connects the tongs by belt or chain to a large crank that significantly increases leverage. For further ease a reduction gear train can be installed (figure 5.41).

Automatic drawing machines are used in industrially settings to produce long fine wires, like the stock used in chain making. The wire to be drawn is wound onto a spool, and its pointed end fed through the appropriate hole in a drawplate. The leading end is attached it to a second spool that is electrically driven. In this way the thin wire is quickly, safely and uniformly drawn and wound onto the drum. Several drawplates can be arranged one after the other (often with a coolant bath between) to effect a large reduction with a single pull.

The last pull with thin wires uses a stone drawplate, in which drilled diamonds or corundum are set into a steel plate. These guarantee accuracy of dimension even during extended use. More recently, sintered hard metal materials set into steel plates provide similar durability at a lower cost.

Drawing wire
Because rolling is easier than wire drawing, roll wire as far as possible before turning to the drawplate. The cross section after rolling is usually hexagonal or square, so sufficient metal must be left to allow for the drawing process to create the desired section.

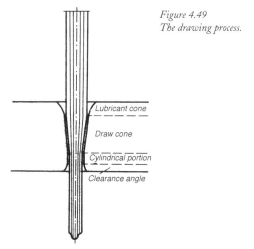

Figure 4.49
The drawing process.

Lubricant cone

Draw cone

Cylindrical portion

Clearance angle

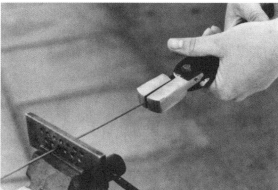

Figure 4.50
Drawing wire with the draw tongs.

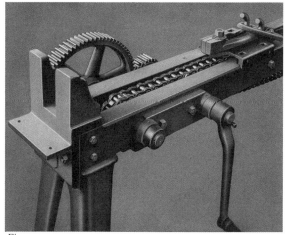

Figure 4.51
Drawbench.

Be sure the wire is free from hard impurities such as iron particles, flux residues and so on. Anneal the piece thoroughly and file a taper about 20 mm long on one end. In thick wire the taper can be created by step rolling. Rub the wire with wax to reduce the friction at the draw cone. Locate the smallest hole the wire can be passed through then begin drawing through the next smallest hole. Grip the point with draw tongs and pull evenly, if possible without stopping. As a rule, no hole can be skipped because to do so risks over stressing the material being worked: the wire will snap or get stuck.

Just as in rolling, regular annealing is important in drawing. Thin wire is wound into a coil and bound with copper or steel wires. Heat the coil with a bushy flame, quench in water, remove the wrapping wire and pickle. Remember to dry the wire completely before continuing to draw it because moisture left on the drawplate will cause it to rust.

When drawing wires of unusual cross section, prepare the strip by making it resemble as closely as possible the final shape. For rectangular or knife-edge wires, for instance, roll a wire through the sheet mill first to approximate the form. To make half round wire, solder two square or rectangular wires together for a short distance along their tips. File this section to a taper, and use it as the draw point to pull the double strand through a round drawplate. The result will be a pair of identical half round wires.

Making a tube

Tubing is made by hammering and then drawing a parallel sided strip of sheet until its edges come together. During bending the outer area of the tube is stretched and the inner is compressed. This explains why the required starting width appears to be a size halfway between what would be calculated for the inside and outside diameter dimensions.

$$C = (D - s) \cdot \pi$$

C	–	the mean circumference in mm
D	–	the outer diameter
s	–	the metal thickness in mm

Prepare a strip of sheet that is a little wider than the measurement given by the formula. This will allow the finished tube to be drawn through several holes to make it smooth and round. File the edges of the strip at a slight angle so they will fit well against each other when they are drawn into contact. Make a taper by cutting a point on one end of the strip. An alternate method, shown in figure 4.52, is to solder a wire whose diameter matches the intended inside diameter to the end of the strip. This allows the tube to remain round and undamaged by the draw tongs.

Hammer the strip into a wooden V-block until its section is slightly more than half round. Direct the hammer blows along the edges rather than the middle of the strip to minimize the tendency to twist like a screw during drawing.

The strip of sheet is annealed and the edges are scraped clean, then the tube is drawn until the seam closes. Avoid the use of drawing wax because it prevents solder from flowing. The drawn tube is closed by soldering with long thin pieces of solder. Pickle

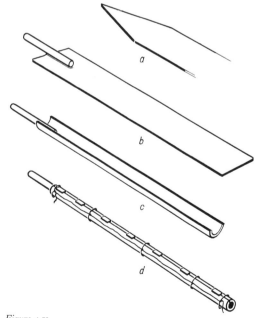

Figure 4.52
Making a tube.
a) prepared trimmed blank with its drawing taper, b) strip of sheet with round wire soldered on as a drawing point, c) gutter shaped prepared tube, d) tube prepared for soldering.

and remove excess solder by filing, then draw the tube through several sequential holes to make it completely round and of the desired diameter.

To make square, rectangular or triangular tubing, start with a round tube with a diameter larger than the intended result. To create a core, draw a copper wire to the intended inside diameter size and shape and coat it with oil. This wire should be at least 40 mm longer than the finished tube, projecting for at least 20 mm out one end. Clean this section of oil and spot solder it into the tube. After filing, this will be the draw point for the operation to follow.

Draw as for wire, starting with the first hole in which the tube makes contact, and proceeding sequentially without skipping any holes. Because there is more stress in this process than in normal drawing, be prepared for some hard pulling. Continue until the tube comes into contact with the core. To remove that wire, first saw off the tip where the two units were soldered together. Working from the back side of the drawplate, feed the core through the hole that formed it; this will not allow the tube to pass through. Grasp the copper wire and withdraw it. Be careful that you don't use the front of the drawplate for this because the cone shaped hole will effectively squeeze the tube onto the core and lock them together. If the tube is to be bent, leave the copper core in place until the bending is finished, then remove the internal wire with acid.

4.7
Annealing and Age Hardening

4.7.1 RECRYSTALIZATION

Earlier it was said that as a metal is deformed the structure is increasingly coerced until all the grains are positioned threadlike in the direction of working stress. This change in structure causes an increase in hardness and tensile strength and a corresponding decrease in ductility. Eventually the metal cannot be further deformed – it will tear and break. To return the metal to its original state it is absolutely necessary to free the structure from its stresses; this is accom-

plished through a process called recrystalization.

The recrystalization process can be divided into three stages that normally follow one another chronologically but can exist within the piece next to each other because of irregular temperature distribution (figure 4.53).

Grain formation

The recrystalization process has several parallels with the crystal formation that occurs when metal solidifies from its molten phase. Grain formation is only possible when the atoms are given enough movement energy in the form of an annealing heat so that they can leave their old positions. The minimum temperature required varies with different metals. Gold, for instance, needs about 400°C, while half that is needed to recrystalize copper and silver. Lead and tin recrystalize even at room temperature. This means that for these white metals deformation and recrystalization – working and annealing – occur simultaneously.

When then the necessary movement energy is added, atoms under particularly high stress are the first to be released. Usually it happens that the first atoms to form new, stress-free grains are at the grain boundaries of the old, deformed grains as is shown in figure 4.54.

Grain growth

If more energy is fed to the piece of metal even more atoms free themselves from the old, highly stressed grains and are deposited on the new grains that have been formed. The newly formed assemblages grow inward into the old structure consuming the stressed grains. In contrast to crystallization from the melt, this process is less limited by orientation. Hardly any dendritic crystals are formed; instead the new structure consists of approximately evenly sized grains with spherical tendencies. The recrystalization process is over when all the atoms from the deformed grains are ordered in stress-free structures. The recrystalization process usually occurs within a few seconds.

Grain size

If metal is heated longer than necessary newly formed grains fuse together to form larger grains. The resulting large grains and reduced grain boundaries affect malleability so metal should not be annealed any longer than absolutely necessary.

If a piece of metal has been slightly or not at all deformed before annealing, no recrystalization ensues and the existing structure remains unchanged. Recognizable recrystalization occurs only after a minimum degree of deformation, with extremely large new grain formation, as can be seen in the diagram (figure 4.55). Because only a few grains were affected by the original deformation there are only a few stress centers so recrystalization is localized.

The greater the degree of deformation the more stress centers are formed and the more grains can develop. Figures 4.56 and 4.57 show schematically the relationship between grain size, recrystalization structure and the degree of deformation. The same process in principle occurs in all precious metals and alloys though with somewhat varying values.

In addition to the amount of deformation, recrystalization structure is affected by annealing temperature. As described above, the minimum temperature required for recrystalization differs for various metals. The more the temperature is raised above this minimum temperature the faster the grains grow and eventually an enlargement of the entire structure occurs. Conditions that contribute to large grain formation are:

– too small a degree of deformation
– too slow heating when annealing
– too high an annealing temperature
– too much time at annealing temperature

The relationship of these influences is shown using the example of gold in figure 4.55.

Large grained structures are unsuitable for mechanical deformation and have a tendency to crack. It is obviously desirable to avoid this, instead trying to create the finest grain structure possible. To achieve this:

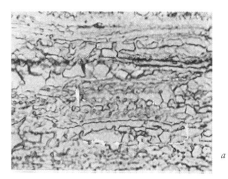

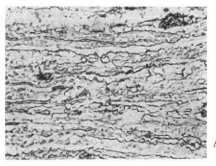

Figure 4.53
The formation of the recrystalization structure.
Steel with 10% C; 90% cold rolled. Magnification = 2000
a) rolled structure, b) the formation of new grains in the deformed structure, c) advanced recrystalization.

• Work the material to its maximum degree of deformation.
• Heat it as rapidly as possible to the required temperature.
• Stop as soon as it is hot enough.
• Do not prolong annealing time.

4.7.2 OXIDATION DURING ANNEALING

Gold and the platinum metals are for the most part unaffected by oxygen. The possible appearance of oxygen-related damage is usually a result of silver and copper so we will focus our attention on these metals and their alloys.

In these alloys the different behavior of both metals in regard to oxygen means that silver absorbs oxygen at higher temperatures, conducts it further to the interior of the metal and there makes possible the oxidation of the copper in the alloy. In addition the copper on the surface oxidizes directly.

The internal oxidation is especially evident in the silver-rich non-eutectic alloys. Though the small portion of copper at the surface barely affects the metal's color, a deep oxidation of Cu_2O is helped by the silver (figure 4.58).

The oxidizing capability values are at their highest in the area of the Ag 800 alloy. The high copper content makes possible a plentiful surface oxidation and in addition enough large alpha-mixed crystals are available to conduct the oxygen to the inside and form Cu_2O layers under the surface (figure 4.59). As the silver content is reduced, the capacity for internal oxidation also goes down as the fine-grained, eutectic structure hinders the diffusion of oxygen. In this alloy oxidation is limited almost completely to the surface. In hypo-eutectic alloys the primarily beta-mixed crystals prevent the diffusion completely and the oxidation is limited to the surface.

In sterling and closely related alloys, the black oxide layer on the surface is easily dissolved by pickling but the dangerous inner oxidation zone is left unaffected. If a thin layer of Cu_2O remains after pickling, the object can be briefly dipped into concentrated nitric acid where the coating dissolves immediately. This process is known as bright dipping.

Repetitious annealing and pickling, called "bringing up the fine silver" causes copper to diffuse to the surface where it is oxidized and dissolved. Eventually a thin, silver-rich surface layer develops. At the same time the deep internal oxidation proceeds further as is shown in figure 4.60. In later polishing the layer of

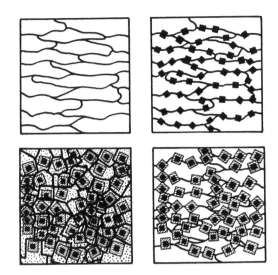

Figure 4.54
The formation of new crystals through grain growth.

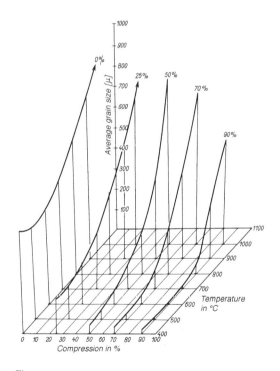

Figure 4.55
The relationship between the degree of deformation, the annealing temperature and the size of the grains with the recrystalization of gold.

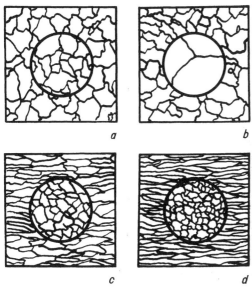

Figure 4.56
Deformation of the structure by plastic deformation (square fields) and the recrystalizations structures (round fields) belonging to them.
a) not deformed, b) deformed 10%, c) deformed 50%, d) deformed 75%.

deep oxidation can become visible as grayish-blue spots called firescale. As well as being unsightly, the layers of internal oxidation can form weak zones at which the metal can peel off and split in layers.

Gold-copper alloys
Even though this alloy has no practical value it is important for the understanding the ternary alloy system. With a low copper content, a thin layer of oxide forms on the surface. This grows slowly because only a few copper atoms are available for diffusion and the gold in contrast to the silver remains completely unaffected. With growing copper content there is some internal oxidation and the external oxidation thickens because of the greater amount of copper available. Here again, the internal oxidation cannot be removed chemically.

Gold–silver–copper alloys
The low gold alloys such as Au 333 behave like the silver-copper system described above. If there is a larger proportion of silver the deep internal oxidation is

Figure 4.57
The relationship between the recrystalizations grain size and the degree of plastic deformation of aluminum. From top to bottom, the reduction in size of the recrystalization structures depends upon the degree of deformation.

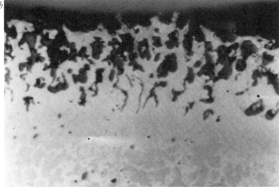

Figure 4.58
Oxidation when annealing.
a) Ag 965 (annealed for one hour, internal oxidation), b) Ag 855
(annealed for 6 hours at 700°C, outer and inner oxidation).
Magnification = 100

Figure 4.59
The advance of oxidation upon multiple annealings of Ag 800.
a) internal oxidation, b) exterior oxidation.
Magnification = 250

promoted (figure 4.61). Copper-rich alloys are oxidized on the surface (figure 4.62), while the oxidation capacity is least in the eutectic alloys.

Figure 4.63 shows an interesting example of an annealed and etched alloy in which the heterogeneous alpha- + beta-mixed crystal structure on the surface has been so dissolved leaving only the well known greenish-yellow "pickle surface" that consists almost completely of gold and silver.

In alloys over Ag 500 the oxidation fostering characteristic of silver is reduced. The copper-rich alloys similar to the gold-copper system oxidize strongly and in some cases even experience deep oxidation (fire scale). Alloys over Ag 750 are the least oxidizable. The thin oxide layer that forms on the surface can be easily removed by pickling.

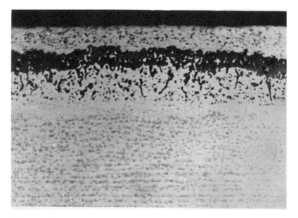

Figure 4.60
The oxidation of Ag 800 upon annealing (annealed repeatedly at 700°C
and pickled each time). A silver-rich top surface, dense CuO layer, het-
erogeneous Cu_2O layer, normal structure . Magnification = 250

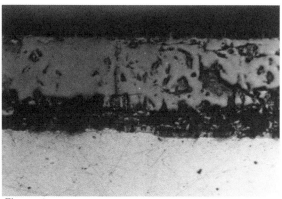

Figure 4.61
Oxidation when annealing. Silver-rich Au 333 alloy (annealed for 3 hours at 800°C). Internal and external oxidation. Magnification = 400

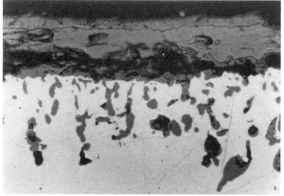

Figure 4.62
Oxidation when annealing. Copper-rich Au 333 alloy (annealed for 6 hours at 800°C). Concentrated deep oxidation. Magnification = 400.

4.7.3 AGE HARDENING
Precipitation processes in the eutectic system

The silver-copper diagram (see figure 1.23a) shows a slightly wavy curve at the end point of the eutectic line that reaches into low temperatures in the solid state. The course of this curve shows that the solubility capacity of the limited mixed crystals is reduced with sinking temperature. The alpha-mixed crystals have a copper content of 90 parts per thousand at the eutectic temperature, the copper content drops to only 10 parts per thousand at 200°C.

The excess copper portion is precipitated out as beta-mixed crystals. So an Ag 965 alloy (figure 4.64) which first solidifies in the form of homogeneous

alpha-mixed crystals decomposes into alpha- and beta-mixed crystals in the solid state after passing the precipitation line. The lower the temperature sinks, the lower the mutual solubility capacity is and the greater is the proportion of beta-mixed crystals in the entire structure. The same process occurs with the reverse symptoms on the copper side of the same diagram with the precipitation of the beta-mixed crystals. The principles hold true also with the ternary Au-Ag-Cu alloy (figure 4.65).

Precipitation in a homogeneous mixed crystal system
Very closely related to the phenomenon just described is precipitation such as that demonstrated by the gold-nickel system (figure 1.51). It makes no difference what the composition is, the alloy always solidifies first as homogeneous mixed crystals. When it is cooled enough to enter the precipitation zone, both metals that are bonded as homogeneous mixed crystals cannot remain completely bonded and the excess metal is precipitated out as a secondary type of crystal at the grain boundaries. The original homogeneous structure becomes a mass of gold-rich or nickel-rich limited mixed crystals.

Transformation of the atomic lattice structure
During cooling those alloy mixtures whose atomic proportions are integral to each other change to a superlattice structure. A typical example is the gold-copper alloy, that has the atomic proportion 1:1. This is approximately the Au 750 alloy. The atoms are ordered in a cubic face-centered lattice structure, with a random distribution of both kinds of metal within the crystal. If the transformation temperature is reached, the lattice structure breaks down to a tetragonal lattice system and the atoms exchange places within the lattice so the gold and copper atoms are ordered in a regular manner (figures 4.66 and 4.68).

With the atomic proportion of $AuCu_3$ (roughly the Au 500 alloy) the cubic face-centered lattice is retained even at the transformation temperature, the gold and copper atoms again ordered in regular rows in the lattice structure.

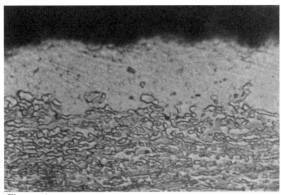

Figure 4.63
Oxidation when annealing. Medium colored Au 333 alloy (annealed multiple times at 800°C and pickled every time). Copper-poor outer zone above the normal structure. Magnification = 800

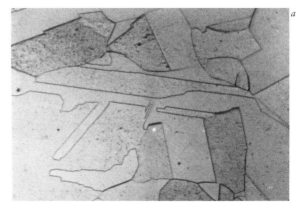

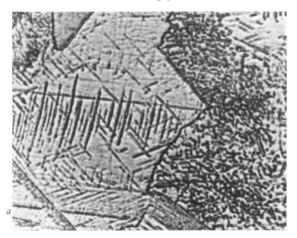

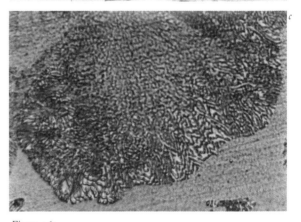

Figure 4.65
Age hardening of Au 585.
a) recrystalization structure, magnification = 200,
b) the decomposition of the mixed crystals (tempered for 3 hours at 400°C) magnification = 200,
c) detail of a eutectically decomposed mixed crystal, magnification = 1000.

Figure 4.64
Age hardening of Ag 965.
a) original homogenous mixed crystals, b) lamellar precipitation of beta-mixed crystals (tempered 4 hours at 500°C).

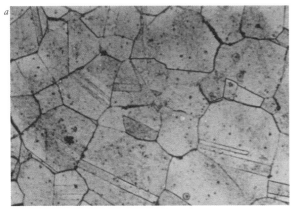

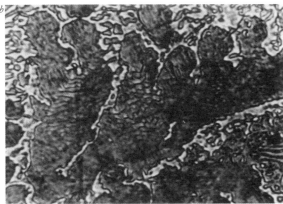

Figure 4.66
Age hardening of Au 333.
a) recrystalizations structure,
b) decomposition of the mixed crystals (tempered for 1 hour at 300°C)
magnification = 250,
c) advancing precipitation of the structure (tempered for 7 hours at
400°C) magnification = 300.

4.7.4 AGE HARDENING OF THE
MOST IMPORTANT PRECIOUS METAL ALLOYS

Silver-Copper

To age harden a silver-copper alloy, the metal is first annealed, then quenched, heat soaked ("tempered"), and allowed to cool slowly. Sterling (Ag 925) permits the highest degree of age hardening because it demonstrates exceptionally strong precipitation effects. It enters the precipitation zone at about 765°C and thus precipitates out a particularly large number of beta-mixed crystals at the grain boundaries. The process can produce an increase from 68 Bhn in the annealed state to over 160 Bhn. In the hyper-eutectic alloys the increase in hardness is less dramatic and in the eutectic composition it is almost unnoticeable.

Gold-Silver-Copper

The eutectic zone stretches out up to 415 parts per thousand gold. While the precipitation zone at 600°C reaches over Au 600 it also reaches the Au 750 alloy at 400°C. This means that actually only the alloys over Au 800 solidify as homogeneous mixed crystals with very slow cooling.

In the Au 333 alloy, the vertical cross section diagram still looks very similar to that of the eutectic silver-copper system. In a similar manner the age hardening reaches its highest values in the homogeneous zone close to the eutectic line (see figure 1.44a).

In the Au 585 and Au 750 alloys the precipitation zone is first reached after the alloy is already solidified homogeneously (see figures 1.47a and 1.49a). The age hardening effect is explained particularly well by the Au 585 alloy. Figures 4.65 and 4.68 clearly show the grain boundary precipitation with this alloy as an example.

The lattice structure transformation zones project up from the copper side into the ternary system as is clear to see in figure 4.69. The simple ordering of atoms as $AuCu_3$ in the area of the Au 500 alloy causes no significant changes in the characteristics. Instead the lattice structure changes toward gold-copper are greater on the reddish side of the Au 750

171

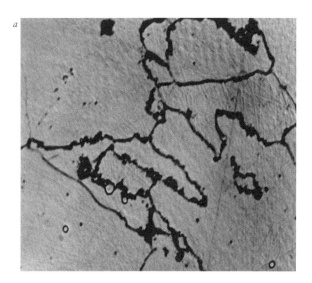

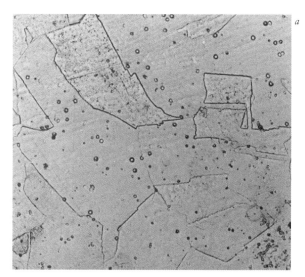

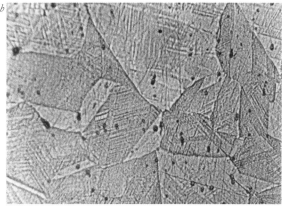

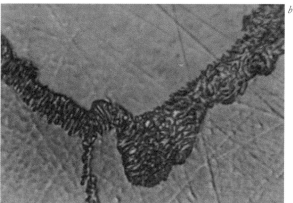

Figure 4.67
Lattice structure changes.
An Au 750 red gold alloy, the rest is Cu. Magnification = 320.
a) original recrystalization structure (annealed at 700°C after defor-
mation), b) structure of the intermetalic phase AuCu (tempered 20 min-
utes long at 350°C).

Figure 4.68
Age hardening of Au 585.
a) the begining of the structural decomposition at the grain boundaries
(tempered 15 minutes long at 400°C, magnification = 100),
b) detail with clearly recognizable eutectic decomposition structure,
magnification = 1600.

alloy. Because precipitation and lattice structure changes occur in both these alloys particularly high age hardening values can be obtained (figure 1.49).

Gold-Platinum
The alloy separates out in the solid state into gold-rich and platinum rich mixed crystals, especially between Au 700 and Au 100. Even in the quenched state this alloy has high hardness values (100-150 Bhn) that can be increased up to 400 Bhn by age hardening.

Gold-Palladium
In this system only homogeneous mixed crystals are formed; there are no age hardening effects.

Gold-Nickel
As with gold-platinum, precipitation occurs in the solid state but this leads only to limited age hardening effects.

Silver-Platinum

Alloys with between Pt 600 and Pt 900 can be worked only if they are quenched at 800°C. Hardness values can be raised up to 200 Bhn by age hardening.

Undesirable consequences

Unfortunately the disadvantages of age hardening in the precious metal working field are still too little known and understood. This is unfortunate because the undesirable consequences of age hardening could for the most part be avoided if recognized.

If an alloy that has a tendency to age hardening is allowed to cool slowly after casting or annealing, it can become less plastic than before. It can even go so far as to make it unsuitable for further plastic deformation. The phenomenon is particularly apparent

with 18K (Au 750 gold) where large grain growth caused by improper handling increases the danger of crack formation.

Benefits of age hardening

Of course age hardening has some positive aspects too, among them increased resistance to wear, and increased tensile strength, which might allow the use of a thinner stock than would otherwise be selected.

The piece of work to be hardened is completely formed, assembled and finished. The working temperature of the solder has to be high enough that it will not flow at the heat treatment temperature. The piece is annealed and quenched at the prescribed temperature then heated to the soaking temperature, where it is held for some time, then removed and

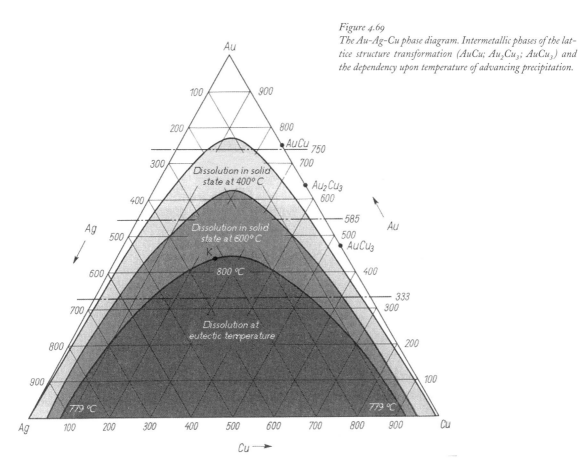

Figure 4.69
The Au-Ag-Cu phase diagram. Intermetallic phases of the lattice structure transformation ($AuCu$; Au_2Cu_3; $AuCu_3$) and the dependency upon temperature of advancing precipitation.

allowed to cool slowly. Treatment directions are as given in the adjacent table. In addition, here are some general guidelines.

- High temperatures cause faster age hardening but the hardness values are relatively low. The degree of precipitation is greater at low temperatures.
- Age hardening works better after deformation and recrystalization than after casting.
- In the heterogeneous portion of the Au 333 alloy, the precipitation goes more quickly than in the homogeneous zones of Au 333, Au 585 and Au 750.
- Higher gold content requires longer age hardening treatment.

The main problem in the practical use of age hardening is maintaining the correct soaking temperature. A controlled electric kiln, like those used for enameling, is required to insure meaningful results. An alternate process uses a mixture of salts that are fluid at the required temperature. These are melted in a stainless steel or Pyrex™ vessel. Check the temperature with a thermometer to insure the correct range, then place the work into the molten salts for as long as necessary to treat it.

4.7.5 ANNEALING EQUIPMENT AND PROCEDURE
Small objects are placed on a soldering block and heated with the soldering torch. Larger pieces are annealed with a melting torch. An annealing plate (figure 4.70) has the advantage of letting the flame surround the object from all sides while the workpiece lies flat.

As with melting, the annealing area should be in the darkest corner of the workshop to allow observation of the annealing colors. Placement near a window risks confusing the process because perceptions are influenced by the weather or the time of day.

An electric kiln with a thermostat is recommended for annealing because:

- The heat is constant and uniform.
- Even larger work pieces can be treated whole and at one time.

- Stresses and changes of shape through irregular heating can be avoided.
- There is no chemical damage as might result from a gas flame.

Reducing oxidation
There are in general no objections to simply annealing those alloys which only oxidize on the surface in air. Deep internal oxidation is more dangerous. If an alloy with a tendency for this has to be annealed a number of times protective measures should be used. This applies also to piece that cannot go into the pickle, or that are already polished.

Vacuum is an ideal solution since no air means no oxidation, but for the small and medium sized workshop such equipment does not pay for itself.

PROTECTIVE GASES
This refers to oxygen-free gases such as ammonia, incompletely burned natural gas or propane and other reducing gases that flow over the annealing metal and so prevent the entrance of oxygen. This equipment is also appropriate only in mass production situations. To achieve a similar effect with simple means, anneal in a kiln after first covering the work with a thick layer of coarse charcoal powder. The burning charcoal protects the metal from oxidation, but has a serious drawback in that it produces highly dangerous carbon monoxide, a tasteless and odorless gas. Obviously this procedure can only be considered when extreme ventilation is in place.

PROTECTIVE SALTS
In large scale production the work pieces are sometimes annealed in salt baths. These are mixtures of salts that melt at a constant temperature, usually over 500°C. The metal is immersed until it is recrystalized, then taken out and rinsed. The procedure offers several advantages:

- By selecting the correct salts, the melting point of the mixture can be precisely controlled.
- The procedure is rapid because heat is transferred directly to the metal.

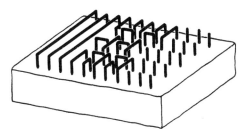

Figure 4.70
A universal annealing and soldering surface.

- The metal cannot oxidize because it is protected from exposure to air through its immersion.

The equipment described for age hardening can also be used as protective salt annealing equipment if the enclosed salt mixture melts at higher temperatures. An ideal salt system has one pot filled with low melting heat treatment salt and the other with high melting annealing salt.

BORIC ACID
Paint object with "Fluxit" or another flux and dip it in boric acid powder. Heat the coated object until the hydrated water is driven off and continue to anneal as usual. Even the polish on the surface is retained with this system. This permits prepolishing of parts that can only be reached with difficulty on the finished piece.

Quenching
Quenching immediately after annealing is important to retain the recrystalized structure. The simplest quenching medium is water, but it is not ideal because it typically removes heat too quickly. Even if age hardening is avoided, sensitive alloys can be stressed by the rapid temperature reduction caused by water quenching. Sometimes the stress cracks formed in this way are only visible during later working.

Many goldsmiths persist in the bad habit of quenching in pickle, though it is without question inadvisable. As described earlier, this process causes particles of acid to become bound to the surface, where they are very likely to cause problems later.

Guidelines for annealing
Work harden the sample by hammering, drawing or rolling to create a fine grain structure. Use a soft flame to achieve annealing temperature, heating only to the lowest threshold of the annealing range for the particular alloy. Do not extend the annealing time any longer than is necessary to insure that the entire piece has reached the correct temperature. Anneal only when necessary to minimize exposure to potentially damaging oxidation. In other words, kccp the heat low, the time short, and the work between annealings as long as possible.

CHAPTER FIVE

Handworking Skills

5.1
The Goldsmith's Workshop

Astoundingly, a goldsmithing workshop more than four hundred years old would not be all that strange to us today (figure 5.1). The bench in the center of the illustration contains the familiar bench pin, small stools and a piece of leather to catch filings. All that is missing from a modern European bench is the cutout shape in the bench top. The familiar drawbench near the left wall could be used to draw thick wires. The tools we see hanging on the walls such as drawplates, files, pliers, hammers, stakes and crucibles are unchanged in their shapes, though today's equipment might be made of better materials.

The most significant change we can see here has to do with heating procedures, such as annealing, melting and especially soldering. The contemporary goldsmith would definitely have difficulties with the muffle kiln shown!

While there is value in tradition, particularly in the field of goldsmithing, modern studio design should take into account the following factors. A well organized working environment is the prerequisite for efficient and healthy work, for both production and one person studios. A basic foundation for this is an appropriately equipped workshop. A young craftsman just starting out is in a position to evaluate the choice of tools and their position in the workspace, while an advanced worker should be equally motivated to take advantage of the latest developments.

5.1.1 EQUIPMENT

In addition to the benefits of improved production, it is also worth remembering that a professional gold-smith will spend hundreds of hours in the studio. For this reason alone, the studio should be well organized and appealing. It is important to locate your studio in a practical, accessible site. You should have a comfortable chair, proper ventilation, and sufficient light. Because each location differs and each goldsmith has his or her individual tastes, it's impossible to describe a universally ideal studio. There are, however, some general guidelines that will apply to most situations.

- The permanent features like doors, windows, and plumbing will start to determine the design.
- Obviously the number of people who will be working in the space, and therefore the number of benches needed, will immediately impact the design. More than this, it should be determined whether the workers benches be near the master's or set apart. In some cases specialized workspaces may be needed for modelmaking, mold making, or production techniques.
- Of course a studio specializing in repairs will have different needs than one specializing in original work. Similarly, the sort of work being made, whether many pieces of lower value or a smaller output of more costly pieces, will also affect the layout.

The example pictured in figure 5.2 is one version of a general model for a goldsmithing workshop. This would be a workable arrangement for an independent master making original pieces and doing repairs.

The center of every goldsmith's workshop is the jewelers bench, where the goldsmith spends more than two thirds of his work time. Useful but less essential is a conventional table for drawing and design work.

As you lay out the studio, consider including these workstations:
- melting and annealing table
- sheet and wire rolling mill
- a workbench with a sturdy vise

- a wooden stump with stakes
- chemical area with ventilation
- electroplating equipment
- scratchbrushing machine
- grinding and polishing area with exhaust equipment

It is always desirable, even if the workshop is only used by one person, to divide the space into two rooms – one "clean" and the other reserved for procedures that make a mess or create dangerous fumes. Of course the size of the two rooms will determine which other activities are located in each space. Many activities, forging and raising for instance, could just as well be set up in either room. There are a few specific exceptions. An enameling area, for example, must be separated from the polishing equipment, because the dust of polishing will contaminate the enamels. It would be ideal to install centrifugal casting equipment in a special room, but it will also work in the dirty workshop. A drill press, lathe, and spindle press can, according to choice, be installed in either room. Of course several miscellaneous items, like a tool cupboard, a safe, storage shelves, seating and such things will also be needed.

5.1.2 THE WORKPLACE

In the same way that a goldsmith's tools and studio have remained virtually unchanged for centuries, so too, has the general working posture, particularly in Europe, where low backless stools are still common. It appears that goldsmiths have been sitting uncomfortably for centuries! Now that we have ergonomically designed chairs, we should take advantage of them. As has become increasingly clear in recent years, improper posture can have seriously debilitating effects on workers.

Goldsmiths should follow the example of other professions such as dentists and physicians to create ergonomically efficient and healthy workstations. The bench described below draws from centuries of experience but seeks to create a design that is comfortable, efficient and versatile.

Figure 5.1 (above)
A goldsmiths workshop. Etienne de Laune, Augsburg 1576. (Kupferstichkabinett, Dresden)
Apprentice at the draw bench on the left, a goldsmith at a kiln (right) and in the middle, goldsmiths chasing and grinding. Around the walls are the goldsmithing tools, still well-known today.

Figure 5.2
Floor plan of a goldsmithing workshop.
1) workbench, 2) drawing table, 3) melting and annealing equipment, 4) rolling mill, 5) workbench with a vise, 6) wooden stump with stakes, 7) chemical working table with a fume hood and suction, 8) electroplating equipment, 9) scratch brushing set up, 10) polishing machine, 11) ultrasonic cleaner, 12) sink and water supply, 13) safe.

179

The bench pin and the table surface in its immediate vicinity is used for working. For the majority of workers, tools are used in the right hand while the left holds the workpiece; for some tasks it might be necessary to brace the left arm against the workbench. Adjacent to this work area are two storage zones for the tools, behind and beside the working area as indicated by item 4 in figure 5.3. Equipment, findings, sheet and wire should be stored close at hand, arranged in a hierarchy so that those tools and materials most frequently needed are closest. A chair for the bench should be comfortable, preferably adjustable in height and easy to roll.

The flexible shaft machine has become increasingly important for the goldsmith and therefore the flexible shaft handpiece must be readily at hand. Of course a goldsmith must have a torch in easy reach. It is important to have the workplace well lit by daylight and artificial light, if possible from the left at an angle. Of course the bench top should be strong and stable, able to remain still even during hammering and filing.

Figure 5.3 shows a contemporary design for a goldsmiths bench that attempts to take all these factors into consideration. Of course each individual's needs and tastes will suggest personal modifications. The table top must be of a sturdy material that will stand up to years of wear. The traditional material is a hardwood like maple, usually cut into strips and glued together. The storage areas on the work table are routed out so the tools cannot fall off the table. This has the additional advantage of keeping the storage areas clearly separated. The table height can be 95 to 100 cm (37-39 inches).

The table shape is developed from a square with sides 100 cm (39") long for ergonomic and functional reasons. You'll see that in this design the cutout is placed in a corner, which makes best use of the space and leaves enough room at the corner opposite the cutout for a pillar that can be used to support equipment such as a magnifying lens, storage bins, tool holders, a light and a flexible shaft machine, all without reducing the bench top surface.

The sides of the cutout are roughly parallel to the

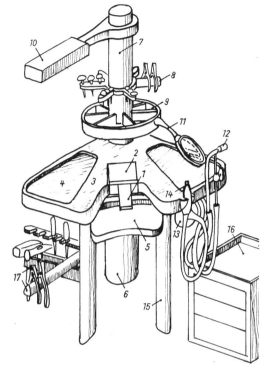

Figure 5.3   The goldsmith's workplace.
1) bench pin, 2) steel plate, 3) working area, 4) tool storage area, 5) filings drawer, 6) front legs of the table, 7) pillar, 8) tool storage area, 9) storage compartments, 10) lighting, 11) loupe, 12) soldering torch, 13) flexible shaft machine, 14) handpiece, 15) supporting leg, 16) storage cupboard, 17) pivoting tool storage.

worker's arms as he sits at the bench. Because it is important that the bench pin be secure, it is best held in place with two bolts secured with wing nuts. These allow for easy removal of the pin if an alternate bench pin is needed. A steel plate is permanently fastened to the bench just behind the pin, where it can be used to cool recently soldered work and to test for flatness.

A substitute for the traditional leather bag or "skin" used to catch filings is a flat tray or shallow drawer. This can be made from a baking pan, with the added advantage of having several pans stacked one inside the other to accommodate various alloys. Some workers like to have a light under the bench in order find dropped parts quickly. A flashlight kept near the bench is a simple alternative.

Concerning the light fixture, a light that can be easily adjusted to meet a range of needs is recommended. Any desk light will work, but if it can be fitted with a diffusing screen (like those used by dentists) it will be even better. The flexible shaft machine can be mounted under the bench top as shown or suspended from above.

Two front legs, one at either side of the cutout, support the bench. Additional swinging holders for tools can be attached to these bench legs. Next to the work place is a tool cupboard which is on rollers.

5.2
The Process of Subtractive Removal

5.2.1 CHIP FORMING

If enough force is given to a vertical standing wedge (e.g. a chisel) the material on each side of the point of contact will be symmetrically deformed. The cohesion of the structure is dissolved and the wedge drives into the material, eventually cutting it in two. When a wedge enters the material at an angle (e.g. engraving), a chip is removed as illustrated in figure 5.4. This provides the basis for all procedures of subtractive forming.

Technically speaking, the intrusion of a cutting wedge into the plastic material creates stresses that lead to elastic and plastic deformation, causing the material to be compressed in that zone. When the stresses exceed the flow and breaking limits of the material, the structure tears apart and the freed material moves along the cutting plane as a chip.

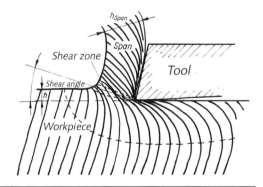

Figure 5.4 Chip formation. As a tool cuts into metal, it first creates compression stresses as indicated by the curved lines. When the stress exceeds the tolerance of the metal, a work-hardened chip is lifted by the shape of the tool.

In figure 5.4 this shear zone is simplified and depicted as a shear plane that is oriented to the cutting direction with the shear angle F. Because the chip is compressed onto itself before it is torn loose, it will be thicker than the removed layer.

$$h_{CHIP} > h : \pi < 45°$$

The proportion between both sizes gives the compression factor

$$l = \frac{h_{CHIP}}{h}$$

The stresses caused by the shearing action affect not only the chip but the adjacent areas of the workpiece, leaving a hardened zone in the path of the tool. For this reason it is sometimes necessary to anneal the metal between chip forming procedures. The structure of the chip that is removed is particularly strongly deformed: it is compressed, torn off and then bent over and rolled up by slipping against the cutting edge. A few highly ductile metals are able to withstand this stress sufficiently to create a chip that rolls off the tool as a long uniform spiral. With most materials the stresses not only tear the chip loose from the parent metal, but break it into small pieces or flakes.

In addition to the ductility of the material, the shape of the tool, speed of cutting, and depth of cut are all contributing factors in the chip forming process. Though there are many intermediate forms, the three basic categories of chip are broken, shear, and continuous.

Broken chips
In brittle materials, the chips crumble into short pieces. Because these pieces fall away readily, fast cutting speeds can be obtained.

Shear chip
In some material, strong compression causes the chip to tear in a lamellar manner. The high degree of heat developed during chip removal fuses the broken pieces together, creating a scab of debris along the

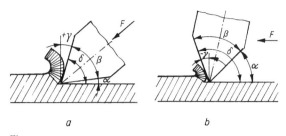

Figure 5.5
Angle at the chip forming wedge.
a) cutting with a positive cutting angle, b) scraping with a negative cutting angle.

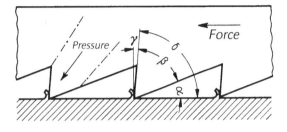

Figure 5.6
Chip formation at the teeth of a saw.

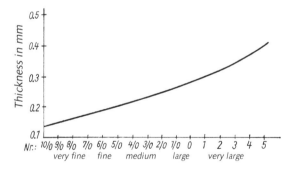

Figure 5.7
Jewelers sawblade designations.

Figure 5.8
A useful storage method for jewelers sawblades.

cut. This kind of chip appears if soft materials are worked at relatively low cutting speeds.

Continuous chip
In this instance the chip is lifted off as a continuous piece of metal and it rolls itself up in a spiral during the deformation. This kind of chip is primarily seen in a soft material with a high cutting speed, as for instance when using a lathe. Though hypnotic to watch, such long chips can be a hindrance and are potentially dangerous.

5.2.2 CUTTING GEOMETRY
The life of the cutting edge and the effectiveness of chip removal depend on having a tool correctly sharpened at the correct angles, as shown in figure 5.5.

Free angle α
The side of the wedge that faces the work piece should not slide directly against the material but should instead be at a slightly steeper angle to minimize unnecessary friction.

Wedge angle β
This angle is formed between the two sides of the wedge, that is between the chip and surface of the parent piece. The greater this angle, that is, the thicker the tool, the more wear resistant and durable it is. A slim cutting edge breaks off easily.

Cutting angle γ
This angle describes the relationship of the upper side of the wedge (i.e. the top side of the tool face) to the work surface. The greater this angle, the more stress is applied at the cut, with the effect of putting greater strain on the tool, but breaking off the chip more effectively.

Cutting angle δ
This angle refers to the distance between the cutting surface and a hypothetical line erected vertically from surface of the work piece at the leading edge of the tool. If the angle is small, the tool is cutting deeply and removing a large chip (figure 5.5). Lowering the

angle of the tool would have the effect of enlarging this angle and of reducing the amount of material being removed. If the cutting angle becomes too small, where it has a negative value, the action is more scraping than cutting.

The relationship of angles
For the cutting angle it is

$$\alpha + \beta = y = 90°$$

with the positive cutting angle (+ y) gives

$$\alpha + \beta + y = 90° \text{ or } \delta + y = 90°$$

with a negative cutting angle (- y) gives

$$\alpha + \beta - y = 90° \text{ or } \delta - y = 90°$$

5.3
Sawing

Sawing is perhaps the second most important process in the chip removal category, exceeded in importance only by filing. The alternative to cutting with a saw is to use a shearing action, which has some advantages. The drawbacks of sawing include loss of material, longer work time, and greater expense because of the breakage of blades. As this would imply, sawing is only done when shears are not appropriate.

Sawing is particularly recommended for:
– thick sheet, wires or rods
– complicated shapes cut from sheet metal
– tubes or wires that would be squashed by shears

5.3.1 HOW THE SAW WORKS
The multiple ranked teeth of the sawblade work as chip forming wedges in that they tear small metal particles loose with every cut (figure 5.6). The chips thus formed are retained in the recesses between the teeth until they can fall out as the blade is advanced. The information given above regarding chip formation applies in general to all sawblades. Minor variations in design depend on the material being worked and the intended cut.

Hard materials are best worked by teeth with a large wedge angle so the teeth do not break off. These blunt teeth are like thick chisels packed close together–there is little room for the newly formed chip between the teeth. If such a blade is used on a soft material, the many chips that are formed have nowhere to go and get packed between the teeth of the blade, causing it to jam. Thin materials, whether hard or soft, require a fine-toothed blade to avoid having the teeth caught on the edge of the material. This is most evident when cutting thin sheet or tubing. Using a large blade for these tasks risks lack of control and breakage of the blade.

Properly designed sawblades will keep within the following guidelines.

Wedge angle	β	50 - 60°
Shear angle	δ	90 - 85°
Free angle	α	40 - 20°
Cutting angle	y	5 - 0°

5.3.2 THE JEWELER'S SAW
The jewelers saw is part of the basic tool kit of every goldsmith. Frames are pretty much universal, the only important difference being the depth of the throat, or distance from the blade to the back of the saw. These range from 6–20 cm (2.5"–7"), the most popular falling near the middle of that range. The length of the sawframe is usually adjustable, which allows for varying tension. Blades are inserted into the frame so the teeth point toward the handle, causing the blade to cut on a downward stroke. Blades are gripped at each end in a plate held tight with a wing nut or a lever cam. Either of these are tightened only by hand and should not require the use of pliers either to close or to release the blade.

Sawblades are made from alloy steel that contains about 1.2–2% tungsten along with 1.2% carbon. The numbering system used to describe the size of sawblades is shown in figure 5.7. It is convenient to arrange a compartmented storage such as the one shown in figure 5.8 to keep the blades separated but within easy reach.

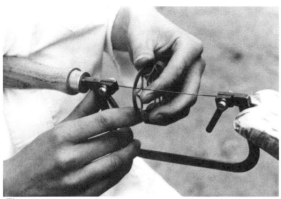

Figure 5.9
Inserting a sawblade into the sawframe.

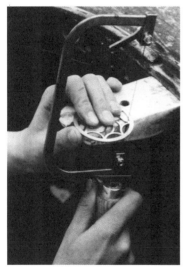

Figure 5.10
Working with the jeweler's sawframe.

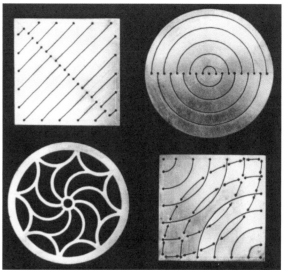

Figure 5.11
Sawing exercises.
Linear cutting (top) and sawn patterns that fit into each other.
(Birgit Karsten, Firma Wilfried Nothdurft, Schwerin)

5.3.3 WORKING WITH THE SAW

As mentioned above, the sawblade is placed in the frame so that the teeth point downward, toward the handle. As seen in figure 5.9, the frame is then compressed by pushing it against the bench pin. When the frame is in this way slightly collapsed, the other end of the blade is made secure, and will create the appropriate tension on the blade as the frame is released.

Start by making a sketch with pencil on paper to refine ideas and make final judgments. When possible the drawing should be transferred to the metal with a fine-pointed scribe; this will make a delicate line. An alternate solution is to glue paper directly onto the metal, or make the drawing on an adhesive label, which can then be pressed onto the sheet. In this case, saw through the paper.

It is usual practice to support the work piece on the bench pin when sawing, guiding the tool into the metal with a fluid movement. Avoid clamping the workpiece because this risks marring the sheet and limits the movement of the saw. Very small objects can be held in a pair of pliers, preferably those with plastic jaws to avoid making scratches.

Guiding the jeweler's saw
The jeweler's saw works when pulled downward with a strong pull. While this represents the main working direction, it is also useful to maintain a little pressure forward, so the saw can feed into the sheet being cut.

The lift, or return stroke should ideally have no pressure, the saw pulled back toward the worker almost imperceptibly. The stroke is never strained, but thick materials will require more pressure than thinner ones. Even so, it is important that in all cases the stroke of the blade is fluid and relaxed, which will make the cut more precise and smooth-walled.

Except for rare special cases when an angled cut is desired, the saw should be kept vertical, as shown in figure 5.10. The blade might be angled against the edge of a sheet to begin sawing, but after the first couple strokes it should be brought to vertical. Note that the effect will be that the hand is beneath rather than in front of the bench pin. In some cases, especially where precise location of a cut is important, it might be useful to start a cut by making a notch with a knife-shaped file. When cutting tubing, it is usually best to rotate the tube as you saw rather than slicing straight down, which has a tendency to snag the blade.

To turn a corner with a cut, continue to stroke the blade up and down while slowly guiding the blade around the turn. If the blade jams, often the result of trying to turn in too few strokes, relax the hand gripping the metal and allow it to reorient to the position where the blade is free. When backing out of a cut line, continue to move the blade up and down.

Piercing, or sawing within a form, proceeds just as described above except that the first step is to drill a hole in each of the compartments to be sawn. One end of the blade is then secured in the frame and the other is fed through the drilled hole before making the blade taut. Periodically brush away the metal chips with a soft brush to properly see the original marked lines. Figure 5.11 shows several exercises used to practice piercing.

5.3.4 SAWING MACHINES

Sawing can become tedious even for those who enjoy it, especially when a great deal of work must be done in thick metal. For those cases it is sometimes worthwhile to use a powered saw, though these will never completely replace the traditional jewelers saw.

Mechanical saws for jewelers are familiar from

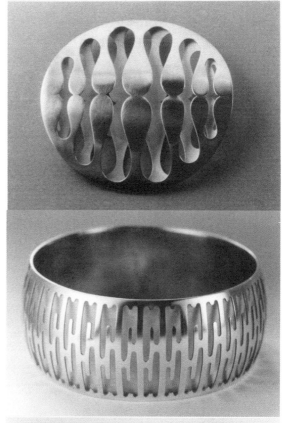

Figure 5.12
Jewelry pieces done using the technique of sawing.
a) brooch, two sawn plates with offset piercings,
b) bracelet, sawn piercings, decked smooth inside,
c) brooch, gold, sawn piercings, assembled offset.
a&b)Rainer Schumann, Dresden. c)Fachschule für Ang. Kunst Heiligendamm.

185

5.4
Filing

Filing is one of the basic skills of the goldsmith and probably the most important chip forming technique used in the studio. Regardless of other techniques employed, it is often through the use of files that the final form and surfaces are brought to their desired shape.

5.4.1 FILE COMPOSITION AND EFFECT

Figure 5.14 shows the parts that make up a file, which include the cut, the body, and the tang. In the case of needle files the tang is replaced by a cylindrical handle that is part of the file.

Files are made from blanks of high quality tool steel or chrome alloy steel that are forged, annealed and ground smooth. For centuries file teeth were cut by hand with a chisel, but it is far more common today that they are cut by machine.

File cuts are available in a wide range of patterns, the most common for goldsmiths being a double cut, in which lines cut on one diagonal are overlaid by a second series of parallel lines that cross at an angle to the first.

The best shape and ordering of the teeth is created when the first cut has an angle of 71° and the overlaid cut falls at 54° toward the axis of the file. The fact that these are different angles, and that the second cut is made slightly shallower than the first achieves a situation where the teeth are not exactly behind one another. Because they are slightly offset in each row, every tooth contributes equally to the chip removal process. If the file teeth were exactly lined up one behind the other, only the first would attack the workpiece, forming grooves in which the following teeth would slide along without doing anything.

Because every tooth of a file is a chip forming wedge with a negative cutting angle, it scrapes rather than cuts the workpiece. To ensure a long service life and to reduce wear, the wedge angle should be as large as possible. The ideal angles for file teeth are:

Figure 5.13
Book cover, silver, sawn designs with engraved effects. Ernst Brepohl, Arnstadt, 1939.

their larger siblings in the woodshop, but generally run at slower speeds. In a bandsaw, the blade is a continuous loop that is stretched between two large wheels, one of them being driven by a motor. The workpiece is held flat on a table and guided into the blade where it travels between the two wheels. The radius of curves that can be cut depends on the width of the blade, but even the finest bandsaws are too coarse for jewelry work. Because of the high purchase price, use of a band saw is generally confined to larger shops.

A circular saw is useful for the small workshop. It is only good for straight cuts but thick rods, tubes and sheet can be cut quickly and cleanly with it. The disk-shaped circular saw blade is sturdier than the band saw and consequently tends to last longer. A small circular saw sold as an accessory for the home craftsman's drill is often sufficient for a small workshop.

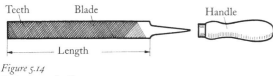

Figure 5.14
Basic shape of a file.

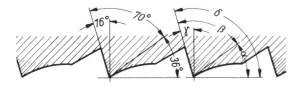

Figure 5.15
Shape of the teeth of a file that has been struck.

Free angle	α	36°
Cutting angle	γ	16°
Wedge angle	β	70°
Shear angle	δ	106°

The effect of the individual teeth is comparable to a graver or to the tooth of a sawblade. As a file is pushed forward, its teeth scrape off small particles of the material that collect in the space in front of the tooth. When the tooth moves out over the edge of the workpiece the chips fall out. If the space between teeth does not allow sufficient space for the chips that are being created, the file "loads" with debris, fails to grab the work, and scratches the surface as the hardened chips are dragged across it. As this implies, the coarser the teeth of a file, the greater the distance needed between the teeth.

When filing soft materials such as lead, tin and aluminum, files with a fine cut tend to fill up and smear. The chips are pressed tightly into the spaces between the teeth by a combination of friction heat and working pressure. Because they cannot fall out and clear the file, the file ceases to be effective. The situation is even more pronounced when working plastics.

When a file jams like this it must be mechanically cleaned with a wire brush or a piece of sheet metal scraped along the direction of the teeth to push out the debris. To avoid the problem, file soft materials with specially designed tools that have a large clearance space between their teeth. Finer work is often better done with abrasive papers.

5.4.2 CLASSIFICATION OF FILES

The cut
The fineness of a cut is expressed by numerals, with higher numbers indicating finer teeth. In this system, "0" is a coarse file, 3 is a medium cut, and 6 is fine. These values are not absolute, however, but are related to the length of the file. A 3 cut on a needle file is in the same proportion of length to tooth size as a 3 on a hand file, but the actual size of the two sets of teeth will be different.

- The largest files are predictably also the most coarse. These require both arms for proper use and are therefore sometimes called *arm* files. Because they used to be packed in straw for shipping, they are also known as *straw* files.
- Mid-range sizes are most common in a metal smithing studio, usually with a cutting surface of about 15–20 cm (6–8 inches). Because they can be controlled with one hand while the other holds the work piece, these are known as *hand* files. As with the larger arm files, they are customarily fitted with wooden or plastic handles.
- Needle files consist of small delicate tools used for specialized work. Unlike the larger files, needle files have a cylindrical handle built into their design, often with a knurled surface to improve grip. While the first two categories are measured along the toothed section only, by convention needle files are described by their total length.

Shapes
Files are manufactured in a staggering variety of sizes, shapes and cuts. It is therefore important to give a full and precise description when ordering files. In addition to the cut, you must specify the shape (parallel or tapered), the length, and the cross section. A typical ordering description, for example, might read like this:

Needle file, cut #3, entire length 140 mm, tapered, triangular.

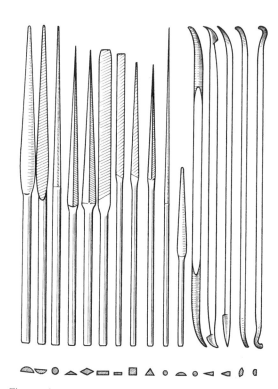

Figure 5.16
Various shapes of needle and riffle files.

Needle files

Name	Form	Name	Form
Round		Knife-edge	
Half-round		Warding	
Crossing (onglette)		Equalling	
Triangle (three-square)		Square	
Barrette		Slitting	

Parallel Files

Name	Form
Warding	
Equaling	
Round-edge Pillar	
Round	

Figure 5.17
Division of files according to their cross section.

Riffle files (also called rifflers) are specialized files used by metalsmiths to reach into tight places that cannot be smoothed by other tools (figure 5.18). Riffle files are forged from square rods that have been slightly bent at both ends to make a double-headed tool. The toothed sections are restricted to these end shapes, the center of the tool generally being left smooth to make a comfortable handle. Rifflers are made in a wide variety of shapes, some with teeth on a convex surface and others with teeth on the concave face. Because of the widespread popularity of grinding burs for the flexible shaft, riffler files are no longer as widely used as they were in the past.

5.4.3 CARE AND HANDLING OF FILES

As described above, large files are supplied with a tapered tang that is intended to be friction fit into a handle. These were traditionally made of a hardwood like hickory or ash, but in recent years plastic handles have gained wider use.

Many handles are sold with a starter hole already drilled, but if this is not the case, or if the hole is too small, the first step is to drill a hole that is about half the diameter of the tang at its largest. The tang is then slid into place and the file is held on a sturdy surface as shown in figure 5.19 and struck several firm blows with a wooden mallet.

A variation on this ancient method is available in handles that have hardened threaded teeth inside the handle. To set such a handle, wrap the file in leather or fabric and set it into a vise horizontally, then carefully screw the handle into place using hand pressure only.

Whatever the choice of handle, it is idiotic to go without a handle out of laziness. Not only will the effective stroke of the file be severely reduced (because your hand is covering half the file), but there is great likelihood the tang will poke painfully into the palm of your hand.

Figure 5.18
Using a riffle file.

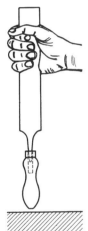

Figure 5.19
Fixing a file into a handle.

Files are best kept in a rack close at hand on the bench. Needle files can be kept handy by sticking them, handle down, into holes drilled into a block of wood. Whatever the storage method, the main point is to avoid having files tossed carelessly against other tools. Both will be damaged. Because they are brittle, it is even possible for files to break by having a heavy tool set down on it. Remember, a file is neither a crowbar nor a stirring stick for molten metal. Use it exclusively for filing!

5.4.4 EQUIPMENT FOR HOLDING THE WORK PIECE

Vises

For particularly large and heavy pieces a leg vise (figure 5.20) of drop-forged steel is both traditional and appropriate, though it is more commonly associated with holding stakes for silversmithing than with goldsmithing.

For smaller pieces the parallel vise (figure 5.21) is better suited because the workpiece is held more securely in the parallel jaws. These vises, also known as bench vises because they are permanently mounted to a workbench, are made from cast iron or cast steel and are available in a wide range of sizes and qualities. As a rule of thumb, buy the best vise you can afford. The improved material and precise machining will reward you with years of reliable service.

A feature that greatly improves the usefulness of a vise is the ability to be rotated on its stand. This allows an optimum angle when filing, for instance, or permits a drawplate to be oriented so that it allows the longest possible drawing room.

Fragile pieces are protected by using protective vise jaws of copper, aluminum, brass or plastic. These are simple forms, either purchased or made in the studio, that hook onto the vise to cushion the grip of the jaws. Some variations use magnets or rubber bands to hold the covers lightly in place. In addition, some vises come with reversible plates that can be secured into the vise with either a toothed or a smooth surface exposed.

Locking pliers

The predecessor of the now ubiquitous *vise grip pliers* was a flat-jawed pliers fitted with an oval ring that slid along the handle to lock the grip once it had been secured on a workpiece. This system is now rarely seen outside of equipment for the backyard grill, but it can be easily rigged up in the studio. In use, such pliers are held against the bench pin as the piece is sawn, filed, or otherwise worked. Of course the more modern vise grips can be purchased in a convenient size and shape, and can be modified if needed for a specific task.

The hand vise

This tool is similar in use to locking pliers, but the jaws are tightened using a bolt and wing nut. While the locking pliers are primarily used for clamping pieces of sheet, a hand vise is useful for wire and nearly finished pieces that might be scratched or bent in a pliers. Cut a notch in the jaws to provide a better grip when holding wire. Figure 5.23 shows the use of a hand vise to secure wire while filing a taper.

The pitch stick

This basic and time-honored tool makes up in versatility what it lacks in sophistication. It is nothing more than a handle-sized length of wooden dowel with one end coated with a layer of pitch. Soften the pitch with a torch and press the piece into place in such a way that a little pitch curls over its edges. After cooling, the work is securely held and can be positioned against the bench pin for engraving, setting, sanding and similar tasks. The size and shape of a pitch stick depends on the characteristics of the workpiece and might be nothing more complicated than a pencil.

The bench pin

The flat surface of a bench pin makes an appropriate support when sawing sheet metal, but for filing, an angled surface at the front of the pin is much more efficient. Use a saw or rasp to create this plane when modifying a new bench pin. To determine the correct angle, sit comfortably in front of the pin and rest a file against it. Note the angle of the file and duplicate it by cutting off the last half inch of the pin. Continue to modify the angle when working until a comfortable arrangement is achieved. It is typical to add a couple small grooves or notches for holding wires and tubes against this angled plane.

Fingers

Even with all these devices available, nothing serves a goldsmith as well as his or her fingers. Used in conjunction with the bench pin, which supports and stabilizes the action, these make by far the most versatile holding mechanism yet devised.

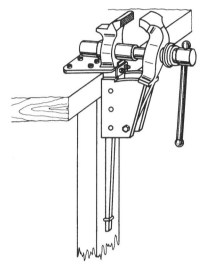

Figure 5.20
A post or leg vise.

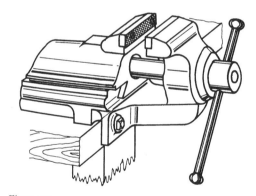

Figure 5.21
Parallel vise.

5.4.5 THE USE OF FILES

Before starting to file, inspect the metal to be certain it is free of flux residue. This can be as hard as 7.5 on the Mohs Scale, making it harder than steel! If you find residue, return the metal to a pickle bath until it is dissolved, then rinse it thoroughly.

When clamping a piece in a vise for aggressive filing, secure the work as close to the jaws of the vise as

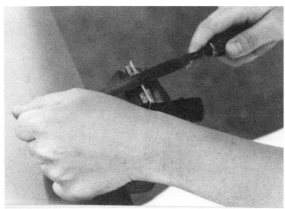

Figure 5.22
Filing metal clamped between protective jaws with a hand file.

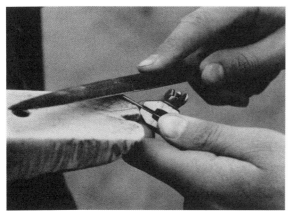

Figure 5.23
Tapering a round wire held in a hand vise.

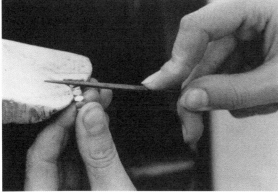

Figure 2.24
Working a piece with has been fixed onto a pitch stick.

Figure 5.25
Working a piece against the bench pin.

Figure 5.26
Working a piece with the hand file at the bench pin.

possible to prevent the edge from bending or feathering when filed. At the same time, don't allow the work to be set so low that the file drags against the vise jaws: this will prematurely wear out the file. Whenever possible, position the piece in the center of the vise, where the grip is strongest.

In proper filing, the tool is pushed forward with a sweeping motion under a moderate pressure and lifted slightly on the return stroke. Early work is done with as coarse a file as possible to efficiently reduce the form. Only when this tool has completed all it can reasonably do should a finer one be used. The rule of thumb here, as with abrasive papers and hammer

191

weights, is to use the most powerful tool that can be safely controlled. To do less not only wastes time but also erodes the form in an unattractive way.

Work moves progressively through the range of files, changing the direction of the stroke with each new tool. This makes it possible to distinguish between the marks left by the two files, and tends to create a more even surface. The metal should be cleaned from time to time with a soft brush to collect filings and make it easier to carefully observe the form.

To obtain an especially smooth surface, dust the teeth of a smooth file with chalk. The chalk dust fills the space between the teeth and retains the small chips that are produced, with the effect of creating an unusually smooth finish.

It should be obvious that the size and shape of a file should be carefully matched to the task at hand. It would be silly to use a huge arm file on a delicate gold earring, and just as ludicrous to shape a large vessel with a needle file. Less obvious but just as important are choices between similar tools, for instance, a parallel flat needle file and the flat side of a tapered half-round needle file. These tools appear at a quick glance to be the same, but remember that each has been designed to achieve a particular purpose. Time spent in considering which is the best file for the job will be repaid with efficiency and a more accurate cut.

Flat surfaces

In order to file a surface absolutely flat, the piece must be securely clamped or otherwise held tightly to a stable surface like a bench top. The file must be guided absolutely straight with every stroke or the surfaces become curved and the edges will be rounded. Because our bodies pivot at the shoulder, elbow and wrist, a curving stroke occurs naturally and must be consciously avoided when filing a straight line. As mentioned above, it's best to alternate the direction of strokes periodically, switching angles as work progresses.

Curved surfaces

Curved surfaces are easiest to file when the work is small enough to be held in the fingers against the bench pin. In this situation the work can be rotated in one direction as the file moves in an opposite arc. When working on a piece clamped into a vise, the file must account for all the curve, often requiring considerable body movement on the part of the worker.

Rounded surfaces

The first step in making a round peg is to create a square cross section along the intended length. This is then reduced to an octagon by filing off the corners, and from there brought to the intended cylindrical shape. During all these procedures, hold the wire in a groove filed into the bench pin. The push stroke of the file tends to rotate the wire as it goes, an action that can be controlled to create a uniform cylinder.

Figure 5.27 shows a collection of forms that have all been achieved from heavy stock exclusively through the use of files. These exercises provide experience in control and appreciation for the value of filing.

5.5
Drilling and Burring

5.5.1 TRADITIONAL DRILLING MACHINES

For centuries the pump drill was such an important part of the goldsmith's art that it came to symbolize the field. Even now, when the flexible shaft machine has been adapted from its original use in dentistry, some older masters continue to favor the pump drill.

In practice a top quality electric motor fitted with a flexible shaft and handpiece can fulfill all the uses of a pump drill, particularly as it offers a wide range of speed control through a rheostat. Having said that, it is still worthwhile to describe the traditional equipment, both for historical interest and for those situations when electric power is not available.

The pump drill

Like most traditional tools, a pump drill is constructed very sensibly, as illustrated in figure 5.28. A drill bit is secured into a three jawed chuck at the end of the

Figure 5.27
Filing exercises.
a) faceted rings and "beaded" rods, b) stepped six sided form, c) constructed and filed hollow forms. (Birgit Karsten, Firma Wilfried Nothdurft, Schwerin)

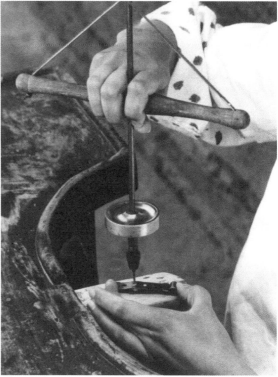

Figure 5.28
Drilling a pearl with a pump drill.

shaft in the conventional way. To prepare for drilling, the shaft is twisted to wind the leather thong around it. This, of course, raises the beam, a piece of wood with a hole in the center. The drill is placed on the metal to be drilled and the beam is pushed down, causing the shaft to rotate. The relatively heavy fly-wheel captures the momentum of this motion and makes the shaft rotate in the reverse direction, wind-

ing the thong around the shaft again, preparing the drill for another thrust. A little practice is required to develop the necessary rhythm, but once a proper pace is found, the beam goes up and down effortlessly.

The bow drill
Because of its delicate touch, this ancient drill has been traditionally used to make holes in pearls. The tool, shown in figure 5.29, consists of a short shaft, pointed on one end, fitted with a chuck on the other, and having a pulley-type wheel attached along its length. It is used in conjunction with a bow, made by stretching a resilient cord on a small green stick.

To use it, grasp a bit in the chuck, wrap the string once around the wheel, and set the point of the shaft into a shallow hole in the front of the bench. The piece to be drilled is held in one hand (here in the right hand) while the other pushes the bow back and forth. This action will of course cause the shaft to rotate.

193

Figure 5.29
Drilling a pearl with a bow drill.

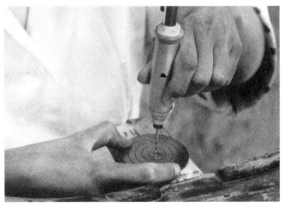

Figure 5.30
Drilling with the flexible shaft handpiece.

194

The flexible shaft

At this point a preliminary remark: in general speech the terms "machine" and "motor" are not clearly enough differentiated. We talk, for instance, of "the flexible shaft motor" or the "polishing motor." In fact the motor is only the drive source and so is a part of the whole piece of equipment, the machine.

The flexible shaft machine will be introduced here in the context of drilling holes, but this is only one of its many uses. Even if it was never used to make holes, it would be a valuable addition to the studio for use in burring, carving and finishing. The flexible shaft machine consists of the following parts.

- Electric motor whose maximum rotation speed is between 5,000 and 18,000 RPM (revolutions per minute). A powerful armature gives the motor a high torque and significant power.
- A variable speed foot control, also called a rheostat. Older versions use a carbon resistance device, but more recently a solid state device has become popular. A benchtop rheostat in which the speed is dialed by hand is also available.
- The torque is transferred with the help of the flexible shaft, a steel spiral housed in a flexible rubber sheath.
- A handpiece is attached at the flexible shaft to grip the tool being used. These are available in over a dozen versions, each with its special features. Some have the familiar, 3-jawed Jacobs chuck, other use a collet, and others include a cam-operated quick change collet. Handpieces vary in size, shape and grip. In every case it is vital that the tool run true to provide long tool life and satisfactory results. Most handpieces include permanently sealed bearings.

For some uses, such as when drilling, it is most convenient to have the machine positioned above the bench, with the tool addressing the work vertically. In other cases, as for instance when grinding and polishing, it is more convenient to have the tool at bench level so the handpiece is oriented horizontally. If the tool is used predominantly in this way it would be best to have it mounted under the bench, out of the way. Of course it's possible to arrange for the motor to be moved from one location to the other as needed, or to have two machines, but this is not usually necessary. If the flex shaft, as it is known, is to be used by several work stations, it can be hung from a sliding track.

A number of accessories are sold to enlarge the use of this versatile machine. One popular device is a table and pillar that allows the flex shaft to be used like a miniature drill press. In this case the handpiece is temporarily clamped in a cradle that is brought into contact with the workpiece as a lever is pulled down. Another useful device clamps the handpiece horizontally against the workbench, positioning it as a miniature grinder or polishing machine. In both cases a key advantage of these tools is that they free up the worker's hands to better guide the work into the tool.

5.5.2 DRILLING HOLES

The location for a hole is best marked with a crosshairs of intersecting lines, drawn with a fine-pointed scribe. Because of a tendency for bits to travel sideways as they begin a hole, a small depression should always be made at the site of a hole before drilling. This can be done with a prick punch, (a pointed steel rod) struck lightly with a small hammer. A spring-loaded device called an automatic centerpunch is an even better method, since it can be operated with only one hand. Simply press this tool downward, and a spring in the handle recoils, snapping the point into the sheet.

Drilling should be done on a small scrap of board so as to avoid making holes in the bench top. In addition to being unsightly, these holes will collect filings of precious metal, creating unnecessary waste. It is also useful to have a small cup of oil or a piece of lubricating wax close at hand. If the drill bit is dipped in this before each use, it will run cooler, which prolongs its life and creates a smoother hole.

As shown in figure 5.30, the tool is held in position, just above the surface of the metal, and the foot pedal is depressed slightly, causing the bit to rotate. The tool is then brought into contact with the metal and held there with only a moderate pressure. Speed can increase somewhat, but should never be fast when drilling metal. The action of the bit is a sideways slicing, and should not be hurried. Neither pressing down on the tool nor increasing the speed will hasten cutting. In fact they have the opposite effect, dulling the bit and prohibiting it from cutting into the metal properly.

It is useful to raise the tool periodically to clear away chips that have formed, especially with a spear point bit, which does not provide for chip removal in its design. It is also helpful to brush chips away from the surface to allow better visibility of the cutting action, (Table 5.1).

Table drill press
While the flex shaft is preferred for making small holes, there is a limit to the size of drill bits it can accept, so many shops also have a full size drill press. These can be free standing floor models, or made to sit on a bench top. Many models include the ability to regulate speed, which is a useful feature. Like the accessory for the flex shaft mentioned above, the advantage of this tool is that it brings the bit to the metal at exactly 90° and allows one hand to secure the sheet being drilled. If the cost of this machine is prohibitive for a small shop, an electric hand drill can often accomplish the task.

Hand drill
The familiar electric hand drill can also prove itself in the studio. Though not as precise or heavy-duty as a drill press, a good drill can be used not only to make holes, but for grinding and buffing as well. A variable speed machine is recommended.

Drill with a micromotor
This is an interesting new development in which the motor is installed in the handpiece itself (figure 5.31). Because of this the torque that is usually lost through the shaft is retained, with the result that the force is more precise and powerful. A foot rheostat controls the speed, which typically ranges from 0 to 30,000 RPM. As with the flexible shaft, drill bits, burs and polishing attachments can be fitted to this machine.

5.5.3 THE EFFECT OF THE DRILL

The effect of the drill is easiest to understand with the simple spear bit, shown in figure 5.32a. The leading edges of a drill bit are two chisel-like blades, usually ground at an angle of 51° that tear into the metal and cut off a chip. These two blades are cut so they meet at a point, typically with an angle of 110-120°.

Symptom	Cause	Remedy
Holes too large, not round. Drill breaks off.	The cutting angle is ground to one side.	Adjust the angles.
Drill cuts only at slow speed.	Drill is dull.	Resharpen bit.
Rough hole; drill breaks off.	Cutting angle is too small.	Adjust the angles.
Drill cuts too slowly.	Cutting angle is too large.	Sharpen the bit.
Drill bit does not turn.	Drill bit is not secure in chuck.	Tighten the collet.
Drill bit becomes dull quickly and breaks	Too much pressure.	Don't push so hard.
Drill bit becomes hot, dulls rapidly, breaks.	Running too fast; not enough lubrication.	Go slow, oil repeatedly.

Table 5.1
Possible mistakes when drilling.

Figure 5.31
Supertronic MC 30/40" micromotor. (Firma J. Schmalz, Pforzheim)

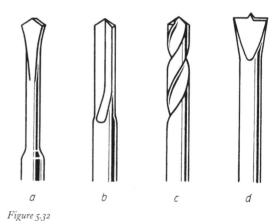

a   b   c   d

Figure 5.32
Drill bits.
a) spear bit, b) "Eureka" bit, c) spiral drill bit, d) pearl drill.

This is necessary to guide the bit to the exact location of the hole and to insure that it moves ahead without deviation. The ground surfaces of the cutters are angled opposite one another so that both are effective in the direction of rotation. An exception is the pump or bow drills, which wind and unwind, and for which the cutting surface should be on the same side. In this way, the two edges come into play alternately with the back and forth spinning movement.

5.5.4 TYPES OF DRILL BITS
Spear or point drills
This basic style of drill bit has two angled facets, referred to above as chisel blades, that meet in a point. The flat area of the bit is widest at the outer edges of these facets, tapering back from there to a waist and then to the shaft that is held in the drill. Because of this tapering, friction against the bit is reduced and a clearance for chip removal is created. This simple bit has several advantages: It is easy to make at the bench, it resists breaking because its taper reduces stress on the length of the bit, and it can be easily filed to create a hole of a particular cross section.

Disadvantages are that the cutting action is slow, control is usually imprecise, and the chip removal system is only moderately effective. Also, because of the tapering nature of the design, continued sharpening of the bit reduces the diameter of the hole it drills. Though small sizes are rarely seen in commercial use, the spear bit is still a useful tool for goldsmiths.

"Eureka" drill
This useful drill bit design is a variation on the spear bit, and has the same cutting and sharpening fea-

tures. Unlike the spear bit, this does not taper, which guides the bit in the hole more securely and means that subsequent sharpenings do not alter the diameter of the tool. Chip removal is facilitated by a flute, or groove that runs along the length of the tool from midsection to tip. This improvement on the spear bit provides greater control, an equally strong bit, and a better system of chip removal.

The twist drill

Twist drills are by far the most common style of bit, no doubt because of their excellent cutting and chip removal abilities, even at fast speeds (figure 5.32c). The disadvantage of this style is the weakness of the shaft, which is made thin by the inclusion of two deep flutes that spiral along the length of the tool. Because these are proportionate to each tool, a delicate bit like those used in jewelry making has a very delicate structure. Especially when used freehand or in imprecise drills, these bits break easily.

The center or pearl drill

In this variation on the spear bit, the cutting edges are in the same line, one that runs at a right angle to the axis of the bit. A small triangular nub stands above this line to make a point for locating the bit and holding it into the hole. This shape is familiar from a carpenter's spade bit, which differs only in size and an elongated guide point. In both cases, advantages of the bit are the creation of a flat "floor" in the hole being drilled, and ease of resharpening. In goldsmithing this is also called a pearl drill because of its use in drilling halfway through pearls and other soft beads that are to be mounted on a post.

Making a spear bit

All of the bits just described can be purchased from suppliers of jewelry tools at prices sufficiently low that it does not pay to make the tool yourself. Nevertheless, it a wise for a goldsmith to have this skill for those inevitable occasions when the exact bit is not available, or is needed in haste. Though the bits are best made of tool steel, mild steel or stainless can be substituted in a pinch. Very small bits, for instance, can be improvised from a sewing needle.

Anneal a piece of round steel wire at one end by heating it to bright red and allowing it to cool as slowly as possible. As shown in figure 5.33a, the top section of the bit is filed to a cylinder of a lesser diameter, which will allow for clearance of the chip. The tip can be left thicker, and is then forged with a hammer to enlarge it, as seen in 5.33b. The point is filed as shown, first with facets that are flat, as if they were a roof on the shaft.

Once they are established and checked for symmetry, each of these "roof" panels is filed again, usually tilting in opposite directions., except in the case of pump and bow drills as mentioned above. The angle of these is critical to insure the drill cuts in the clockwise direction of rotation used by drill and flex shafts. Angling these facets the wrong way will make the bit useless.

The waist of the bit is filed to a pleasing shape and the tool is checked for accuracy by drilling lightly into wood. When you are sure it is ready, the tool should be hardened. Heat the bit to bright red and quench it immediately in water. In order to reduce the brittleness created in this operation, the bit is sanded to remove its black scale and gently heated until it shows a straw color, when it is quenched again. Be careful not to overheat. It is an indicator of the low temperature needed to say that for small bits the tempering process could be done with a common match! The final cutting surfaces are sharpened on a fine oil stone, with 600 grit paper, or on a separating disk spinning in the flex shaft.

For extremely small bits, a straight pin can be shaped as minimally as the bit shown in 5.33d. Though far from precise, this simple tool can be very effective, particularly since holes this small are typically seen in thin material.

5.6
Milling

5.6.1 THE EFFECT OF THE MILLING CUTTER

The action of milling, or grinding, is perhaps best explained by looking at a face milling cutter, (figure 5.34). A number of cutting teeth are positioned all

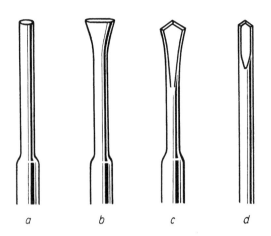

Figure 5.33
Making of a spear bit for a pump drill.
a) the filed rough form, b) forged cutting head, c) finished filed shape, d)
spear bit make from an ordinary pin.

around the spinning tool. In a milling machine the workpiece is pushed against the tool (feed movement), while the milling cutter spins in the opposite direction on a stabile shaft (main movement). The depth of the cut is determined by raising or lowering the tool as the material passes beneath it. Each tooth of the cutter is a chip forming wedge and therefore must be made from high quality tool steel, precision cut to the appropriate angles.

The plain or face milling cutter is used to smooth a surface by removing a layer of material. Other cutters are available in a wide range of profiles, enlarging the potential of the milling machine to cut contours, channels and even threads. Though milling is a vital part of general metalworking, it does not come into goldsmithing, except in its use in making tools for the studio. A small scale variation on milling – the use of burs and cutters – is very useful and important.

5.6.2 BURS

Since these tools were adapted from dental technology a couple decades ago, they have proven themselves in the goldsmithing studio. Tedious work that was formerly done with rifflers or sandpaper can now be achieved more efficiently with burs and grinding wheels. Though useful throughout a piece, they are most appreciated for their ability to reach into con-

cavities and small recesses, some of which cannot be worked by any other means.

Burs are used in the flexible shaft machine. To facilitate changing from one bur to another, many burs use the same size shaft – 3/32 inch (2.34 mm). The popularity of burs have led to a proliferation of styles that defies description here. Instead we will look at a couple general families of burs as defined by their use, understanding that many variations are possible within each style. These are shown in figure 5.36.

• A *tapered bur* is used to broaden a drilled hole to a conical shape.
• *Cylinder burs* (also called *rotary files*) are used to smooth surfaces, clean up solder seams, or convert a round hole into an oval. If the cylindrical head has teeth on it's front end (*front cutting bur*) it can be used to create a flat bottomed hole for setting a stone.
• *Stone setting burs,* shown here at c, are a useful combination of a cylinder and a tapered bur. Once a hole is drilled, this bur can be used to shape the cavity to accommodate the underside (pavilion) of a round faceted stone.
• *Ball burs* are particularly well suited for finishing work on hollow hemispheres or similarly curved surfaces. If the bur has a hole like the example shown at 5.36d, it can be used to clean up around a peg soldered into position to hold a pearl or bead.

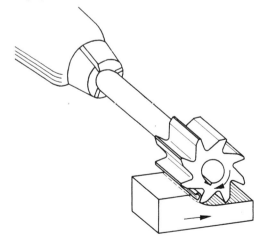

Figure 5.34
Chip forming using a barrel bur.

Figure 5.35
The use of a flexible shaft motor for setting and burring. A hammer handpiece with various inserts, flexible shaft handpiece with burrs, various burrs and the handpiece.

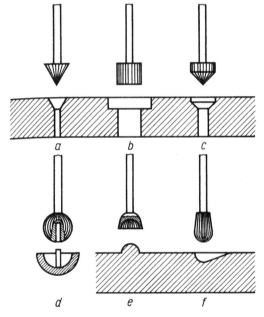

Figure 5.36
Various shapes of burs.
a) conical bur, b) barrel bur, c) stonesetting bur, d) ball bur (this type has a hole in it to accommodate a pearl peg for cleaning out a pearl cup), e) cup bur, f) pear bur.

- The head of a *cup bur* has a hemispherical hollow that contains sharpened cutting edges. It is useful for shaping rivet heads and prong tips.
- Dozens of *specialized burs* in a variety of shapes make it possible to clean up areas that would otherwise pose a difficult problem.

When enlarging a drilled hole to a conical opening, the handpiece is held vertically and brought down to the workpiece. To smooth a piece with a cylinder bur, the handpiece is held horizontally and swept across the work in a fluid movement. Experimentation with burs will soon show the preferred position for each.

For all applications, the rule of thumb when using burs is to combine high speed with minimal feed pressure. That is, let the tool find its own cutting pace rather than force it into the metal. Pressing too hard not only stresses the tool but often creates a rippled surface. Burs designed for coarse work will have a few large teeth, while those intended for finishing have many small teeth.

Whenever grinding with burs, it is vital to protect your eyes with enclosed goggles. The nature of the activity is to throw off chips, and often the craftsman's face is close to the work to see details clearly. This is a recipe for trouble, and only a foolish goldsmith would risk his vision needlessly.

5.7
Turning

5.7.1 APPLICATION POSSIBILITIES
Lathe turning is a widely used process in manufacturing and is part of virtually every metalworking program in a polytechnic or trade education, yet it is commonly overlooked by goldsmiths. This is too bad, because there are several ways in which a lathe will serve a jeweler. A lathe can be used, for example, to make or modify equipment such as mandrels, setting tools and punches. Forming tools like dapping punches and circle cutting tools can be made or repaired, and finished items like wedding bands and bracelets can be trued up and even polished by mounting them on a lathe.

It goes beyond the purpose of this book to describe turning in great detail, but it deserves inclusion in this section on chip forming processes. Readers wanting more information are encouraged to seek additional literature and education.

5.7.2 HOW IT WORKS
Turning is a chip forming procedure with a rotating cutting movement in which the workpiece is

mechanically rotated and cut by a tool that is brought into contact with it at a tangent. In a metalworking lathe, the tool is contrived to be advanced along the axis of the workpiece by a hand-operated or machine controlled feed movement. Figure 5.37 illustrates these several actions.

Tools for lathe cutting are made of special alloys to stand up to the high stress at the tool face. The quality of the tool, the material being cut and the speed of the lathe all contribute to the life of the tool, and are all within the powers of the worker to regulate. Optimum speeds for various sorts of turning can be found in reference books.

5.7.3 LATHES

Of interest to goldsmiths is the fine machinists lathe, a small version of a standard metalworking lathe, characterized by a precision motor, a hand-driven feed mechanism and an overall small size. As with all lathes, the machine consists of a frame, a motor and drive assembly, a headstock and a tailstock.

Mounting a workpiece
It is paramount for successful turning that the work be properly mounted in the chuck. For this reason, only top quality jaws and centers should be used. In the best situation, a workpiece will be mounted in the chuck so it is tight, centered, undamaged by the grip and easily removable.

The chuck sits on the headstock of the lathe (the part connected to the motor) and usually has three jaws similar to those found in a drill. The jaws are made so they can also hold ring-like parts by grabbing them on the inside. Face-plate turning, in which the work is not supported except for its contact with the chuck, is limited to objects whose length is roughly three times the diameter of the chuck. Larger pieces should be supported in the tailstock. In this situation, a "live center" or point riding on ball bearings, is set into a depression in the center of the rod being turned. In this way the tailstock supports the turning without significant friction and with very little obstruction of the working zone. Better than a fixed center is a ball bearing-mounted free center because no friction is developed in the centered

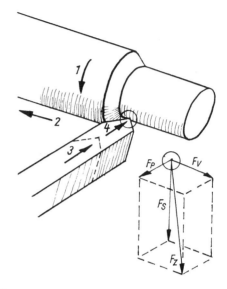

Figure 5.37
The movement process while turning.
1) cutting direction, 2) forward movement pressure, 3) tool movement from its starting position, 4) cutting and adjusting movement.

drilling. For facing angular workpieces chucks with two or four jaws are used as shown in figure 5.38.

Tool carriers
The cutting tool for a lathe is clamped in a *tool carrier* which is mounted on the frame of the machine as seen in figure 5.39. This is mounted in such a way that it touches the workpiece exactly at its equator.

The simplest tool carrier is the *clamping dog*, whose clamping plate is made parallel with an adjustable screw and then pressed against the turning tool with a tightening screw. The height of the turning tool is made perfect by strips of shim metal placed under it. A practical variation is a *quick change tool holder*, which allows the tool to be rapidly changed, positioned in height and fixed in place.

Production shops use a star-shaped *revolving tool holder* that is fitted with several tools, any of which can be quickly brought into position as needed. Such a tool greatly speeds work because the machine does not need to be stopped to change tools.

To drill holes with the lathe, a bit is chucked into the tailstock then brought into contact with the rotating workpiece that is chucked into the headstock.

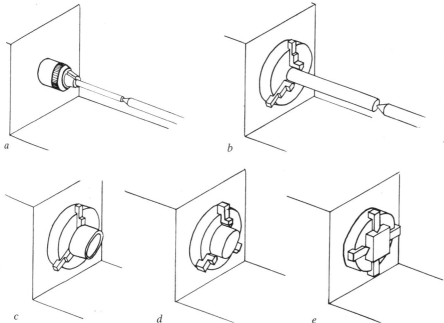

Figure 5.38
*Various ways in which a workpiece
can be mounted in a lathe.
a) rod in chuck, held and guided by
a floating-center tail stock,
b) rod in three-jawed chuck,
c) tube chucked from inside with
three-jawed chuck,
d) round disc clamped from the
outside in the three-jawed chuck
for facing cutting,
e) square plate, chucked from outside in a four-jawed chuck.*

a   b

c   d   e

Turning tools

Years ago lathe tools were simply made of a medium grade tool steel, but current practice is to attach small pieces of high strength tool steel onto bars of less expensive mild steel. In this way the cutting edges have excellent wear resistance at a fraction of the cost of making the entire tool of this expensive material. The working surfaces are usually made from high speed tool steel, carbide steel, or exotic high strength materials like diamond. Figure 5.40 shows some of the most familiar tools used on the metals lathe, each of which has a specialized purpose.

Different turning tool shapes have been developed according to the intended purpose.

a   *Straight turning tool* for rough cutting when face- or spindle-turning.
b   *Bent turning tool* for finishing when facing or longitudinal turning.
c   *Inside turning tool* for shaping inside cylinders and inside cones.
d   Inside corner turning tool for sharp corners on the inside of cylinders.
e/f   *Pointed and wide turning tools* for finishing when facing or longitudinal turning.

g   *Parting tool* for engraving grooves and cutting.
i   *Lathe threading tool* for external and internal thread cutting.

5.8
Forging

5.8.1 THE CONCEPT

We can say that forging is the original metalworking technique. In forging the metal is worked between hammer and anvil to create a desired shape. Blacksmiths use the term forging to distinguish work on hot metal, using the word "hammering" for other cases. In goldsmithing, however, a better definition would be this: Forging is the process of altering the cross section of a piece by striking it with a hammer in such a way that no metal is removed.

Because of their inherent plasticity, precious metals and their alloys are usually forged cold (i.e. at room temperature) and only rarely struck when hot. Sometimes forging is used to prepare a cast ingot for further treatment by rolling, drawing and so on. Other times forging is used to create a finished piece, relying on hammering as a central process in the development of form.

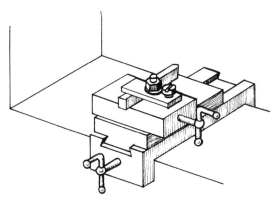

Figure 5.39
Fixed the lathe bit into the tool holder.

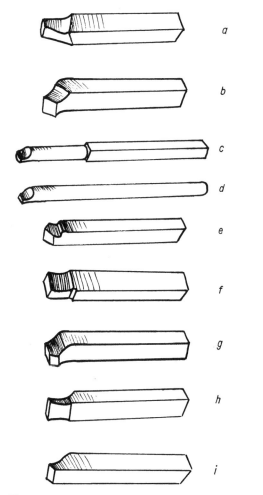

5.8.2 THE DEFORMATION PROCESS DURING FORGING

Ball peen and forging hammers are designed to achieve radical displacement of material. Both intrude deeply into the metal and displace material adjacent to the impact. They seriously alter the shape of the block.

The blow from a ball peen hammer displaces the structure all around the point of impact, whereas the metal beneath a forging hammer stretches only in one axis, namely at right angles to the peen. The block is lengthened in this direction. This important distinction accounts for the ability of the forging hammer to control the direction of flow during forging. In the case of both these hammers, the surface is dramatically altered and needs to be beaten smooth periodically as work progresses.

Where only minor changes in form are needed, the ball peen and cross peen hammers are replaced by planishing hammers. Crowned (lightly domed) faces are used on flat surfaces and absolutely flat faces are used on curved surfaces like bracelets.

5.8.3 HAMMER SHAPES

Perhaps the most basic hammer shape, and another icon of the metalworker's art, is a simple *forging hammer*, also called a *mechanics hammer*, shown in figure 5.41a. Variations on this, called a *goldsmiths hammer*, *tinsmiths hammer*, and *cross peen hammer* can be found in almost every trade that works metal. In every case, the distinguishing feature is a blunt wedge-shaped peen at a right angle to the handle on one end, and a flat or slightly crowned face on the other.

In all the hammers described, a wooden handle is stuck through the eye of the hammer and wedged tightly. The handle should be made of ash or a similar hardwood with elongated grain so it will be strong and still somewhat elastic. The body of the hammer should stay soft, but it is helpful if the striking surface is hardened. A steel with a carbon content between 0.38% and.05% is used. The faces of a metalmith's hammer must be free of all scratches and pits. If a mark is accidentally made in a hammer, a good smith will immediately stop work to polish it out, knowing that using a scarred tool is a waste of time.

Figure 5.40
Lathe bit shapes.
a) straight lathe bit, b) bent lathe bit, c) pointed lathe bit, d) internal and corner lathe bits, e) cut-off lathe bit , f) wide turning bit, g) offset lathe bit, h) Stechmeisel, i) threading lathe bit.

Of course every workshop has occasion to drive nails, pound a chisel or in other ways use hammers in a way guaranteed to mar their surface. For this reason, be certain to equip your shop with a traditional carpenter's hammer for these occasions.

Most hammers have two faces, the exception being small specialty hammers made to reach into tight places. In some cases the two faces of a hammer are in the same family, such as planishing faces. At other times a single hammer will combine faces from two different families, as for instance in a forging hammer, which combines a cross peen with a planishing face. Here are some popular hammers.

Goldsmith's or *Bench hammer*. This top quality hammer is used for small scale forging and shaping. The face is round and slightly crowned. The opposite end is a cross peen.

Raising hammers. Both striking surfaces are cross peens with different curvatures. The corners are slightly rounded to prevent marring the metal.

Forging hammer. This hammer has a sharper peen than the raising hammer and typically has a squarer body. The other end is a flat face, usually round or octagonal, slightly crowned and polished smooth.

*Ball Peen hammer (*sometimes called a *machinists* or *embossing hammer)*. The striking surface forms a hemisphere and the opposite end a smooth, round face. These are available in a range of sizes.

Planishing hammer. The two faces of this hammer are circular and well polished. One face should be flat for working on curved surfaces and the other slightly crowned, for striking flat surfaces.

Finishing hammer. Hammers in this large and diverse family have polished faces and can be square, round or rectangular, either flat or convex.

Chasing hammer. (figure 5.42) This familiar icon of goldsmithing is used to strike small tools.

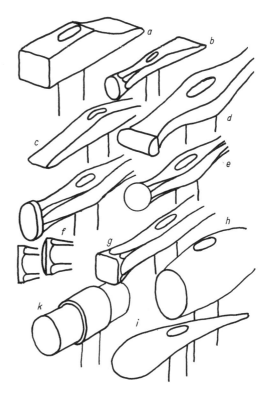

Figure 5.41
Goldsmithing and silversmithing hammers.
a) machinists hammer, b) bench hammer, c) forging hammer, d) raising hammer, e) ball hammer, f) planishing and smoothing hammer, g) tray or plate hammer, h) wooden mallet), i) horn mallet, k) plastic mallet.

Accordingly, its flat face is unusually large for its light weight, the better to "find" the tool. The handle is best made of a close-grained wood and sanded so thin it is springy. The back peen of the hammer is a small sphere that is useful for texturing or making rivets. The handle is shaped to an oval that makes a comfortable grip.

MALLETS
By definition, a mallet leaves no hammer marks on the surface of a workpiece. These were traditionally made of wood, but are now available in several kinds of plastic, including nylon, Delrin and other plastics. These are typically cylindrical, the striking surface is flat or slightly convex with rounded edges. While more expensive than wood, these mallets have the

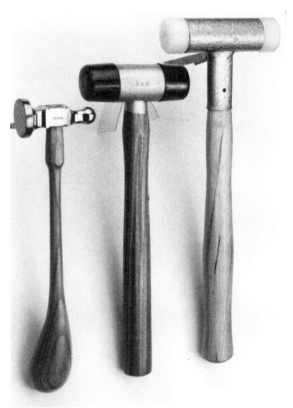

Figure 5.42
Special hammers. Chasing hammer, "Nyloflex" plastic hammer with changeable hammer faces, bounceless plastic hammer. (Firma J. Schmalz, Pforzheim)

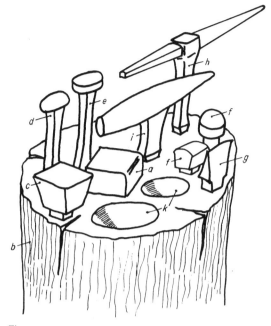

Figure 5.43
Anvils and other stakes.
a) bench block, b) wooden stump, c) flat anvil, d) "fist" stake, e) bottoming stake, f) small horned stake, g) splitting chisel stake, h) blowhorn stake, i) T-stake, k) depressions in the wooden stump for sinking and forming.

advantages of being somewhat heavier and lasting longer than their wooden forebears.

Horn mallets. This is a traditional mallet made out of the solid end of a cow's horn. The natural conical shape is retained, creating a flat face on one end and a blunted point on the other. These have been eclipsed by the less exotic but more practical plastic mallets, and are difficult to obtain nowadays.

5.8.4 ANVIL AND STAKE SHAPES

Figure 5.43 illustrates some of the scores of anvils and stakes used by metalsmiths. The best stakes are made of top quality tool steel, well shaped, polished to a mirror finish, and hardened on the surface to minimize marring. Though the proper material is steel, these tools are traditionally called *irons*.

As with hammers, anvils and stakes should be kept in a state of high polish. In proper use the hammer never strikes the anvil or stake directly, which would make a mark. If such a blemish occurs, the stake should be sanded and polished to return it to its original state. Some studios cover their stakes and anvils with a cloth containing a little oil to inhibit rust.

Bench anvil. This is a small steel block used at the bench for delicate hammering operations such as riveting or light forging, (figure 5.46). The block should have at least one polished surface and one crisp edge. It is useful to have one edge rounded. Sizes vary, but usually fall between 50-100 mm (2"–5").

Wooden stump. Though some stakes are made to fit in a vise, far more common is a tapered square peg made to secure each stake into a wooden stump. Because the wood provides a mass that will absorb the blow, the force does not bounce back. In addition, wooden stumps are inexpensive and weighty enough to stay in position. It is typical to also carve some shallow depressions in the wood for sinking, thereby enlarging the usefulness of the tool. Stumps have been a part of metalsmithing studios for centuries, and nothing has come along to improve on them.

Flat vertical stake. This simple but useful stake is not unlike the bench anvil, consisting of a rectangle of steel, in this case attached to a tapered foot for securing into a stump.

Dome stake. This is a sturdy stake, usually about 20 cm high (6") that can be mounted in a wooden stump. The striking surface is usually hemispherical and is always polished. It is used for forging, raising and planishing, and is made in several different sizes. Especially in the larger versions, this is also called a *mushroom stake* because of its shape.

Bottom stake. This tool is used to form and planish the bottom of a vase or bowl, and may be round, oval or square, always with a polished flat top. It is advantageous to have a bottom stake with both sharp and rounded edges.

Figure 5.44
Small stake heads of different sizes with an extension arm and stake holder. (Firma J. Schmalz, Pforzheim)

Flanging stake. This stake looks like a large stone mason's chisel and has a sharp-edged striking surface with one flat side and the other side at an angle.

Small stakes. This family of stakes includes a range of shapes used to make spoons, lips, spouts and ornaments. Most are only about 12 cm high (8") and come in many different cross sections, with both rounded and sharp edges. It is particularly useful if a whole set is available. By also having an extension holder and extension arm, these small stakes can be used in a wide range of applications, including the often problematic walls of hollow containers.

Horn stakes; Also called *T-Stakes* (figure 5.43). Horn stakes are available in several styles. One type consists of two conical horns of different sizes. Another, similar tool, has two tapered "horns" one of which is flat on its top surface. In both of these cases the top surface of the stake runs parallel to the floor. In a third type, the conical horns slope downward, usually terminating in a bluntly rounded tip. These versatile stakes can be used for bending bracelets, raising, forging and planishing.

Further stake shapes. Along with the standard shapes described above, a silversmith might sometimes need special stakes which he makes for himself. These can sometimes be modified from stakes on hand, but sometimes they must by cast for the job. The inventory of such "irons" in different shapes and sizes is the pride of the silversmith and is the basis of his work.

Mandrels (figure 5.45). These are a sort of stake with specialized uses that give each tool its name. Bracelet mandrels are generally round or oval, and ring mandrels are always round, sometimes with a milled channel to accommodate a stone culet. Bezel mandrels are available in round, oval, square and rectangular versions, though the round is undoubtedly the most useful. The photos in figures 5.48 & 5.49 illustrate some of the uses of a ring mandrel.

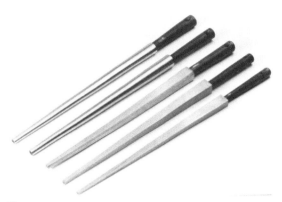

Figure 5.45
Various mandrels. Ring mandrel, angular mandrel, bracelet mandrel.
(Firma J. Schmalz, Pforzheim)

Figure 5.46
Hammering a workpiece with the peen of a hammer on the bench block.

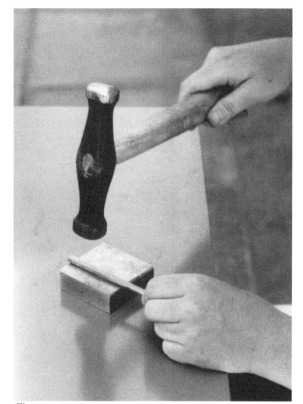

Figure 5.47
Forging a rod on the bench block.

5.8.5 THE CARE OF TOOLS

It is important to understand that every mark on a hammer face or anvil will be stamped into the workpiece with every blow. It is therefore essential to maintain these tools in pristine shape, taking care with their use and storage. Tools that are used infrequently should be protected against rust with a thin coating of oil.

5.8.6 THE EFFECT OF DIFFERENT HAMMER SHAPES ON THE MATERIAL

Flat striking face

Figure 5.50 illustrates the effect of different hammer shapes as they impact on metal. As seen in the first drawing, the effect of a flat hammer face is a vertical force distributed over a relatively large area. This means the force per unit area is relatively small. As explained earlier, the friction between the hammer face and the metal further limits the ability of the metal to move sideward, with the effect that a flat-faced hammer is not especially effective as a tool for moving material.

The structure of the metal under a blow is condensed. First the grains directly under the strike surface are deformed and press outward against their neighboring grains outside the pressure field. Because the force of the blow is distributed so broadly, the effect of this is usually small, limiting the use of the flat faced hammer to finishing, where this effect can be very helpful. The edges of the striking face should be slightly rounded so they don't leave dents. The hammer with a flat striking face is well suited as a finishing and planishing hammer.

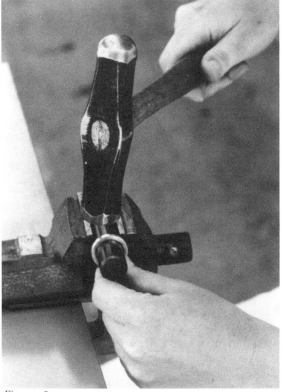

Figure 5.48
Forging a ring on a round ring mandrel.

Figure 5.49
Forging a ring on a parallel ring mandrel.

Crowned striking surface
In this situation, (not illustrated), the primary force is again vertical, but this time with some of the impact pressing outward. This fact, combined with the reduced friction of the face against the metal, results in a blow that achieves greater deformation than the flat faced hammer with the same amount of force. If the striking surface is equally rounded on all sides, the effect will also be equal on all sides. The relationship between the vertical and the sideways forces can be modified by the degree of curvature; the more strongly rounded the hammer shape, the deeper the hammer will intrude into the material under it. That is to say, a highly crowned hammer will move more metal faster and leave more dramatic marks.

Spherical striking surface
The logical extension of a crowned face is a ball peen, as seen in figure 5.50b. Here the force is concentrated into a small area of surface contact, with the result that a high pressure is developed. The force of the blow is strongly vertical, but includes strong forces pushing outward. Naturally with ball peen hammers the deformation forces are always uniformly concentric just as with the slightly crowned hammer.

Wedge shaped rounded striking face
The force delivered by a cross peen hammer is vertical and outward, but unlike the ball peen, this outward force moves in only two directions, perpendicularly forward and back from the wedge-shaped face. Because of its limited surface contact, the hammer

207

bites deeply into the metal, and delivers its force effectively. Because this hammer allows for maximum control over the direction of deformation, it is preferred for rapid forging.

5.8.7 PRELIMINARY FORGING

Preliminary forging has more to do with the internal structure of the material than with its eventual shape. All cast ingots should be forged for the following reasons:

- Through powerful forging, dendritic crystal growth and large grains are broken and recrystalized by subsequent annealing to create an evenly distributed fine grained structure.
- Rolling and drawing apply force primarily to the surface of a block, leaving the core section barely affected. Vertical hammer blows, by contrast, affect the metal throughout, and lead to a more homogenous structure.
- Hand forging is often the most efficient way to bring the ingot to a size and shape ready to be rolled or drawn.

For preliminary forging to achieve these desired results, the material must be strongly deformed. Proper forging, therefore, requires a heavy hammer and a stable smithing surface. When forging a square or rectangular rod, the cross peen is used to deliver close, evenly spaced blows at a right angle to the axis of the bar. This is done on a flat anvil, first on one side, then on its opposite side, and then on the remaining two sides. After hammering all four sides, the surfaces are made smooth throughout with a slightly crowned hammer, starting first on the corners, which might otherwise crack. The rod is then annealed and the process repeated until the ingot approaches the desired shape.

The ingot used to make wire is often a round rod, which should be reduced to a square cross section for rolling through the mill. This is done with a crowned hammer, taking care to keep each side perpendicular to its adjacent sides.

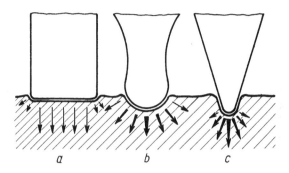

Figure 5.50
The effect of various hammers upon the structure of the material. a) flat, b) spherical surface, c) wedge-shaped striking peen.

5.8.8 PRECISION FORGING

Though the term *smith* derives from *smite* or "strike with a tool," over the years the trade has evolved to the point where the term goldworker is probably more accurate than goldsmith. This neglect of basic hammering skills is unfortunate, because forging offers interesting shapes and a unique design process. In addition, forging offers a unique opportunity to synthesize process and form. Whenever possible, I encourage smiths to leave the hammer marks on the piece, in this way demonstrating the truth to materials so essential to this process.

The following basic exercises are a useful way to approach forging, but bear in mind that these samples are intended only to present the basic vocabulary of the process of forging. A talented goldsmith will combine these and invent new forms to create innovative jewelry. These exercises can be worked in copper or brass, which is recommended for training exercises.

Forging exercises
A faultless material of the highest possible ductility is the prerequisite for successfully carrying out forging operations. Sterling silver (Ag 925) responds very well to hammering, as does a gold alloy of Au 750 or higher. Both these metals have a ductility of over 40%. Forging is possible, though, with all silver alloys and any gold over Au 500, which is to say, 12K or higher. In order to leave the object at its highest possible

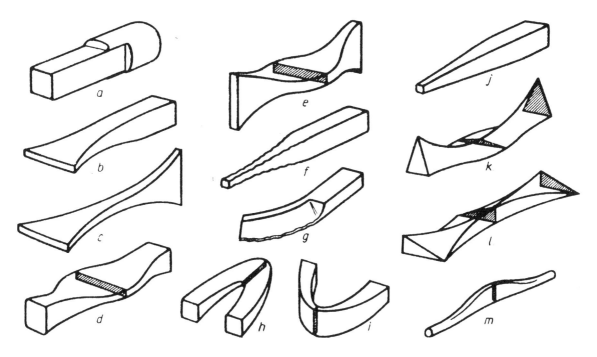

Figure 5.51
Elementary forms of cross section change when forging.

toughness, it is preferred, where possible, to end with a hammering rather than an annealing operation. Of course it is also possible to heat harden some alloys.

Figure 5.51a
In this exercise a round rod is forged with a slightly crowned planishing hammer against an anvil. After striking one surface with overlapping, evenly-spaced blows, rotate the rod 180° and repeat the pattern of blows on the reverse side. Rotate the bar 90°, watching carefully to see that the side just formed is perpendicular to the anvil, and holding the rod tightly so it doesn't turn in the hand. Strike a series of blows as before, always being careful that each adjacent side is at a right angle. If the form distorts and forms a rhomboid cross section, the rod must be hammered into a six-sided rod, then rounded and finally squared off again.

Figure 5.51b
By forging one end of a square rod of two opposite sides, you will create the first fundamental forged form – a wedge-like widening of the end of the rod.

Figure 5.51c
If opposite ends of a rod are forged at right angles to each other, the result creates another basic forged shape in which a surface transmutes into an edge and vice-versa. To increase the widening force of the hammer, use the cross peen of the hammer along the axis of the rod. The rod can be widened significantly by striking a fan-like pattern of hammer blows.

Figure 5.51d
If the same blows are directed at the center rather than the ends of a square rod, the resulting form will take the shape shown in this example.

Figure 5.51e

This exercise combines the two preceding ones, widening the center section and the two ends on opposite axes.

Figure 5.51f

To create a taper, a rod must be forged thoroughly on all sides, preferably with a cross peen hammer placed at right angles to the axis of the rod. In the early passes, hammering begins at the top of the taper and progresses all the way to the end. As the taper emerges, hammering is confined to the lower part of the rod, always working on all sides in opposition.

Figure 5.51g

If a square rod is struck more on one side than the other, a rectangular cross section is formed. If the blows are delivered to the edge of the bar, and limited to one side only, the rod will curl away from the force of the blow, and the section will become triangular.

Figure 5.51h

Here a square rod has been bent into a graceful curve, then forged at the height of the arc, widening the metal here and accentuating the curve.

Figure 5.51i

In this case the rod was bent then forged out flat at the bend using a horn stake.

Figure 5.51j

To refine a taper, start as described above in figure f, then move to lighter blows to smooth out the surface. To convert the taper to a round form, strike the corners to create an octagonal cross section, then strike the taper while rotating it.

Figure 5.51k

In this exercise, the square rod is forged out like a roof by striking with a slightly crowned hammer on opposite edges of the top surface of the bar. As shown in figure g, striking one side only will cause the rod to curve. Proceed by working alternately on the near and far edges of the bar, creating a triangular cross section with a straight axis. The pitch of the angle will be determined by the angle of the hammer blow. The midsection is altered by additional striking, making it shallower and wider than the ends.

Figure 5.51l

In this variation of the previous sample, the sloping surface alternates to one side, then the other, and back to the first, creating a wavy rhythm of planes and edges.

Figure 5.51m

In this case a round rod is forged flat on one side in its middle with a crowned planishing hammer.

All of these basic forms can be used as design elements, translated directly into pieces of jewelry. These samples only begin to hint at the rich variety and beauty of forged shapes, which become especially active when repeated on a larger form. These exercises use a short straight bit of rod, but it is also possible to start by forming a rod or bar into a ring that can be soldered then forged on a mandrel or stake.

Of course many ideas first come to life on a drawing board, but forging is a particularly fine example of the way designs can come spontaneously from working directly with metal.

Making a solid band ring

The ring illustrated here, (figure 5.52), is most often made today through lost wax casting, but for generations it was made by forging. The techniques are still viable, and this ring is a valuable exercise in perfecting hammering skills. In addition, there are slight differences between a cast and worked form that are made clear by making this ring. The instructions that follow describe the process as starting with a rod, but it is also possible to cast a "blank" that supersedes the first couple steps.

• Start with a square rod as thick as the thickest part of the ring. Step roll the rod in the wire mill on both ends to make the shank.

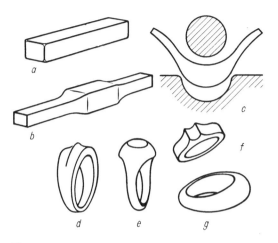

Figure 5.52
The making of a forged band ring.
a) rough bar, b) basic form with step-rolled shank, c) bending it around
on in wood or plastic, d) to g) various shapes of the band ring.

- If the shank is to be flat, these sections can be further reduced in the flat rolling mill.
- Even out the tapers just created by striking with a slightly crowned hammer on a curved stake or the horn of an anvil.
- Carve a half round groove in plastic or endgrain wood roughly to the outer dimension of the proposed ring. As shown in 5.52c, set the annealed ring blank into position with a steel rod or ring mandrel on top. Strike the mandrel with a large mallet, forcing the ring to curve around the rod. The thickest section of the form must be curved first; the thinner areas of the shank will follow easily, being malleted in any convenient way until the ends are brought together.
- Both ends of the shank are fitted together and joined with hard solder, after which the shank can be made truly round. The ring size should be a little smaller than needed to allow for hammering and filing as the ring is brought to its final shape.
- Figures 5.52d through 5.52g illustrate variations that can be worked on the basic ring form. In each case, use a hammer first to rough out the form, then follow with files, burs, and sandpaper.

Making ring shanks

Where the preceding description applied to large rings made entirely through forging, here we turn the process to the creation of smaller shanks that can be fitted with settings for stones or other ornaments. There are two general ways to proceed.

In the first, follow the instructions above, forging a square rod so its thickest section is in the middle and it tapers evenly toward each end. This is pounded into a wide groove as before to bend it around, and the ends are soldered together to form a ring. From here the shank can be trued on a mandrel and filed to a graceful shape. The only disadvantage with this approach is that the shank has a seam in the thinnest place.

The other way to proceed starts with a similar square rod, but in this case it is thinned in the middle section, as shown in 5.53a. This can be done by hammering over a curved stake (like the horn of an anvil) or by repeated back and forth rolling in a flat rolling mill. To get started, the rollers must be opened wide enough to allow the entrance of the bar, which is set into the mill with an equal length projecting on each side. Tighten the rollers as much as possible and roll a little in each direction, re-tighten, and so on, until the desired thickness is reached.

Once the shank form has been achieved, the process continues in more or less the same way, bending the shank, soldering it closed, and truing it up through use of a mallet, followed by filing.

Figures 5.53c, d and e illustrate a few of the many shapes that can be made this way.

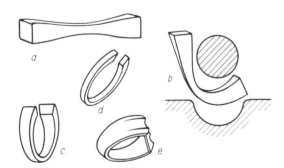

Figure 5.53
The making of a forged ring shank.
a) step-rolled basic shape, b) bending the form on wood, c) to e) various
shapes of ring shank.

Figure 5.54
Forged rings. silver. (Fachschule für Ang. Kunst Heiligendamm)

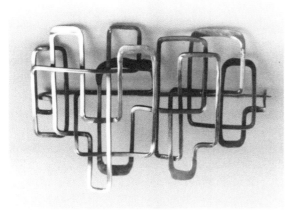

Figure 5.55
Brooch. Silver, forged from one piece. (Fachschule für Ang. Kunst Heiligendamm)

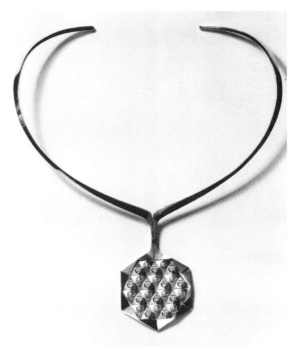

Figure 5.56
Neckpiece. Gold, pearls, diamonds. The cross section of the neckpiece was obtained by forging. (Oskar Stork, Berlin)

5.9
Bending

5.9.1 STRUCTURAL CHANGES

Metals have the useful feature of being bendable in two distinct ways: elastically and plastically. To clarify the difference, imagine a metal rod set across two supports, as diagrammed in figure 5.57. In elastic deformation, the deformation lasts only as long as the load is in effect. When the load is removed, the rod returns to its original shape. When the load is sufficient to create a permanent bend – when the sample no longer springs back to its original shape – the bend is called plastic deformation.

Permanent bending

Permanent deformation begins in the zones furthest distant from the neutral seam as seen in figure 5.58. In a manner of speaking, the spaces between atoms have become too great or too compressed to allow further mobility. The atoms have no "choice" but to shift on slip planes.

Bending (as distinct from forging) can be defined as a variant of plastic deformation in which the zones of the structure are affected differently. (In forging the zones are affected more or less uniformly). In the example shown in figure 5.59, the boundary zones 1 and 4 are affected only plastically and the core zones 2 and 3 are deformed only elastically. When the load is removed, the elastically deformed portions want to return to their original positions and tensile or compression stresses can develop.

On the other hand, the portions of the plastically deformed boundary zones (1 and 4) do not return to their original shape, and prevent the internal region

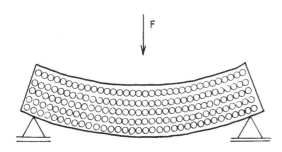

Figure 5.57
Elastic bending. The change of the entire shape and the structure.

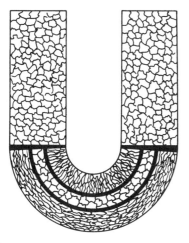

Figure 5.58
Rough sketch of plastic deformation and structural change in bending.

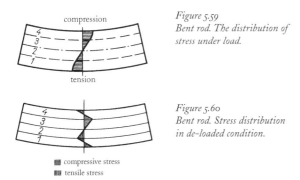

Figure 5.59
Bent rod. The distribution of stress under load.

Figure 5.60
Bent rod. Stress distribution in de-loaded condition.

▤ compressive stress
⦀ tensile stress

from doing so as well. Even though only the outer regions have been severely stressed, the entire piece is put under tension as a result.

As the load is increased, the areas closer to the neutral seam undergo plastic deformation, while the areas under the greatest strain are pushed even further and may break. This will appear as surface cracking. A tough metal, i.e. one with limited ductility, should be annealed frequently during a bending process.

The choice of an alloy for a given job must balance the need for ductility with the importance of wear resistance. A metal with a low elastic limit will be easy to form but also easy to deform, or bend out of shape. Au 585 (14K gold) is hard to bend into a ring shape, but will stand up to years of wear. Au 750 (18K gold) is easier to bend into jewelry, but will be knocked out of shape easier.

If wire has been annealed irregularly, some areas have larger grains than others. These recrystalized areas give way easily under pressure (deform plastically) while the work hardened regions respond to the same pressure with a springy, elastic deformation.

5.9.2 PLIERS

From early times, metal workers extended the power and precision of their fingers through the use of pliers. These simple tools have evolved into a huge range of variations, but their essential character has been unchanged over the centuries.

Pliers construction and usage

Pliers consist of two double-ended levers with a shared fulcrum, (figure 5.61). The two clamping jaws form the mouth of the pliers, which is closed by pressure on the handles. The distance from the fulcrum to the handle accounts for the grip of the tool, the best results being achieved with short jaws and long handles. Not surprisingly, this is exactly the case of traditional jewelers pliers, where strong pressure, a tight grip, and careful control are all needed.

The very best grip is achieved immediately adjacent to the fulcrum or pivot of the pliers, but work grasped in this location has a tendency to slide away slightly toward the tips of the jaws. This phenomenon

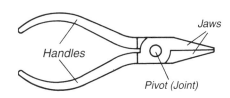

Figure 5.61
The basic shape of a pair of pliers.

can be diminished by roughening the inside surface of the jaws, but this is not usually appropriate for jewelers, who prefer smooth surfaces to avoid marring their work.

This is not usually a problem since maximum pressure is not typically the highest priority for a goldsmith when using pliers. Of greater importance is the ability to form sheet and wire with great precision, for which a large assortment of pliers of various shapes are needed.

Pliers are usually made out of unalloyed tool steel, but some specialty pliers are made of steel that includes chrome, vanadium or molybdenum. Pliers are available in a range of sizes to accommodate different size hands. Most fall in the range of 13 cm and 16 cm (5"- 6") but especially delicate "Geneva" pliers with a length of only about 12 cm are sometimes useful. Pliers are described by the shapes of their jaws, the most common of which are described here.

Flat pliers

The working surfaces of this style are flat and rectangular. The sides of both jaws, seen from the top view, are parallel. Pliers made for jewelry will have smooth jaws, but if you acquire a pair with serration on the inner jaws, these can be removed with a file or a silicon carbide disc on the grinding machine. Of course it is also possible to grind the overall shape of the jaws to a special shape if needed.

Chain-nosed (pointed flat nosed) pliers

The jaws on this style taper to a point and have flat, smooth interior surfaces. This might be considered a variation on flat jaw pliers.

Half-round forming (shank bending) pliers

The working surface of one jaw is flat while the other is slightly curved; both are smooth. These pliers can be purchased or created from flat or chain nose pliers. This style pliers is extremely useful for bending ring shanks or any other curved form. Because its curved jaw echoes the shape of the curve, it resists the marring that is inevitable with flat-jawed pliers. The flat jaw, which contacts the convex side of the curve makes contact only on a tangent, so marring is reduced to a minimum.

Round-nosed pliers

This pliers has jaws in the shape of elongated cones, coming almost to a point. These delicate pliers are useful when making or handling small rings, but they must be used with care. Because of the small contact surface, the working pressure is great and dents are easily made in the workpiece.

Special pliers

Many variations of the basic types described have been developed in the course of time to meet special requirements.

- A hybrid of two basic types yields the *round-flat pliers*, whose jaws are flat near the joint but turn into two round cones at the tips.
- In the *rounded hollow pliers* one jaw is a normal round nose while the other jaw has a hollow semicircular channel that corresponds with it.
- The jaws in *riveting pliers* are carved away so that only the points touch. They are used for earrings, hinges, and pin backs where it is useful to grip only the ends of a pin.
- The *box pliers* are somewhat similar, but in this case one jaw is flat while the other is arched, or hooked, to reach into an enclosed form.
- One jaw of the *ring bending pliers* has the shape of a broad "V" running along its length, while the other is a more familiar elongated tapered rod. These are usually of heavy-duty construction, and are useful for bending thick sheets or wires.

Storing pliers

Pliers should be kept on the bench so they are close at hand, easily identifiable, and comfortable to take up. A traditional method is to straddle them over a stout wire as shown in figure 5.62. Another proven method is to make a rack from a strip of sheet metal, and attach this across the front of the bench near the bench pin. Another device consists of a stand with holes drilled in a rotating disk. These can be purchased or easily made in the studio. Whatever the method used, avoid setting pliers into the sweeps drawer where they become lost and tangled up with all the other bits and pieces there. Time wasted in searching for the right pliers is inefficient and frustrating.

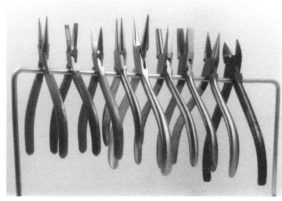

Figure 5.62
Various kinds of pliers:
– Geneva pliers (round, flat, chain-nose)
– normal pliers (round, flat-rounded, half-round forming pliers
  flat, chain nose)
– side cutter

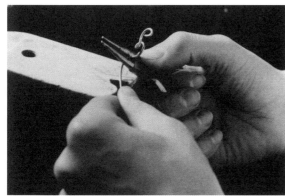

Figure 5.63
Bending wire with the round nosed pliers.

5.9.3 BENDING WIRE
Bending with pliers

It is obvious to point out that thick pieces of metal are more difficult to bend than thin ones. And of course, some metals are tougher than others. Pliers are used to extend the strength of the hands, to provide access to small shapes that are difficult for the fingers to grasp and to create improved leverage. Even so, there are limits to what pliers can do.

It is wise to experiment with various pliers and thicknesses of stock to determine in advance what can be reasonably accomplished. A thick ring shank in Au 585 (14K gold) can be bent only with great difficulty and will probably by deeply marred in the process. It is best to know this in advance, and devise an alternate method.

It is important to choose the appropriate pliers for each particular job. As a rule of thumb, whenever making or altering a curve, use a pliers with a similar curve, preferably with a flat jaw on the outside tangent. Always use your fingers as much as possible (guaranteed, no dents!) and then use pliers only after considering the effects of their use.

Even with strong hands and the correct pliers, it is never possible to bend wire into an absolutely crisp right-angled bend. To achieve a sharp corner, notch wire with a square file as shown in figure 5.64b and d. This process of course weakens the wire, which should be soldered before additional work is attempted. The deeper the notch, the sharper the bend, but the more fragile the corner until it is soldered.

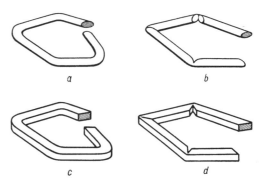

Figure 5.64
Square frames.
a) round wire with rounded corners, b) round wire with sharp corners,
c) square wire, rounded corners, d) square wire, with sharp corners.

215

Bending using other tools – Making round jump rings
Whether wire has been purchased, made by drawing, or made by rolling, before making jump rings it should be checked to be certain it is free from imperfections, burs and nicks. To guarantee perfectly round rings, the wire must be uniformly annealed. In the case of fine wire this can be achieved by wrapping the wire around a brass cylinder, which evens out the heat and reduces the risk of localized overheating. For larger wire, make a coil the size of a small plate, keeping each strand tightly held with all the others. Wrap this with brass or stainless steel wire and anneal with a bushy torch flame that is kept constantly moving.

Any rigid rod can be a mandrel for making jump rings: nails, dowels, and brass rods or tubes are all well suited. It's handy to have a collection of various sized mandrels ready at hand when needed. These may be plain, but many goldsmiths prefer to alter their mandrels to insure that the end of the wire is well anchored onto the mandrel before they bend up rings. Popular methods include a hole drilled in the rod, a slot cut about ⅛ of an inch in from the end, and a groove into which the wire can be laid for gripping in a vise.

When making a large number of rings, consider the simple device shown in figure 5.66. The mandrel in this case is a brass rod that is bent to include its own crank. It is set onto two pieces of wood that are gripped in a vise in such a way that the wire being

wound is passed between them and held with a certain amount of friction, which establishes a uniform tension in the coil.

An electric hand drill or flexible shaft can also be used to wind jump rings on a mandrel, but it is vital to run the machine slowly. The mandrel extending from the drill should not exceed 10 cm (4"). Goggles should be worn when operating the drill.

For smaller jobs, a hand vise can be used to make a short mandrel easier to hold, as shown in Figure 5.67. This is set against the bench pin and rotated, care being taken that each coil lays tightly against the preceding one.

In some cases it is helpful to anneal the coil while on the mandrel, depending on the intended use of the rings. If the coil does not slip off, it is removed by pulling backwards through the drawplate as shown in figure 5.70, where the coil is caught against the face of the plate and the core is pulled out with drawtongs. The coil might then be pickled and polished or scratchbrushed, again depending on the use.

Making oval jump rings
Oval rings can be made by wrapping two round rods held side by side, over a flattened rod, or on a strip of material whose edges have been rounded by filing. Wrap the mandrel with layers of masking tape, then wrap the wire tightly, keeping the coil neat. Heat the whole unit, which has the double purpose of annealing the wire and burning away the paper to provide clearance for removing the coil from the mandrel.

To make very small oval jump rings, start with a copper mandrel that has been flattened to the appropriate shape. Wrap a wire around it tightly, then heat the whole unit, annealing both wire and mandrel. Grasp one end of the mandrel in a vise and the other in draw tongs and pull hard. This will stretch the copper, elongating it and making it slightly thinner so the coil can slip off.

Closed and open springs
The previous section described coils that are made with the intention of cutting them to make jump rings. There are some cases, though, where the coil is

Figure 5.65
Examples of practice exercises. Scrolls bent and constructed from flat wire.(Birgit Karsten, firma Wilfried Nothdurft, Schwerin)

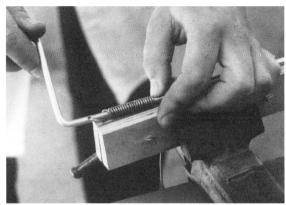

Figure 5.66
Winding the jump ring spiral at the vise.

Figure 5.67
Winding jump rings at the bench pin.

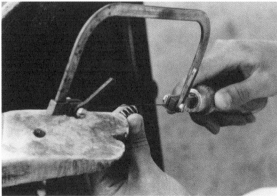

Figure 5.68
Sawing the jump rings that have been spread apart.

the end product, as for instance when making miniature springs for mechanisms, or making a lacy ornament to go around a stone. In both these cases it will
be necessary to create a coil with evenly spaced turn-
ings. Of course it is possible to wind a tight coil then
simply pull it from each end, stretching it out until it
does not completely retract. This will work, but the
spaces are rarely uniform.

A better solution is to wrap two wires side by side.
"Unscrew" one of the wires after turning, and they
will both be seen to have a uniform gap between each
turning of the coil.

Another way to achieve this effect is illustrated in
figure 5.71, in which a template coil has been made
and slid onto the mandrel. This is a winding of hardened brass that is made on a slightly smaller mandrel,
and is about two centimeters in length. It makes a
tight fit on the mandrel, and is held in position with
a finger as the mandrel is turned and the wire passes
over it.

Making twisted wire
Twisted wire is an ancient and versatile ornament. To
make small sections, grasp the ends of a piece of wire
in a vise, pulling the loop taut to find the center. Slide
a short length of tubing over the wires to make a handle, and slide a bit of rod or a stamping tool into the
tip of the loop as shown in figure 5.72. Keep a firm
backward pressure on the wire while turning, and
rotate the handle until the wire has the desired look.
There will be a little spring back, so overwind by a
turn or two.

For a longer twist, repeat the arrangement but
make a small hook to fasten into the jaws of a drill.
Keep the wire under light tension as the drill rotates
slowly.

Jig work
This device is used to make multiples of complex
forms or continuous loops in wires. To make a bending jig, hammer nails of an appropriate diameter into
a hardwood board, then cut the heads off. The pegs
should project only as far as needed, perhaps 5 mm
(¼"), so the wires can be easily lifted off the jig.

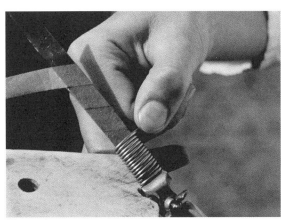

Figure 5.69
Making long oval jump rings. The jump ring mandrel is wound with sticky paper or tape.

Figure 5.70
Removing the jump ring coil using a drawplate.

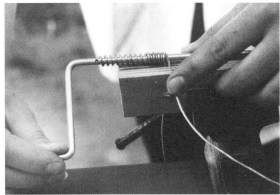

Figure 5.71
Making a spiral with regular distances between the windings.

An adjustable jig can be made as shown in 5.73. Start with a sheet of brass about 1 mm thick and 10 cm (4") on each side. Layout a grid of a convenient size, and drill holes at each intersection, then screw the brass to a suitable hardwood board, drilling the holes into this as well. Make a collection of pins from nails that fit the holes snugly and arrange them into whatever pattern meets your needs.

Unusual shapes can be accommodated by cutting a template from brass sheet and soldering on it a couple of pins in such a way that it will fit into the grid already established.

WIRE BENDING WITH THE WIRE BENDING JIG

The jig is easiest to use if it is securely fastened in a vise or onto a workbench. Start by using pliers to bend a loop into a wire so it can be securely anchored onto the first pin. Wind the annealed wire around the jig, keeping the wire taut, with pliers if necessary. When the wrap is complete, use a small screwdriver to pry the coil free. Figures 5.74 and 5.75 show work made in such a jig.

Straightening wire

STRAIGHTENING BY HAND

Often small irregular bends in a section of wire can be smoothed out by selective bending with fingers. Sight down the length of the wire to determine precisely the location and amount of the unwanted bend, and fix it.

STRAIGHTENING ON THE SURFACE PLATE

As illustrated in figure 5.76, a piece of wire can be straightened by tapping it against an anvil with a hammer or mallet. Set the wire so the "hump" is up, leaving a void between two points of contact, then tap this lightly until the wire is flat. In the case of round wire, rotate the sample and strike softly to avoid flattening the wire.

STRAIGHTENING BY STRETCHING

In many cases a distorted piece of wire can be made straight with a simple pull. Grip the wire firmly in a well-anchored vise, grasp the other end tightly with a drawtongs, and give a sharp tug backward. You will

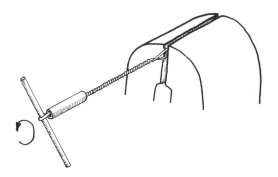

Figure 5.72
A simple method of twisting round wires.

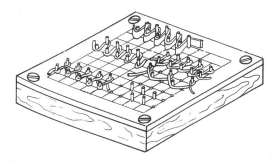

Figure 5.73
A wire bending jig with examples of how it is used.

feel the wire stretch, and often see a remarkable difference in the piece.

Another method, shown in 5.76b, is to rub a wood-
en dowel along a wire while it is held under tension.
Alternately, rub the wire along a dowel that has been
positioned into a vise, as shown in 5.76d.

Pliers can be used to twist a bent piece of wire back
to straight, as shown in 5.76c. Round wire is the most
forgiving here, but with specialty wires like square or
triangular, it is important to wind and unwind exactly the same amount.

5.9.4 BENDING SHEET

Bending by hand
As with wire, the best tool for bending sheet is always
the hand, which cannot be equaled for sensitivity and
delicacy. But as with wires, there are cases where a
tool is needed to increase finger power.

Bending with pliers
Sheets can be bent with the same pliers used for
wires, but they almost always prove limited. Because
of the hinging nature of pliers, they grip at only a narrow zone, which in the case of sheet always falls at the
edge. This makes them useful only for strips of sheet
such as bezels, ring shanks, and settings.

A parallel jaw pliers is commercially available that
uses a slipping joint to overcome this problem. These
are recommended when working with sheet metal. If
you find yourself frequently dealing with the same

Figure 5.74
*Neckpiece, gold. The links were bent up on the jig. Erhard Brepohl,
Arnstadt, 1954.*

219

Figure 5.75
*Pendant with shell cameo, gold. The frame ornamentation was
bent up using a jig. Erhard Brepohl, Arnstadt, 1954.*

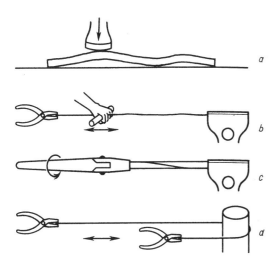

Figure 5.76
Straightening wire.
a) on the surface plate, b) by rubbing, c) using pliers to twist it,
d) by rubbing back and forth using two pliers.

gauge of sheet, you should consider altering a pair of flat or chain nose pliers just for this use. File or grind metal from the inside of the jaws, taking the most away near the joint and feathering to nothing at the tip. Check frequently by grasping a sheet of metal with the pliers and examining their grasp closely. Stop filing just before the shape is correct to allow for sanding and polishing.

Bending with other tools
For centuries, lead has been a popular material for forming silver and gold. It is soft enough to yield under a hammer blow but resilient enough to push against the workpiece to give it form. But lead has some drawbacks. Simply handling a block of lead is enough to allow traces to enter the body, causing a health risk. Also, when small bits of lead are left on silver or gold and heated in subsequent soldering or annealing operations, they contaminate the precious metal and cause pits that can only be corrected through drastic and time consuming repairs.

For centuries these drawbacks had to be accommodated because there was nothing else that quite filled the bill. Today a new generation of plastics called ure-

thanes is available in several grades of "springiness" and is recommended as a replacement for lead.

Figure 5.77 illustrates several ways to bend up a form, using hammers, mallets and mandrels in a solid base. Use the following guidelines and common sense to modify this technique to your own needs.

As shown (5.77a), it is sometimes enough to select the appropriate hammer face and strike it against a flat but yielding surface. For deeper grooves, pound or carve a channel into plastic, wood or steel, and work the metal into the groove, either with a mandrel or the peen of a mallet. If a lead block is used, slide it into a latex surgical glove to prevent contamination.

Bending right angles
It is impossible to create a crisp right-angled bend simply by hammering sheet over a form. To make a sharp bend the sheet must be notched, or *scored*, to remove metal from the bending area. In the case of a narrow strip this can often be achieved with a triangular and then a square file, as described above.

To score a wider sheet, either engrave a V-groove or clamp a straight edge into position and drag a scoring tool along it to create the same groove. This tool can be purchased or made by bending the tip of a file tang at a right angle and filing it to a point. However it is achieved, the groove must be most of the way through the sheet, at which time the pieces can be bent up with finger pressure. Because this area is fragile, it should be reinforced with solder right away.

When a small radius (or rounded edge) is acceptable, a corner can be made by using a mallet to pound a sheet over a steel stake as seen in figure 5.80a.

Bending rounded edges (figure 5.80b)
To create a rounded edge, file or grind the appropriate form on the corner of a stake, anvil or block.

Half-round bending (figure 5.80c)
After starting the bend on a stake with a rounded edge, the form can be refined over a piece of thick steel on which the edge has been made round as shown here. It is sometimes possible to use a vise to press the metal against the steel.

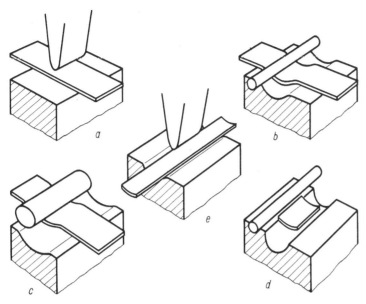

Figure 5.77
Bending strips of sheet metal.
a) with the hammer onto a lead block,
b) with a mandrel onto a lead block,
c) with a mandrel onto a wooden block,
d) with a hammer onto a steel swage block,
e) with a mandrel onto a steel swage block.

Making a rolled edge (figure 5.80d)

A rolled edge can be made by starting as above, then inserting a wire of the appropriate diameter. This "inside mandrel" allows the metal to be hammered forcefully without fear of collapsing the rolled edge. Use a flat mallet to lock the wire in place and a cross peen to cinch it closed. It is often useful to make a block of wood with the corresponding negative shape to press the metal uniformly over the wire.

Folding over an edge (figure 5.80e)

Start by hammering a right angle as shown in 5.80a, then anneal and mallet the flap over a sharp-edged stake like the one shown, which can be purchased or made from a piece of steel sheet. Anneal again and mallet the area closed on a flat anvil.

5.9.5 BENDING TUBE

When bending a tube there is always the danger that it will kink. It's usually possible to achieve a gentle curve when bending a thick-walled tube just using your hands, but for other situations it will be necessary to insert a core to support the interior as the tube is bent. A tube with an unsoldered seam is almost impossible to bend, even with a core.

Figure 5.78
Bending of sheet with a steel mandrel onto a lead block.

221

Figure 5.79
Brooches, silver, bent up from strips of sheet metal. (Fachschule für Ang. Kunst Heiligendamm)

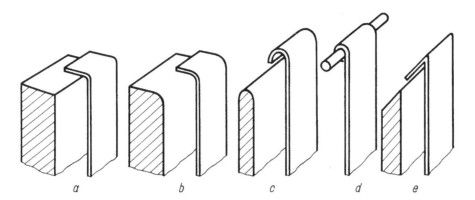

Figure 5.80
Folding over and rolling an edge. a) bending a right angle, b) bending over a rounded edge, c) bending over half-round, d) rolling (wiring) the edge, e) folding over sharply.

a   b   c   d   e

Inserting a metal core

In this time-honored, but labor intense method, a tube is plugged up with a metal rod that is then removed with acid after bending. For silver and gold alloys over Au 500, mild steel is recommended because it can withstand the heat of the repeated annealings that will probably be needed. If no annealing is to be done, an aluminum core can be used. For higher karat gold alloys, copper is usually used.

After the tube has been bent, cores are removed with acids that will attack the internal support without harming the tube. For steel the preferred etchant is diluted sulfuric acid. Aluminum is etched with hydrochloric acid, and copper is removed with nitric acid. In large tubes, the core itself may be a tube, which means there is less metal to be etched away.

Bending when filled with sand

This procedure has been used for years in the plumbing and sheet metal trades with thick tubing and can be successfully adapted to precious metals. The advantages of this method are the ease of filling and emptying the core, and the fact that the tube can be annealed midway in the process.

Seal one end of the tube, either by soldering on a cap, or with a cinch and fold. Dry, fine-grained dry sand is poured into the tube, tapping it frequently so the sand packs uniformly. When the tube is completely filled, the other end is closed up in the same manner. After the piece has cooled, it can be bent in the hands. Locate the solder seam on the inside of the curve so it is compressed rather than stretched. It is

possible to anneal without removing the sand, but the piece should be allowed to air cool; quenching could trap liquid in the tube that would cause a rupture when heated. When the desired curvature is obtained, the tube is opened up by cutting off the end and the sand shaken out.

Bending with a plastic core

For small tubes, a flexible plastic core can be used to provide internal support when bending. Nylon fishing line is a useful choice, and is available in large sizes from specialty sporting goods stores. Select a cord that makes a snug fit in the tube and coat it with a thin film of oil for lubrication. Use a length of cord that provides sufficient material to grab onto when it's time to pull the cord out.

The tube can be bent in the fingers, but annealing midway in the process will not be possible. When the bend is complete, grab onto the cord and pull it out. If a bit of the nylon breaks off inside the tube it can be burned out, but be warned of the noxious fumes that will result.

Tube bending equipment

This specialized equipment allows all manner of tubing to be bent without resorting to internal supports. Rollers are used on the inside and outside of the bend, and because they are perfectly matched to the contour of the tubing, the moment of force is spread over a large area. This prevents kinking. The tube is clamped at the segment being bent, then rolled and bent around the with supporting and bending rollers.

Figure 5.81
Tube bending equipment.

5.9.6 MAKING JUMP RING CHAINS
Fundamentals

A wide range of chains are mass produced by machines to satisfy the great demand for pendant, necklace and decorative chains. There are still cases, however, when a goldsmith is called upon to make a chain by hand, for instance when no commercially made chain proves suitable for a design, or when using a material that is not commercially made up into chain. Some chains are used to support pendants, and should play a secondary role in the overall design. A chain that is too large or ornamental will take attention away from the pendant and perhaps cause it to hang awkwardly. Other chains are designed as individual pieces of jewelry themselves.

Necklace and bracelet chains can be subjected to significant stress, for instance if the chain is snagged on something in use. For this reason, links are usually soldered. Beyond this, each link constantly rubs against its neighbors, so a sufficient thickness of wire must be chosen.

Standard measurements:
  – Bracelets are about 18 cm long (7").
  – Pendant chains between 42 and 45 cm (16-18").
  – Decorative chains 37 to 60 cm (15-24").

Thin chains are made from wire, usually round wire, thick chains and those with larger links are made from tubing to reduce cost and weight.

Cable chains

This family of chains is perhaps the most basic. It consists of interconnected jump rings that link together at a right angle to their neighbor. That is, each ring has a ring through it, which has a ring through that and so on (figure 5.82a).

ROUND LINKS

If the inside diameter of a jump ring is only slightly larger than the two rings that link through it, the chain is called a *closed* cable chain. To create this relationship, select a mandrel with a diameter only slightly larger than twice the thickness of the wire being used (figure 5.82b). When bending jump rings, use two pairs of pliers and open the ring by twisting it side-to-side rather than by opening out the circle.

Goldsmiths who do a lot of work with chains might find it useful to modify pliers for this purpose. Grind the points of a chain nose pliers to be slightly more narrow than usual and file half round grooves into each face of the jaws, directly opposite each other. Round these grooves to match the contour of a ring and sand the edges smooth to avoid marring the wire. These pliers pick up rings comfortably and grip them tightly for easy bending, (figure 5.83).

Soldering the links of a chain poses a unique challenge; each ring should be joined but not fused to its adjoining links in the process. To make solder joints invisible on the completed chain, use only tiny snippets of solder. There are several strategies for approaching chain making, each with its proponents.

• Solder each jump ring as the chain is assembled. A disadvantage of this method is the need to cool the chain after each operation. The entire sequence would be: insert link, close with pliers, flux, position solder, heat, quench, repeat. Though effective, the process is tedious.
• Another approach is to assemble the chain completely and suspend it tautly on the soldering bench. Rotate the rings so each seam is upwards, then flux and solder in one procedure.
• A variation on this method is to solder half of the rings as independent units before assembling.

223

Position in a taut line as before, but in this case every other ring will already be soldered. Be certain that the already finished jump rings are turned so the solder seams have no contact with neighboring jump rings.

- This method combines the best factors of each of the preceding suggestions. Start by soldering half of the jump rings closed and set them aside. Take up two rings onto one of the unsoldered rings and close it to make a cluster of three. Make many of these units, laying them on the soldering block as you go. Flux the joints and solder each ring closed.

   Take up two of these units on another unsoldered ring and twist it closed; you will now have a cluster of 7 links. Solder the ring closed. Continue in this way, joining two 7-units to make a 15-link section, and so on until the chain is complete.

The basic cable chain may be easily modified further by altering the size and shape of the jump rings, by changing the shape of the wire or by combining different types of jump rings. Several possibilities are shown in figure 5.84.

A variation on the cable chain just described can be created by soldering two links together at right angles. In this case the positions of the horizontal and vertical jump rings are clearly fixed.

OVAL LINKS

The length of the links can be different but the thickness of the jump ring mandrel must be at least twice the wire thickness to prevent the links from twisting (figure 5.82c).

Divide the planned amount of wire into two parts and wind jump rings from one half with a right hand turn. The other half is wound towards the left. If the jump rings made in this way and arranged alternately the chain will hang straight; otherwise it assumes a spiral twist. To differentiate them, one kind of jump ring is left oxidized black, the other is pickled.

Oval jump rings are connected together just as the round ones were. Turn the rings so that the seams of each two jump rings are next to one other.

Now the whole chain is pickled, because half of the jump rings are still blackened. The chain is placed into a watery solution of borax or flux and simmered to prepare it for soldering. The chain is then heated slightly on a steel block so that the flux dries onto it.

Hang the chain on a hook-shaped stand and use soldering tweezers to straighten the links. The solder is placed in position and the chain is allowed to hang free for soldering; i.e. it is not stretched taut.

After soldering the chain is pickled and drawn through a square drawplate to standardize it. This is simultaneously the best check on the durability of all the chain links.

If jump rings are to be twisted, first construct them as normal jump rings and twist them only after they

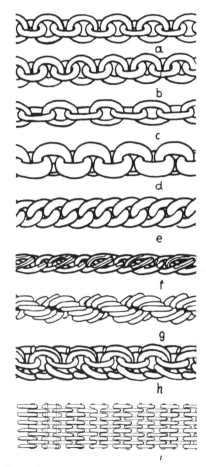

Figure 5.82
Hand made chains.
a) simple chain, b) close chain, c) chain with oval links, d) pea chain ("Rolo"), e) cable chain, f) Parisian chain, g) rope chain, h) Garibaldi chain, i) Milanese chain.

Figure 5.83
Grooved pliers for making chain.

Figure 5.84
Variations of a the simple chain.

have been soldered. For this purpose a hook is screwed into an edge of the workbench and a similar hook is clamped into the hand vise. Pull the chain taut and rotate the tool slowly to twist each individual jump ring.

Multiple cable chains

Two or more cable chains can be soldered together in a parallel construction to create a wide chain. Make the chains as described above and lay them on the soldering block, using pins to secure them into position if necessary. After soldering the chain can be flattened with a mallet or passed through a rolling mill with the jaws in an open position.

CABLE FROM STRIP

This is a special form of cable chain in which the links are bent up from thin strips of sheet and are slightly domed for stability, (figure 5.82d). This traditional chain, also known as a *pea chain*, can trace its history back many centuries, and was common as a component of bridal jewelry even recently.

The links are made by cutting pieces from sheet metal and forming them as shown in figure 5.85. The forming tool is made by filing a sphere on the tip of a round steel mandrel fitted into a wooden handle. A diameter of about 4 mm is typical, but of course many sizes could be used. If hand pressure alone is not sufficient to dome the links, a cord or thong is made into a loop and set over the tool as shown. This is caught with the foot where it will provide increased downward pressure as the tool is rotated by hand. The

Figure 5.85
Shaping a link of a pea chain.

225

formed rings are linked together and soldered, typically by hanging the chain from a hook over the soldering block.

Loop-in-loop

This extensive family of chains has a rich history. It was used by virtually every culture that worked precious metals, often with a delicacy that we still marvel at today. The chain is made of loops of wire that are soldered or fused closed before they are assembled into a chain. In the days of charcoal soldering, when it was difficult to locate heat precisely, this had an obvious advantage.

The loop-in-loop chain has a striking effect, almost like a flexible tube of precious metal. A commercial version is available as a machine-made chain, which is more commonly seen than the handmade variety, especially in small sizes. While the work is repetitive and demanding, the beauty and purity of the handmade chain is exceptional.

BASIC LOOP-IN-LOOP

This chain, as well as the many others derived from it, is made from many identical loops, each soldered or fused to make a continuous circle. These loops are then stretched into long ovals with round nose pliers. This prepares for assembly and tests the joints, which is advantageous because the chain can be difficult to repair. If a loop on a complete chain breaks, an attempt is usually made to solder it closed in place. If this is unsuccessful the chain must be taken apart back to the site of the break and then rewoven after a new link is inserted.

The relative sizes of wire gauge and link diameter offer a huge range of possibilities: experiments in base metal are recommended to determine the ideal sizes for a particular project (figure 5.86). The rings are made by wrapping wire around a metal rod or wooden dowel, then cutting the coil with scissors or a separating disk. The ends of each circle are brought together and each link is fused (fine silver or high karat gold), or soldered with very tiny bits of hard solder. The rings are then stretched on the tips of round nose pliers; defective links are set aside for repair.

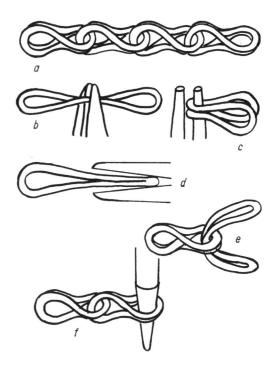

Figure 5.86
Making a simple foxtail chain.
a) the organization of the links, b) a link made from a round jump ring, c) bending the link around, d) pressing a loop flat, e) pushing it into the previous link, f) enlarging the newly formed link.

Each link is pinched in its center to make a figure-eight, or hour glass shape. The first link is bent at its waist so what had been the top and bottom of the eight stand opposite each other. Let us call these two open ends of each link "wickets." It's helpful to insert a small twist of wire into the first link to provide something to grasp until the chain itself is large enough to be easily held.

A second ring is shaped into an "eight," and threaded through the two wickets of the first link. In some cases it might be necessary to squeeze one end of the "eight" so it fits through the former link. In this case, use a scribe to pry the link open so the next one can be passed through it. The chain continues in this way, each link passing through both ends (wickets) of the preceding link.

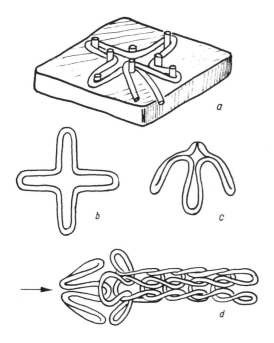

Figure 5.87
The making of a loop-in-loop chain with four loops.
a) wire wound around pegs, b) link soldered together, c) pre-bent link,
d) construction of the chain.

DOUBLE LOOP-IN-LOOP

This variation can be made in several versions; a variant with four loops will be used as an example. Each link is created by winding wire around the pegs of a jig. In this version, the result is a clover leaf shape (figure 5.87). These links are soldered closed and the ends of two opposing loops are bent up at an angle. If necessary, the loops of the second link can be compressed to allow them to fit through the loops of the first link. Once they have been inserted, the loops are opened up again with a pointed mandrel and bent around so they can in turn be pierced by the next link. The chain continues in this fashion until the desired length is achieved.

The construction process leaves the chain irregular and inflexible. To correct this, anneal the assembled chain and pull it through a wooden drawplate. Though a steel drawplate can be used, wood is preferred because it does not risk damaging the chain. To facilitate the drawing, twist a scrap of wire through the end link to grasp with the drawtongs.

Curb chain

In this variation on the cable chain, simple interlocking soldered links are twisted so they lie flat. The origins of the chain can be traced back to mail of medieval knights. Links in a curb chain can be round or oval, and made in almost any size (figure 5.82e).

When determining link dimensions, remember that the inside diameter will be contracted as the ring twists. The chain is most effective when the links are snug against each other, but of course they must not bind up. As a rule of thumb, the inside diameter should be about 2¼ times the thickness of the wire being used. As with any chain, it's a good idea to make a couple inches of sample in base metal before cutting links of gold.

Each link is set into place, soldered, and twisted, one by one. Parallel jaw pliers are useful in this operation. The seam must be in the direction of the main axis of the chain and lie in the middle of the half of the ring sticking out, (figure 5.88). Bend a steel wire to the same curve as the links and use it, held in pliers, as a bending tool. The U-bend is fed through the new link, gripped behind the ring with parallel pliers and the link is shaped by twisting.

To even out the finished chain and to guarantee that it hangs well, insert a piece of scrap wire through the last ring on each end. Grasp one end of the chain in a vise (the wire will prevent damage to the chain) and hold the other in vise grip pliers or draw tongs. Pull forcefully. If the chain is still not straight, rub it between two hardwood boards while under this tension, or roll it carefully through the rolling mill.

CURB CHAINS WITH CONNECTING LINKS

This combination of curb and cable chain is offered as a proposal for further variations (figure 5.89). The jump rings are hung together as double rings in pairs and soldered together. They are connected with oval double jump rings.

Parisian Chain

Wind wire around a mandrel as described above. Though many sizes are possible, a recommended size for a sample chain uses a wire with a thickness of 0.6

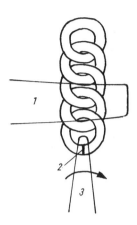

Figure 5.88
Twisting the links of a cable chain. the pliers are depicted as transparent). 1) the parallel pliers, 2) the seam of the new jump ring, 3) the grooved pliers.

Figure 5.89
A cable chain with connecting jump rings.

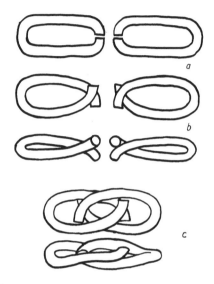

Figure 5.90
Parisian chain.
a) original shape, b) the jump rings bent over themselves, c) the jump rings assembled as a chain link.

mm wrapped around a 4 mm copper mandrel. After wrapping, the coil and mandrel are passed through a rolling mill to flatten the entire unit. This will yield oval shaped rings, as shown in figure 5.90. These are sawn on the short side and inserted, two into each other, where they are soldered to make a link. Each link is fabricated in place onto its immediate predecessor as the chain is built. After construction, each link is twisted slightly by grasping it with two pairs of flat nose or parallel jaw pliers. Finally the chain is filed smooth on both sides and sanded.

Rope chains

The jump rings in this popular chain are so closely interconnected that the chain is similar to a rope. In order to reduce weight, hollow links are often used. Of course the appearance is the same for solid or hollow links (figure 5.82g). Round jump rings are sawn open and stretched on a mandrel made just for this purpose. The mandrel is mostly tapered, but ends in a cylinder of exactly the correct diameter so that when a ring is pressed to this section the gap at the sawn seam is exactly the size of the wire being used. Links are soldered together with each successive ring clamped in this way onto its predecessor.

Binding wire is wrapped around the chain as it is being assembled to hold the rings into position (figure 5.91). The success of this chain depends on correct proportions: the inside diameter of each loop should be three times the thickness of the wire being used.

Garibaldi chain

Wind round wire onto a round mandrel whose diameter is roughly three times the thickness of the wire, keeping the wind loose. Cut the wire at intervals that allow each link to consist of two circles, i.e. two full turns around the mandrel. Two of these are "screwed" together and soldered so their open ends are facing each other. After the first double link is completed, a round unit is fed into it and completed by coupling it with another round unit. These are soldered and the next link is added on, etc. The chain is completed by malleting it flat.

Milanese band

This band is not a chain in the usual sense and has limited flexibility, but makes an interesting watch band or bracelet. The building block – it can't really

Figure 5.91
A rope chain, wound around with binding wire for soldering.

be called a link – is an open coil of wire. These will be needed in two versions, one wound clockwise and the other counter-clockwise. Both will need to have a uniform spacing between the windings, which is done by wrapping two wires side by side.

Start with two identical round wires of a manageable length, say around one foot long. Hold these side-by-side against a round mandrel and wrap as if they were one wire, going slowly enough to insure that they lay flat against the rod. When the wrapping is complete, slide the coil off the mandrel and "unscrew" the two units, taking care not to bend them. Cut these identical coils into pieces equivalent to the intended width of the band.

Repeat the process with one variation. Wind the other direction. Keep these units separated from the first. We'll call them A and B coils.

Set an A coil next to a B coil and push them together until they engage like cogs on gears. Slide a straight length of wire through the coils at the area of overlap, somewhat like sliding a hinge pin into position. Bend the ends of this wire at a right angle to hold it in place temporarily. This wire will later be soldered and trimmed away.

Continue in this way, always alternating A coils with B, (they won't mesh otherwise). When the band approaches the correct length, solder each end of the wire to the tip of one of the coils. Cut away excess wire and file the edges to make it smooth and attractive. It is typical to follow this step with a light malleting to flatten the band. The surface can also be filed and sanded to convert the round wires to facets. Of course you must be careful not to file too far.

Variations

Part of the fascination of chains is the vast wealth of variations they contain. Each of the preceding examples can be altered by changing the size, shape, pro-

portion and materials to create an infinite selection that will accommodate every need (figures 5.92–5.94).

BALL CHAIN

This familiar chain can be found on everything from key chains to wash basins. Connecting links look like miniature barbells—a short round wire with a ball on each end. These are held in links made from seamless tubing, short sections of which are cut off and burnished to secure a connector at each end. Small versions are made by machine and do not lend themselves to hand production, but here is a variation that can be made at the bench.

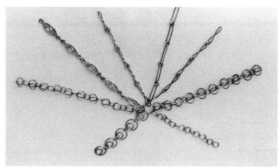

Figure 5.92
Practice exercises for various decorative chains. (Birgit Karsten, Firma Wilfried Nothdurft, Schwerin)

Figure 5.93
Examples of various cable chains.

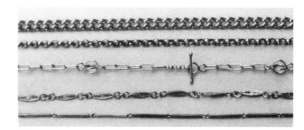

Figure 5.94
Various hand made chains. Cable chain, "pea" chain, cable chain with decorative links, cable chain with filigree parts, chain of rods.

229

Example: ball bracelet, diameter 10 mm.

Hemispherical domes are formed from thin sheet with the dapping block and punches; a hole is drilled in the center of each dome. The smaller connecting bar can be capped with jump rings, or with a small piece of tightly fitting tubing that is soldered in place. In either case, one end of the connecting bar is completed in advance, and the other is capped after the bar has been inserted through the dome (figure 5.95c).

Sub-units consisting of two open hemispheres joined by a connecting bar are completed, then they are joined by soldering the rims of two hemispheres onto each other to create a hollow bead. This soldering operation is, of course, delicate and requires careful control of heat to avoid having pieces seize up. The chain continues in this way until it reaches the desired length. A ball-shaped screw clasp is an obvious choice of clasp for this chain.

Knitted mesh tube (crochet)

This is not a chain in the true sense because it is not made of individual links. Instead, it is a flexible tube made from a single thin wire that is woven into a mesh of many interlocking loops. Mesh tubes from ancient times can be found that are more than two

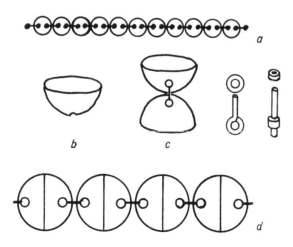

Figure 5.95
Ball chain. (the links are depicted as transparent).
a) machine made chain, b) hemispherical dome, c) construction to the half-spheres, d) the half-spheres soldered together.

thousand years old. The monk Theophilus, writing in the Middle Ages, described in the 62nd chapter of his third book how chains were made for the cast incense censer.

> *If you want to make chains, first draw fine or coarse wire from copper or silver and with the help of an awl bend three, four, five or six loops, depending upon the size, as you will, depending upon the weight relations hips of every censer, whether it is small or large.*

Mesh tubes illustrate interesting problems in the history of metalworking techniques. In addition to marveling at the skill involved in looping the wire into a decorative mesh, we can't help but be impressed with the labor involved in preparing materials. First, a cast rod was forged as thin as possible, then drawn out to make a long, thin, flawless wire. We take this for granted today, but can imagine the difficulty of creating such a strand in a 14th century workshop. How, for instance, did they make the drill needed to create the smallest hole in their drawplate?

Process

The technique can be practiced with copper wire before moving on to sterling or gold. A typical size wire is 0.2 mm (32 B&S gauge). Use a hooked needle, size 6. Unlike conventional knitting, which uses two needles, the structure of the wire itself holds the mesh together, so only a single needle is needed.

DIRECTIONS FOR A SIX-LOOP MESH

Wind wire around your fingers three times, then tie the bunch together by wrapping the short end of the wire around the middle. Bend up the ends to create a shape that might be seen as a six-petaled flower (figure 5.96a). Bend the points up and tie the lower end together so the loops stand next to each other like a funnel (figure 5.96b).

Select any loop at random and pass through it a loop created from the "feeder" wire that is still on its spool. Figures 5.96c, d, and e show the desired effect. The next drawing shows how a hooked needle is used to pull the wire through each loop. Lay the feeder wire horizontally across one of the loops, inside of the funnel shape, and reach through a loop with the hooked needle. Snag the wire with the hook and pull it back through the loop, using the fingers to flatten it out (figure 5.96f, g).

Continue in this way, moving around the original six-lobed funnel shape to make the chain. Note that these drawings show the structure as flat in order to make the sequence clear; in fact the chain grows as a hollow cylinder.

The finished mesh chain can be given a more even shape by pulling it lightly through a steel or wooden drawplate. The mesh may be drawn a little or a lot depending on taste, but be warned that tight compression will result in a stiff chain.

5.9.7 FILIGREE

Since ancient times, *filigree* and *granulation* have been linked together in so far that the wires and balls were soldered onto the recipient metal with the help of a eutectic fusion. In folk jewelry traditions, however, filigree developed into a linear style; one in which granules were of lesser importance to the design, or omitted altogether. For this reason, filigree is dealt with here as a separate section, but readers are reminded of the value of combining the two techniques. Filigree falls into two styles: open work (pierced lattice), and filigree that is soldered on a metal surface.

Filigree jewelry can be made from all gold and silver alloys, but because of its association with traditional folk jewelry, silver is most commonly seen. Standard sterling (Ag 925) is recommended because of its easy shaping and resistance to oxidation.

Filigree wire
The visual effect of the filigree is the result of delicate markings ("beads") on the standing edge of a flat wire. The term literally means *beaded wire,* as derived from Italian: "filo"= wire; "grana"= grain or bead). This flat wire combines delicate effect with sufficient stability.

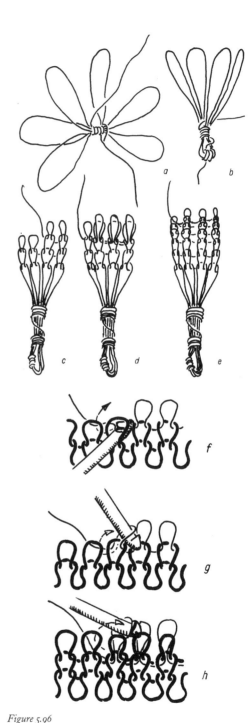

Figure 5.96
The making of a woven tube.
a) the wires bound together, b) the wire bundle, c) a simple knitted row, d) doubled row of knitting, e) further development of the mesh, f) drawing the wire through, g) lifting the wire up, shaping of the mesh, h) formation of the doubled row of knitting.

Figure 5.97
Bracelet. Antiqued silver, soldered with filigree ornamentation.
(Manaba Magomedova, Tiflis)

Figure 5.98
Cigarette box (detail). Silver, gilded. Open-work filigree. (Krasnoje
Goldsmithing School, Volga, Russia)

The wire used in filigree can be made in two ways. Twist together two thin round wires. Because large quantities are typically needed, use a flex shaft or drill to twist a long segment. Make the twist as tight and even as possible then flatten the twisted strand in a roling mill or by planishing it lightly.

Threaded wire is less traditional but preferred because it is easier to make and work. Cut a large coarse thread onto a round wire, using a threading die as if making a bolt. Again, because a large quantity of this wire will be needed, it is beneficial to find a mechanized way to produce it. One method is to clamp the thread cutting die in a vise, pass the silver or gold wire through it, and clamp the end of the wire in a drill. The wire can then be mechanically "screwed" through the die, where it will be cut with a winding coil. Keep a slight tension on the wire throughout the process, and proceed slowly. After cutting, the wire is flattened by passing it through a rolling mill. The result will be a flat ribbon of metal with a delicate pattern on each of edge of the strip.

In either case, twisting or cutting, anneal the wire carefully to prepare it for filigree work.

Soldering filigree

Work is usually shaped directly on a drawing. Use pliers to bend the filigree wire to shape, cutting with small scissors or flush cutting wire snips. For some designs, a bending jig might prove useful. It is com-

mon to enhance the design with small balls (called shot). These are much larger than the grains used in granulation, and are made by cutting pieces of sheet or wire and heating them on a soldering block. They will draw up into spheres with a tiny flat section on the underside; this helps prevent their rolling away when they are being soldered onto the filigree unit. Small coils of thin wire or jump rings made of twisted wire are also familiar embellishments for filigree constructions.

To solder a filigree wire pattern onto a base sheet, flux the parts and sprinkle them with very tiny chips of solder. Do not set the solder directly on the sheet, where it will spread outward and leave an unattractive blemish. By having the solder on the filigree wire, it must pass through the filigree to reach the sheet.

Filigree mesh

Not all filigree is soldered onto a base. In cases where the filigree is to remain open, it is supported in a solid frame, for instance of stout square wire. It is typical to subdivide frames into smaller compartments, which not only increases strength, but allows small sections of filigree to be assembled individually (figures 5.98 & 5.99). Usually the frames are made first, then the smaller ornaments are formed from the prepared filigree wire. Parts are shaped with pliers or with a pattern jig as demanded by the design. Traditional filigree patterns are often symmetrical, in which case small units will be repeated many times. They should be checked against each other to insure regularity.

The finished frame is set onto a flat soldering surface and filled with the ornamental units. They can be positioned and soldered all at once, or handled in smaller sections. Because it would be very time consuming to place solder chips on each of the joints, solder filings are dusted over the surface after all the contact points are painted with flux.

Sculptural filigree

Because properly made filigree units have such a high degree of structural integrity, they can often be treated like solid metal. This means that filigree-filled frames and disks can be bent into cylinders and domes by forming them with pliers or in a dapping die. These units can then be soldered up into beads and other three-dimensional units.

Finishing

Gold and silver filigree can be finished like any other type of fabrication. A popular variation is to pickle the finished object to achieve a uniform matte surface, then polish only the high-standing edges of the filigree. The result is a delicate but dramatic contrast that emphasizes the fine detail of the filigree edge. Another finish widely used in European folk art is to gild the backing plate and use rivets or screws to connect the lattice of filigree over it.

Figure 5.99
Chest. Silver, open-work filigree. (Venice, end of the 17th century. Green Chamber, Dresden)

5.10
Educational Trade Exercises

It is fitting to conclude this chapter on benchwork with examples of exercises used in Germany to train and instill confidence in students intending to pursue a career in goldsmithing. By separating issues of technical skill from design, we are able to focus attention on proper use of tools and the development of benchworking skills.

Success in these exercises is not subject to the mood of the professor or the charm of the worker. This rigorous system teaches understanding of technical process and confidence. The examples that follow have been drawn from the training program of the Master Goldsmith Wilfried Nothdurft in Schwerein and from students of Professor Friedrich Becker in Düsseldorf.

FILING

These excercises provide all the difficulties a person might encounter while sawing. The geometric patterns instantly reveal the quality of the sawing.

SAWING, FILING

These bars have been given original and interesting shapes entirely through the use of files.

Figure 5.100
Sawing and filing exercises, brass plates, 55 mm x 55 mm, 1 mm hick

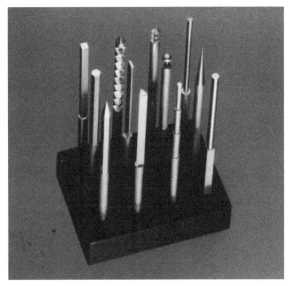

Figure 5.101
Filing exercises, brass rods, 150 mm long, 6 mm thick

SAWING, BENDING

Because we are so familiar with the shapes of letters, they tell us instantly if they have been poorly made. Letterforms are used in these examples, cut from sheet and formed from wire.

SAWING, BENDING

These examples use the repetition of gcometric forms to test bending and soldering skills.

Figure 5.102
Lettering design as sawing and bending exercises. The base plat is 120 mm x 30 mm, 6 mm thick.

Figure 5.103
Exercises for bending wire and soldering. silver on brass, 50 mm x 59 mm, 1 mm thick.

STAMPING

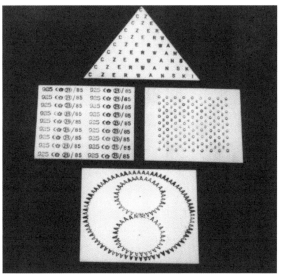

Figure 5.104
Punch work exercises. Brass plates, 500 mm x 50 mm, 1.5 mm thick

Practice is the key to making uniform marks with stamping punches. Through practice and concentration, detailed patterns of great regularity can be achieved.

SOLDERING

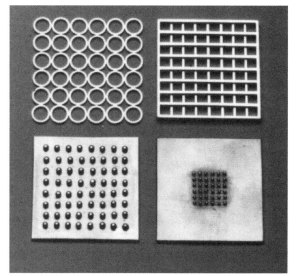

Figure 5.105
Soldering exercises, Silver, 35 mm x 35 mm, 1 mm thick.

Small repeating units are soldered onto a sheet to practice control. Again the regularity of geometric patterns is used to make errors instantly recognizable.

Figure 5.107
Conical bezels, brass, 1 mm thick.

These are all bent up from developed layout projections, the angular ones are scored with mitered cuts; the seam and miters are soldered. The sphere is put together from two halves, all the other forms are constructed from developed layout projections.

Figure 5.108
Constructed hollow bodies, average diameter approximately 40 mm (1½"), 1 mm thick.

TURNING

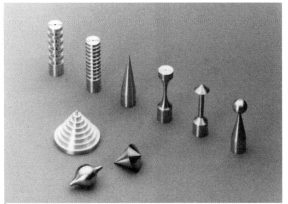

Figure 5.109
Turned shapes, brass.

These exercises are used to gain familiarity with the possibilities of lathe turning. In addition to being interesting forms, these examples teach precise measurement.

FORGING

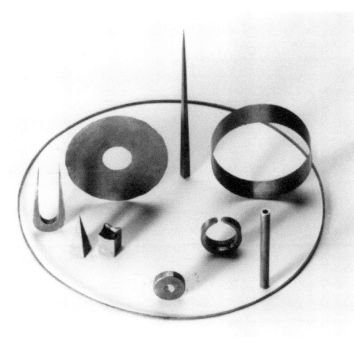

The simple thick copper washer (bottom center) forms the basic shape from which all the examples shown were developed with a hammer and an anvil. In some examples the disc was sawn in to the hole.

Figure 5.106
Forging exercises. Clockwise from bottom:
- *Plate with a hole in it outer diameter is 21 mm, inner diameter is 5 mm, 5 mm thick (approx. 1" with ¼" hole). All the shapes started from this shape.*
- *Four sided prism with concave upsetting, 12 mm x 12 mm, 16 mm high,*
- *U-shaped 57 mm high.*
- *Disc, outer diameter 70 mm, inner diameter 19 mm, 0,4 mm thick.*
- *Needle, 5 mm x 5 mm, 127 mm high.*
- *Hoop, diameter 68 mm, width 17.4 mm, 0.4 mm thick.*
- *Tube, outside diameter 6 mm, height 62 mm, 3.4 mm thick.*
- *Hoop, 1.4 mm x 1.4 mm, 210 mm diameter.*
- *Open ring, inside diameter 20 mm.*

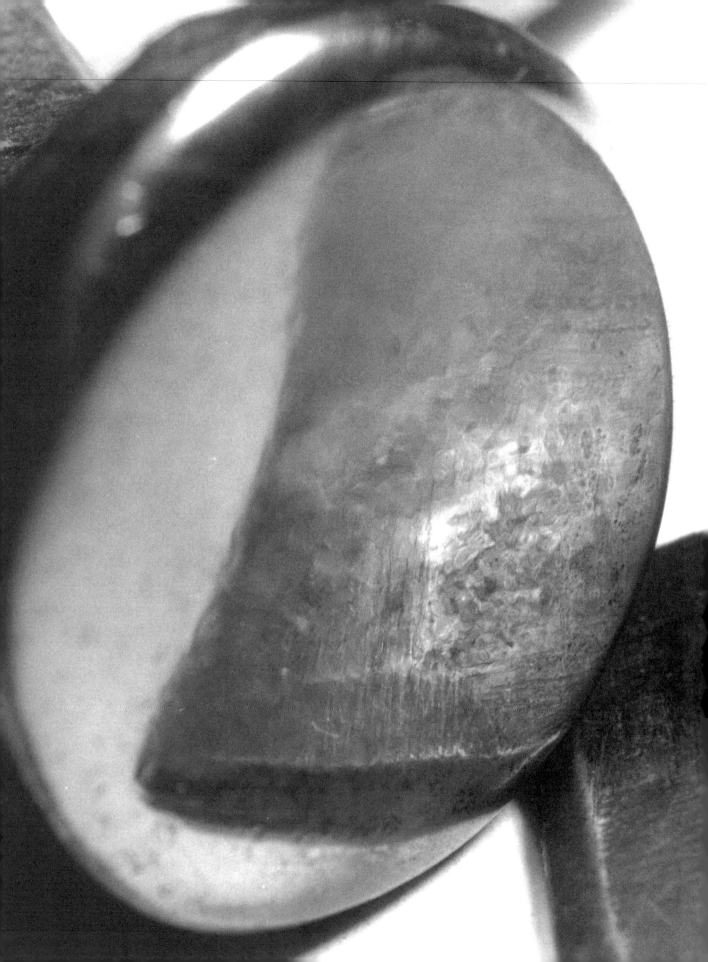

CHAPTER SIX

Silversmithing

6.1
Explanation of Terms

FORMING

This comprehensive term encompasses the wide range of procedures used to convert flat metal into volumetric form. It includes the techniques associated with silversmithing and hollowware, as well as processes usually used for relief such as repoussé and die forming. By and large, sheet material is struck with various steel or wooden hammers or with different kinds of steel punches onto soft or giving surfaces (wood, felt, leather, lead, pitch) or onto different shapes of steel stakes. All metals with sufficient ductility can be worked with these methods – precious metals and their alloys, copper and malleable brass, aluminum and steel.

SINKING

In this forming process, blows are struck against a sheet on the inside of a form while it lies over a hemispherical depression. It is the simplest way to create a dish or hemisphere. In a small scale the process is called *dapping*.

PRESSING

Hammering from an ingot, particularly with the aid of heavy machinery.

PLANISHING

The sheet is smoothed and stretched with a slightly crowned hammer on a smooth steel anvil from the center out to the edges in a spiral pattern. The primary use of this process is as a finishing technique.

STRETCHING

A hammering process in which malleable material is pinched between two hard surfaces – usually a steel hammer and a steel stake – in a way that causes it to thin and simultaneously bend into a volumetric form.

RAISING

The process of bending sheet metal by small increments over rigid forms to create a vessel. The process starts with sinking or the creation of flutes that are then hammered in such a way that the metal is compressed. The initial shape for raising can be a disc or a developed pattern projection. Examples of uses include dishes, beakers, chalices, coffee or tea pots.

RAISING IN

In this extention of raising, (also called *necking in*) metal is brought inward from a vertical position to create a form that is smaller in diameter at the top than at the base or belly of the form.

UPSETTING

Technically this is a process in which metal is pressed down on itself, and is seen in riveting, stonesetting and other applications. In silversmithing the term refers to a process of hammering directly down on an edge with a cross peen steel hammer to thicken the rim. This increases the visual impact of an edge while also stabilizing it.

LAPPED JOINT

This is a specific kind of seam used when a form will sustain the stress of hammering, as for instance when making a cylinder that will be hammered into a curvilinear form. The edges are prepared by hammering a wedge or tapering strip on the edges to be joined. These are then overlapped and soldered, in this way greatly increasing the amount of surface-to-surface contact. After planishing, the form is of a uniform thickness, which would not be the case if the edges were not tapered first.

REPOUSSÉ AND CHASING

These separate but related techniques are used to create relief by hammering sheet metal into a semi-resilient material like pitch, lead or soft wood. While the hammer is occasionally used directly on the metal, both processes are typically associated with smaller scale and the use of steel punches.

6.2
Deformation When Shaping and Forming

Forming is a chipless deformation method. At a microscopic level, the material is subjected to the same kinds of stresses and structural changes described earlier. Issues of elastic and plastic deformation, slip planes allowing for the relocation of crystals, and the recrystalization process that occurs during annealing are all the same as described earlier in conjunction with rolling and drawing.

Of particular interest in the hand forming methods described here, however, is the difference between local and general stresses. The following example provides insight into the subtle but critical stages of a deforming process.

In the first case, imagine a disk of metal placed on a flat lead block and struck with a dapping punch, as shown in figure 6.1. The pressure cone forms first directly under the punch, where contact is first made. Because the lead does not offer much resistance, the

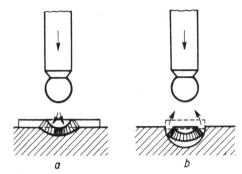

Figure 6.1
Forming process using chasing and punching.
a) a portion of the entire metal sheet is formed, b) the sheet metal piece is entirely formed.

disk is plastically formed – if we pull it out now we'll see that it has been domed. Continued hammering locates the stress on the highest curve of the dome, the place where the stresses were first applied. Because this is the area that was first deformed and has therefore taken the most stress, continued work might cause it to tear. The lower part of the dome, meanwhile, was never significantly stressed. This will create an uneven structure after annealing, because the stressed areas at the top of the dome will recrystalize properly (because of their fine grain structure), while the unstressed lower regions of the dome that were never stressed will be left with large grains after annealing. This is a heat hardening effect.

Compare that with the same process done in a dapping block, shown in figure 6.1b. In this case the outer parts of the disk are the first to make contact with the support (the dapping die) and are stressed as the form is compressed. The further the deformation proceeds, the greater is the compression and the larger is the area affected by it. As before, deformation is made possible by shifts in the atomic lattice structure, but in this case the metal is made thicker at the outer regions and thinner at the center. The location of stresses are exactly the opposite from the first case; the maximum stress lies in the outer edges of the dome, the structural changes decreasing towards the middle. In the center of the disc the original structure and the original metal thickness remain unchanged. Though perhaps less obvious, these principles apply to all forming processes.

6.3
Stretching

Stretching resembles planishing, but its intention has to do with form, where planishing is primarily associated with surface concerns. Stretching is nothing more than carefully located and controlled hammer blows that locally deform a metal sheet. Stretching can be used to flatten an irregular sheet, to redistribute stresses from a previous operation, or to create a dome from flat sheet.

A stretching hammer, like a planishing hammer, will be of steel, have a slightly crowned face and be well polished. Hammerheads that weigh 500 and 1000 grams (17 & 35 oz.) are typical. An anvil or a flat rectangular stake is used as the supporting element, because by definition stretching will always include a rigid support beneath the blow. To practice, use copper or brass that has been given a matte surface by scrubbing with pumice. Such a surface will reveal hammer blows clearly.

Proper stretching requires sensitive hands and focused attention. The workpiece is held against the stake or anvil securely, because it is this angle that will determine the affect of the blow. The hammer is brought into contact with a confident vertical blow. The hammer should never tilt as it strikes, because this would create a half-moon imprint where the edge of the hammer makes contact.

Though apparently simple, proper stretching requires a thoughtful understanding of internal stresses with a sheet. Practice and close observation are needed to master the technique. Figure 6.2 illustrates a few of the situations in which stretching can be used. In every case, follow these general guidelines:

- Blows should not be set too close together.
- Blows are always placed from the center outward in a circular manner, regardless of the shape of the sheet.
- The outer rim is worked a little or not at all to prevent the creation of a wavy edge.
- Rectangular and oval sheets are worked in the long direction.

After the sheet has been thoroughly stretched, like the example diagrammed in figure 6.2a, it is rotated at an angle against a harsh light to show up any irregularities. If the piece has bumps, they are the result of striking too hard in those spots. It's tempting to try to pound them flat, but this will have the reverse effect. They are the result of having been struck… hitting them again will only make matters worse.

Instead, the proper method calls for careful blows all around the bump. This will deform and harden those areas, causing the sheet to eventually be drawn flat by the stresses created around the bump. Often such bumps lie very close to one another: they are evened out together (figure 6.2f). The stretching is repeated as often as necessary until the domed area disappears. Naturally the sheet must be annealed periodically throughout the process.

Irregular surfaces in a triangle or the corners of a square pose a slightly different set of stresses, and should be struck in the sequence shown in figures 6.2b and d.

As illustrated in figure 6.2g and h, long strips of sheet are often deformed through cutting or rolling such that one side becomes longer than the other. The solution is to carefully stretch the concave or shorter side, which will restore the piece to its rectangular shape. After stretching the piece should be uniformly planished to create an even pattern of stress, and then annealed. Use only light blows to avoid damaging the sheet.

Besides making sheets flat, stretching can be used to create curved forms, most usually the shape of a shallow round dish. These forms are uniquely stable and lend themselves to use as lids, bases, and components in larger forms. In the pure state, this is a musical instrument called a gong.

Start with a disk of uniform thickness and set it at a slight angle on a polished anvil or flat stake. Strike around the edge of the disk with a slightly crowned polished hammer. The result is a very local thinning of the sheet that presses the displaced metal upward, away from the anvil. Strike another blow immediately beside the first and so on, moving inward in a spiral pattern toward the center of the disk. Tilt the form

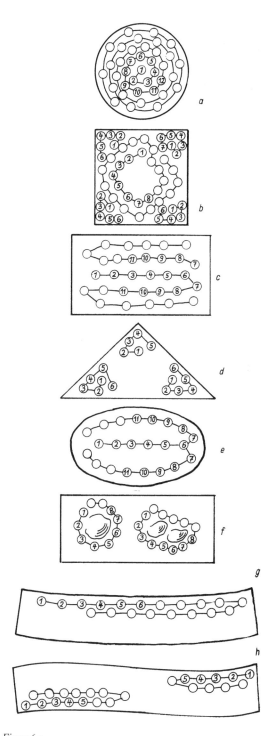

Figure 6.2
Strips of sheet metal.
a) circular sheet, b) square, c) rectangle, d) triangle, e) oval, f) bulges in the sheet metal, g) and h) stretched metal sheets.

as necessary so the hammer blow is consistently trapping the sheet squarely on the anvil.

Because the outer zone has been strengthened by the first series of blows, continued working pushes the metal toward the direction of the still unworked middle of the sheet. The workhardened outer rim does not yield, so the stretched metal has no place to go but outward, or into a dome.

6.4
Sinking

Sinking is one of the most basic techniques of silversmithing. A flat sheet, often a disk or oval, is pressed into a wooden hemispherical depression with domed hammers or mallets. The wooden form can be carved in boards and clamped temporarily to the benchtop for use, but a better arrangement uses a section of tree trunk cut to a convenient length, perhaps 60 cm (20") high. The cut sections should be made level so the log will be stable. Round and oval depressions are carved into the endgrain surface with gouges and sanded reasonably smooth. It is usual to have several sizes and depths, but of course these can be modified as needed.

Hammers and mallets of various sizes and weights can be used, depending on the thickness and malleability of the metal being formed. A medium weight plastic mallet that works well on thin sterling will clearly be ineffective on thick bronze. The curvature of the hammer will be similarly variable. A broad, slightly crowned face is appropriate for thin metals being only slightly deformed, where a smaller ball peen that will localize force is recommended for tougher, more dramatic sinking. In some cases a mushroom stake might be used instead of a hammer.

Rounded dish
This is the simplest shape of a sunken dish, it is a section out of a sphere (figure 6.3). If the form is to be used as a dish, a ring can be soldered on later to hold it level.

The first step is to draw and cut out from heavy paper a pattern or template of the intended shape,

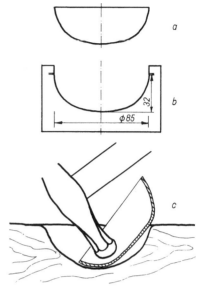

Figure 6.3
Sinking of a curved bowl.
a) side view, b) pattern, c) working in the wooden depression.

(figure 6.3b). This step becomes especially important as work becomes more complex and the cost of materials increases, so it is a good idea to make it part of the process even in these first exercises. Though it is omitted in the examples that follow for reasons of brevity, pattern making is always understood to be part of the process.

The drawing of the side elevation is transferred onto tracing paper, which is folded in half on its middle axis to check for symmetry. Transfer the lines to a piece of cardboard, using something as rigid as matte board for larger shapes. Allow the template to extend beyond the form at the top as shown, and draw lines to indicate the center and the proposed rim. In addition to using the template to check progress, it can be saved as a reference for future objects. With this in mind, it is helpful to write down on the template when you're finished all the information you might later find helpful, such as the thickness and diameter of the starting piece, the dimensions of the finished dish, and the time it took. Though this might seem unnecessary in such a simple example, the habit will prove valuable as you proceed to more complicated forms.

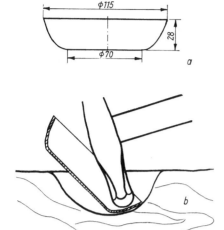

Figure 6.4
Sinking of a flat-bottomed bowl with low sides.
a) a side view, b) hammering in the wooden depression.

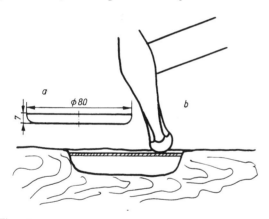

Figure 6.5
Sinking of a flat-bottomed bowl with a high ridge.
a) a side view, b) hammering in the wooden depression.

This form, like all those that follow, starts with a disk that is cut and filed smooth around the edge. Follow the filing with a burnishing action to make the edge consistently smooth and even. This has the double advantage of protecting your hands from injury from sharp edges and reducing the risk of edge tears. Make a small hammered impression at the exact center of the disk with a centerpunch. Again, these steps, though not repeated below, are assumed for all the samples that follow.

Select a depression in the sinking block that most

closely resembles the proposed dish and lay the disk at an angle across it (figure 6.3c). Starting from the outside edge, strike a pattern of overlapping blows about a half inch in from the rim. Follow this with another circle of blows, just inside the first, continuing in a spiral to the center of the disk. The force of the blows should be sufficient to cause the form to curve, but not so strong that it puckers at the edge. The wooden form should provide a hollow space beneath each hammer blow. If this is not the case, move to a smaller and deeper depression. The sound of proper sinking is a dull thump.

Try to deliver blows of consistent force, which will keep the form regular. If some blows are stronger than others, the dish will have bulges. These should be removed by striking lightly around them until they are incorporated into the curve of the dish. The series of blows from the outer rim to the center is called a *course*. After the first course, check the dish against the template to determine if further sinking is necessary. If it is, anneal the dish, pickle, rinse, and dry it, then repeat the process, starting at the outer edge and moving again to the center.

Flat-bottomed dish with a low rim
In the case of a dish with a flat base, (figure 6.4) follow the same procedure but stop striking at the point where the walls of the form meet the bottom. It might be that only two or three concentric circles of blows will be needed to make up a course. If the form is not deep enough, anneal and repeat as necessary to create the form. The bottom might become slightly deformed and can be flattened by setting it on a flat anvil and tapping it with a mallet.

Flat-bottomed dish with a high rim (plate)
When the proposed form consists mostly of a flat bottom, (figure 6.5) the easiest method is to carve a wooden form that closely resembles the desired curve, as shown. Sink the disk into this form, striking only along the edge. It often happens that the upper part of the walls of the dish are curved inward. This can be corrected as shown in figure 6.6 by using a slightly crowned planishing hammer on a flat anvil or stake.

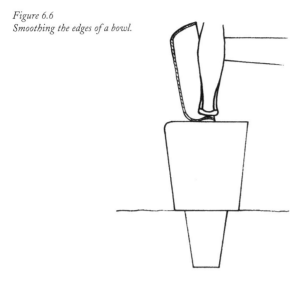

Figure 6.6
Smoothing the edges of a bowl.

strike it gently with a slightly crowned planishing hammer. This will press it outward against the walls, pulling it tight like stretching a sheet on a bed.

If the floor is not perfectly flat the bowl will rock when set on a table, which is undesirable. It is better that the floor curve slightly upward, into the bowl, which will leave only the outer rim of the floor to make contact with the table. This is made as true as possible through hammering, then the bowl can be rubbed on a sheet of sandpaper taped to the benchtop to leave the foot absolutely level.

The upper edge of the dish is marked with a surface gauge or by holding a pen on a stack of books so that it is rigidly level at exactly the correct height. File the rim down to this line and sand it as necessary to make an appealing edge.

6.5
Planishing

Planishing is the process of pinching metal between two hard forms to make it smooth and to refine the form. In the case of each of the bowls described above, sinking into a wooden form is followed by planishing over a polished steel stake that closely mimics the curvature of the form. For these simple bowls a single stake will probably suffice, but in more complicated forms it is not unusual to switch between several stakes in the process of planishing.

As has been repeated often before, the faces of planishing hammers must be polished to a mirror finish. Use a hammer that is heavy enough to move the metal under impact, but not too heavy to use for a long time. For these simple forms, a light planishing hammer will be sufficient. The hammer finds a spot on the stake and strikes it repeatedly as the form is moved around beneath the hammer. Unlike the sinking blow, this should have a solid feel and make a ringing noise.

In the examples above, particular care will be needed to refine the transition from the flat floor as it curves up into the sides of the dish. To make the floor itself flat, set the dish on a smooth hard surface and

6.6
Raising

Stretching and sinking are very useful techniques, but they are limited to open shallow forms like the dishes described above. There is no doubt that the process called raising, in which sheet metal is compressed and stretched over rigid forms by careful placement of blows, offers dramatically wider potential. The process is more difficult than sinking because it requires sensitivity to the shape of the form, angle of the metal and direction of the blow, but the wealth of forms it can create justify the time and practice needed to master it.

Raising cannot be learned from a book, but will come from diligent experimentation. A person who enjoys the process will spend more time at it, with the inevitable result of increased skill and greater pleasure in the process. What follows is a description of the concept of raising that will perhaps give a glimpse into the geometry of raising, catching the reader's interest and compelling him to take up a hammer and give it a try. Though silversmithing, where the emphasis is on larger forms, is distinct from goldsmithing, it was not unusual in the 18th century that a single craftsman would work in both arenas, and we are seeing a return to that breadth of range today.

245

Dish with a flat bottom and a high rim

For a first example, let us take a bowl like the one shown above in which a sheet has been formed through sinking into a flat-bottomed dish with curving sides. This is as far as sinking can take it. Let us now raise the walls to be vertical, and to have a crisp right angle where they meet the floor.

Work can be done on steel or wooden stakes, the latter being slightly preferred in this case because they are less likely to scar the metal. Stakes like those shown in figure 6.7 can be made in the studio from any hardwood; maple is the most frequent choice. Clamp the stake into a vise that is securely mounted to a stable bench.

Unlike sinking, which thins the sheet slightly, raising is primarily a compression process. As the metal is pressed upward it is gathered and therefore thickens. This will be impossible to see on an example like the dish being described, but in a tall narrow vase the metal thickness at the rim can be three times that of the starting disk.

Raising is done with a rounded cross peen hammer or plastic mallet. Hammers can make the work progress faster because of their greater weight, but can also make a misdirected blow all the more troublesome in the hands of a beginner. It is typical to learn with a mallet and then proceed to steel tools, but each person should try both ways to determine which seems right for them.

The dish is given its shape through sinking as described above. While it is possible to start raising from a flat sheet, it is usually considered easier to give the vessel at least a general depth through sinking. The work is annealed, pickled, rinsed and dried, and concentric pencil lines are drawn on with a compass about 10 mm (½") apart. These are a visual reference that will help guide the hammer blows.

The vessel is held against the stake as shown in figure 6.8, angled so there is a space beneath the metal just adjacent to the point of contact. It is this "hollow" that makes raising work, so pay particular attention to it. The idea is simply to lever the small area just there against the fulcrum created by the point of contact with the stake. If there is no hollow, that is, if the

Figure 6.7
Raising blocks for working pieces into different firms.

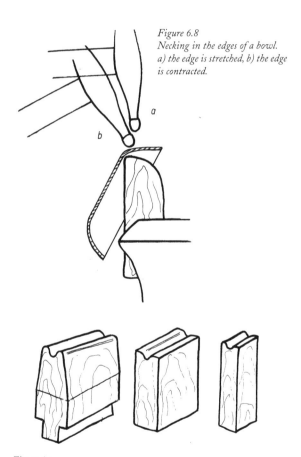

Figure 6.8
Necking in the edges of a bowl. a) the edge is stretched, b) the edge is contracted.

Figure 6.9
Folding blocks for different size plates (or blanks).

metal is angled so it rests on the stake, the blow is useless. It traps the metal and either thins it (if using a metal hammer) or has no effect at all. If the angle is such that too much space is exposed beneath the hammer blow, the deformation is too great at a localize spot. Subsequent blows must either tear the sheet or undo some of the bend just made.

Work always proceeds in concentric circles, moving from the center of the disk outward, or in this case, from the point where the wall meets the floor out to the rim. Blows are again hollow, falling as they do "on air." It is far more important to have the angles right than to deliver a powerful blow. If the leverage is working as it should, relatively little force is needed to deform the sheet.

The correct hammer angle is shown in 6.8a, in which a vertical blow collects the metal and compresses it against the form, pushing it slightly in the direction of the center of the disk as it does so. This compression stroke will move the metal faster, offer greater control, and result in a more rigid form when complete. The other angle, (figure 6.8b) is incorrect and will push the metal upward against the stake. In addition to having less control and effectiveness, this blow will thin the sheet and yield a sharp fragile edge.

Work will fall into a natural rhythm, usually striking 3–5 blows as the disk is rotated against the stake before the holding hand adjusts to a new grip. Try to keep the angle and force of the blows equal and the position of the form on the stake consistent. Failure to do this will permit the vessel to get lopsided. If this happens, correct it as soon as possible in whatever method seems best. This could be as easy as bending it in your hands or returning it briefly to the sinking stump. Such a diversion is obviously a nuisance that adds extra time to the process. As raising proceeds upward the metal thickens and work hardens, making it more difficult to deform. You can expect to need heavier blows as you approach the top of a form. The higher the raising, the more pronounced this will be.

If a single course was not sufficient to raise the walls as far as desired, the piece is annealed and raising is repeated against the same wooden stake. It is possible to start from the same point (where the walls meet the floor) but probably that area was correctly shaped in a single course since only a little deformation was necessary. It is more typical that each subsequent raising commences from slightly higher up the wall. In every case, the course should continue all the way to the rim.

Suggestions on finishing this form are included in the following example.

Beaker with conical, straight walls
There are many ways to raise a beaker like the one in figure 6.10, each with its advantages and proponents. To attempt to discuss them here would be more confusing than helpful, so we will select one popular method and content ourselves with that. Readers who go on to pursue silversmithing will discover other methods both in their experimentation and continued reading, and are encouraged to try every possible technique before settling on a favorite.

The intention here is to allow even students of goldsmithing, who do not foresee extended work with this technique, to have an opportunity to learn first hand the forces involved in transforming a flat sheet into a straight-walled vessel. It is an exciting process, and one that cannot help but inform one's understanding of the behavior of metals.

The tools required for the beaker are raising and planishing hammers, a wooden V-stake (also called a valley stake), a wooden raising stake like the one used in the preceding example, a bottoming stake and a

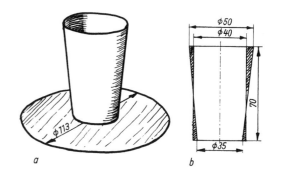

Figure 6.10
Raised cup.
a) disc blank and final form, b) simplified side view for calculating.

form that matches the contour of the walls of the beaker for planishing.

To determine the correct size starting disk it is first necessary to draw out the intended form. As mentioned above, a template should be cut from stiff cardboard. From this information it is possible to determine the average or *mean* diameter, in this case about 4 cm. This can be used in the following formula to calculate the starting disk.

$$d_1 = \sqrt{d_2^2 + 4\,d_2 h} = \sqrt{4^2 + 4 \cdot 4 \cdot 7} = \underline{11.3 \text{ cm}}$$

This is only a theoretical value based on the supposition that the sheet thickness does not change and the beaker is cylindrical with straight-walled sides. In practice the form is a cone, and the walls will thicken slightly. In addition, because this is a handworking procedure, there are many opportunities for minor irregularities to affect the process. For this reason we will either complete the calculations and add some extra as a margin for error, or simply substitute the following rule of thumb formula.

diameter of the disk   =
    proposed height + widest diameter of the form

In this example we start with a 120 mm disk (4¾"). Experience tells us that a beaker of this size should be hammered up from metal about 0.8-0.9 mm thick (19-20 B&S). If it is thinner, folds occur too easily at the rim; if it is thicker the work is too difficult and tiring.

As mentioned above, mark the center point with a punch to create a dimple that will not disappear during repeated annealings, and will provide an anchor point for the compass when we draw guidelines. Those should be in pencil, and will of course need to be redrawn after each heating. A line that marks the baseline, or the place where the bottom meets the walls, can be drawn with a divider.

Using this line as a guide, hammer the disk against a raising stake as shown in figure 6.11. This will locate the baseline and cause the walls of the beaker to start

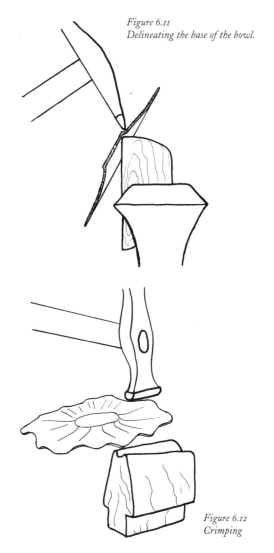

Figure 6.11
Delineating the base of the bowl.

Figure 6.12
Crimping

to rise up. The amount of height is not critical at this point. The purpose of this step is to create a work-hardened area that will prevent the bending of the next step from deforming the floor of the beaker.

The disk is held against the wooden valley stake and struck with a cross peen hammer to create radial folds, figure 6.12. These should be evenly spaced around the disk, and need not be very deep. Their purpose is to quickly pull the flat sheet up into a dish, from which raising will commence. If the floor has become warped during this process, it should be made flat again. Anneal, rinse, pickle and dry.

With the disk held firmly against the angled edge

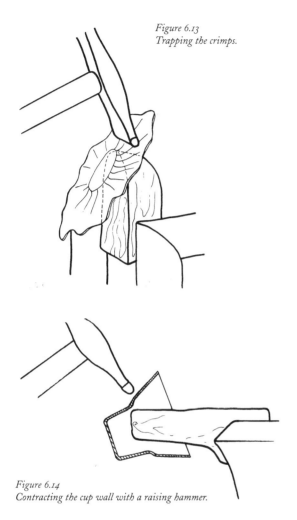

Figure 6.13
Trapping the crimps.

Figure 6.14
Contracting the cup wall with a raising hammer.

of a raising stake, each of the folds is methodically hammered down onto the stake, rotating the form and working from the baseline up. The first blows of each fold should fall on the top of the curve, or that section that was pressed most deeply into the valley stake. As mentioned before, work will become increasingly difficult as hammering proceeds up the walls toward the rim. Use slightly heavier blows to compensate.

Care must be taken that the folds are not accidentally hammered closed. This will stress the metal and almost certainly cause it to tear along the crease. If a fold starts to close up, which is usually the result of a misplaced hammer blow, interrupt the raising process immediately to correct the problem. It is sometimes

possible to open out a narrow fold by hammering on the inside of the form as it lays on a flat stake or anvil. If the fold is nearly closed up, it might be necessary to use the wedge of a narrow cross peen hammer, driving it into the fold with a mallet as you would drive a wedge into a log to split it. Follow any such repairs with annealing.

If the hammer blows are positioned exactly perpendicular to an imagined radial line, each course of blows will land exactly where the preceding blows fell. This causes tremendous stress on certain areas of the sheet. To prevent this, angle the hammer blows very slightly, tilting first to the right and then the left on successive courses. This will create a herringbone pattern of interlocking but not quite superimposed blows. In most cases the first course will reduce the folds but not make them completely disappear. Anneal the sheet and repeat the process just described, starting from the baseline again and proceeding to the rim, again directing first blows in each section to the highest point of the fold.

Continue in this manner, annealing after each course of raising. Subsequent courses will start slightly above the baseline. If the form starts to curve outward, taking on the shape of a trumpet, raise a course or two starting at the midpoint of the form and proceeding to the rim.

It is natural, particularly as arms and hands start to weary, to pay less attention to the angle and location of hammer blows. Don't. Proper raising is a straightforward matter of geometry that requires care with each blow. In every case, pay attention that the form is angled to provide a consistent "hollow" beneath the hammer, that the blow is falling vertically onto the stake, and that the hammer is firmly grasped so it doesn't spin out at the moment of contact. It is better to make a smaller number of careful blows than to pound on the form in a hit or miss fashion.

In this example a single generation of folds were made at the beginning of the process. Another method is to repeat the use of the valley stake a second time as soon as the first folds are smoothed away. Silversmiths who have mastered that technique maintain it is the quickest way to develop a deep

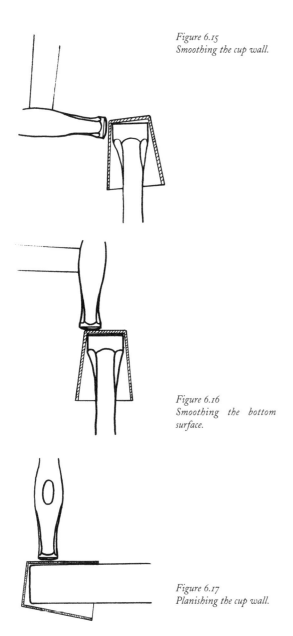

Figure 6.15
Smoothing the cup wall.

Figure 6.16
Smoothing the bottom surface.

Figure 6.17
Planishing the cup wall.

a general way, seeking out and correcting irregularities by stretching with a planishing hammer. It is usual at this stage that the hammer blows are widely spaced. Examine the form both by eye and by running your fingers along it in several directions. Test the form against the template.

Attention is next given to the corner where the walls of the beaker meet the floor. At this point the highly stressed walls meet the unstressed floor, creating a disparity in tension that makes the corner dangerously susceptible to splitting. No blows are struck directly on the corner, and those that are described below are relatively light compared to the planishing done elsewhere.

Mark the baseline one more time with a pencil compass, the original scribed line by now having disappeared through stretching. Set the beaker over a bottom stake as shown in figure 6.15 and strike a light pattern of blows about 2 mm below the baseline with a slightly crowned planishing hammer. Hold the beaker tightly against the stake.

Repeat the process on the floor as shown in figure 6.16, taking special care that the blows are light enough that they do not stretch the floor. This will cause the floor to bell outward and create a vessel that will not sit squarely on the table. It is a difficult problem to correct but an easy one to avoid: Go lightly!

In preparation for planishing the form is annealed and scrubbed with pumice powder. The shiny blows that will result from the polished hammer face show up dramatically against this matte surface. Position the beaker against a stake that closely matches the curve of the walls. Something as simple as a heavy steel pipe will suffice, as long as its surface has been sanded and polished smooth.

With a little practice you will develop the sensitive touch and rhythm that make planishing successful and enjoyable. Move lightly over the surface, overlapping blows and constantly examining the surface to insure a uniform effect. On a curved surface like this, using a crowned planishing hammer will create light-catching hollow facets; more blows will be needed because the meeting of two curved surfaces, hammer and beaker, allows for very little surface contact. It is

form. The second set of folds should be offset from the first to even out stresses.

Because forming has been done on wood rather than steel, the result at this stage is rough looking. When the form has reached its intended height, it is refined and smoothed on a steel stake, first with a wooden or plastic mallet, then in planishing where steel is used both inside and outside the form.

The first stage of finishing is to go over the form in

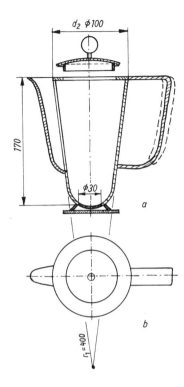

Figure 6.18
Calculations for a pot.
a) cross section, b) top view.

6.7
Making a Coffee Pot

After working though ideas as sketches, a technical drawing is made to actual size (figure 6.18). This will provide not only important measurements, but a consistent guide as work proceeds. From this, make a template in matte board. In the example being shown here, the body of the pot will be made from sterling sheet 0.8 mm thick (20 gauge B&S), cut into a fan shape and bent up to make a cone from which the final curvilinear form is developed (figure 6.19).

To develop the pattern for the cone, draw the profile of the cone to actual size. Extend the two sides by drawing lines with a ruler to find their point of intersection. Set the point of a compass at this point and adjust the pencil to fall on the top of the cone. Draw an arc. Reset the compass so the pencil falls on the lower edge of the cone and draw another arc.

To calculate the distance of this arc needed to make up the desired cone, consider that the end of the cone is a circle. The question then becomes, how much metal is needed to go around this circle? The pertinent formula is

$$C = \pi \cdot \text{diameter}$$

If the diameter of the large end of the cone is 100 mm, the distance needed along the arc is 314 mm. This is measured with a flexible ruler or a string and marked. The resulting point is then connected to the original center point with a ruled line. This piece, which does not include the original silhouette of the cone, is the pattern that will make a cone of the correct dimensions. This piece is cut from paper and checked, then transferred onto sterling sheet.

A conventional butt joint in which the two edges meet squarely against one another will not withstand the stress of the forming that will come later, so a special lap joint should be made. Hammer or file a tapering slope along a 10 mm strip of each edge of the fan-shaped piece. This will provide for generous overlap but because of the taper will not result in a bulge. The form will be bent into a cone and tied with binding

251

also possible to use a flat-faced planishing hammer, which will create a different but equally attractive faceted surface.

Go over the entire form two or three times, tapping lightly from baseline to rim each time. Avoid the temptation to overwork the corner. Additional work rarely improves the symmetry and risks splitting the vessel.

Mark off a line along the rim and file if necessary to make an even edge. Follow this with sanding, then planish the lip, holding the beaker in your hand. This process, called upsetting, will thicken the edge, making it more rigid and visually important. Finally, check that the beaker sits flat on the table. If it rocks slightly, invert the vessel on a sturdy table and tap the center of the bottom lightly with a round peen wooden or plastic mallet. Test the results frequently and stop as soon as the beaker rests on its outer edge.

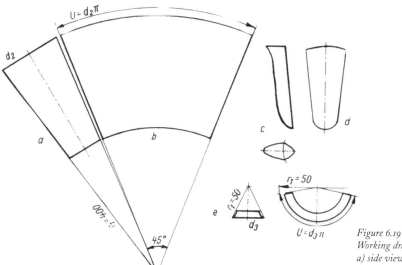

Figure 6.19
Working drawing for the pot.
a) side view of the vessel's body, b) pattern, c) side and
top view of the spout, d) front view of the spout, e)
pattern and side iew of the pot's base.

wire for soldering, but when it is cinched in this position the edges will have a tendency to slip over top of one another. To prevent this, saw a 5 mm line into the sloped section about 5 mm from each end. On one side of the cone, bend the small fingers of metal downward. On the opposite side bend the fingers upward. When the cone is formed around a mandrel, these two areas will engage and provide a lock to prevent the edges from slipping past each other.

Bend the form over a stake or mandrel and tap the raised fingers down with a mallet. Use heavy binding wire to tie the form closed, pulling the seam up tight with a Z-bend of the binding wire. Tying a cone is tricky at the best of times, and will be facilitated by having the assistance of a friend. Flux the joint well and solder it with a generous amount of hard solder. It is possible to solder parts of the seam, mallet the gaps closed and resolder, but it is best to complete the whole seam in a single operation.

After pickling, excess solder is filed and scraped away and the seam is lightly planished over a stake to create a uniform thickness. If necessary the form should be trued to a symmetrical round cone.

The smaller end of the cone will become the bottom of the pot, and is raised to create a pleasing curve and to reduce the size of the opening at this end of the pot. Work over a wooden stake, following the same procedures described for the last project (figure 6.20). It is important that the form remain symmetrical.

When the raising reaches an attractive curve, measure the opening and cut a disk of silver slightly larger. This is sunk in a wooden block to create a dome that will fit neatly over the bottom of the cone. File the edges of both pieces perfectly flat, then solder the two together. This completes the body of the pot, which can now be planished.

As described above, rub the form with pumice after pickling to create a matte surface that will show up the planishing marks clearly. Work over an appropriate steel stake with a polished planishing hammer to refine the form and create a uniform surface. As shown in figure 6.21, a mushroom stake is used to planish the bottom and blend the solder seam into the body of the piece. The walls of the pot are planished on a T-stake or similar tool that conforms to the curve of the cone (figure 6.22).

The next step is to design and fabricate the spout. The goal of this unit is to pour well, break the stream cleanly when pouring stops, and blend harmoniously into the form of the pot.

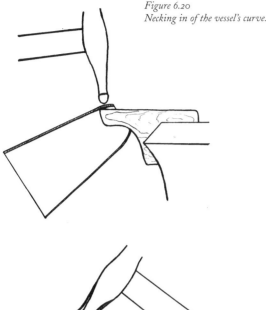

Figure 6.20
Necking in of the vessel's curve.

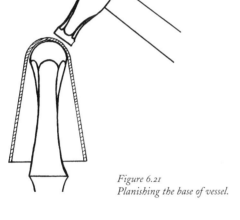

Figure 6.21
Planishing the base of vessel.

Figure 6.22
Planishing the wall of the vessel.

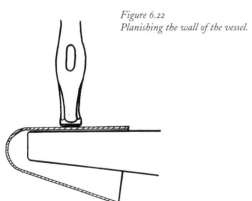

In this example, the spout is made of a single piece, the pattern for which is shown in figure 6.19d. This is cut out and formed with a mallet into a wooden groove, using other hammers or stakes as necessary to develop the form. Hold the spout up to the body of the pot periodically to check for attractive symmetry.

The spout will be positioned over the seam to camouflage it. File the edges of the spout as necessary to allow it to fit perfectly against the pot. This can be a tedious chore, but will be rewarded with an easy and attractive seam. With the completed spout held in position, draw an ink line around it on the pot. Drill and snip or saw a hole about 2 mm inside this line to open a hole for the spout.

Clean and flux the edges and set the spout into place, holding it there with binding wire. This is easier to write about than to achieve, but use a heavy wire and some ingenuity to configure an arrangement that will grasp both the spout and the pot.

Place a generous number of solder chips on the two millimeter ledge that lies inside the spout and heat the entire unit with a powerful flame. Be careful not to set solder on the outside of the pot where it risks flowing into the planishing marks. Such solder spills will not only be tedious to remove, but will destroy the continuity of the planished surface. After pickling the rim can be removed with files, burrs and rifflers.

The top of the pot is closed with a decking sheet that will be soldered on the top of the cone. Before doing that, cut out a circle and fit it with a rim that will be on the inside of the pot. This will provide a better seating for the lid and makes the whole pot appear more substantial. Bend up a ring into a bracelet-like form and solder it to what will be the underside of the top plate. If this piece is slightly conical, the effect is improved. When this is done and smoothed with files, the unit is soldered onto the top of the pot.

Make a lid by slightly doming a disk and fitting it with a ring that fits neatly into the collar just mentioned. Mount an appropriate knob on the top of the lid with a silver rivet.

The handle of the pot is made from a strip of silver 3 mm thick and 25 mm wide, curved around and soldered on. Decorative wooden pieces are carved to attach to this, adding heft, contrast and heat insulation to the handle. Shape the wood so as to blend into the design and attach with silver rivets. Compete the pot by polishing it with a brass brush then heating and pickling it several times to bring up the fine silver finish. A final brass brushing is used to create a warm luster.

6.8
Making a Bellied Container

This shape builds on the previous exercise, and uses several techniques described there. The curvilinear form could be raised from a disk, but the work will go much faster if it is derived from a cone. As before, a pattern is generated from a drawing of the profile of the pot. In this case, first draw the curved vessel, then superimpose over it a cone that falls on the mean form that divides about in half the amount of expansion and contraction. This is shown in figure 6.23, and illustrates that for the belly of the pot, the cone will be stretched, while at the neck the cone will be pressed inward.

As before, prepare a lap joint by hammering and filing a sloping edge on each side of the cone blank. Use small tabs near each end to catch the edges from slipping past each other when the cone is wired up for soldering. Planish the soldered seam to make it flush and the same thickness as the rest of the pot, then use a permanent marker to draw a line around the cone at the points of greatest curvature, both inward and outward. Continue to refer to these reference points throughout the forming of the piece.

As was seen in the previous example, the position of the metal on the stake and the location of the hammer blow are critical – that's what makes raising work. Because metal is not transparent, it is of course impossible to see the location of the supporting stake, so we use our ears instead. In every case, raising requires that the hammer fall on an unsupported section that is near a supported section that acts as fulcrum. A proper raising blow will always sound hollow. To locate the point where the metal is in contact

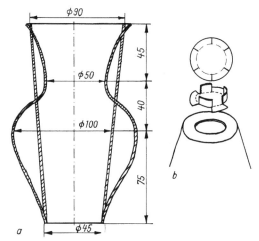

Figure 6.23
Wide bellied vessel.
a) simplified sectional view, b) base plate with folded sides.

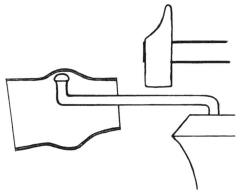

Figure 6.24
Hammering out the bulge.

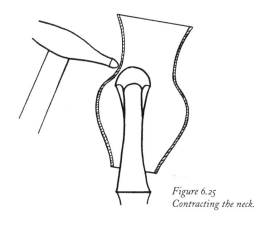

Figure 6.25
Contracting the neck.

with the stake, tap the hammer lightly until you find a place of solid contact.

Because a hammer cannot reach into the inside of the cone to pound the curve outward, an ingenious tool called a snarling iron is used. This steel tool, shown in figure 6.24, is mounted in a strong vise and struck a heavy blow along its midsection. The recoiling action of the springy tip of the iron is used to mimic a hammer blow from inside by holding the cone firmly over the stake. Each blow will show a bulge indicating the location of the tip of the iron. Work with this tool around the surface, stopping to anneal after each course and continuing until a check of the template reveals that sufficient pounding out has occurred. This process usually results in a lumpy surface that is smoothed and refined over stakes with an appropriate curve.

As seen in figure 6.25, the neck of the pot is compressed over a narrow stake with a cross peen hammer. Guidelines may be drawn with pencil to help keep the raising symmetrical. Here again, the critical thing is to strike the metal just above the point of contact where the metal is unsupported. It might require several courses to close the neck to the proper dimension, annealing between each one.

When the form is pleasing, it can be planished as described above. To attach the bottom, raise a 5 mm lip inward and planish it to make a crisp corner. Cut a disk of metal just slightly smaller than the bottom and notch it as shown in figure 6.23 to create an even number of tabs. Bend up every other one of these to a right angle and insert the disk into the pot. The flat tabs will be on the inside of the lip and the other will show on the outside. Press the tabs with a mallet, then hammer them down firmly with a steel hammer working over a bottom stake. Flux generously and solder, then planish again, stretching the bottom slightly to make it rigid.

6.9
Goldsmithing Forming Work

As the following examples illustrate, the skills of silversmithing have many applications in the jewelry scale of a goldsmith. It is for this reason that every metalworker should develop at least a general understanding of raising and sinking, because they will help him in a variety of ways. These exercises are simple, but begin to point out the relevance of silversmithing to all kinds of sheet metal deformation.

Hemispherical button
This very simple and versatile element is made in a dapping block, shown in figure 6.26 and is analogous to the sinking process described at the beginning of this chapter. As shown, dapping dies are available in two forms: as a cube with hemispherical depressions on all sides, or as a thick sheet of steel with all the depressions on one side. In both cases, a set of ball-ended steel punches completes the set. Dapping tools are expensive but with care will last unchanged for many years. To preserve the tool, protect it from moisture so it won't rust and use the tool only for its intended purpose.

Set an annealed disk into a cavity that is a little larger than its diameter. That is, the disk should fit down inside the depression. Select the dapping punch that makes a perfect fit in that particular hole and strike it a firm blow with a coarse-faced hammer. Do not use a planishing hammer, because its face will be scarred by the steel punch. Be careful that you do not use a punch that is too large for a depression: this will make a nasty gouge on the punch.

There is no need to continue hammering once a solid sound is heard. The metal is now resting on the dapping punch and has no where else to go! Move the dome to a smaller depression and repeat the process, always shifting to the appropriate punch, until the intended form is created.

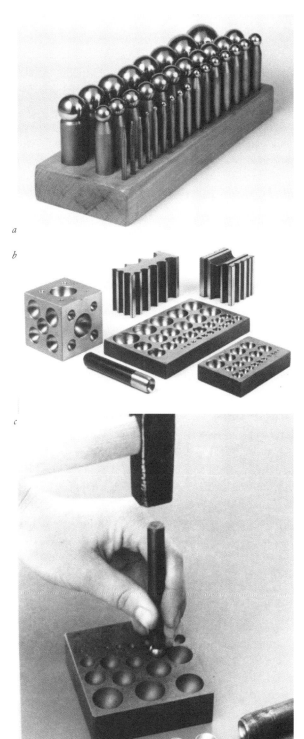

a

b

c

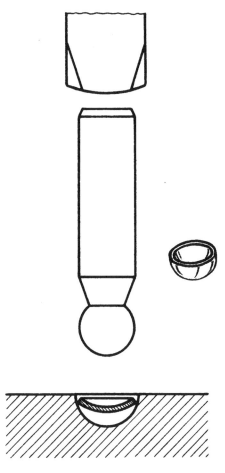

Figure 6.27
Making a hemisphere in
the dapping block.

Figure 6.26
Sinking with round dapping punches and dapping die.
a) a set of ball punches, b) different dapping dies, c) sinking in the
dapping block.

Figure 6.28
Raising on a dapping punch with the goldsmiths hammer.

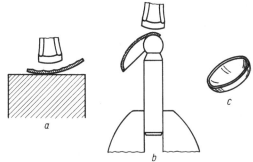

Figure 6.29
Making an oval bowl on the dapping punch.

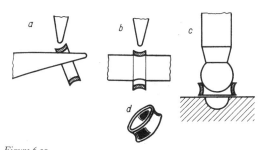

Figure 6.30
Making a concave marriage band.
a) forming with the raising hammer on the anvil's horn, b) further hammering out of the concave band, c) stretching the concavity, d) finished ring.

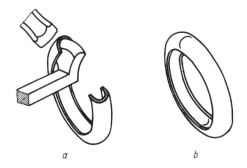

Figure 6.31
Making a raised convex bracelet.
a) forming the convexity of the bracelet on th stake, b) finished bracelet.

Oval hollow dish

As useful as it is, dapping is restricted to circles. In this similar case, an oval of sheet metal is pounded into a hollowed (or volumetric) form. This might be described as a miniature oval bowl.

After cutting out the piece and smoothing its edges, the form can be generated by stretching as described in the first section of this chapter. In this case, hold the oval on an anvil or similar flat surface and strike a spiraling series of blows with a ball peen hammer, starting in the center and moving outward, figure 6.29a. Decrease the force of the blows as you proceed, ending with only a light tapping near the rim. This process may be repeated several times, or reworked with a smaller peen, to deepen the curve.

An alternate way is to work the flat oval into a wooden depression carved for this purpose. Use a ball peen hammer (or dapping punches) to drive the metal into the wood, in this case working from the perimeter toward the center. It is natural for the form to curl upward along its longer axis; simply invert the form on the benchtop and press down on it to straighten it out. As with the other method, this process can be repeated several times to create a deep hollow. The outer rim can be given additional curva-

ture by working it in a raising operation over a dapping punch secured in a vise. This is shown in figures
6.28 and 6.29b.

High domed ring
This shape has uses as a finger ring, but is sometimes
also needed as a component for a vessel or other
object. Start with a simple band ring, making certain
it is well soldered at its joint. As shown in figure
6.30a, angle the ring on a mandrel and tap it with a
cross peen hammer as it is rotated. Reverse the ring
and repeat the process, alternating from one side to
the other until the form is complete.

If several pieces like this were needed, it might be
worthwhile to carve or turn a groove into a steel or
plastic rod as illustrated in figure 6.30b. This would
make the process much faster.

In either case, the contour can be pushed a little
further with a dapping punch as shown, working first
on one side and then the other. Set the ring over a
depression in the dapping die to insure that the tip of
the punch is not flattened by accidentally striking a
hard surface.

Convex domed bracelet
As in the previous exercise, a strip of metal is bent
into a circle and soldered. It is then laid into a V-
groove in a wooden or plastic form and struck near its
edge with a narrow cross peen hammer or mallet,
moving around the entire form. The bracelet is rotated and an identical series of blows is struck, again just
inside the rim. The piece is annealed and the process
repeated, taking care that the hammer strikes are
neatly spaced and of consistent force. The bracelet is
planished over a stake as shown in figure 6.31.

Hollow h-ring (bishop's ring)
This ring (figure 6.32) is developed from a pattern
roughly like the one shown in figure 6.32a. The overall length will determine the size of the ring, and the
distance of the arc at the extreme left and right will
combine to make the circle or oval of the top. It is
usual to cut a pattern of paper to double check
dimensions before cutting out sheet metal.

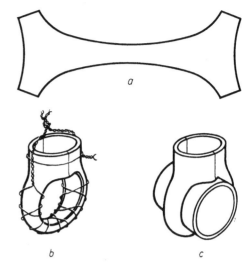

Figure 6.32
Making a hollow constructed ring.
a) the sheet metal blank, b) finished outer form prepared for soldering,
c) preparation for finishing.

258

Scribe axis lines down the center of the form as reference points during forming. Start by bending the two halves that will make up the top of the ring in a wooden form, using a cross peen mallet. As the ring starts to curl up, move to a V-groove in a wooden block (or work on pitch) and strike the ring shank with small dapping punches to make it rounded. Continue bending and shaping all sections until the ring form comes together. File or saw the seams to make them fit perfectly, and tie the unit closed with binding wire, as in figure 6.32b. The inside of the ring is decked with a tightly fitting tube, shown in 6.32c, that is soldered into the ring and then cut off.

Closed hollow ring
This unusual ring, (figure 6.33), takes full advantage of silversmithing techniques, though the small scale might disguise the fact the most of the ring is made by raising. Start with a pattern like the one shown in figure 6.33a, in which the narrowest section is roughly three times the width of the intended shank. In the example shown, the depression for the pearl seat is made by hammering the center of the blank into pitch with a dapping punch.

To form the ring, the blank is held against a wooden groove and tapped with a small hammer in the same way described for the convex domed bracelet above. This will simultaneously dome the shank and curl the blank into a ring. Continue in this way rotating the ring and using whatever small punches can be found until the ring brings itself up to a complete circle. Refine the seam and solder the ring closed.

After pickling and drying, continue to tap lightly against the ring as it rests either on a curved surface, either of wood or steel. In this way the shank will eventually be pulled up to a closed tube, which is then filed to perfect the form.

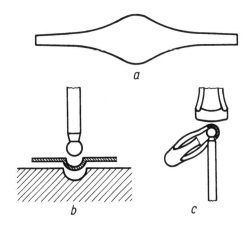

Figure 6.33
Making a hollow consructed ring.
a) sheet metal blank, b) sinking the middle portion, c) pulling in the shank over the dapping punches.

CHAPTER SEVEN

Machine Tools

7.1
Functional Principle of the Press

A die forming press is used for blanking, cutting and forming processes that have use in the small studio but are particularly important for large volume production of components from sheet. There are many types of presses, but each will have some sort of frame, drive (motor or crank), toolholder and guides.

Specific detailed information about individual presses will be found in the instruction manuals that come with the machines and in specialized literature, to which the reader is sent for additional help. For our general explanations here, a few typical examples will convey the sense of the process.

Every press suffers a loss of force because of friction of its parts. In other words, the theoretical force developed by the press is diminished by the time it gets through to the tool. The phenomenon is particularly evident in the single spindle press, where the degree of effectiveness (η) is only

$$\eta = \frac{W_{AE}}{W_{AI}} = 0.2...0.6$$

W_{AE} - effective working capacity
W_{AI} - induced working capacity

To simplify the following explanations we will ignore this loss of effectiveness, though in industrial applications, in the process of determining what can be expected of each machine, it would be calculated with the following formula

$$W_{AE} = W_{AI} \cdot \eta$$

7.1.1 DROP PRESS

This basic machine (figure 7.2) which causes a weight to be dropped onto a workpiece has been a standard tool in the industrial workplace for the last 200 years, and continues to be an important tool in metalworking. In its most basic operation, a conforming die is made of a rigid material, typically hardened steel. The negative component is attached to the bed or anvil of the press and the positive is fixed into the ram, or the part that travels.

The ram is pulled up with a pulley, traveling along guide rails that insure a consistent and controlled path when it is dropped. A piece of annealed metal is set into position in the die and the ram is released.

The advantages of the drop press are in its simplicity, both in construction and operation. Disadvantages are that the weight of the ram (therefore the power of the press) is limited to what can be pulled up with the pulley. Also, the guides offer only limited precision, and the work time is relatively slow.

Because it is so elementary, the drop press provides a useful example to illustrate the physics of this category of machine. The following description refers to

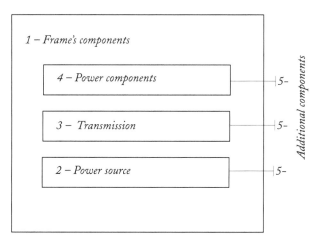

Figure 7.1
Construction of presses.

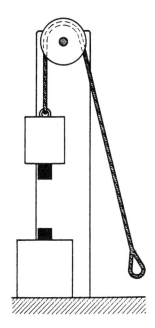

Figure 7.2
Drop hammer.

figure 7.3, which should be consulted to understand the following definitions:

Mass of the ram m = 20 kg
Starting height h_1 = 2 meters
A bump of h_3 = 5 mm height is to be pushed out of a sheet with the forming die.

How large is the effective press force F_P for this?
If the ram is drawn up high to the starting position with muscle power (1→2), the work used for this is transferred over to the system and is stored as potential energy (2).

$$E_{pot2} = F_G \cdot h_1 = m \cdot g \cdot h_1$$
$$= 20 \cdot 9.81 \cdot 2\text{Nm} = \underline{392.4\text{Nm} = 392.4\text{J}}$$

E_{pot2} – potential energy in Nm
F_G – force of gravity in N
h_1 – height drawn to in m

If the ram is released from this starting position (2) it falls onto the sheet to be shaped (2 → 3). Upon striking (3) the mass of the ram m has covered the distance of the height of the fall h_2, achieved the speed v, thereby creating the kinetic energy E_{kin3}.

$$E_{kin3} = \frac{m}{2} v^2 = m \cdot g \cdot h_2$$
$$= 20 \cdot 9.81 \cdot 1.995\text{Nm} = \underline{391.42\text{J}}$$

E_{kin3} – kinetic energy upon impact in Nm
m – weight of the ram in kg
v – speed on impact in m/s
h_2 – height of the fall in m

This kinetic energy – the force of the descending ram – gives rise to the working capacity W_A which is used to overcome the resistance to deformation of the sheet in the 5 mm long working traverse h_3 (3 → 4).

$$E_{kin3} = W_A = F_P \cdot h_3$$

W_A – working capacity in Nm
F_P – effective press force in N
h_3 – working traverse of deformation in m

In the deformation phase, the ram has to cover the working distance h_3 and the kinetic energy required for this is produced from the following sum:

$$F_P = \frac{W_A}{h_3} = \frac{391.42}{0.005} = \underline{78\,300\text{ N or }78.3\text{ kN}}$$

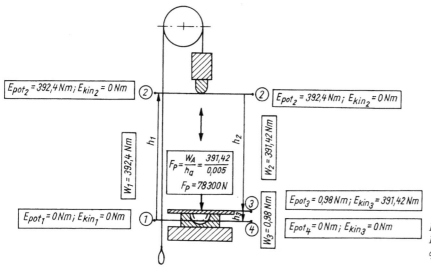

Figure 7.3
Energy, work and compression power
of the drop hammer.

According to this the available press force for deformation is:

$$W_{kin3} = E_{pot2} - W_{kin2} = (392.4 - 391.42)Nm$$
$$= 0.98 \, Nm$$

or, for example from the conditions

$$W_{kin3} = m \cdot g \cdot h_3 = 20 \cdot 9.81 \cdot 0.005$$
$$= 0.98 \, Nm$$

According to the formula for the conservation of energy, the entire potential energy E_{pot2} must be used up when the ram has reached its resting position (4) after the end of the deformation.

$$E_{pot2} = W_A + W_{kin3}$$
$$m \cdot g \cdot h_1 = F_P \cdot h_3 + m \cdot g \cdot h_3$$
$$392.4 \, Nm = 391.42 \, Nm + 0.98 \, Nm$$

Normally the working capacity produced by the press is completely converted for overcoming the resistance to deformation of the material. That is to say, all the power of the press is spent on pounding the sheet metal into the die.

If W_A is too small, the bulge is not completely pushed out: a second blow of the ram might be necessary to press the metal fully into the die. On the other hand it is also possible that W_A is too large, and is therefore not completely used up in the deforming process. This excess of energy is absorbed by the tool, damaging and possibly destroying it. It is obviously important to understand the forces involved in order to deliver the correct amount of force, for instance by reducing the height of the drop.

This smaller working traverse, h_3, will reduce the force of the ram and result in a greater effective press force F_P as illustrated by the formula

$$h_3 \to 0; \; : F_P \to \infty$$

This dangerous relationship, charted in figure 7.4, must be watched for with all presses!

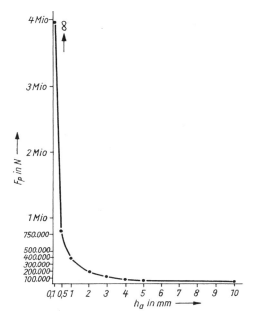

Figure 7.4
Relationship between the press power and the work distane.

7.1.2 FOOT OPERATED PRESS

This popular press (figures 7.5 and 7.6) uses the pressure of a foot on a pedal to force a ram into a vertical descent. Like the drop press, this has the advantage of being easy to build and modify, but has several disadvantages. The amount of force that can be delivered is modest, and extended use of the press leads to fatigue. The monotony of the action, in which the foot presses and lifts while the hands insert a workpiece into the die, can lead to accidents unless workers take frequent breaks to relieve the tedium.

In practice, the pressure of the foot against the pedal is transferred to the long arm of the foot lever, which carries the kinetic energy F_B into the ram. According to the law of leverage the force of the foot is increased depending upon the transfer relationship of the lever.

Figure 7.5
Foot operated press.

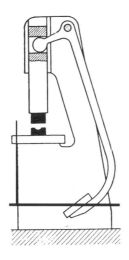

Figure 7.6
Foot operated press.
F_N = 40MN
H = 70mm,
h = 1300 mm
(Pressenwerk
Morgenrothe-
Rautenkranz).

$$F_F \cdot l_1 = F_B \cdot l_2 \ \text{bzw} \ \cdot \frac{F_F}{F_B} = \frac{l_2}{l_1}$$

F_F – foot power in N
F_B – kinetic energy in N
l_1 – long lever arm
l_2 – short lever arm

The ram is set into an accelerated motion by the kinetic energy, so that it reaches the speed V and kinetic energy E_{kin} – which is again the same as the working capacity W_A – upon impact with the work.

This produces the relationship

$$E_{kin} = W_A$$

$$F_B \cdot h_2 = F_P \cdot h_B$$

The ram in a kick press slides along a stable path, making the machine appropriate for cutting operations (also called blanking), in which precise alignment of the die parts is critical. Because the working traverse is the same as the thickness of the sheet being cut, a great cutting force is obtained.

Example
What foot power (F_F) is necessary if a round disc (d = 50 mm) is to be cut from a 1 mm thick sheet (CuZn 37; σ_B (tensile strength) = 290 N/mm²)?

l_1 = 1500 mm
l_2 = 200 mm
h = 100 mm

At the foot pedal it is

$$F_F \cdot l_1 = F_B \cdot l_2 \qquad (1)$$

As the ram descends kinetic energy develops which is used as working capacity

$$F_B \cdot h_2 = F_P \cdot h_A \qquad (2)$$

The press force F_P is used as cutting force F_S for separating the material.

$$F_P = F_S = d \cdot \pi \cdot s \cdot \sigma_B \qquad (3)$$

To answer the question (1) is converted as F_F, then (2) is converted as F_B and is inserted in (1):

$$F_F = \frac{l_2 \cdot F_F}{l_1} \quad (1) \qquad F_B = \frac{F_F \cdot h_A}{h_2} \quad (2)$$

$$F_F = \frac{l_2 \cdot h_A \cdot F_P}{l_1 \cdot h_{2V}}$$

Now (3) is inserted for F_P

$$F_F = \frac{l_2 \cdot h_A \cdot d \cdot \pi \cdot s \cdot \sigma_B}{l_1 \cdot h_2}$$

$$F_F = \frac{200 \cdot 1 \cdot 50 \cdot 3.14 \cdot 1 \cdot 290}{1500 \cdot 99} \, N = \underline{61.3 \, N}$$

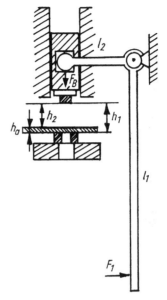

Figure 7.7
Action of the foot lever press.

$$E_{rot} = 2\frac{m}{2} \cdot v^2_U = 2\frac{m}{2} \cdot w^2 \cdot r^2$$

and because $\quad w = \frac{\pi \cdot n}{30} \quad$ then

$$E_{rot} = m \left(\frac{\pi \cdot n \cdot r}{30} \right)^2 = \underline{1.1 \cdot 10^{-2} \, m \cdot n^2 \cdot r^2}$$

This rotational energy is transformed through the spindle into kinetic energy E_{kin} which moves the ram. When the tool makes contact with the workpiece it has working capacity wA, which is used to deform the metal. As before, this force should be calculated to be exactly the force needed for this material and this deformation. If too much force is delivered it will damage the dies and the press.

Advantages of the spindle press
- Because of the secure dovetailed guide of the tool carrier, alignment of dies is precise.
- As above, this press can operate at a short working distance, and therefore is capable of delivering tremendous force. This means, for instance, that a relatively small amount of effort is needed to cut thick material.

7.1.3 SCREW PRESS OR HAND SPINDLE PRESS

The central unit of this simple device is a threaded rod that passes through a stout frame, figures 7.8 and 7.9. The familiar C-clamp is a variation on a screw press. In the case of a table mounted press or larger model, additional force in turning the screw is provided by a pair of weights mounted on opposite ends of a horizontal bar at the top of the screw, which is the ram.

The rotating weights are set in motion by hand. They could be described as two points of mass that move about the point of rotation at the distance r with the circumferential speed v_U. The effect of this is that the two masses develop the rotational energy.

$$\frac{E_{rot}}{2} = \frac{m}{2} \cdot v^2_U = \frac{m}{2} \cdot w^2 \cdot r^2$$

E_{rot} – rotational energy in Nm
m – rotating mass in kg
v_U – circumferential speed in m/s
w – angular velocity in s^{-1}
r – rotations radius in m
n – revolutions per minute in min^{-1}

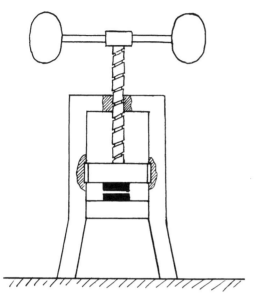

Figure 7.8
Rotary hand press showing only the most important parts.

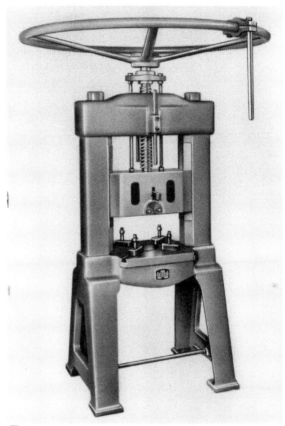

Figure 7.9
Dual standing rotary hand press.
F = 250 MN, H = 250 mm, h= 2150 mm (Pressenwerk Morgenrothe-Rautenkranz).

- When deep drawing, this press delivers consistent force over a long path. That is, the threaded spindle delivers the same amount of force after making contact as it does at the moment of contact. This is not the case with the kick press described earlier.
- The spindle press is a versatile machine, suitable for blanking, deep drawing, stamping, bending, pressing, flattening and so on.

Frictional spindle presses
This is a variation (figures 7.10 and 7.11) on the screw press just described with the important distinction that in this family of machines hand power is replaced with force supplied by an electric motor. The same rules of physics and leverage are applied, with the result that significant forces can be developed. For this reason it is critical that these presses be well constructed of heavy duty materials. Where the presses described above are used primarily to form small units and components, these presses can be used to cut out and deform entire pieces of flatware.

An electric motor is mounted on the top of the machine and engaged to alternately lower or raise a threaded spindle. To achieve this with a motor that is turning in single direction, the motor turns a horizontal axle on which are mounted two wheels, looking somewhat like a barbell (figure 7.10). This axle can be slid left and right, and is slightly longer than the large flat wheel that connects to the threaded ram. With the axle in one position, the vertical motor-driven wheel is put into contact with the leather covered outer edge of the large wheel, causing it to screw downward. When the metal has been deformed, the axle is shifted and the same motor rotation unscrews the ram, lifting it so the workpiece can be removed from the die.

267

Seen in physical terms it is a "rotating mass" and takes up the energy E_{rot} :

$$E_{rot} = \frac{I \cdot w^2}{2}$$

Because of its geometric shape the drive plate has the inertial moment:

$$I = \frac{m}{2} r^2$$

The angular velocity is obtained from:

$$w = \frac{\pi \cdot n}{30}$$

So the rotational energy in the case at hand is:

E_{rot} − rotational energy in Nm

$$E_{rot} = \frac{m \cdot r^2 \cdot \pi^2 \cdot n^2}{2 \cdot 2 \cdot 30^2} = \frac{m \cdot r^2 \cdot \pi^2 \cdot n^2}{3600}$$

I − inertial movement in kgm²
w − angular velocity in s^{-1}
m − mass in kg
n − revolution per minute
r − radius in meters

If the ram strikes the material, the rotational energy E_{rot} stored in the drive plate as working capacity W_A which has to be used up for deformation upon the working traverse h_A.

Example
The drive plate of a friction screw press has a mass of 200 kilograms and a radius of one meter, (m = 200 kg, r = 1 m). When striking onto the material it achieves a revolution count n = 150 min⁻¹. How great is the working capacity?

How much press force is available for blanking from a 2 mm thick sheet?

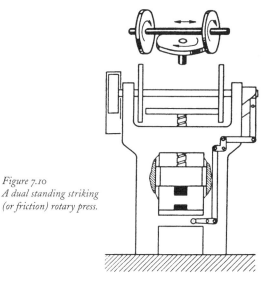

Figure 7.10
A dual standing striking
(or friction) rotary press.

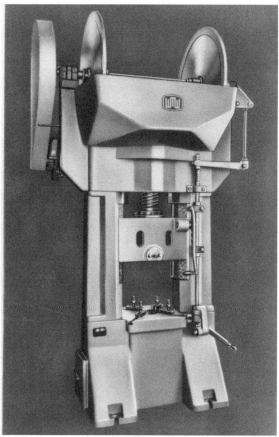

Figure 7.11
A dual standing striking rotary press.
E = 630 MN, H = 224mm, h = 2800mm. (Pressenwerk Morgenrothe-Rautenkranz)

$$E_{\text{rot}} = W_A = \frac{m \cdot r^2 \cdot \pi^2 \cdot n^2}{3600}$$

$$= \frac{200 \cdot 1^2 \cdot 3.14^2 \cdot 150^2}{3600} \text{ N} = \underline{12.325 \text{ Nm}}$$

The following features characterize the friction screw press:

$$F_P = \frac{W_A}{h_A} = \frac{12.325}{0.002} = 6,162,500 \text{ N} = \underline{6,162.5 \text{ kN}}$$

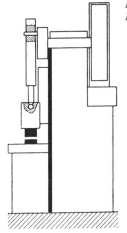

Figure 7.12
Eccentric press.

- The high working capacity produces a very high press force in a short working traverse.
- The degree of the force can be influenced by changing the forming time, so that the allowable nominal load of the press is not exceeded.
- The press works relatively slowly; if the outer zone of the drive wheel is used it then results in a higher acceleration.
- This is the reason that such presses are suitable for heavy blanking, stamping and similar press work. The slow pressure is useful when pressing but especially lends itself to deep drawing.

7.1.4 ECCENTRIC CAM PRESSES

In this family of presses, a shaft is mounted at the edge of a wheel that is turned by an electric motor, shown in figures 7.12 and 7.13. This eccentric, or off-center pivot lifts the rod then presses it down, an action that is converted to a vertical path by attaching the other end of the rod to a carrier running in a guide. The configuration is identical to the cylinders in an internal combustion engine, except in that case the cylinders create the force, which is transferred to the wheel. Here the wheel has the force (from an electric motor), which is transferred to a piston, or ram, traveling in a vertical path.

The uniform rotational movement of the eccentric shaft is translated into an accelerated lifting movement of the ram. That is, the motor runs at a consistent speed, but the ram is lifted and lowered at a rate affected by the position of the rod at its particular

Figure 7.13
Single standing eccentric press. Partial view with the cover of the puncher open. F = 160MN, H = 4...60 mm, hges = 1700 mm, stroke number 110 min⁻¹.

269

moment during that rotation of the wheel. There is a point when the rod is at its maximum extension and its deepest thrust. The latter is shown in the right-hand drawing of figure 7.15.

These could be called 0° and 180° respectively, and are the dead points of the ram: the lifting motion reverses and at this moment the lifting speed is zero. Halfway between these dead points the lifting speed of the ram passes through its middle position, 90° and 270° respectively, at which point it achieves maximum speed (figure 7.14).

The eccentric shaft is affected by the constant torsional moment

$$M_\mathrm{d} = F_\mathrm{T} \cdot r = F_\mathrm{T} \cdot \frac{H}{2}$$

M_d — torsional moment in Nm
r — radius in m
F_T — tangential force at the on the eccentric in N
H — lifting height of the ram in m

The constant tangential force FT produces the relationship between the momentary position of the eccentric stud − expressed with the crank angle − the respectively effective press force FP. Because the push rods are usually significantly longer than the radius of the wheel shaft, its deviation from the vertical is so small it can be ignored. This allows us the following simple formula to determine press force.

$$F_\mathrm{P} = \frac{F_\mathrm{T}}{\sin \alpha}$$

Figure 7.15 illustrates how the tangential force F_T is transformed through the pushing force F into the actual effective press force F_P. The eccentric stud is $\alpha = 90°$ at the horizontal position and because sin 90° = 1 is applicable.

$$F_\mathrm{P} = \frac{F_\mathrm{T}}{1}$$

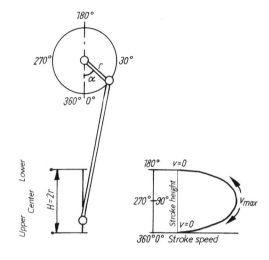

Figure 7.14
Operating method of the piston mechanism.

$$F_\mathrm{P} = \frac{F_\mathrm{T}}{\sin \alpha}$$

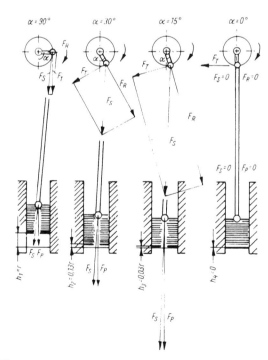

Figure 7.15
Translation of tangental power by way of the piston into compress force.

The tangential force F_T and the press force F_P are equally large at this position. At the dead point position $\alpha = 0$, that is $\sin \alpha = 0$ applies.

With the nearing of the dead point, the press force achieves unacceptably high values, endangering the tool and the machine (figure 7.16). Therefore eccentric presses typically accept as the maximum allowable press force:

$$F_{PN} = 2\,F_T$$

The correct degree of angle for the position of the eccentric pivot is determined according to this formula:

$$F_P = \frac{F_T}{0} = \infty$$

As a result of this the ram of the hub may only be used in the zone $\alpha = \sin 90° - 30°$. Each press will be accompanied by an instruction manual that will describe the proper set up for specific conditions.

$$\frac{F_T}{F_{PN}} = \frac{1}{2} = \sin \alpha \quad \text{that is} \quad \alpha_N = 30°$$

In practice the height of the wheel or the location of the table can be adjusted as required for a specific job. In addition, the pivot point of the push rod on the drive wheel is sometimes adjustable; this will affect the length of the stroke, which will become shorter as the attachment point moves toward the center of the wheel.

7.1.5 OTHER STYLES OF ECCENTRIC PRESSES

The *open front eccentric press* offers access to its table from all sides and provides a table whose height is easily adjustable. Among its drawbacks is the fact that this type of press can only be used for light work because the ram is guided only on one side and the eccentric is only attached at one side.

The *double sided eccentric press* offers a secure column guide, the eccentric is supported on both sides but the table can only be got at from one side.

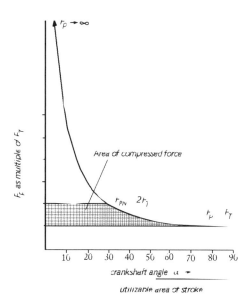

Figure 7.16
Dependency relationship of the compressive force on the angle of the crankshaft.

The *automatic columnar punch press* (figure 7.17) has its drive mounted below the table. The drive moment is conducted by the crankshaft further over the connecting rod and they traverse onto the four guide columns of the ram punch. This permits steady operation of the machine despite the great speed of the ram, whereby the ram is kept in its optimal position by the four columns. As shown in the illustration, feed and take-up wheels send a strip for blanking automatically through the dies.

7.1.6 THE HYDRAULIC PRESS

The hydraulic press is fundamentally different from the mechanical presses described above, not only in the way it works, but also because of its unique applications. A familiar application of a hydraulic press is the car jack used in service stations, which is illustrated in figure 7.19 and described below.

Force, that we'll identify as F_I, is introduced and affects the piston surface A_{K1} – the surface of the press piston K_I which is in this way pressed down against a fluid; valve V_I shuts itself while V_2 opens.

Figure 7.17
Automated punching press.
E = 25 MN, H = 6 mm, h$_{ges}$ = 1300 mm. (Pressenwerk Morgenrothe-Rautenkranz)

The drive force (F_I) moves the pump piston (K_I) on the path (h_1). This action causes a specific amount of fluid to be displaced. Because it cannot spread out in any other way, this force is transmitted to the surface of the working piston (A_{K1}) and moves it on the working path h_1.

$$F_2 = \frac{A_{K2}}{A_{K1}} \cdot F_I = \frac{h_1}{h_2} \cdot F_I$$

The piston surface and the height of the ram are in a reversed relationship, so a relatively small initial force acting upon a small piston surface, transmitted over a relatively long path is transformed into a large press force with a short stroke at the large piston:
If the piston K_1 is withdrawn (i.e. if the handle is lifted), the position of the valve labeled V_2 remains unchanged. Valve V_1 opens and new fluid is sucked out of the reserve container, allowing the same action to be repeated, with the effect of raising the piston K_2 further. The result of all this is that repeated up and down motions of the lever at F$_I$ result in a lift motion at F_2 that has much more force than what was originally put into the system. A child can lift a car!

When the piston has been raised high enough, the valve labeled V_3 is opened, allowing the fluid to flow

Figure 7.18
Hydraulic single standing press.
F = 100 MN, H = 250 mm, h$_{ges}$ = 220 mm.

into the reserve container and releasing the piston to return to its lowered position.

This basic arrangement can be designed to accommodate various needs. If an electric motor is being used, it is connected to a pump that converts the power of the motor to a hydraulic system (i.e. a pump) which then drives the press. An alternate design is shown in figure 7.20.

In small shops, simple presses use hand pressure to deliver force to the hydraulic press. In industrial

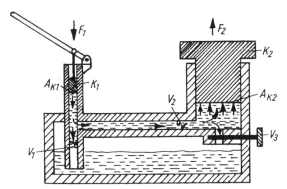

Figure 7.19
Principle of hydraulic force transmission.

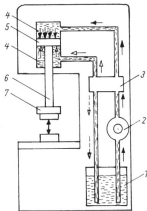

Figure 7.20
Hydraulic press.
1) resevoir
2) hydraulic motor
3) regulators
4) pressure container
5) pressure piston
6) press rod
7) punch

applications, this power is delivered by rotary hydraulic motors that create continuous fluid pressure that are arranged to both lower and raise the piston.

The hydraulic press has several advantages:

- The speed, height, length and number of each stroke can be easily changed and set.
- The full nominal press force is available in all lifting zones.
- The press is not sensitive to overloading.

Disadvantages of the press are that the absence of a flywheel requires a heavier pump than might be needed in an alternate press, and the relatively slow speed of operation, which makes the hydraulic press unsuitable for most blanking and cutting operations.

7.2
Cutting and Blanking

7.2.1 TERMS
We'll use the word "cutting" to describe the chipless separation of metals and nonmetals. There are at least three categories of cutting, diagrammed in figure 7.21.

a) *Shearing.* Two jaws of a shear create a sharp angle and create a localized pressure that exceeds the strength of the material, tearing it apart along the line of the blade. Examples include scissors, shears and similar tools with angled sides.

b) *Knife edge cutting.* In this case the cutting action results from a sharp edge on just one side of the action, for instance as the piece lies upon a solid flat surface as shown here. Examples would include cutting dies and chisels.

c) *Parallel shears.* In this situation, a pair of cutting surfaces with parallel faces are pressed closely alongside each other, trapping the material between them and tearing it in a motion similar to the shearing described in (a). This is a common method in blanking tools.

The last mentioned arrangement is of greatest importance in manufacturing because of its wide application. Dies of appropriate size and shape can be mounted into presses that squeeze the parts together. There are several advantages in this system:

- It is efficient, using a single press to accommodate a variety of parts.
- Parts are consistently identical.
- The system allows very close tolerances.
- This kind of blanking lends itself to automation, yielding great productivity and safety.

The primary disadvantage of blanking dies is their initial high cost, which limits their use to high volume production runs through which this cost can be amortized.

273

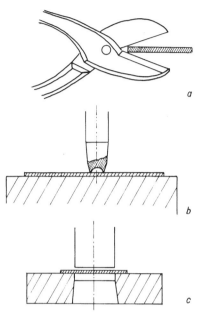

Figure 7.21
Cutting possibilities.
a) shearing cut, b) wedge cut, c) parallel cut.

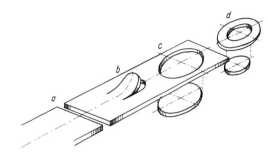

Figure 7.22
Parallel cuts.
a) sheared, b) notched, c) blanked, d) pierced.

7.2.2 CLASSIFICATION OF THE BLANKING TOOLS
Types of blanking cuts can be assigned to the following categories, shown in figure 7.22:

a) *Shearing*, in which parts are cut cleanly away.
b) *Notching*, in which material is partially cut but not removed.
c) *Blanking*, also called *hollow cutting*, in which a piece of material is completely removed from within a larger piece.
d) *Piercing*, similar to blanking, but in this case the part that is cut out is the scrap.

In all blanking arrangements it is critical that the two parts slide precisely alongside each other. There are many ways to guarantee this: a few of the most common solutions are illustrated in figure 7.23. In the first example, the punch is mounted into a tool carrier that moves on a prepared track. In (b) an upper plate guides the punch and holds it vertical. An example of this is the popular circle cutting die found in many goldsmiths' workshops. In the third example we see a superstructure built into the die to anchor and direct the punch. In the example shown at (d), the vertical

punch reaches past the workpiece on one side where it is sheathed in die, which will keep it running true.

7.2.3 BLANKING PROCEDURES
The two main elements – punch and die – run past each other with very little distance between them. This clearance is called the cutting play, and is critical to the performance of a blanking die. The concept is familiar from common scissors, which pivot on a single axis to scrape the two edges against each other. We have all had the frustrating experience of trying to use scissors in which the pivot has come loose. The result is that the edges do not run tightly against each other, resulting in poor cutting or none at all.

Figure 7.24 illustrates what happens as a blanking die is brought down upon a sheet of metal.

a) *Elastic deformation*. At the first moment of impact, the punch bends the metal uniformly, pressing it slightly into the cavity of the die. If the stroke were reversed at this point, the metal would spring back.
b) *Plastic deformation*. With continued stress, metal is deformed more drastically: the grains are pressed along their slip planes. If the piece was removed at this point, the mark of the tool would be evident.
c) *Crack formation*. As the tool penetrates further into the die the stress is localized in a very small area. The grains are so heavily deformed that they lose cohesion: the grain boundaries are dissolved, cracks form and the piece is completely torn away. Another description would be to say that the cohesive forces within the lattice structure are exceeded by the external cutting force.

Figure 7.23
Methods of gulding stamping
(or punching)
a) free-standing punch
b) plate guidance
c) vertical column guides
d) rear support

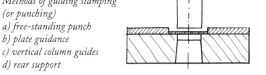

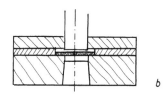

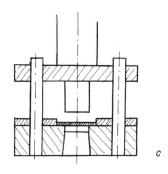

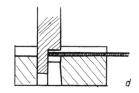

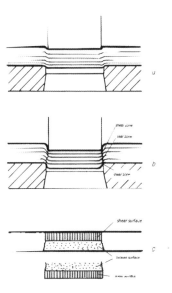

Figure 7.24
Steps in cutting.
a) plastic deformation, b) points of rupture between the shear zones, c) shear and fracture surfaces in the cut piece and remaining metal.

F_s – cutting force in N
A_s – shear surface in mm^2
l – length of the shear surface in mm
s – material thickness in mm
τ – shearing resistance in N/mm^2

The shear surface, or area being cut, is a product of the length of the cut and the material thickness. The size of the surface area of the cut portion has no bearing on the issue. The relationship between shear and tensile strength can be written as

$$\tau = 0.8\, \sigma_B$$

To compensate for friction of the material and inevitable dulling of the tool, we calculate about a 20% higher value for the tensile strength and in this way calculate the required cutting force with this formula:

$$F_s = s \cdot l \cdot \sigma_B$$

d) *Springback resilience.* When the metal tears the force of the press is no longer acting against the sheet. This allows the original elastic deformation to spring back, having the effect of locking the parts, suddenly expanded, into the die. The punch is pressed further down to eject the cut away part. A part of the die called the stripper is laid against the workpiece to hold it down as the punch is withdrawn.

The resistance of a material to the action of the punch depends on the size of the shear surface and the thickness of the material to be cut. The necessary cutting force can be calculated by this formula:

$$F_s = A_s \cdot \tau \text{ or } F_s = s \cdot l \cdot \tau$$

275

7.2.4 CUTTING TOOLS

Free blanking tools

The free blanking tool (figure 7.25) has no direct guide, and is suitable for simple parts. Some models have a stripper to hold the workpiece as the punch is withdrawn. The punch is held in position in relation to the die by a press or similar frame. This press is most suitable for limited production.

Platen blanking tool

In this more sophisticated arrangement, shown in figure 7.26, a guide plate is positioned over the die plate. The layers in between serve as spacers and as a guide for the strip of material. The guide plate also forms the stripper. This configuration is much safer than the open tool because there is no possible way to get the fingers accidentally under the punch.

Column-guided cutting tools

The punch is indirectly guided by the columns that are fixed into the die base (shoe), as in figure 7.27.

Cutting tools with rear guided punch

In this arrangement, seen in figure 7.28, the punch is fitted with a rod or bar that slides into a fitted hole in the cutting die. It is longer than the stroke of the punch and therefore remains in the hole even when the punch is withdrawn, providing alignment for the next stroke. Though many variations are possible, this is a typical open cutting tool.

Cutting tool using a rubber pad

It is typical that production runs in the jewelry industry fall into the middle range of volume – the number of pieces needed is too small to justify the cost of a complicated blanking die, but too large to make handwork reasonable. A recent development called rubber blanking provides a valuable middle ground.

In this arrangement, diagrammed in figures 7.29 and 7.30, the cutting edge is one side of the metal only, as first explained in 7.21b. The effect is similar to tearing a piece of paper against the edge of a table. The upper part of the punch consists of a piece of rubber that is contained in a steel cylinder or similar

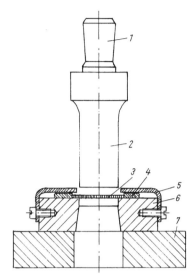

Figure 7.25
Free-standing cutting tool.
1) tension tenon, 2) cutting punch (or stamp), 3) blank, 4) material guide, 5) stripper, 6) cutting plate, 7) base plate.

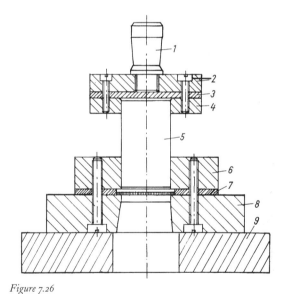

Figure 7.26
Plate guided cuting tool.
1) tension tenon, 2) stamping head plate, 3) pressure plate, 4) stamping retention plate, 5) cutting punch, 6) guiding plate, 7) intermediate layer, meterial guide, 8) cutting plate, 9) base plate.

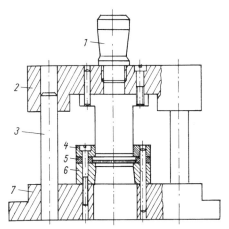

Figure 7.27
Column or rod-guided cutting tool.
1) tension tap (or tenon), 2) upper stamp guide, 3) guiding columns, 4) guiding plate, 5) intermediate layer, 6) cutting plate, 7) base plate with guiding rods.

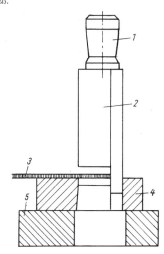

Figure 7.28
Cutting with rear guided stamp.
1) tension tenon, 2) cutting stamp with support rod, 3) meterial, 4) cutting plate with guiding slit, 5) base plate.

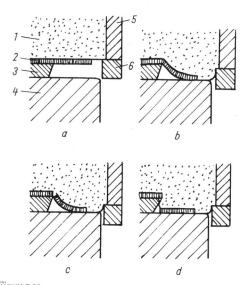

Figure 7.29
Operating method of a rubber cutter.
1) rubber block, 2) part to be cut, 3) cutting plate, 4) base plate, 5) container, 6) tension plate.
a) rubber block sitting on top, b) edge bent, c) edge pressed against base plate, d) edge ripped off.

construction. This will focus its compression on the workpiece where it is needed. A hardened steel die in the shape of the piece to be cut out is place on the bed of a press; the piece of metal is placed on top of this. As the punch descends, the sheet is pressed against the die by the rubber pad. As pressure increases, the metal is deformed over the die, draping over it like fabric. As the bending radius becomes even smaller, the increasing stresses focus on the edge of the sheet where it is pulled tightly against the sharp edge of the die, where it will tear.

The cutting die, made of hardened steel, should be about five times as thick as the metal being cut to allow enough room for the rubber to accomplish its task of stressing the metal to the breaking point around its perimeter. The cutting die should have a clearance angle of about 4°; that is, the die tapers slightly inward from the cutting edge to the base where it is mounted into the press. The die is typically screwed onto the bed of the press from underneath.

Though this process will work with almost any kind of rubber, cheap pads will quickly wear out and require additional pressure and therefore longer time in the press. A recent development is a unique rubber-like material called urethane. It has the ability to recover from high stress even after many uses. This material is available in several grades, called *durometers*. Material with a higher number will have reduced flexibility and is therefore recommended for cutting.

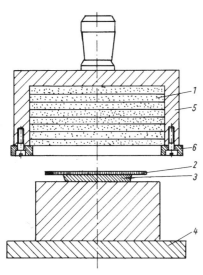

Figure 7.30
Cutting tool with rubber plates.
1) rubber plates, 2) part to be cut, 3) cutting plate, 4) base plate,
5) container, 6) tension plate.

7.2.5 ELEMENTS OF THE CUTTING TOOL
The cutting punch

In a simple cutting die, the punch slides through the die with the aid of some kind of force, for instance a hammer blow or the descending ram of a press. It is common to make the punch from heavy stock, turning it down to the appropriate thickness only in the region of the die end. This will give the die increased stability. In larger arrangements, the die is mounted into a clamping plate, which has a hardened punch head plate to help take up the force of the blow. These elements can be observed in figures 7.25 and 7.26.

Cutting die

The die hole, which is of course the exact shape of the piece to be cut, is made in tool steel and then hardened through heat treating. The angle at the top of the die is precisely square to the walls of the hole, which are perfectly vertical for a couple of millimeters. The lower section of the die hole opens out conically with an angle of no more than 3° to allow the cutoff part to have clearance and to therefore drop out. The space between the punch and the die must not be so tight that the two units jam up against each

other, but should be as tight as possible within that guideline. If there is a gap between the punch and the die, the cutoff part will have a bur.

Punch guiding

It is imperative that the parts of a punch make a perfect fit into one another. This demanding requirement has been made easier in recent times through the development of high strength castable resins. One element of the die is created in steel then filled with a resin, temporarily in its liquid state. The die is treated with graphite powder to allow the parts to be separated after the resin cures.

In the case of platen guided blanking tools (figure 7.26), the guide plate is connected to the cutting die. The thickness of the guide plate depends on the tensile strength and thickness of the material being cut, but in all cases it must be sufficient to hold the punch precisely in position throughout the blanking procedure.

In the case of dies with column guides (figure 7.27) the stabilizing guide components are independent from the actual tool. This is an advantage because it means the dies themselves can be simpler, and the same press can be used for various tools.

Strip guiding

In a die like the familiar circle cutter, the spacer that separates the upper and lower parts of the die can also serve as a locator for the strip. If we feed a piece of sheet metal into the die until it presses against the spacer, a fixed, determinable distance from edge to hole is established. Or to say it another way, if we repeat the action a dozen times, the holes in a dozen different sheets will always be the same distance from the edge because of the locating ability of the spacer.

Limiting feed

In a normal blanking operation, a hole is cut and the strip is advanced for the next cut. Determining the amount of advance is important in order to make the process efficient and to limit waste. Two systems are in common use.

In the first, a stud, or stop is placed at the far side of the hole, as shown at #2 in figure 7.32. The strip is fed into position and the first hole is punched. The strip is then slid forward until it is stopped by the stud. After the blow the stud retracts, allowing the strip to be advanced, but it pops up again and is in position to stop the strip as soon as it advances far enough for the next piercing.

A more precise but also more complicated system of tracking a strip through a die is illustrated in figure 7.33. In this case a separate die is used to notch the outer edge of the strip, in a manner not unlike film-strips or tractor-feeding punches on computer paper. In this case the notch is cut open to the edge, and is keyed to the action of the main punch. When the primary die is brought down to punch out, in this case, a rectangle, a second die is nibbling off a small section of the edge at a precise distance away. This section will be caught up on appropriate pins to position the strip for precise blanking at that point.

7.2.6 MULTIPLE BLANKING TOOLS
Follow dies

When several holes are to be made in a workpiece, the appropriate punches can be positioned in sequence, as for instance in figure 7.32, where the die is cutting a rectangle with an oval hole in its center. The strip is fed into position for the first cut, then advanced to the second and so on. The holes are cut one after another until the last step when the work-piece itself is cut out and ejected from the die.

Total blanking tools

In this arrangement, shown in figure 7.34, both inner and outer shapes are cut with a single stroke of the machine. As illustrated in the washer cutting die, the upper unit presses down on the sheet to cut out the outside dimension, i.e. the larger circle. Simultaneously, a section of the die equal to the width of the washer (#1 in the drawing) is raised to support the disk from below. The smallest punch, equal to the hole in the washer, then descends from within the first die where it presses the center hole out and ejects the plug. The parts of the die are separated, the die is cleared, the strip advanced and the process can be repeated.

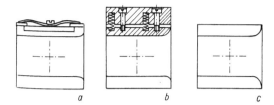

Figure 7.31
Strip leads (guide mechanisms).
a) and b) spring loaded leads, c) fixed lead.

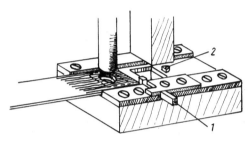

Figure 7.32
Serial cutting tool with advancement stops.
1) cut edge stop and 2) insert pin.

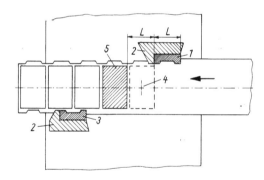

Figure 7.33
Serial cutting tool with advancement stops.
1) first side cutter, 2) fixed stop, 3) second side cutter, 4) hole punch,
5) cut-out punch.

7.2.7 MAXIMUM UTILIZATION OF MATERIAL
It is important to determine the most efficient and economical placement of cutouts on a strip. Depending on the shape of the piece being blanked out, this might involve simply advancing the strip the correct amount, but in other cases it might be necessary blank out different parts from the same strip.

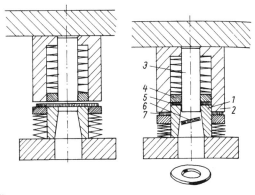

Figure 7.34
Comprehensive cutting tool shown before and after cutting.
1) stamp, 2) cutting plate for cutting out, 3) punch and 4) cutting plate
for punching holes, 5) cut part, 6) punched out scrap, 7) scrap strip.

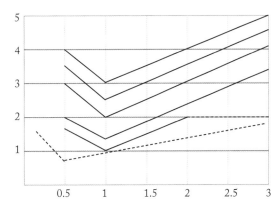

Figure 7.35
Diagram for calculating the edges and border widths.

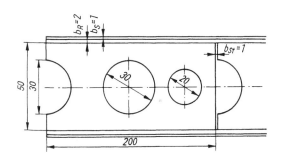

Figure 7.36
Example of strip utilization.

280

The following formulas use strip width B and feed length L to determine the optimum material usage. Refer to figure 7.35 for the following examples.

The width of the stock between blanks and edge are determined by the relationship between sheet thickness (s) and the length of stock between blanks. The distance of the shortest stock between blanks – in this case 10 mm – is determined from the drawing.

Example 1
How much waste will result in the blanking operation shown in figure 7.36?

$$\text{Strip width } B = b_T + 2b_R + 2b_S$$
$$= 5 + 2 \cdot 0.2 + 2 \cdot 0.1$$
$$= \underline{5.6 \text{ cm}}$$

$$\text{Strip length } L = l_T + b_{St}$$
$$= 10 + 0.1$$
$$= \underline{10.1 \text{ cm}}$$

width of part – b_T – width of the blanked part
length of part – l_T – length of blanked part
width between blanks – b_{St} – distance between parts
width of edge – b_R – distance between part and edge
side waste – b_S – waste from the side cutter

Necessary material surface area for a part
$$A_W = B \cdot L = 5.6 \cdot 10.1 \text{ cm} = \underline{56.56 \text{ cm}^2}$$

The surface of a blanked part

$$A_T = b_T \cdot l_T - \left(\frac{r^2\pi}{2} + r_2^2\pi + r_3^2\pi\right) = 5 \cdot 10 \text{ cm}$$
$$- \left(\frac{1.5^2\pi}{2} + 1.5^2\pi + 1^2\pi\right) \text{ cm} = \underline{36.26 \text{ cm}^2}$$

The surface of the waste $A_A = A_W - A_T$
$$= 56.56 - 36.26 = \underline{20.3 \text{ cm}^2}$$

The cost comparison produces the following values:
Proportion of waste

$$A_V = \frac{A_A}{A_W} = \frac{20.3}{56.56} \cdot 100 = \underline{35.89\%}$$

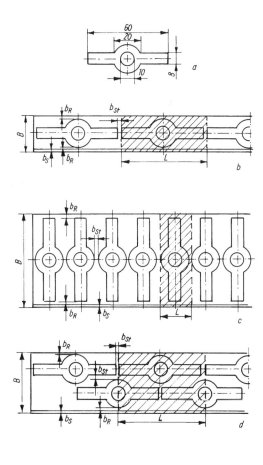

Example 2

A ring shank blank is to be cut out with a follow punch tosol. What configuration offers the least amount of waste?

Some of the possible solutions are assembled in figure 7.37. In the case of examples (a) and (b), the amount of waste can be easily measured because it surrounds the blank. If we calculate the area of the entire rectangle, less the area of the ring blank itself, we are left with the waste portion. In the case of the later examples, the amount of waste is reduced because of overlapping the forms, so the calculation is a little more difficult.

If the parts lie parallel to each other, as in example (b), the amount of waste, or W_A, equals 38%. In example (c), W_A = 33%, or not much better. The solution tried in (d) is better, using 41% of the sheet, but the tooling would be more expensive, either requiring a second tool, or an arrangement that would allow the tool to be shifted to the alternate position with every other blow.

In this example, the best solution is shown in the final example, where W_A = 48%. As this example demonstrates, each situation presents unique challenges and requires special consideration.

7.3
Bending

7.3.1 TERMS

It often happens that the pieces cut with the blanking tools just described are then taken to another class of equipment in which they are deformed, or bent to a desired shape. Though the action is different, the affects of work hardening, plane dislocation and other qualities of deformation are identical with handworking operations and are consistent with the descriptions given previously. We might say the metal does not know how it is being shaped: whether by hammer or in a press.

The four basic types of sheet metal forming are illustrated in figure 7.38.

Figure 7.37
Strip metal use for different arangements of the punched parts. Edge width b = 1mm, margin between pieces b =1mm, side cutter b=1 mm. a) punched out part, b) to e) various arrangements of the parts of the strip.

Material utilization

$$W_A = 100 - A_V = 100 - 35.89 = \underline{64.11\%}$$

a) *Simple Bending.* The metal is trapped and pressed until it assumes the shape of the die.

b) *Roll Bending.* The metal is curled by the downward stroke of the die, in which the contour of the form presses the metal ahead of itself to impose a rolled or cylindrical shape.

c) *Relief Stamping.* One side of the die has a specific contour, into which the metal is pressed, either by a mated die, or with a resilient material that will temporarily take on the contour of the die. In this case the thickness of the metal remains unchanged.

d) *Stamping.* In this case the thickness of the workpiece is affected as the metal is pinched between two rigid dies. This process is sometimes referred to as *coining*, a reference to an ancient use of the technique to produce metal currency.

7.3.2 SIMPLE BENDING AND FORMING

Bending in a die is very similar to bending by hand. As shown in figure 7.39, the metal is pressed as the ram contacts it, and deforms as the sheet is pressed into the die. The metal is stretched on the outer surface, where friction against the die contributes to the dynamic of the situation, and is compressed on the inside of the bend.

When force is removed the object will springback slightly; the amount of this depends on the hardness and tensile strength of the metal and the size of the bending radius. This simply says that a tight bend, which puts the metal under considerable compression, will show more springback than a more gentle bend. To reduce the amount of springback, follow these guidelines.

- Relieve the stress in the material by annealing.
- Choose the smallest possible bending radius.
- Narrow the bending clearance somewhat at the actual bending spot to additionally compress the material.
- Use a smaller bending angle on the tool so the workpiece takes on the required angle of bend after the spring back.

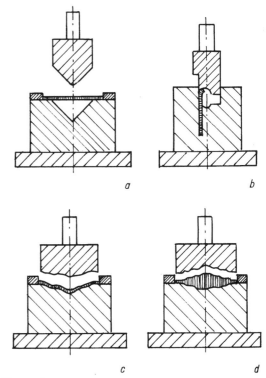

Figure 7.38
Types of bending.
a) V bend, b) roll bend, c) form bending and stamping, d) embossing.

Because some degree of springback is inevitable, proper tool design will accommodate this in the angles of the tool. If the desired angle is 45°, for instance, and springback will be 2°, the angle of the tool should be 47°.

In order to avoid crack formation and overstressing of the material, the bending edge should lie at right angles to the direction of rolling.

7.3.3 BENDING AND FORMING TOOLS

A bending die is not significantly different from a cutting die. In this case, as described above, the action consists of a piece of metal being trapped between two hard forms. As before it is important that the two parts of the die, the ram and the die block, be in proper alignment. The amount of force needed will depend on the thickness and tensile strength of the metal and the amount of deformation required.

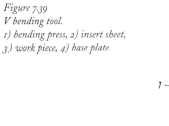

Figure 7.39
V bending tool.
1) bending press, 2) insert sheet,
3) work piece, 4) base plate.

A simple example of a forming die is the familiar dapping block described earlier. In common practice this is used freehand, without the benefit of a frame to keep the parts of the die in alignment. This is possible in the case of dapping because the spherical nature of the form means that even an angled stroke will seat properly into the dapping die.

In that case the disk being domed is free to move slightly in the hollow of the die. In more complicated pieces this would result in a misshapen piece, so holding devices are built into the lower part of the die to keep the blank in place during forming. Springy *counter holds* can be installed in the forming die which serve as *knock outs*. The nature of the tool should be explained using two further model examples.

V-bending die
In this simple die, illustrated in figure 7.39, the angled die presses a sheet of metal into a V-groove. The guides shown at #2 are sufficient to keep the material in position until the force of ram carries it into the die. Because the die is open or exposed, there is no need for a device to eject the piece from the die.

Triple action bending die
This more complicated machine is diagrammed in figure 7.40. The strip is put into position in the die and held in place by guides, seen in (a). In the first phase, (b), a ram descends onto the metal pressing it into a die and forming a U-shape. The support (called a *counter hold*) beneath the form is spring-loaded, and

lowers with the impact of the ram. In the next phase, shown at (c), a pair of dies are driven horizontally to press the sides of the U around the ram. When these parts of the die are withdrawn, the vertical die is raised and the piece is lifted out of the die by the counter hold from below.

7.3.4 ROLL BENDING (CURLING)
In a case like the forming operation shown in figure 7.41, the top edges of a form are rolled into a tube-like rim. Notice how the curvature is the result of the shapes built equally into the upper and lower dies. This allows the piece to be removed, which would not be the case if all the forming happened within one die.

The counter hold beneath the object is spring loaded and will eject the finished piece when the die is opened.

7.3.5 FORMING
Forming dies
As used here, we will distinguish forming from bending with this distinction: forming is a process in which a decorative contour is imparted to the metal, and in which the thickness stays the same. The effect is familiar from handworking in the process called repoussé. In die forming, the desired contour is carved into a die as a negative impression, then the metal is pressed into the die where it takes on the shape. In a traditional arrangement, called a conforming die, the ram will have the same shape as the die, less the thickness of the sheet. The two parts fit together like a hand in a glove. In practice conforming dies are used in platen or column guided presses, and often follow the use of cutting or bending dies.

The process of making a conventional steel die is exacting and complex. First the general shape of the tools are made by a machinist, who selects a grade of steel that combines the necessary properties. These blanks are then given to the steel engraver, who uses a combination of machining, engraving, grinding and chasing to create a positive of the intended form. If a high volume is foreseen, and knowing that dies will wear out and need to be replaced, this master die is

283

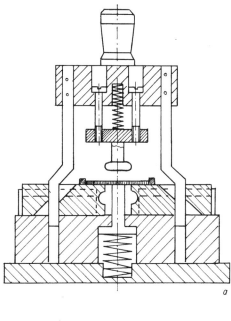

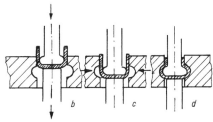

Figure 7.40
Wedge (or piston) driven bending tool.
a) overview, b) U-form deformation with spring-loaded bending
press, c) forming the rounded shell with the wedge press,
d) finished piece.

refined, hardened and kept aside specifically to make
other dies.

As seen in drawings (a) and (c) of figure 7.42, this
die can be used to press its imprint into the block that
will become the lower piece of the die. If the relief is
significant, some material will be cut away with chisels or other cutting tools to prepare the die for the
impact and reduce the amount of displacement
required. The lower die, which will be the front or
outside of the finished piece, must be particularly well
finished. When this is done the piece is hardened and
tempered. The ram is then pressed again into the die
to insure a perfect match of the two halves, then the
ram is also hardened.

Etching can be used to refine the fit of complicat-

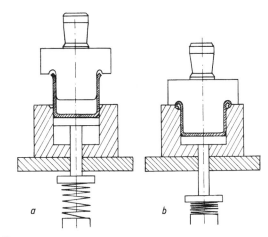

Figure 7.41
Roll bending tool with divided rolling cylinder to flare the edge of the
vessel. a) before and b) after forming.

ed die pieces. To do this a thin coat of lacquer is
painted onto the ram, which is pressed slowly into the
die. Points of contact squeeze the lacquer off, leaving
the high spots exposed. When the steel is submerged
in acid, these areas are eaten away. The process is
repeated as many times as necessary until the parts fit
together perfectly.

Specific forms will dictate whether it is easier to
start with the positive or negative impression, but as
can be seen, either half of the die can be used to generate the other.

Forming and bending with a rubber pad
A popular alternative to expensive conforming dies is
a nonconforming die in which one part of the pair is
a sheet of rubber that will temporarily take on the
shape necessary to press metal into a die, then return
to its original form when pressure is released. Not
only does this have the advantage of not requiring a
matched pair of steel dies, but because of the softness
of the rubber, dies can be made of wood or plastic.

In nonconforming dies like this, the solid piece can
be either the ram or the negative die, depending on
the shape being created. In the example shown in figure 7.43, the desired contour is created in the lower
unit. The metal is placed into the die and a pad of
rubber is pressed against it, where it will take on the

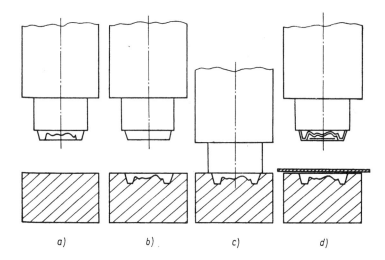

Figure 7.42
Making a matching punch and die.
a) hardened metal punch with annealed die,
b) hardened die with annealed punch, c) punch
pressed into die, d) hardened punch and die in
operation.

a)   b)   c)   d)

contour of the die and press the metal into every crevasse.

The process works particularly well with gentle transitions and soft forms, but can create crisp detail, particularly with thin metal and a properly carved die. As mentioned earlier, this same process can be used as a cutting die, which means that care must be taken when it is forming (as opposed to cutting), what is wanted. In addition to removing sharp edges, there is an advantage to positioning the form with a relief angle of 7-10° which will allow the metal to flow better and thereby minimize stress.

7.3.6 COINING

As described earlier, the term coining is used to identify forming processes in which the thickness of the metal is altered. This is, predictably, the case with the change in your pocket, which makes the term easy to remember.

In single sided coining, the workpiece lies on a flat base that has been grooved or textured to prevent the piece from shifting. The negative relief is worked into the upper punch. As the punch descends, material is displaced from the deeper lying regions of the relief into the raised ones and excess metal is pressed out around the edges as a flange. This has the advantage of preventing the die from impacting on the base or anvil, which would damage it.

Particularly when the piece calls for significant

relief, a slower action (as can be produced in a hydraulic press), is preferred over a fast impact, because it allows time for the metal to flow from one region to another.

If the relief is to appear on both sides, as with a coin, the images are carved in both the upper and lower units of the die. When a flange is not wanted, the relief is carved into a lowered recess and the amount of metal (i.e. the size of the initial blank) is carefully calculated.

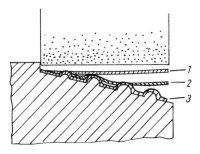

Figure 7.43
Forming metal sheet with incremental blows with a rubber pad.
1) starting blank, 2) midway in the process, 3) completed form.

285

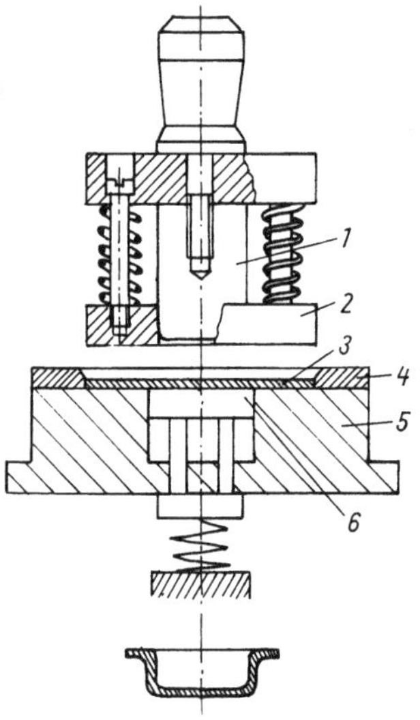

Figure 7.44
Deep drawing die with ejector.
1) punch, 2) suppressor,
3) card/board, 4) inlay plate,
5) draw-radius, 6) ejector.

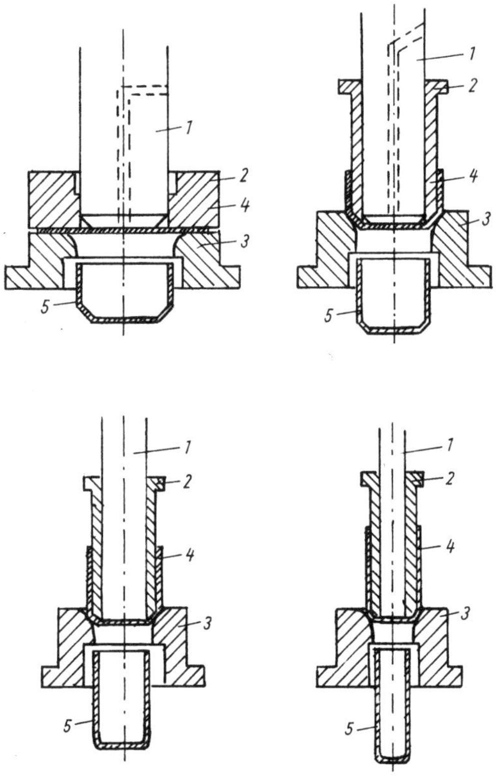

7.4
Deep Drawing

The term deep drawing refers to a specific kind of forming in which sheet metal is pressed into dies to create hollow forms. On a large scale, this process creates beakers, cookware and similar vessels. On a smaller scale, deep drawing is used to make bezel cups, caps and various small cylindrical parts.

7.4.1 PROCEDURES AND TOOLS

The essential ingredients of the tooling are shown in figures 7.44 and 7.45, and are known as the drawing punch, drawing die and blank holder. When the ram descends it presses the blank, typically a disk of annealed metal, into the cylindrical die chamber, gathering the appropriate amount of metal and forcing it into an oversized, general shape called a preform.

This is a complicated process (from the metal's point of view) in that some material is stretched radially, while other neighboring portions are compressed in a tangential direction. These forces work against one another to keep the thickness of the material relatively unchanged throughout the drawing. The walls of the container get longer.

Particularly when thin metal is being used there is a danger of folds or crimps appearing on the walls of the form. To prevent these from forming, the blank holder is used to sustain constant pressure against the metal, holding it taut. At the end of the stroke the ram is lifted and the spring-loaded knock out pushes the drawn object out of the mold. Alternately, some dies are designed to allow the finished article to fall out a hole in the bottom, as shown in the last drawing of figure 7.45.

It is rare that a completed form can be made in a single die. If the diameter of the container is less than 60% of the diameter of the original blank, it will be necessary to sequence the drawing operation through a series of dies. In each successive case, (figure 7.45) the container is reduced in diameter. The size and shape of the blank holder is important in keeping the walls of the form smooth throughout the operation.

Figure 7.45
Deep drawing die for multiple draw levels.
1) stamp, 2) suppressor, 3) draw-ring, 4) output form, 5) end form.

7.4.2 DETERMINING THE BLANK

Whether a form is made through hammering, spinning or deep drawing, it is always vital that the blank, or starting disk, be the correct size and shape. Normally a careful drawing is made of the desired form and dimensions are taken from it. It is better to make careful calculations than to rely upon approximations. Proper understanding of the blank refers to this formula

$$m = V \cdot \rho = A \cdot s \cdot \rho$$

A – surface of the sheet metal in cm²
s – thickness of the sheet in cm
V – volume of the sheet in cm³
ρ – density of the metal in g/cm³

This assumes the following correlations exist between blank and container.

- They have the same density; logical because they are made of the same metal ($\rho_1 = \rho_2$).
- They have the same weight, because nothing is cut away or added ($m_1 = m_2$).
- The metal thickness remains the same, because this measurement should not change with deformation ($s_1 = s_2$).

Understanding all this, it appears clear that the surface area of the blank and the finished form are the same!

$$A_1 = A_2$$

In the case of symmetrical, cylindrical containers the starting blank will be a disk. The diameter of the disk is calculated as shown in this example. Because the thickness is relatively thin compared to the diameter of the form, we can leave it out of the calculations.

Example 1
What is the diameter of a blank needed to make the cylindrical container shown in figure 7.46a?

blank = container
$$d^2_1 \frac{\pi}{4} = d^2_2 \cdot \frac{\pi}{4} + d_2 + \pi \cdot h$$

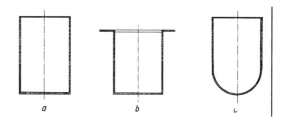

Figure 7.46
Pattern calculation.
a) cylindrical vessel, b) cylindrical vessel with rim, c) cylindrical vessel with rounded bottom.

From this we can derive:

$$d^2_1 \frac{\pi}{4} = \frac{\pi}{4}(d^2_2 + 4 \cdot d_2 \cdot h)$$

$$d_2 = \sqrt{4^2 + 4 \cdot 4 \cdot 6}\ \text{cm} = \underline{10.58\ \text{cm}}$$

The following formula is given as a generalization.

$$A_1 = A_2$$

$$d^2_1 \frac{\pi}{4} = A_2$$

$$d_1 = \sqrt{\frac{4 \cdot A_2}{\pi}}$$

The surface formula for the container is inserted at the position A_2 in the calculation.

Example 2
What size blank is needed to make the container shown in figure 7.46b, which has a horizontal shoulder around the rim? Note: the metal needed for the flange can be added to the dimension of the floor to make the diameter d_3.

$$d_1 = \sqrt{\frac{4}{\pi} A_2} = \sqrt{\frac{4}{\pi}(d^2_3 \frac{\pi}{4} + d_2 \cdot \pi \cdot h)}$$

$$d_1 = \sqrt{d^2_3 + 4 \cdot d_2 \cdot h}$$

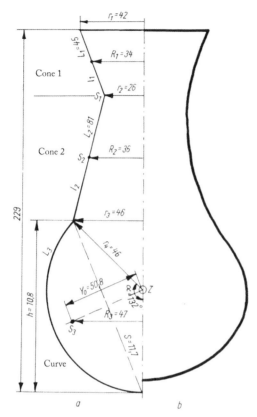

Figure 7.47
Pattern calculation for a curve-bottomed vessel.
a) elemental divisions, b) cross-section overview.

Example 3

What is the size of the blank needed to produce the cylindrical container with a rounded bottom, as shown in figure 7.46c.

$$d_1 = \sqrt{\frac{4}{\pi} \left(d^2{}_2 \frac{\pi}{2} + d_2 \cdot \pi \cdot h \right)} = \sqrt{2 \left(d^2{}_2 + 2 d_2 \cdot h \right)}$$

Though these examples are using symmetrical geometric forms, it is more typical that the intended design involves a more complex arrangement of curves and contours. To calculate the metal needed for these forms, the shape is divided into segments that can be described as basic geometric forms like cylinders, cones and spheres.

Calculating the blank from the mass

If there is a finished product at hand that can be used as a model, an alternate calculation can be made, using weight rather than surface dimensions. This is an easy process, and especially useful for complex forms.

The mass of the round blank is determined with

$$m = V \cdot \rho$$

Because the round blank is formed like a round cylin-

$$m = \frac{d^2{}_1 \cdot \pi \cdot s}{4} \cdot \rho$$

dar, its volume is inserted.

$$d_1 = \sqrt{\frac{4 \cdot m}{\pi \cdot s \cdot \rho}}$$

Next d_1 is converted
Because weight and thickness do not change significantly during working, these quantities can be inserted into the formula to determine the size of the blank needed.

Example 4

A silver beaker of a known weight is to be produced by deep drawing. How large a disk is needed?

$$m = 123.6 \text{ g}$$
$$\rho = 10.3 \text{ g/cm}^3 \text{ for AgCu 10}$$
$$s = 0.08 \text{ cm}$$
$$d_1 = \sqrt{\frac{4 \cdot m}{\pi \cdot s \cdot \rho}} = \sqrt{\frac{4 \cdot 123.6}{0.08 \cdot 10.3 \cdot \pi}} \text{ cm} = 13.82 \text{ cm}$$

Blank diagram

If there will be recurring need to determine the size of blanks for similar shapes, it will be worthwhile to generate a table like the one shown in figure 7.48. In

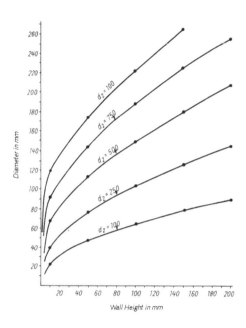

Figure 7.48
Pattern diagram.

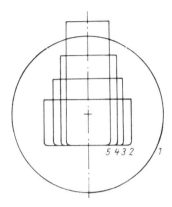

Figure 7.49
Determining the stages of deep drawing (die forming).
1) blank, d_1 = 174mm, 2) 1 draw, d_2 = 100mm, 3) 2 draw, d_3 = 80mm,
4) 3 draw, d_4 = 65mm, 5) last draw, final product, d_5 = 50mm,
h = 137mm.

this example, a cylindrical shape has been calculated for several diameters, using the formula described above.

$$d_2 = \sqrt{d_2{}^2 + 4 \cdot d \cdot h}$$

It is worth pointing out that the lines thus created are not straight, which confirms the complexity of the issues involved, and further makes the case against simply relying on a general rule of thumb.

7.4.3 STAGES OF DEEP DRAWING

As mentioned previously, only shallow vessels and forms can be drawn in a single stroke. Most cases require several drawing strokes, or stages. These are shown in figure 7.49, as explained below.

For the first draw it is: $m_1 = \dfrac{d_2}{d_1}$

For further drawings: $m_2 = \dfrac{d_2}{d_1} \ldots \dfrac{d_n}{d_{n-1}}$

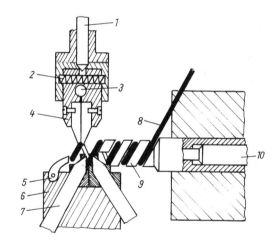

Figure 7.51
Link-making part of the automatic (curb) chain-making machine.
1) Locking or closing rod,
2) tension spring,
3) jaw's bolt,
4) resistance piece,
5) chain-bending clamp,
6) cutter,
7) wire,
8) winding threads,
9) winding mandrel.

m – drawing proportion
d_1 – blank diameter in mm
d_2 – outer diameter after the first draw in mm
d_N – outer diameter after the nth draw in mm

Experience tells us that the first draw will generate a value of between 0.55 and 0.60 mm for m_1. Subsequent draws (mn) will yield 0.75.....0.80 mm.

Example
Deep drawing of the beaker shown in figure 7.49 will go through the following stages:

$d_2 = m_1 \cdot d_1 = 0.6 \cdot 17.4 = 10.4$
rounded to 100 mm

$d_3 = m_2 \cdot d_2 = 0.8 \cdot 10.0 = 8.0$
rounded to 80 mm

$d_4 = m_2 \cdot d_3 = 0.8 \cdot 8.0 = 6.4$
rounded to 65 mm

$d_5 = m_2 \cdot d_4 = 0.8 \cdot 6.5 = 5.2$
rounded to 50 mm

7.5
Bending Wire

As has been demonstrated in the preceding pages, many hand techniques for shaping sheet metal have been adapted to industrial application. The range of equipment for bending wire, however, is relatively limited. In many cases it is still most practical to have wire elements bent by hand, even though this is slower.

Figure 7.50 shows a commercial wire bending machine and hints at the range of shapes it can create. It will be noted, however, that these are generally flat and limited to wires of a uniform diameter. While bending machines can conceivably be created to mechanize any task, the complexity and cost is often prohibitive. In those cases we return to jigs, bending mandrels and the use of pliers in a talented pair of hands to create wire forms.

Bending machines like the one illustrated supply the wire from a drum or large spool mounted on the top or side of the mechanism. It is fed into a bending arm that pushes the wire against a mandrel or jig. The arms and jigs are interchangeable to create a range of parts. Cutters are brought in to snip the piece when bending is complete, and the piece is usually ejected, for instance into a bin below the machine. Through the use of eccentric wheels and cams the machine is designed to insert, bend, rotate, bend and snip a length of wire in a single rotation of the motor. The high cost of these machines is offset by their great efficiency in producing basic shapes like paper clips.

Figure 7.50
A commercial wire bending machine with a few of its thousands of possible shapes.

7.6
Chainmaking

The observation just made about the relative ineffec-
tiveness of wire bending machines does not apply
when it comes to chainmaking equipment. In this
specialized situation, highly effective ingenious
machines have been developed that produce high
quality precious metal chain with consistently fine
results. Because chain design does not change dramatically from year to year, the high cost of these
machines can be spread out over a long term of use.

Figure 7.51 shows the workings of a curb chain-
making machine. It is indeed hypnotic to watch the
precisely controlled action as the wire is fed in, wound
around a mandrel to make a ring, cut, bent, inserted,
bent and so on. Each action is controlled by a cam or
transfer ram attached to the drive shaft of a motor,
with the result that watching the machine operate is
a delightful opportunity to see many parts moving in
great precision. The speed of the machines is impressive, moving so fast that it is difficult at first to make
out the action. A typical machine will produce 20
meters of chain in an hour!

In most cases the chain links are soldered closed,
typically by pinpoint electrodes that spot weld the
joint with local heat. Solder is introduced in the form
of a core that is manufactured into the wire used to
make the chain. Some machines also have the ability
to hammer or bright cut the links as part of the
process.

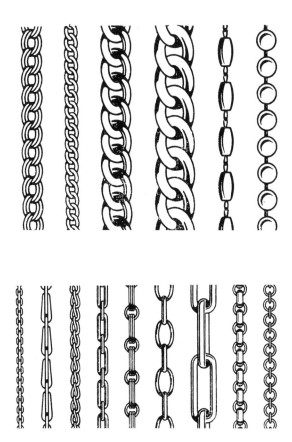

Figure 7.52
*Compact and relatively inexpensive machines can produce a wide vari-
ety of manufactured chains like the ones shown here.*

Joining Techniques

8.1
Soldering

Pieces of metal are permanently joined in a process called soldering, in which metal material (solder) is melted and flows into the structure of the heated parts through capillary action, where it unites the pieces by diffusion. The action of the solder is assisted by flux, a chemical that reduces the formation of oxides that will interfere in the process.

The solder is generally an alloy, as opposed to a pure metal, and is formulated with consideration for its working temperature; a temperature at which the melting solder will fill a seam. This is generally just above the liquidus temperature of the solder alloy. In the case of silver soldering, more properly called silver brazing, the working temperature of the solder is below that of the pieces being joined. This distinguishes the process from welding. Solder alloys are available in many temperature ranges, each requiring a flux that is active at the same point.

8.1.1 SOLDERS

In a well made solder joint, especially in precious metal alloys, the solder flows into the structure of the workpiece, as illustrated in figure 8.1. The parent metal is heated to a temperature at which its grain structure is open, allowing the solder to be drawn into the microscopic openings by capillary action as soon as it is fluid. More than that, the solder dissolves the metal it is attaching, creating the situation in the diagram, in which a new alloy (part solder and part parent metal) is formed along the edges of the seam. Each time the joint is reheated this process goes further, with the result that an early seam on a piece that goes through several heating has a fully homogenized blending that cannot be detected even with magnification.

In general, goldsmiths work with high melting solders whose working temperatures are close to the melting points of the workpiece. This is usually done to insure a strong joint and a close color match. As a rule of thumb, the difference between the working temperature of the solder and the melting point of the metals being joined should be at least 50 K. If the piece is heated to temperatures approaching or in excess of its solidus point, the metal starts to break down, forming reticulated surface convolutions.

There are cases, for instance in delicate wire work such as filigree, when an even greater gap between solder temperature and the melting point of the work metal is advised.

In a properly made joint, the solder reaches its liquidus temperature and flows instantly and completely into every crevasse of the seam. Every working goldsmith has had the experience, however, of having the solder draw itself up into a ball. This can be caused by several factors. If the workpiece has not been sufficiently heated, the heat from a torch will cause the solder to ball up since it cannot flow into the seam. The solution here would lie with better preheating.

It is also possible that the wetting action of the solder has been compromised by oil or a similar foreign substance in the region of the joint, either on the workpiece or the solder. The solution here is to clean all components before attempting to solder.

The third reason that solder might not flow is that it is not in contact with the workpiece. We often forget that the subtle textures of our work might be enough to keep the solder elevated, where it will overheat and not be subject to capillary action.

Soft solders

The term soft solders refers to a large family of alloys characterized by a relatively low melting point and a gray-white color. The most important and common of these contain tin, typically alloyed with lead. The phase diagram for the lead-tin alloy shown in figure 8.2, is similar to the copper-silver diagram.

The mixture of 61.9% tin forms the eutectic, or lowest melting combination of these two metals. It becomes fluid at 183.3°C, (362°F). The lead can dissolve a maximum 19% tin in its alpha-mixed crystals; this solubility is reduced as the temperature decreases. Unlike the silver-copper system, the precipitation process cannot be stopped by quenching.

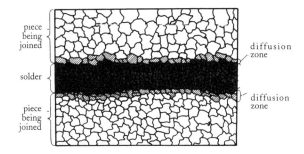

Figure 8.1
Structure of a solder joint.

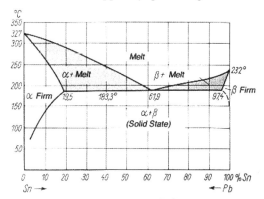

Figure 8.2
Pb-Sn relationship chart.

In practice the most commonly used solder alloys contain 50–60% tin. These offer a practical mix of ease of flow, strength and solidification time. When working on food containers or utensils, the danger of lead poisoning requires that a lead-free solder be used. An alloy of 96% tin and 4% silver (*Sta-Brite*) is often used in such cases.

The melting point can be further lowered by the addition of other metals, most notably cadmium, but this is not recommended because of the health risk associated with that material. Nevertheless, in the interest of thoroughness, let us here give the composition of one of the low melting alloys, Woods Metal:

4 parts bismuth (Bi)
2 parts lead (Pb)
1 part tin (Sn)
1 part cadmium (Cd)

This unusual metal melts at 65°C (149°F), which is lower than the boiling point of water. Because of the toxic nature of cadmium, use of Woods Metal is not recommended, but an understanding of the material is important because it might be encountered in the course of repair work.

It is generally considered bad practice to use tin-bearing solders except in cases where they offer the only possible alternative. Soft solders have several disadvantages:

• They are not nearly as strong as silver solders, which are roughly 8–10 times stronger. The tin solders can be scratched easily and will not withstand hard use.
• Because of limited diffusion, the solders sit on the surface of the metal, unlike silver solders. Because of this, they do not have the holding power to stand up to serious deformation.
• The gray color of tin solder is unattractive, particularly on colored alloys like copper and brass.

Hard solders
As was described in the first chapter, zinc and cadmium lend themselves very well to lowering the melting points of precious metals and have been used for centuries as the principal alloying ingredients in silver solder and gold solder. In recent years as the danger

of cadmium has become more widely understood, it has been removed from alloys, leaving zinc to take the major role.

Silver-bearing alloys, some of which are listed in table 8.1, are widely used in industry because they offer high strength, heat-resistant joints. Many copper-silver and copper-silver-zinc alloys are commercially available. Because of their yellow-red or gray-red colors, they are rarely used in jewelry work, though they have applications in other products of a metalsmith such as lamps, sculpture and so on. For precious metal work, alloys will always contain at least 65% silver or gold.

In the case of gold, where laws closely govern the purity of the completed object, solders are formulated to retain the correct proportion of gold while lowering the melting point. Such a solder, for instance, will have a lower melting point than Au 750 (18k) sheet and wire, but will assay out with the same precious metal content. Such a solder is called plumb.

Gold solders are grouped according to their gold content, as seen in table 8.2. It will be obvious that a goldsmith needs to know the solidus point of the alloy of which a piece is being made in order to select the appropriate solder for it. To take a specific example: Au 585, a 14 karat gold, with its balance mostly silver (i.e. green gold) or mostly copper (i.e. rose gold) has a high melting point and could be soldered with an alloy whose working temperature is around 900°C. That same solder would not be appropriate for the same Au 585 alloy in a yellow color, because that alloy will start to melt at 810°C.

8.1.2 FLUXES

Effect of fluxes
Anyone who has ever heated metals knows that they have a tendency to acquire a dark oxide scale as they are heated. Some metals acquire a scale very quickly, (copper, for instance) while others, such as high karat gold, resist oxide formation. But all metals except platinum will form a scale that will prevent solder from flowing into the structure of the metal.

Trying to solder onto scale is like gluing two pieces of rusty metal together. The glue probably won't hold, but even if it does, you have only joined the "skin" of the metals, so the joint is weak.

Type	Composition in % Mass		Active Zone in °C	Density in g/cm³	Tensile Strength in N/mm²	Distention in %	Preferred Use
	Ag	Additive					
L-Ag30Cd22	30	Cu, Cd, Zn	680	9.2	480	31	Copper Copper alloys
L-Ag34Cd20	34	Cu, Cd, Zn	640	9.1	530	32	Copper Copper alloys
L-Ag40Cd20	40	Cu, Cd, Zn	610	9.3	530	21	Copper Copper alloys Gold doublée
L-Ag50Cd10	50	Cu, Cd, Zn	650	9.5	430	30	Copper Copper alloys Silver alloys
L-Ag65Cu29	65	Cu, Zn	740	9.7	380	25	Jewelry, utensils
L-Ag65Cu26	65	Cu, Zn	730	9.7	420	30	Jewelry, utensils
L-Ag65Cu23	65	Cu, Zn	720	9.7	420	30	Jewelry, utensils
L-Ag65Cu20	65	Cu, Zn	700	9.7	420	30	Jewelry, utensils

Table 8.1
Silver solders.

Composition in % Mass		Active Zone in °C	Density in g/cm³	Preferred Use
Au	Additive			
75	Ag, Cu, Zn, Cd	820	15.3	Hard solder for Au 750
75	Ag, Cu, Cd	725	15.1	Soft solder for Au 750
58.5	Ag, Cu, Zn	850	16.1	Extra-hard solder for Au 585
58.5	Ag, Cu, Zn	820	15.3	Hard solder for Au 585
58.5	Ag, Cu, Zn	775	15.3	Medium solder for Au 585
58.5	Ag, Cu, Zn	760	15.3	Soft solder for Au 585
33.3	Ag, Cu, Zn	790	12.3	Hard solder for Au 333
33.3	Ag, Cu, Zn	760	12.3	Medium solder for Au 333
33.3	Ag, Cu, Zn	740	12.4	Soft solder for Au 333
56	Pd, Ag, Cu, Cd	920	17.2	White gold Au585 and Au750
83.3	Pt, Pd, Ni	920	19.9	Jeweler's platinum

Table 8.2
Gold and platinum solders.

Flux is a chemical added to a solder area in preparation for a joint. In order to accomplish the several tasks required for a successful seam, flux should

- dissolve oxide residues.
- inhibit the formation of further oxides as the soldering commences.
- promote the wetting and therefore the flow of the solder.
- be easily removable when the soldering operation is completed.

Melting zone
Each flux is formulated to be active in a specific temperature range, which must be selected in consideration of the metals being soldered. Because oxides start to form well below the melting point of solders, it is important to use a flux that becomes active well below the melting point of the solder. Obviously a flux that does not become active until the moment when the solder is supposed to flow cannot fulfill its task of keeping the area around the joint clean.

An ideal flux is one whose active zone starts before the melting point of the solder, and is still active at the melting point of the solder. Further, it will be beneficial if the flux itself melts quickly, allowing it to flow out into a protective puddle as soon as heat is applied. And finally, a good flux will have the ability to dissolve oxides for a relatively long period. Even a flux that has all the other attributes will not do much good if it cannot prevent new oxidation for the duration of the soldering process.

Flux consistency
Ideally, flux will have low viscosity and surface tension. These attributes will allow the flux to spread like water or thin syrup over the work. In cases where the surface is heavily textured, a thick flux would be a disadvantage because it might not penetrate into narrow crevasses. Similarly, a material with a high surface tension, in other words, a material that draws itself naturally into a ball, would make an inappropriate flux.

At the same time, the flux should not be so thin (watery) that it slides off the workpiece as soon as it

is heated. Not only would this leave the metal exposed to oxidation, but the sliding action might take the solder chips along with it. Every goldsmith has had occasion to use flux to temporarily glue solder into place.

Surface cleaning
A good flux also has the capacity to carry away certain dissolution products that form during the soldering process. This material, called slag, can lodge in a seam and prevent the solder from making proper contact with the workpiece.

Solubility
Having done all this, a flux must be easily removable. In the case of soft solder fluxes, the gummy residues that remain after soldering will dissolve in soapy water. Borax or fluoride-based residues of hard solder fluxes can be dissolved in boiling water or pickle.

Soft soldering flux
ZINC CHLORIDE, $ZnCl_2$
This time-honored liquid, also called soldering water, can be easily made in the studio as needed. Sheets of zinc are set into a beaker of hydrochloric acid, where they will bubble and dissolve. Continue adding zinc until it no longer goes into solution, which will indicate that the acid has been transformed into a saturated salt. This is important, since the acid would corrode the workpiece if it were not converted. The reaction can be seen here, which also shows the formation of the gas that we see go off as bubbles.

$$2\,HCl\quad + \quad Zn\quad \rightarrow$$
hydrochloric acid zinc
$$ZnCl_2\quad + \quad H_2$$
zinc chloride hydrogen gas

When the zinc chloride has formed, it is mixed with an equal amount of clean water to make a flux. The material is clear and almost odorless, so be certain to mark it well. Left to dry out, zinc chloride will form a white powder, which is strongly hygroscopic, or hungry for water. If it takes up water, which it can sometimes do from moisture in the atmosphere, it will form (hydrochloric acid) gas with water:

$$ZnCl_2 \quad + \quad H_2O \quad \rightarrow$$
zinc chloride water
$$ZnO \quad + \quad 2\,HCl$$
zinc oxide hydrogen chloride

The gas formed dissolves the oxides at the soldering area and converts them to chlorides.

$$2\,HCl \quad + \quad CuO \quad \rightarrow$$
hydrogen chloride copper oxide
$$CuCl_2 \quad + \quad H_2O$$
copper chloride water

The zinc oxide from the first reaction and the metal chlorides shown in the second reaction are dissolved into molten zinc chloride, which is the active ingredient of the flux.

Though it is effective, the use of this flux is limited because the presence of excess moisture (which can come from the air) will produce hydrochloric acid that can corrode the workpiece, and of course, cause skin irritation. In electrical technology and precision machining, these drawbacks are sufficient to require a different flux.

AMMONIUM CHLORIDE (SAL AMMONIAC) NH_4Cl
Sal ammoniac is a white powder which can only be made fluid under high pressure between 53°C and 600°C. It is soluble in water. The powder is pressed into a block, (the salamoniac stone) that can be touched with a hot soldering iron to clean it and coat it with a layer of flux. Sal ammoniac is used as a flux with niello.

$$2\,NH_4Cl \quad + \quad CuO \quad \rightarrow$$
ammonium chloride copper oxide
$$CuCl_2 \quad + \quad 2\,NH_3 \ + \ H_2O$$
copper chloride ammonia water

Flux mixture
The melting point of sal ammoniac is too high to make it an effective flux for tin-bearing solders all by itself, but when mixed with some of the zinc chloride flux, an effective material can be created. The lowest

melting point of the combination (180°C, 356°F) is achieved with a proportion of 28% ammonium chloride and 72% zinc chloride. The mixture of both materials forms zinc ammonium chloride, $Zn(NH_3)Cl_2$ at high temperatures by decomposing the hydrogen chloride gas which fosters the soldering process.

$$ZnCl_2 \quad + \quad 2NH_4Cl \quad \rightarrow$$
zinc chloride ammonium chloride
$$Zn(NH_3)_2Cl_2 \quad + \quad 2HCl$$
zinc ammonium chloride hydrogen chloride

To make this flux, both salts are mixed in the desired proportion and dissolved in water.

While this is an effective flux and one that offers considerable flexibility in its ability to accommodate a specific soldering range, it must be noted that even in this combination the flux has the ability to create hydrochloric acid that can damage the workpiece. It is therefore important to thoroughly rinse, or even better, neutralize the piece after soldering.

COLOPHONY, $C_{20}H_{30}O_2$
Colophony is a distillation product of the resin of pine trees. The honey-yellow soft resin melts between 100°C and 200°C. Unlike the fluxes described above, this naturally occurring flux is harmless and the residues, rather than being corrosive, actually protect the completed piece. The oxide solubility is, unfortunately, not as great as with the other fluxes, so it requires thorough cleaning of the metal before soldering can be attempted. Because of the limited oxide resistance of this flux, soldering should be accomplished as quickly as possible.

Proprietary fluxes
Though it used to be necessary for metal workers to create their own fluxes, it is now far more common to purchase fluxes ready to use. They are available from most hardware stores and any shop that sells welding supplies. Generally these are formulated to combine the cleaning power of the acid-based fluxes with other ingredients that neutralize the acid. Even so, there are always traces of acids or acid-forming compounds in these fluxes, so care should be taken to clean to completed joint well.

Another class of soft solder flux uses grease or Vaseline as a base. These fluxes generally have no acid problems, but pay for this with limited oxide prevention power.

Hard soldering fluxes

Borax is the classic hard soldering flux of the goldsmith, so much so, in fact, that at one time members of the profession called each other "borax brothers." Though now the traditional slate grinding plate and solid cone of borax have all but disappeared from the studio, borax is still the most important ingredient in hard solder fluxes. Boric acid, another form of the same compound, is used to preserve a polished finish on an item being repaired and is the best hope against unsightly firescale.

Despite their similarity, borax and boric acid behave differently and therefore bring different things to the process. Both materials form a glassy melt at glowing temperatures and dissociate to make boron trioxide, B_2O_3. This reacts with the oxides of the metals being heated to form borates, for example:

$$CuO + B_2O_3 \rightarrow Cu(BO_2)_2$$

copper oxide   boron trioxide   copper metaborate

At temperatures below 900°C (1650°F), boric acid is deposited as a thick glassy layer on the surface of the metal, as diagrammed in figure 8.3a. While this provides some protection against oxidation, the film is so thick it also prevents further penetration of additional boron trioxide, which would assist in the oxide protection. This explains why boric acid is not recommended as a flux when working below this temperature.

When the temperature is raised above that point, as for instance when soldering brass and nickel silver, the glassy film becomes fluid enough to allow for further penetration of boron trioxide. This is shown in figure 8.3b.

Borax, on the other hand, breaks apart to form boron trioxide and sodium metaborate when heated to its melting point. The boron trioxide dissolves metallic oxides to form metaborates. These are dissolved by sodium metaborate and carried away so new boron trioxide can arrive at the oxide layer in order to work in the same manner (figure 8.3c). The process will continue until the boron trioxide is used up or the oxide is completely dissolved.

Making your own flux

While plain borax can be used as a flux, it has several disadvantages. It becomes active at a temperature where some oxides have started to form, it puffs up when heated and it does not dissolve in water. It is therefore much more common nowadays to use commercial preparations that have been formulated to reduce or resolve these shortcomings. These go by several trade names, (e.g. Handy Paste Flux), and can be purchased from any welding or jewelry equipment

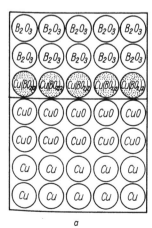

a   b   c

Figure 8.3
Effect of flux on the metal oxide surface. a) boric acid, melted, under 90°C (194°F) and b) above 90°C, c) borax, melted.

supplier. In some cases, refiners will supply a flux specially formulated for a special alloy.

An exception to this, however, arises in silversmithing, when copper-bearing alloys like sterling silver are going to be heated many times. In these cases, where the risk of firescale formation is especially strong, additional care is recommended. The joint being soldered is prepared as usual and painted with a proprietary borax flux. The piece is set onto the soldering pan, warmed slightly and then dusted with borax powder to create a protective film across the surface. Because of the relatively high melting point of borax, an even better solution is to mix up the following recipe:

2 parts borax
2 parts potash (potassium carbonate)
1 part cooking salt

This mixture is also recommended as a flux for melting and was previously mentioned in that context. This mixture has a significantly lower melting point than plain borax, which accelerates its ability to protect sterling silver. Soldering proceeds as usual; remove the glassy flux coating by boiling the piece in water.

8.1.3 HEAT SOURCES

Soldering irons
Though their use is rare in jewelry fabrication, there might be an instance when a metalsmith needs to use a soldering iron. Certainly work in tinplate and pewter will call for one. The most familiar and popular version consists of a resistance coil that is heated electrically. A small version, called a soldering pencil, has the advantage of being a lightweight tool with low heat and a thin point that reaches into tight places. When more heat is needed, another electric tool, this one shaped like an electric drill can be used. For very large pieces there is nothing better than the traditional thumb-sized block of copper mounted on a steel rod that is equipped with a wooden handle. This version is heated in a gas hotplate or the flame of a torch.

In every case a wire or block, usually copper, is heated and used to melt the soft solder. The surface of the copper will become covered with oxides that will prevent efficient transfer of heat. To correct this, clean the tool periodically with files and dip the tip of the iron into flux now and again. To reduce the build up of oxides on the copper tip, coat it with a layer of hard silver solder because this will oxidize much slower.

Natural gas (City or Town gas and Stink gas)
Natural gas is familiar in our everyday life: households and businesses are supplied with it through an interconnected system of pipes that generally run under the street. Because it was first made available in communities, it is also known as "town gas" or "city gas" Where it is available the initial cost of having pipes installed by a licensed plumber (the only way to go) is offset by inexpensive fuel and ease of use.

When used with compressed air, natural gas produces flames in the vicinity of 1100°C (2000°F). When bottled oxygen is introduced into the flame, temperatures of 1800°C (3275°F) are possible.

Natural gas torches are widely available and can be used for annealing, soldering and melting. Because the pressure is low and controlled at the source of supply, no regulators are needed. These torches are versatile, simple to use and traditionally require little or no maintenance.

On the other hand, there are significant disadvantages as well:

– natural gas is poisonous
– as a gas-air mixture it is explosive
– because of impurities mixed in (especially sulfur compounds), town gas can be so strongly contaminated that the metals can be damaged, particularly when melting

Propane C_3H_8
As goldsmiths continue to relocate in less urban areas where natural gas lines are not as easily available, propane is gaining increased use in the field. Many smiths find it cleaner, safer and more flexible than natural gas. It is familiar through its use in backyard grills and camping trailers, and because of those applications it is becoming very easy to find a source for refilling tanks.

Main Constituent in % Volume	Density in kg/m³	Combustion Point in °C	Maximum Air to Gas Ratio for Combustion, in % Volume	Flame Temperature in °C		Theoretical Amount of Air for 1 m³ Gas in m³
				atmosphere	with oxygen	
City Gas						
50 Hydrogen H_2 34 Methane CH_4 8 Carbon Monoxide CO	.68	560	6 : 35	1100	1800	3.86
Earth Gases						
80...90 Methane CH_4 1...14 Nitrogen N 3...7 Ethane CH_3-CH_4	.85	645	5 : 13	1700	2790	9.55
Propane						
100 Propane CH_3-CH_2-CH_3	2400	510	2.3 : 9.5	1900	2750	23.8
Acetylene						
100 Aceylene HC = CH	1171	335	3 : 82	2325	3200	11.9

Table 8.3
Characteristics of combustible gases used in soldering.

Propane becomes fluid under pressure and in this state can be stored in steel bottles. The usual arrangement is to keep about 80% of the contents as a liquid, with the remaining volume as a gas. This compensates for changes in temperature that will make the fuel expand or contract. This is called liquid propane *gas* or LPG, and is the usual form, the one available through hardware stores, camping suppliers and welding shops.

At temperatures above 20°C (68°F) the vapor pressure of propane is 0.75 MPa. One kilogram of liquid propane produces 511 liters of gas, which means that the familiar squat white tank, which holds 20 pounds (9.072 kg) of liquid contains 4, 636 liters of gas.

Like natural gas, propane is poisonous and explosive when mixed with air. It is heavier than air and will therefore accumulate at the floor in the event of a leak, adding to its sinister potential. Because the gas is under pressure in the tank, a regulator is needed to control the force of the escaping gas. Hose connections need to be stronger than with city gas, just in case the regulator is incorrectly set and allows too much pressure into the hose. Pure propane is odorless but commercial propane has small amounts of butane, ethane and pentane added to create a characteristic smell.

Propane has these advantages over town gas.
– greater heat content
– a greater air requirement
– a slower speed of combustion
– higher heat value
– no significant accompanying impurities

Acetylene
This highly combustible gas is well known for its use in welding. When used with atmospheric air (commonly called a plumber's torch, or a Prest-o-lite) acetylene is capable of producing a flame with a tem-

301

perature of 1800°C (3270°F). When pure oxygen is combined with the gas in an oxy-acetylene torch the resulting flame achieves an impressive 3000°C (5400°F).

Though rarely done in the industrialized west today, it is possible to make acetylene in a small, portable gas generator. The gas develops from the reaction of carbide with water:

$$CaC_2 + 2\,H_2O \rightarrow C_2H_2 + Ca(OH)_2$$

calcium   water   acetylene   calcium
carbide   hydroxide

The generator is filled with a certain amount of water and a steel basket filled with pieces of carbide is hung in it. A reaction begins. The gas developed drives the water from the carbide, the gas generation stops. If gas is removed, the water surface rises again creating a self-sustaining reaction that replenishes the supply as gas is used. The generator is equipped with a safety switch to guard against excess pressure – with proper care it is not dangerous. One kilogram of carbide produces about 300 liters of burnable gas.

Like propane, acetylene forms an explosive mixture with air. As with any gas, all fittings must be checked regularly and returned to an authorized dealer if any problem is detected. Never modify a fitting on a gas tank! If you detect a gas odor, clear the area, open windows and doors and call a qualified specialist.

In most goldsmithing studios, where the need for acetylene is relatively small, it is more typical to purchase acetylene in steel tanks. These can be as small as a coffee thermos or as large as a person. The sizes usually used in American studios are called "MC," the smallest, or "B," which is about two feet tall and 8 inches in diameter. The larger sizes are typically leased, while the smaller tanks are often purchased.

Acetylene does not readily become a liquid like propane, so it is dissolved in acetone. This mixture is absorbed by either diatomaceous earth or a felt-like material that is packed into the tank. The internal pressure of a tank is .8 MPa; one liter of acetone absorbs 360 liters of acetylene.

Because the gas is under pressure in the tank, a regulator is needed to control the rate at which it is allowed to escape. Without a regulator a full tank

would eject the gas so fast it would blow out the torch. As a tank empties, the flame will lose power. Most regulators allow for pressure to be set, though some are preset by the manufacturer. The usual pressure for most torches is around 0.2 MPa. Consult the technical information supplied by the manufacturer with each torch to determine the correct setting.

In order to make it impossible to confuse the various valves and steel tanks used with torches, standardized color designations and different kinds of connections are required by law for the valves. (see table 8.4.). As a rule of thumb, fuel gases and their hoses are red; oxygen tanks are usually either orange or green.

Torches

Regardless of style, materials or scale, every jeweler works with torches. Every torch has it special properties and each goldsmith has a favorite torch, but there are many elements that are common to all. For one thing, fuel and air are always mixed in the tip to create a combustible mixture. In some case this air is drawn from the atmosphere as the suction of the fuel gas passing through the tip pulls it into the tube-shaped nozzle. In other cases air is supplied through a second hose, either as atmospheric air driven by a compressor or in the form of pure oxygen. In these cases, both the fuel and air has its own regulating valve.

NATURAL GAS TORCH

A classic jewelers torch uses natural gas mixed with air from the worker's lungs. A familiar model, shown in figure 8.4a, delivers the gas through a thin tube that is controlled with its own valve. Air is blown in a continuous stream to create a flame suitable for soldering. In this case the tube is held directly in the mouth, so the jeweler is forced be very close to the work.

In the model shown in figure 8.4a, the gas supply is controlled by a valve and the air is supplied through a rubber hose a couple feet long. This allows greater mobility during soldering and allows the worker to sit more comfortably. Though it requires some practice to develop breath control, this style torch has the advantage of low cost and instant, almost infinite control.

Table 8.4
Characteristics of gas tanks
and their fittings.

Gas Type	Color Code	Reduction Valve Connection Type	Tank Pressure in PPI
Propane	Red	Left-hand thread W 21.8 x ¼"	0.75 at 20° C
Acetylene	Yellow	Gripping connector	1.8
Oxygen	Green or Orange	Right-hand thread R ¾"	1.5

It was a logical extension from here to include a bellows, in which a mechanical device was used to supply air. The development of electrically driven air compressors offered a further logical extension. In a torch first associated with glassworkers, natural gas is mixed with air delivered from a compressor. This torch has proven itself very useful in the goldsmithing studio, where the flame can be made soft enough to evaporate flux or hot enough to melt even platinum alloys.

The traditional glassblower's torch is appropriate for a goldsmith. Either compressed air or pure oxygen can be added, making this torch extremely versatile. It can be used for everything from delicate silver brazing to welding platinum.

Annealing, melting and large hollowware work require a larger torch to keep the worker's hands a safe distance from the heat of the work. Large torches are generally about 40 cm (15.7") long with a mixing tube with an inside diameter of about 10–12 mm (½"). The air for combustion was traditionally supplied by a foot bellows, but it is far more common nowadays to use an electrically driven air compressor.

Separate valves are used to control the gas and air flow. When the gas burns alone (i.e. without introducing any air) this torch will create a soft, low temperature flame that is useful for preheating the workpiece to dry off flux.

When a small volume of air is supplied to the torch the flame, which was yellow, will become blue and form a soft-edged bushy flame. This medium temperature flame is appropriate for soldering bezels or wires of small diameters because the heat of the flame is still limited.

If the air supply is increased the flame will become sharper, more narrow, and paler blue. This flame is well suited for annealing because it develops the heat required for it and uniformly washes over the annealed articles.

If the air supply is increased still further a pointed conical flame forms at the head of the torch opening in the direction of the stream of air. It consists of two flame cones one within the other. If insufficient oxygen is available, the outer cone is brightly illuminated

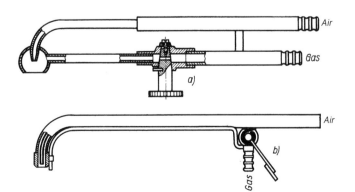

Figure 8.4
Gas soldering torch, mouth blown air.
a) gas supply with regulator screw, air supplied by hose,
b) gas supply regulated by pressure lever, air directly supplied through soldering tube.

because unburned soot particles glow; with a saturated oxygen component this outer flame cone is bluish, the inner one dark.

Because of the unburned carbon monoxide the inner cone of flame is reducing and the flame temperature in this zone is low. The outer cone is an oxidizing flame, or one in which there is more oxygen than can be consumed by the volume of gas present. The highest flame temperature occurs just in front of this sharp pointed flame. When soldering, the torch should be held far enough away from the work to allow this "hot zone" to reach the metal and do its work. If the torch is too close and the inner cone is touching the metal, there is a significant reduction of temperature. This slows the soldering operation (or even makes it impossible) and is obviously something to avoid.

In general the first step is to "wash" the piece to be soldered with a soft bushy flame until the flux no longer bubbles. The bushy flame is then made sharper by adding air and the workpiece is heated further until it glows evenly. At this point slightly more air is introduced to create a hot pointed flame. The hot zone just in front of this cone is directed at the solder area. If it was sufficiently preheated the solder will flow quickly and fill the seam cleanly.

If the workpiece as a whole was not preheated correctly, soldering temperatures are created only at the surface in the vicinity of the solder. In this case the solder melts but cannot fill up the seam. Instead the solder fuses with the metal being joined and alloys itself; this is called a "cold joint" and is much weaker than a proper seam.

Large work is traditionally placed on a turntable to allow it to be rotated into the flame to make it easier to heat evenly. In the case of very large pieces it is sometimes necessary to use a second torch or to work on a bed of glowing coals to create the appropriate temperature.

PROPANE TORCH

Most natural gas torches can be used with propane, but in each case it is wise to check in person with a local authority. Take your tank and torch to a welding shop and ask for instruction in its proper use. Propane torches are usually used with pure oxygen or com-

pressed air, but they can be set up for use with a foot bellows or blowpipe. In the latter case it is important that a backflow valve be in place to make it impossible to accidentally inhale the gas.

Propane can also be fitted with a gas/atmosphere torch, an arrangement in which the flow of pressurized fuel gas sucks air into the torch where it swirls to form a burnable mixture. In this case the torch has a single valve that controls the flow of the fuel gas. As more fuel is released it automatically draws in more air, keeping the mixture at its proper proportion. This torch has interchangeable torch tips to create flames of different sizes.

The intensity of the flame is controlled by the regulation of the gas supply. Because of the high gas pressure a particularly high pressure hose must be used in the supply line.

ACETYLENE TORCH

Acetylene tanks can be purchased or leased from local suppliers in several sizes. The smallest is called the MC, and the one most typically found in jewelers' studios is called a B tank. This stands about two feet high and can be easily carried by hand. The size of the tank depends upon the need. Larger sizes are available for commercial and industrial applications: consult with a welding supplier for recommended sizes.

In order to be used a tank must be equipped with a regulator, a device that allows the gas to leave the tank at an even pressure, along with a recommended flashback protector. These can be purchased through local welding companies or jewelry suppliers and are universal to all torches and tanks.

Perhaps the most common jewelers acetylene torch is the gas/atmosphere type, in which the force of the gas moving through the torch head draws the necessary air into the tip where it is mixed with the gas to make a combustible fuel. These torches can be instantly recognized in that they have only one valve. As the flow of gas is increased, the quantity of air is automatically increased to maintain the same, precalculated proportion.

This versatile torch is easy to use and offers a wide range of flames, especially when the torch is outfitted with a variety of tips. The resulting flame is focused, contained and significantly hotter than a natural gas/air torch. It can be used equally for gold and silver work, and lends itself to everything but the extremes of very tiny and very large work.

Hotter flames can be achieved when acetylene is used with pure oxygen. In this case a tank of oxygen, fitted with its own regulator, is connected to the torch. Many manufacturers make torches for this fuel combination, which is widely used for welding steel. The extremely high temperatures that can be reached (over 3000°C, 5400°F) make this an excellent torch for fusing, melting and large scale work, though care must be taken to avoid accidental melting.

Torches made specifically for jewelry work have very small flames that allow tremendous control in directing the flame onto a piece. This hot local flame has particular use in repair, where even jewelry set with stones can often be soldered without danger of heat spreading to the gem.

EQUIPMENT FOR MICRO WELDING AND SOLDERING
This family of torches has tips that resemble medical syringes, yielding flames that look like pencil points. Though small, these oxygen-fed torches achieve the same high temperatures as their big brothers, reaching 3000°C (5400°F). Torches are manufactured to work with either propane/oxygen or acetylene/oxygen. Research which fuels are available before purchasing a torch because they cannot be interchanged.

Because of the high temperature delivered by these torches, heat is fed in more rapidly than the thermal conductivity of the metallic workpiece can carry it away. Normal preheating of the workpiece is unnecessary; the flame can be focused directly on the solder seam. Because the flame is so intense and local, large surfaces and thick parts cannot be soldered with a miniature soldering flame.

As mentioned before, all tanks will require a regulator, and these are made to be specific for each gas. In order to prevent accidents, each family of gas uses a different nozzle size, making it impossible to screw an incorrect regulator onto a tank.

WATER TORCH EQUIPMENT
The familiar formula for water, H_2O tells us that for every atom of hydrogen two atoms of oxygen exist.

Figure 8.5
Water torch. (J.Schmalz Company, Pforzheim)

These are, of course, ideal ingredients for a torch, a fuel and the oxygen necessary to combust it. An ingenious torch uses the electrolytic decomposition of water to create the fuel for a torch, commonly called a water torch (figure 8.5).

In the equipment a 29.4% potassium hydroxide solution is decomposed. In the watery solution KOH dissociates to K^+ and OH^- An electrolytic reaction occurs:

cathode
$K^+ + e^- \rightarrow K$
(unstable in water)

anode
$OH^- - e^- \rightarrow OH$
(unsaturated atom group)

The immediate reaction with the water is

$2K + 2H_2O \rightarrow 2KOH + H_2$
$2OH + H_2O \rightarrow 2H_2O + \frac{1}{2}O_2$

The machine operates on regular household electricity, with the electrolysis controlled by a transformer and rectifier to regulate the quantity of gas produced. The electrolyte is regenerated by additions of distilled water; the proportion of KOH remains unchanged. The equipment, which operates very economically, uses a micro-torch with needle tips; the flame temperature lies in the range of 2000°– 3000°C (3600°–5400°F).

A larger flame can be created by interposing a "booster," which has the added advantage of making

305

Figure 8.6
Universal micro soldering and welding unit. (J. Schmalz Co. Pforzheim)

a reducing flame. The gas is run through a container with methyl alcohol before it arrives at the tip:

$$CH_3OH \ + \ \tfrac{1}{2}O_2 \ \rightarrow \ CO \ + \ H_2 \ + \ H_2O$$

8.1.4 SOLDERING SURFACES

One of the most universal and time-honored soldering surfaces used by goldsmiths is a rectangular block of charcoal. This is made from a knot-free piece of wood and is generally treated to inhibit it burning up quickly with use. To protect the block against breaking if dropped, notch the corners and wrap it with stout wire. Charcoal has the advantage of providing a reducing environment and allowing for the surface to be sanded smooth when worn, but also has the disadvantage of continuing to burn after soldering is completed. To avoid the risk of fires, sprinkle water on the block at the end of each soldering session.

Lightweight firebricks, such as are used to line electric kilns, make excellent soldering blocks. They can be easily cut with handsaws and abraded smooth on any coarse flat surface such as sandpaper or even concrete. They reflect heat back reasonably well and do not catch fire.

Asbestos was formerly used in soldering surfaces but today we know enough about its health risks to completely ban it from the studio. Microscopic asbestos fibers are taken into the lungs where their barbed points damage the delicate cells and can cause inflammations that lead to cancer. Do not use asbestos and asbestos containing materials!

Several heat resistant materials are available. They can be pressed into sheets for use as soldering blocks. Each has its advocates and detractors: experience and personal soldering style are probably the most important factors in choosing a block that suits your needs.

8.1.5 SOFT SOLDERING PROCEDURES

Because of the contamination inherent in using a low melting metal like tin on a precious metal, no responsible goldsmith will use soft solders except as a last resort. As mentioned above, the development of micro torches makes possible joins that would have been difficult or impossible only a generation ago, for which the soft solder was, in fact, the last resort.

Though tempting, it is not recommended to use soft solder because the piece has been ruined by previous use of a low temperature solder. It is better practice to convince the customer of the advantage of hard soldering and to explain the importance of completely removing the tin, which will of course raise the cost of the repair.

Recent improvements in adhesives now make them a viable alternative to the lead-tin solder used for years as a repair tool. When applied well, glues can have as much strength as solder without the complication of contamination.

Tin soldering has the following drawbacks:

- The strength of the solder is significantly lower than hard solder.
- After a piece has been joined with soft solder, no more hard soldering can occur: at hard soldering temperatures, the tin solder eats into the precious metal through alloy formation.
- If soft solder residues end up in a crucible of precious metal, the entire alloy becomes unusably brittle because of the formation of intermetallic compounds.
- All scrapers, files, tweezers, soldering surfaces, fluxes and solders used for soft soldering should be stored in a special box.
- Work surface and sweeps drawer must be carefully cleaned before and after working with soft solder.
- Scrap containing (or that might contain) tin or lead should be stored separately from normal filing residues.

SAFETY NOTE: Tin solder and all the equipment for soft soldering can on no account come in contact with precious metals and the tools for working them!

Cleaning for soldering
The first step in all soldering is to insure that no film of dirt, grease or oxides coats the surfaces to be joined. An easy way to insure that the metal is exposed is to rub the surface with a scraper, sandpaper, or a Scotch-Brite pad. The solder is treated in the same way. Other cleaning methods such as pickling, brass brushing, glass brushing and treatment with harsh soaps are all possible as long as the end result is clean metal.

Fitting
Careful fitting of parts to be soldered will result in an easier process, a stronger joint and a cleaner seam – three good reasons to devote as much time as necessary to insure that the fit is very good! Because the strength of soft solder is significantly less than hard solder, special configurations are sometimes needed to compensate, as illustrated in figure 8.7.

• If a setting or a bezel is to be soft soldered onto the piece, attach a tightly fitted frame to one unit first with hard solder, then soft solder the walls to this unit (8.7a).
• When two pieces are soldered nose-to-nose, the limited surface areas are insufficient to make a solid joint with soft solder. In these situations a strip or collar of metal is added, preferably by attaching one side with hard solder (8.7b & c).
• When an ornamental element of a ring cannot be attached (or reattached) to a shank with hard solder, the solution is to make a tube of metal to equal the correct ring size. The upper portion of the ring is soldered into place with soft solder, then the shank is slid over the tube and carefully soldered into place. The excess tube is removed to leave a solid and almost invisible construction (8.7d).
• This faux rivet is used to secure a panel, such as an enameled unit, that cannot be soldered. The pins are hard soldered onto the base unit, then the panel (into which carefully located holes have been

drilled) is slid into position. Small jump rings made from square wire are fitted over the pins and slid into place. They are soldered with a small amount of soft solder, then shaped with files or a cup bur to resemble a rivet (8.7e).

Applying the flux and soft solder
Flux is applied to the entire area to be joined. Liquids can be brushed on, or squirted from the tip of a dispenser in which they are sometimes supplied. Paste flux can be applied with a brush, but a disposable cotton swab (e.g. *Q-Tip*) is a more convenient tool.

When using a soldering iron, the tip is first cleaned then coated with solder. When a flame is used, the solder is cut into small chips in the same way as is typical for hard soldering. This process is made easier if the solder wire is hammered or rolled into a thin strip. Cut the solder pieces as small as possible so they will melt efficiently. Larger pieces tend to roll up into a sphere as soon as heat is applied and require coaxing with the point of a scribe to make them flow into a seam.

In some cases it is useful if one of the parts being joined is coated with a smooth layer of solder: this process is called tinning, and the pre-coated metal would be described as tinned. To accomplish this,

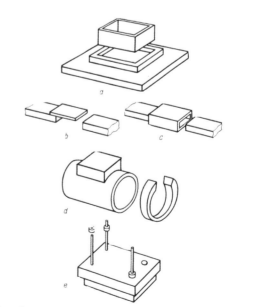

Figure 8.7
Enlargement of the contact surfaces for soft soldering.

either flux the surface and scatter small pieces of solder around it, or load the tip of a soldering iron with excess solder and use the iron to "paint" the solder across the surface.

Solder pieces are set across a fluxed seam and heat is directed from beneath where possible to draw the solder into the joint. Because the workpiece retains heat, be careful not to move the work until the solder has had a chance to solidify, a process that can take as long as a minute in some cases.

Flowing the solder

When using a soldering iron, (the old-fashioned, heavy block of copper heated in a flame), solder is introduced into a joint by first loading a thick layer onto the iron in much the way that a paintbrush is loaded when painting a house. The cleaned and fluxed metal is then heated by laying the iron onto it. When it reaches the correct temperature, the solder will flow off the iron into the joint. If more solder is needed, the iron is reheated, recoated with flux, and again set against a block of solder to reload it.

When using an electric soldering gun (which is much more common today), it is typical to feed solder into a joint as needed directly from the coil of solder wire. First, plug in the tool and allow it ample time to heat up. It is frustrating and inefficient to attempt to solder with a cold tool. Clean the tip of the gun by touching it into a can of flux. If the tip is very dirty, turn off the power and file it until clean metal is revealed. Prepare the joint as above, making it clean and well fluxed, then hold the tip of the gun on a single spot to bring the workpiece up to temperature. Test this by tentatively touching the tip of a solder wire near to the place where the tip is in contact with the workpiece. When the solder starts to flow, slide the tool along the seam, simultaneously feeding a little more solder into the joint.

When using a flame, remember that the temperature needed for soft solder is considerably less than what most torches achieve. Use a slow, bushy flame, and keep the torch several inches from the workpiece. Clean, fit and flux the joint, and lay small pieces of solder across the seam. Heat the areas adjacent to the seam, avoiding the solder itself with the flame. The idea is to heat the metal and allow that heat to melt the solder. Play the torch lightly across the surface, pulling the torch away frequently to allow time for the heat to flow through the piece. Remove the torch as soon as the solder starts to flow.

If for some reason the solder does not flow, or does not go where you want it to go, resist the temptation to apply more heat. That will not solve the problem and will create a mess! Soft solder fluxes have a narrow active range: when overheated they burn, leaving a thick black residue that is difficult to remove. The trick in soft soldering with a flame is in knowing when the correct temperature has been reached. If the solder has not flowed by this point, stop, cool the piece, clean it and start over.

Cleaning

An experienced worker is sometimes able to use exactly the correct amount of solder and make it go exactly where it is needed. In other cases, excess solder must be removed. The ideal tool for this is a scraper, which is dragged across the surface to slice off thin layers of solder. Be patient: it's better to take many thin slices than to try to cut too deeply. Because soft solder is so much more malleable than sterling, it is quite easy to feel the difference when the tool reaches through the solder and touches the piece itself. Keep in mind that it might be necessary to make scrapers to reach into tight corners. Files and burs can also be used to clean away excess solder but bear in mind that they will fill quickly, and that they must be thoroughly cleaned before using the tools again on precious metals.

Pickling is unnecessary because soft soldering occurs under the annealing temperature of the precious metal alloys. If done properly, the only change on sterling will be a mild tarnish than can be removed with a rouge cloth or a light buffing.

8.1.6 HARD SOLDERING PROCEDURES

In this connection "hard" means not only high melting, but also refers to the greater strength of the joint. Hard solders have significantly more strength than the soft solders just mentioned because hard solders diffuse into the internal structure of a metal. Such a soldering withstands high stresses during rolling, forging, bending and forming. Because of the small difference between the flow temperature of the solder and the melting zone of the metals being joined, more extensive preparations are necessary for hard soldering. Greater knowledge of flame control is required to create a durable connection without damage to the metals being joined.

Cleaning

The preparations mentioned above for soft soldering apply here as well. The workpiece and solder must be clean and the parts must make a perfect fit. This is particularly important in hard soldering because this solder does not bridge a gap, but instead migrates into the structure of the pieces being joined.

Cleanliness of solder and pieces refers not only to the removal of oxides (tarnish) but to invisible finger oils and the white pickle finish as well. Failure to clean pieces thoroughly will invite a tenuous joint that might hold for a while but will fail eventually.

Fitting

The secret to good soldering is in careful fitting. If the pieces fit together perfectly, the operation is easier, the clean up goes faster and the finished joint is invisible. Time spent on this procedure is repaid by efficiency in later steps.

In proper soldering the gap must be large enough to allow flux and solder to penetrate the seam. Ideally there is enough solder to completely fill the joint without having excess that must be filed off. Experience is the best teacher of the correct amount to use.

The solder seam should be a maximum of 0.1 mm wide with goldsmithing work – that is, about the thickness of a razor blade. In the case of hollowware, the gap can be double this width. When made fluid by heat, solder will be sucked into the narrow crack of a well prepared seam by capillary action and will result in a clean joint of great strength. It is also possible, with a little experience, to flood a bad seam, but this poor craftsmanship will show up in the final polishing. In addition, such a joint is not as durable as a properly made seam.

Pieces that have been stressed should be annealed before fitting is attempted or you might end up doing the work twice. If a ring, for instance, has been ham-

mered round and then made to fit neatly at the joint, it will expand when first heated, opening the joint enough to prevent solder flow. To prevent this, anneal immediately after forming and only then complete the fitting operation.

All enclosed hollow bodies must be drilled before heating to allow the release of the air trapped inside. This air will expand when heated and if not given a means of escape, will either pop out a seam or cause the form to explode.

Because of the strength of hard solder, thin pieces can be joined without the reinforcing plates suggested for soft soldering. Even so, it is good practice on thin sections to angle the facing planes of a butt joint so as to increase the surface areas being joined (figure 8.8a).

Similarly, when a stress situation is anticipated on a vertical rod (figure 8.8b) it is preferable to either drill a hole in the plate or create a foot on the wire. Though small differences, either of these devices will increase the amount of surface involved in the seam dramatically.

Figure 8.8c illustrates a situation in which a seat is soldered into a bezel. In the case on the left, the bezel simply sits upon the sheet; on the right we see a variation in which the plate that makes up the seat is allowed to project below the outer bezel. It has been fitted into a hole in the base sheet, locating it and again significantly increasing its purchase on the work. This joint has the additional advantage of being easy to solder from the back.

It is typically difficult to align hollow pieces for soldering, as seen in figure 8.8d. Insert a thin sheet, which will permit easy adjustment of the pieces and provide a ledge on which the solder can be set. After soldering the excess metal is sawn off.

When a joint will have to withstand considerable stress, such as wide ring shanks or a broken spoon handle, the method shown in figure 8.8e is recommended. Slots are cut into the workpiece at right angles to the seam and a narrow connecting strip of sheet metal is inserted and soldered together into place, along with the seam. Excess is of course trimmed away in finishing.

Often a piece must be inserted into a ring shank, either to change the size or to replace a damaged section. In order to keep this piece secure when soldering and to guarantee the greatest possible stability in later use, it is filed to a dovetail shape just at the ends of the shank, inserted and soldered in place. (figure 8.8f).

Attaching a shank to an ornamental element on a ring is often difficult because the pieces shift just as the solder flows. In almost all cases a simple and useful remedy is to file a step at the ends of the shank. Often only a thin ledge is all that is needed to support the shank during soldering (figure 8.8g). When the shank is correctly wrapped with binding wire, as illustrated in figure 8.12a, the soldering operation is precise and efficient.

When attaching a bezel to a sheet, there can be a problem with solder spills around the outside of the bezel. A trick to avoid this is to premelt ("sweat") the solder onto the bottom edge of the bezel first, then set it into place on the sheet and reheat. Solder has an affinity to its first place of contact: if it is already coating the bezel, it is likely to stay there rather than spread onto the sheet.

Special problems present themselves when soldering layers of sheet, where the surface area is greatly increased, and possible warping makes it difficult to guaranty tight seams. A common solution is to premelt or "sweat" solder onto one of the units. This can then be placed into its proper location, and if necessary, clamped there as shown in figure 8.9. These clamps are not commercially made, but are simply bits of steel or nickel silver wire bent to shape as needed.

When solder is to be fed into a seam from outside it is helpful to roughen the areas being joined with burs or sanding disks. This will create tiny channels along which the solder can flow. For long joins, it is helpful to create a tapering seam, or a gap that is slightly wider at the beginning than at the end. This arrangement will pull the fluid solder into the seam, propelling it all the way to the end.

Solder seams on hollowware
When hollowware is developed from volumetric forms bent up from sheet metal (a process called seaming), the sheet is cut according to a pattern, bent around and soldered together. This seam is strongly stressed during the subsequent hammer work and therefore must be particularly durable.

To increase the contact surfaces, hammer both edges of the join and file them to a slope to make an overlap joint (figure 8.10a). The purpose of the slope is to create an overlap that remains the same thickness as the rest of the piece. A problem arises when bending up a form like the one shown because the two sides slide across one another as binding wire is tightened.

The solution to this problem is a keyed seam as shown in figure 8.10c. A pattern is created and lengthened slightly to allow for the overlap. The distribution of the keys is illustrated in figure 8.10b.; both outer keys always have to be on what will be the inside of the form. The keys are cut with a saw and bent up. The other edge is hammered thin and filed so it fits between the prepared keys. The form is pulled into a cylinder and the keys are tapped down with a mallet.

Typically the form is then secured with binding wire, well fluxed and soldered. After pickling the joint can be planished smooth on a polished steel stake and the form can be raised without thought of the joint.

Assembly
Because of the high temperatures and longer heating needed when hard soldering, it is often necessary to arrange an assembly that does not rely on hand grip alone. Ideally the parts will be fixed securely so the metalsmith's attention can be focused on the location and progress of the heat. Assuming that one hand is needed to hold the torch, it is useful to have the other hand free to manipulate parts or add more solder if needed.

Every assembly is different and each goldsmith will need to invent unique arrangements as needed to hold parts together until the solder flows. The basic methods below describe some general situations, but creative interpretation is called for!

SOLDERING TWEEZERS
It's a good idea to have separate tweezers for working under the torch because this will inevitably damage the tips slightly. Soldering tweezers are longer than standard tweezers (to delay the transfer of heat) and

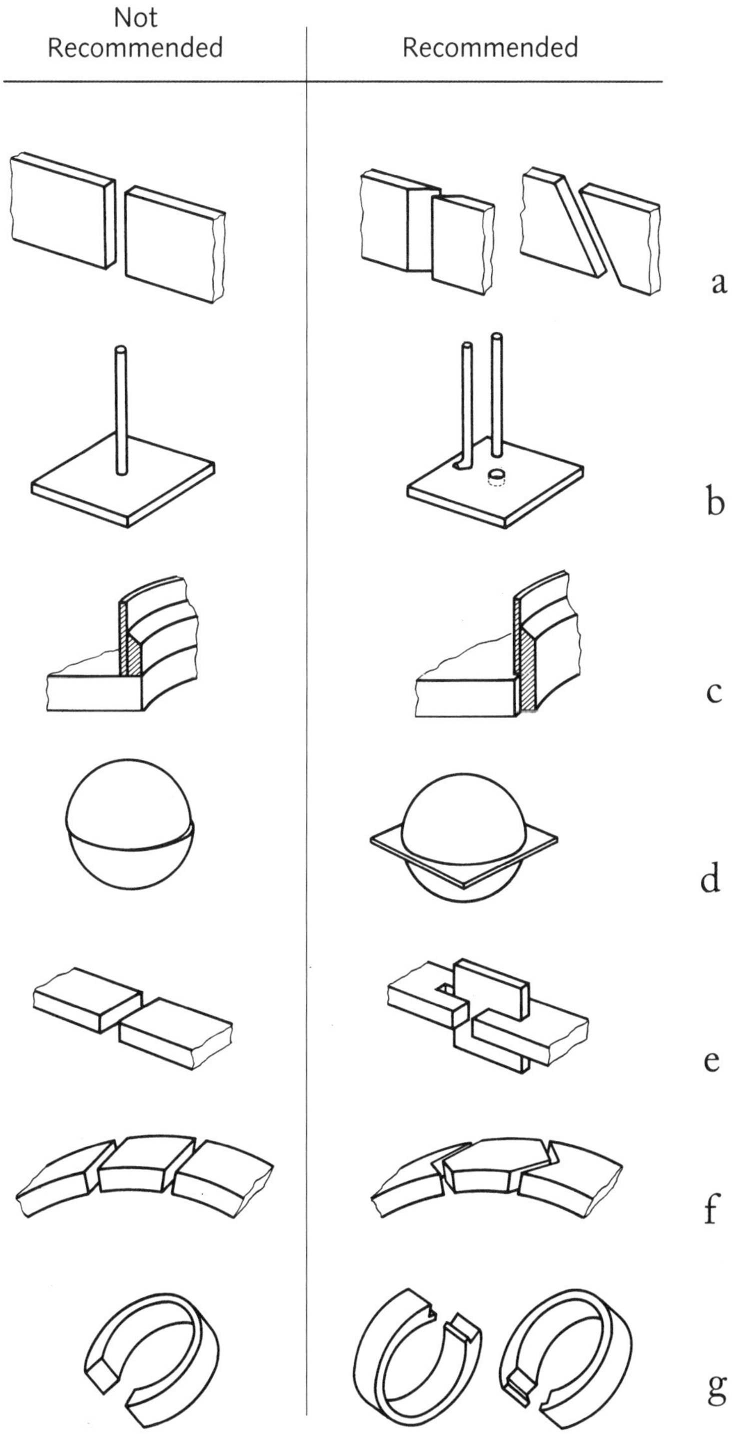

Not Recommended	Recommended	

Figure 8.8
Enlarging contact surfaces for
hard soldering.

a — Scarfed or beveled edges

b — Securing a post by drilling an
anchor hole or flaring the base

c — Attaching to the broadest edge

d — Providing additional material
where needed

e — Reinforcing a joint

f — Keying a joint to increase
surface area

g — Notching a ring shank to accept a
head or other addition

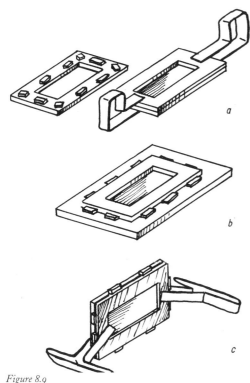

Figure 8.9
Soldering a plate.
a) pallions spread on the back side, b) pallions placed on the outside,
c) soldering joint on a frame.

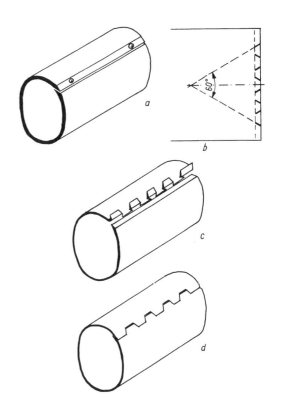

Figure 8.10
Soldering joint preparation for silversmithing work.
a) lap joint, b) cutting the tabs, c) prepared and d) finished lap joint
with tabs.

are usually made of heavier steel for the same reason. A variation, called self-locking or cross-lock tweezers, holds pieces without needing to be constantly pinched in the fingers. These are especially useful in setting up work for soldering, but have the disadvantages of creating a heat sink. Be cautious about attaching steel elements to work, especially small pieces, because they can make it difficult to bring the work up to soldering temperatures.

The best locking tweezers consist of quartz rods between which the parts are held. These have significant advantages: heat conductivity is very minimal, neither flux nor solder stick to the tweezers, the quartz jaws are easily replaced if broken, and the jaws lock in any desired position through a clamping device.

A soldering board with adjustable clamps (figure 8.11) provides an infinite range of adjustments, but

can sometimes require a lot of fussy work to get all the pieces arranged. The time-honored methods of pins, wire and hand methods are often still the best.

SOLDERING SURFACES
The charcoal soldering block has proven itself for generations.
• If it has been properly prepared it is only partially burnt and therefore has a long life span.
• Because it absorbs very little heat, work heats rapidly.
• The surface can be easily made smooth with a coarse file or sandpaper.
• It is relatively easy to carve depressions or to scratch grooves to hold pieces.
• Parts can be pressed into the charcoal to hold them in place.

• Pins and other soldering aids can be pressed directly into the charcoal.

The primary liability of charcoal blocks is the fact that they continue to glow as burning embers and can be a fire hazard. In addition, the cost of blocks has recently gone up, making them more expensive than some other alternatives.

According to occupational health and safety laws, asbestos soldering surfaces may no longer be used. In recent years they have been replaced by asbestos-free, heat resistant materials that are shaped into blocks and panels. Various manufacturers offer a range of similar materials. Each worker should experiment to discover the combination of durability, heat reflection and softness that works best for his or her personal soldering style.

Whichever material, it is sometimes helpful to modify the soldering block, especially in production situations. If, for example, several wires are to be soldered onto a round setting at regular intervals, it will be handy if the soldering surface has suitable guidelines cut into it beforehand.

The ingenious goldsmith will have in his drawer a little box with various kinds of studs, bent pieces of metal and other supports that can be used to arrange parts against each other to support them for soldering. Useful bits and pieces can be made from old nails, paper clips, scraps from die making, lumps of charcoal, a tangle of binding wire and so on. Often

Figure 8.11
Soldering board equipped with adjustable third hands. (J. Schmalz, Pforzheim)

something as simple as a small piece of steel sheet bent to a particular shape can be the solution to an otherwise complicated situation.

In other cases, assembly is made easier with graver stitches, small fingers of metal that are created by cutting into the sheet with a sharp steel tool.

BINDING

The use of steel wire is another time-honored method to secure pieces for soldering. On the positive side, it is versatile, inexpensive and straightforward. The principle drawback is that some forms are very difficult to wrap securely. Figure 8.12 illustrates a few such shapes, and suggests some solutions, each of which is described below.

Binding wire is annealed steel wire covered with a layer of black iron oxide to decrease the likelihood of solder sticking to it. For jewelry, wire around 0.6–0.4 mm (22-26 B&S) is typical. Silversmithing calls for a thickness of at least 1.0 mm (18 B&S). To increase thickness, twist two or three wires together.

When using binding wire you should be aware of these factors:

• Iron expands significantly less than precious metals and jewelry alloys.
• The black iron oxide on binding wire can merge with the workpiece and become permanently soldered in place.
• When fine wire stands free from the piece it is easily overheated to the breaking point.

Figure 8.13 illustrates several ways in which binding wire can be used. Of course each unique shape will require its own clever solution. Because steel binding wire does not expand as much or as fast as silver or other hollowware metals, a piece can be severely distorted if the pieces are tied too tightly. To avoid the problem, wrap the wire loosely then cinch it by grasping it in flat-nose pliers and giving a half turn. This will result in a zigzag bend that will expand along with the piece being soldered.

As shown at mid-height on the form in figure 8.12a, it might be necessary to insert shims of metal to direct the tension of the wires to a specific location. Though steel, brass, or copper can be used, these risk

313

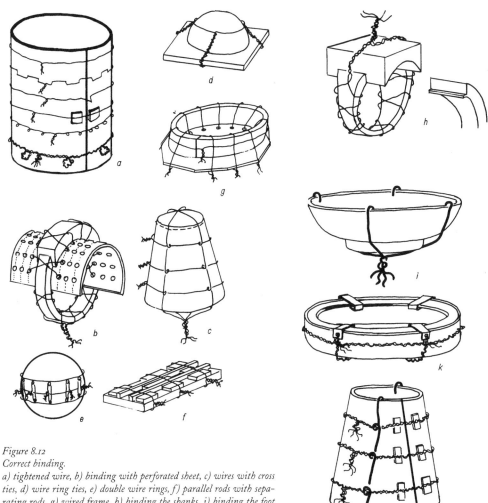

Figure 8.12
Correct binding.
a) tightened wire, b) binding with perforated sheet, c) wires with cross ties, d) wire ring ties, e) double wire rings, f) parallel rods with separating rods, g) wired frame, h) binding the shanks, i) binding the foot of the bowl, k) binding frames, l) binding with wire of similar material.

scratching a silver object. If possible, fine silver should be used; its higher melting point and softness make it ideal.

A useful holding device is illustrated in figure 8.12b. Small holes are drilled into a thin steel plate that is then curved to fit inside a ring. This arrangement provides many options for placement of wire to tie the pieces together. Figure 8.12f shows how a bezel can be tied onto a base plate if the opening is to be later sawn out

In exceptional cases where no other method of fastening can be devised, it is possible to drill into the workpiece and bind pieces with wire of the working material, for instance, using sterling wire when work-

ing on a sterling object. After soldering the excess wire is removed and the binding wire, which has been soldered in place, is filed smooth.

CLAMPS

Small, hair pin-shaped devices called clamps have several advantages. They are easy to make and apply, often reusable, and avoid the shrinkage problems mentioned above. In many cases these are made from whatever wire is close at hand. Heavy binding wire and nickel silver are preferred. Figure 8.13 illustrates a variety of shapes and their application. Of course, each situation might require special modifications.

PINNING INTO THE SOLDERING SURFACE

An alternate way to join pieces for soldering is to anchor them onto the soldering block. Charcoal or firebrick blocks work particularly well for this. Figure 8.14 illustrates the use of pins to hold delicate parts in specific arrangements. In figure 8.14d, the ends of two pins are bent into loops which hold onto a wire securely. Pins are also useful when soldering chains. As seen in figure 8.14e, a chain can be stretched taut with pins for soldering.

Figure 8.13
Different clips.

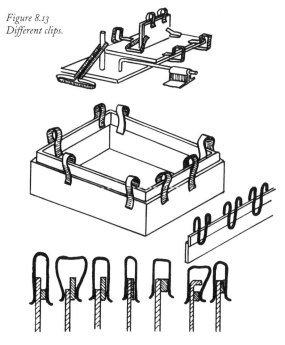

Figure 8.14
Use of pins.

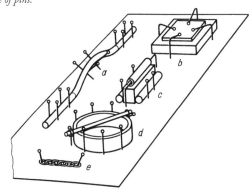

Soldering investment

This specialized method (figure 8.15) is especially recommended when joining many small pieces. Rather than wires, a plaster-like material called investment is used to secure the pieces during soldering.

First the individual parts are painted with flux then heated until they are left with a layer of glaze. The pieces are then assembled by pressing them into wax or modeling clay. Of course, it is necessary that the pieces touch each other. A temporary wall of cardboard, plastic, or tape is laid around this construction and sealed with modeling clay. Conventional casting investment can be used but a special formula, called soldering investment, is preferred because it dries faster. Mix the investment with water according to the manufacturer's instructions and pour it over the work. A thin layer of investment is sufficient; too much material only extends the drying time required.

Allow the investment to dry, removing the wall after about 10 minutes to speed up this process. Invert the piece and use a fine blade to scrape away wax and/or investment from solder seams. Pre-heat the entire unit (either with a bushy flame or in a kiln) to ensure that all moisture has been removed. Add flux and solder at each point of contact and heat with the entire unit with a torch until the solder flows. After checking to be certain all the joints are solid, quench in water and the investment will fall off.

ASSEMBLY ON ACID SOLUBLE FORMS

In some extreme situations this unusual method is indispensable. The example here, shown in figure 8.16, demonstrates the fabrication of a sphere made of a lattice of wires. The concept is to create a form in a metal that can later be removed with acid. In this example we'll imagine a copper sphere and Au 750 (18k) gold wires. First, two hemispheres are made from thin copper sheet and soldered together. The lattice work is constructed on the copper sphere and soldered in sections (8.16b).

When the fabrication is complete, drill holes in the copper wherever possible to reduce the amount of metal present. The remaining copper is removed by etching the entire unit in a strong solution of nitric acid. Adequate ventilation will of course be required. Because the gold is impervious to this acid it will

315

Figure 8.15
Plaster soldering. Parts are arranged inside a frame pressed into plasticene, then investment is poured over the arrangement.

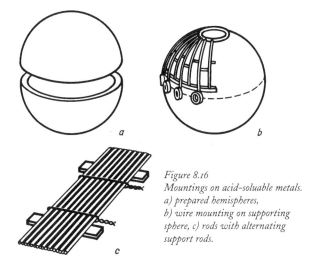

Figure 8.16
Mountings on acid-soluable metals. a) prepared hemispheres, b) wire mounting on supporting sphere, c) rods with alternating support rods.

remain untouched while the copper is completely dissolved. When all traces of copper are gone the piece is retrieved and thoroughly rinsed.

A variation on this method is shown in figure 8.16c. In this case wires are kept at even spacing by separating them with a metal that will later be etched away.

Applying flux and solder

In most cases flux is applied along a solder seam with a fine-pointed watercolor brush. An inexpensive version of this delicate brush facilitates accurate placement of flux and solder. In some situations the entire piece is dipped into flux; it might be necessary to thin it slightly with water. Use a small tip-proof container like an inkwell to keep the flux convenient on the soldering bench. This can be refilled as necessary from the jar in which flux is purchased.

A glance at a jewelry supply catalogue will reveal several brands of flux: each goldsmith should experiment to discover his or her favorite. A borax-based flux (e.g. Handy Flux) has the advantage of creating a glaze that can withstand several reheatings. Understanding this, it is important to allow work to air cool between soldering operations. If the work is pickled or rinsed, the flux will be removed. With care however, it is possible to establish a thick flux coating at the outset that will sustain multiple heatings. Note that this longevity is not a property of fluoride-based fluxes, which are sometimes identified as "self-pickling."

Solder is usually used in the form of small squares (pallions) that are cut from sheet. Clean a sheet of solder with sandpaper or Scotch-Brite then use scissors or shears to cut parallel linesalong one edge. The resulting fringe will probably curl and should be straightened out with pliers. Cut another series of parallel lines at right angles to the first, catching the chips in a small dish. Most goldsmiths prefer to cut a small supply of solder so that it is ready at hand when needed. Be careful, however, not to cut so much that it will become oxidized before use. The three grades of solder (easy, medium, and hard) must be kept separated and clearly marked. Small, air-tight containers are preferable.

Solder is laid into position either with the flux brush or tweezers. To use the brush, moisten it with a drop of flux, touch it lightly to the solder and the piece will adhere. Lay the solder in position and twirl the brush gently to release the chip. Alternatively, use fine-tipped tweezers to carry solder to its intended location.

Wherever possible, position the solder so that it straddles the seam or at the very least is in contact with both units to be joined. Long thin strips of solder will nestle into a seam as illustrated on the right in figure 8.17.

As mentioned previously, the quantity of solder must be sufficient to fill the seam without leaving excess. This is learned through experience. Students are encouraged to study each joint immediately after soldering to determine if the correct amount was used. A well-made joint will draw all the solder into the seam, leaving little or none to be filed away. Another lesson of experience is to complete as many joints as possible with each soldering.

When sheets are being soldered one on top of the other, a special method called sweat soldering is recommended. In these cases, solder is distributed and pre-melted onto the backside of the top piece. The lower piece is fluxed and preheated until it approaches the solder range, then the units are then put together and heating continues. Solder flow will be visible at the edge of the top piece, looking like a bright flash of mercury.

A special form of sweat soldering is required when cladding one metal onto another. This might happen, for instance, when soldering a layer of gold onto a sterling base. In this case, cut a pattern of criss-crossing grooves with a sharp scribe or graver into the silver surface. Pre-melt solder onto the gold, then set the two pieces together. The grooves will facilitate even distribution of the solder, ensuring a strong bond and preventing lumps.

Making the solder flow
When using jeweler's solder, it is always necessary to heat the entire piece. This is usually done with a rhythmic, circular motion of the torch, watching color changes in the metal to ensure that pieces reach temperature equally. Start with the torch on the perimeter of the work, slowly bringing it to bear on the solder seam. In an ideal situation, heat flows from the workpiece to the joint, reaching soldering temperature just as the flame is directed at the seam.

Solder flows toward heat. To use this principle, direct the flame in such a way that it will draw the solder into or through a seam. If, for example, you want to solder a thin jump ring onto a thick plate, start by bringing the plate up to temperature. The ring, because it is so much smaller, will quickly overheat if it is in the flame. If the plate is first made hot, the solder will jump there and then travel to the ring.

Solder is available in several grades that melt at slightly different temperatures. The most familiar in silver soldering are:

Hard	788°C	1450°F
Medium	738°C	1360°F
Easy	719°C	1325°F

The idea behind these three alloys is related to the fact that the entire piece must be heated. In complex pieces that require many solder joints, the first round of joints are made with hard solder which flows at the highest temperature. Subsequent joints are made respectively with medium and easy. In each case the piece does not need to be brought to the temperature of the preceding joint. Although they are useful, solders of different temperature are not absolutely necessary. Each time solder is reheated it diffuses deeper into the structure of the work, effectively raising its melting point. It is not uncommon for professional goldsmiths to accomplish most of their work with a single grade of solder. Hard is preferred because it is the best color match with sterling.

A rare and frustrating situation can occur when solder is overheated. It is possible that the zinc in the solder can eat into sterling, leaving a small rough depression. This blemish is very difficult to repair; take pains in the future to lift the torch away as soon as the solder begins to flow. With experience a goldsmith learns to read heat through color. If solder is not starting to flow when it should, resist the urge to continue heating. Cool the piece, clean it if necessary, reflux and try again.

Preventing the flow of solder
In theory it is possible to prevent solder from flowing, or to direct it away from certain areas, by coating those areas with an insulating material such as chalk, powdered rouge, or a fine clay like yellow ochre. In practice this is not recommended. The degree of insulation these coatings provide is no match for the ability of metal to conduct heat, so they offer a false security while effectively camouflaging the important

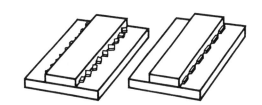

Figure 8.17
Incorrect and correct position of solder pallions.

color-reading that allows a goldsmith to perceive temperatures. Further, if solder does flow beneath a coating, it becomes rough, gray and unattractive.

Experience and control are always better than protective coatings: faster, safer, and cleaner. A "natural" antiflux method is to heat a piece without flux, which will cause it to oxidize. Scrape away the oxide only in the area to be soldered, and apply flux only to the seam.

Clean up
It is a sign of controlled soldering to have little clean up, but almost all joins will require a little finishing. In most cases, clean up waits until all soldering is completed, until that moment when the goldsmith says in relief, "The jewelry piece is out of the fire!" Cleaning up solder seams too soon risks the seam opening during later heatings, and increases the risk of unsightly firescale.

After the last soldering the work is allowed to soak in warm pickle to remove oxides and flux glass. This latter is harder than you might expect and will damage tools if not dissolved away. Files and burs are used to smooth large blemishes; needle files, rifflers, sandpaper and grinding wheels on the flexible shaft are used to smooth smaller areas.

Scrapers (triangular and other shapes as made for specific pieces) are used to remove excess solder adjacent to a seam. With a little practice, these versatile tools can create a smooth flat surface that is ready to be polished.

8.2
Fusing and Welding

8.2.1 BASICS
Though it applies elsewhere, the term welding immediately makes us think about joining steel. In reality welding can also be used by jewelers, silversmiths and brass founders. The technical definition of welding is "a union of metallic materials using heat or pressure or both, without addition of other materials." The process depends on homogeneity, the notion that if atoms are sufficiently excited and in close proximity they will be drawn together by mutual bonding forces.

In the oldest method, forge welding, the principle can be clearly seen. The contact zones of the two steel parts are heated to white heat in a blacksmith's forge. At the correct moment, force is applied in the form of directed hammer blows that press the soft steel units together, closing any gaps that may have existed and squeezing the fluid surface of each piece against the other. When done correctly, the bond is formed immediately and is as strong as the parent metal. If necessary the join areas can be heated again and forged together until completely homogeneous unification is completed.

According to the same principle, a layer of gold is fused onto the sterling or brass body in the making of double, a clad material sometimes known as bi-metal. The parts being joined are heated without contact with air and then immediately pressed together under high pressure where they diffuse completely into each other.

A more localized process, commonly called fusing, uses a sharp flame to bring adjacent pieces to temperatures at which their surfaces become fluid (i.e. liquidus). The various parts will diffuse into each other, creating welded units that are as strong as the metals being used.

In the modern procedure of fusing no pressure is necessary, as it is possible to heat the parts to be joined so quickly at the seam with the extremely high heat of the welding/fusing flame that the edges of the seam melt and either directly or with the help of a similar addition material bond with each other.

In welding the pieces are always at risk of melting because the process operates in the liquidus zone. In the case of steel, which is a relatively poor conductor of heat, edges can be molten without exposing nearby areas to risk. The jewelry metals – silver, gold, copper and their alloys – conduct heat much better, which means that melting temperatures are quickly spread throughout the whole piece. This is the reason that hard soldering was invented in the first place, to achieve welding-like strength at temperatures that approach but do not reach the melting point.

Nevertheless, there are times when welding (a.k.a. fusing) is used by goldsmiths. When seaming a vessel that will be worked with hammers, welding might be used because of its great strength. In a case like this,

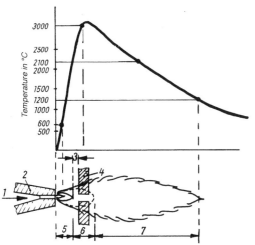

Figure 8.24
Welding flame.

a) temperature curve of flame, b) flame form. 1) burning gas mixture $C_2H_2:O_2 = 1:1, 1$; 2) tip of torch, 3) distance from the tip of flame to work piece, 4) work piece, 5) core of flame with surrounding flame, 6) area for welding, 7) dispersed outer flame.

if the surface is roughened by melting it is not a great concern because the hammer blows will repair the surface.

Platinum is typically joined by welding and, like steel, it allows very close work to be done without fear of melting adjacent areas. Note that because of its high melting point platinum welding can only be accomplished with an oxygen flame. Protective lenses should be worn to protect eyes from harmful rays.

8.2.2 GAS WELDING

Welding can be done with a high surge of electricity, and in fact in commercial welding of steel, this is the most frequently used method. Though miniature arc welders have been developed for jewelry, such as the popular "Sparkie", they are used mostly for specific assembly line tasks. Far more common in studio welding is the use of a torch whose flame is fed by oxygen and a combustible gas like acetylene, propane or butane.

Several manufacturers sell torches that produce a small very hot flame. These can be used to weld even heat-conductive metals like gold and silver because they deliver so much heat to a localized area. With these torches it is even possible to repair areas near to

stones: the piece can be heated, joined and cooled before the heat is able to travel to the gem.

8.3
Granulation

The ancient technique called granulation is a specialized version of fusing in which tiny spheres "granules" are attached to a piece with such a delicate fillet that they appear to be simply set into place. The result is a rich yet delicate pattern of great beauty.

The revival of granulation in our century has been accompanied by many wrong ideas and misunderstandings, many stemming from the incorrect notion that the secrets of a mysterious process were long lost. To better understand granulation, we should therefore start by examining the myths and laying them to rest.

8.3.1 HISTORICAL SOLDERING PROCEDURES

From ancient times right up to the Middle Ages, two different procedures were used depending on the requirements of a particular piece. One used an alloy with a slightly lower melting point than the work piece to fill seams; this of course is hard soldering as we practice it today.

The other method used a eutectic solder created at the location and at the moment of diffusion, in the process we have come to call granulation. This method was used to attach the dividing struts in Egyptian cloisonné inlays, to join the wire ornaments in German disk fibulas, and to attach bezels and filigree onto book covers in the Middle Ages.

To achieve the localized diffusion of granulation, a copper compound is applied to the base, then an organic substance is added to it. The carbon in this compound will act as a reducing agent, joining with oxygen and drawing it away in the form of carbon dioxide. This organic substance often does double duty, serving simultaneously as a glue to hold pieces temporarily and as a flux. The units to be joined (which might be granules, but can in fact be any shape) are set into place and the work is dried. Heat is applied gently, traditionally with a charcoal fire, until the piece reaches a precise temperature. The copper compound, acted upon by the glue and flux, forms a low-melting alloy exactly at the point of contact. This eutectic alloy diffuses between the two units, base and ornament, and welds them together.

In most of the many centuries this process has been used, goldsmiths knew only as much as their eyes and instincts could show them. With modern measuring devices we are now able to confirm the temperature differences that make this possible.

- On *fine silver* (melting point 960.5°C, 1760°F) the process yields a silver/copper eutectic alloy with a solidus temperature of 779°C, 1434°F.
- On *fine gold* (melting point 1063°C, 1945°F) the resulting gold/copper alloy (Au 820) has a melting point of 889°C, 1632°F.
- Copper in small amounts also alters the melting points of high karat gold/silver alloys. Etruscan pieces made of alloys in the range of ⅔ gold and ⅓ silver (melting point 1060°C, 1940°F) can be joined with the granulation process because the eutectic alloy drops to a melting point of 860°C, 1580°F.

With all this going for it, we might wonder why eutectic joining went out of fashion. To save money, alloys were made of a lower value, reducing the proportion of gold in order to create a more affordable alloy. These lower alloys do not react the same way as the richer blends, so the "eutectic magic" of granulation could no longer be used. For example, in silver alloys like sterling, the eutectic temperature remains unchanged at 779°C, 1434°F. In lower karat gold/silver/copper alloys, the introduction of small amounts of copper at a joint has almost no effect. With the introduction of alloys of lower gold content, eutectic soldering was forgotten and replaced by the use of the hard solders. When work was no longer done in high karat alloys, eutectic diffusion was displaced from the technical vocabularies and then the design repertoire of goldsmiths.

This was to change early in the twentieth century when archeological discoveries of the work of antiquity (particularly the outstanding masterpieces of the Etruscans) wakened an interest in granulation. This surge of interest led to a hectic and often misguided attempt to "rediscover" this lost art, though in fact

eutectic diffusion has always been practiced by some metalworkers somewhere, often in very basic folk art traditions. Research has shown that granulation was never really "lost" and was accurately described by Pliny, Herodotus, Theophilus and others.

8.3.2 METALS

Pure gold and silver can be used for granulation, as can alloys with high proportions of pure metal. For gold, alloys over Au 750 are recommended; for silver, though sterling (Ag 925) can be used, mixtures with a higher percentage of silver are recommended. Gold and silver can be mixed, as can different alloys. It is possible, for example, to fuse gold granules onto silver sheet, or to use golds of different karats in the same piece.

Making the granules

Roll a sheet of metal as thin as possible and use scissors to cut parallel lines, making a fringe. Cut across this at a right angle to create tiny squares (pallions) as is done when cutting solder. Alternately, it is also possible to snip a fine wire into short pieces. For extremely fine granules, catch the dust made with a coarse file.

In order to prevent the pieces from melting into each other in the next step, the small pieces are moistened and stirred into powdered charcoal with a miniature whisk. This will coat each piece with a fine layer of powder. Sprinkle a half inch layer of charcoal powder into a crucible then distribute the gold pieces over it. Add another layer of charcoal powder and sprinkle in more chips, continuing until the crucible is full.

Set the assembly into a kiln and heat it until the crucible glows red. Use a spoon to lift out a small sampling, which is dropped in a container of water. If the granules have formed spheres, the heating is done and the rest of the batch can be retrieved. The contents of the crucible are poured into a container, rinsed and then dried.

It is also possible to simply set the gold pieces on a charcoal block and heat them with a torch, a method that is particularly useful when only a few granules are being made. A disadvantage with this method is that the spheres tend to have a small flat facet, especially in the larger granules.

To sort granules by size, make a graduated series of sieves using either commercially obtained screens or disks drilled with holes of different sizes. There are several approaches to this; many use a tube to rank the sieves in sequence, enabling the granules to be sorted and stored in each section according to size.

Eutectic soldering of the granules
Any of the following copper compounds can be used to create eutectic solders.
- Malachite, basic copper carbonate $CuCO_3$. $Cu(OH)_2$. Pliny records that in ancient times this stone was pulverized and used for soldering.
- Copper (II) oxide CuO. This material can be derived, as it was in antiquity, be saving and grinding the scale that forms on copper during annealing.
- Copper (II) hydroxide $Cu(OH)_2$, which is transformed into black copper (II) oxide upon heating with an alkaline base.
- Copper (II) chloride $CuCl_2 \cdot H_2O$. In earlier times, this was obtained by annealing a piece of copper sheet painted with salt.
- Copper sulfate $CuSO_4 \cdot 5\ H_2O$.

Make a solution that includes one of the copper compounds above along with a glue (gum tragacanth is preferred) and a hard soldering flux, in roughly equal proportions. This solution is painted onto the cleaned surface and the granules are set into position, typically with a fine-pointed brush. To avoid a boiling action that would dislodge the granules, the piece is slowly dried, for instance under a lamp.

The work is then heated with a reducing flame to a temperature at which the copper is released from its compound. This is ideally done by heating from beneath the piece. As the work is heated the organic glue will turn black then lighten and disappear. At the precise moment the eutectic temperature is reached, the trace amount of copper at the site of each point of contact will go into the alloy and diffuse into the granule and the base, making a metallic bond at that point. This is the decisive moment! If a timid goldsmith stops too soon, the bond is not sufficiently strong and some of the granules will fall off. If the

heat is allowed to linger, the higher temperature will start to melt the pieces together, destroying the delicacy that makes granulation so beautiful.

If granules fall off, it is possible to clean the metal and repeat the process, but it's always better to have all the granules adhere in the first firing.

Fusing the granules in place
This method is used with particularly fine granulation. No metallic bonding material is used; instead, the surface is painted with diluted flux. After their original heating, the granules in this case are not pickled, leaving them with a slight coating of oxide. They are set into position with a tiny bit of flux that acts as a glue. The piece is then heated to just that point at which the surface shines like a mirror; that is, where it reaches its liquidus temperature. At that moment the granules will fuse to the surface, their form being held intact by the oxide coating. Every goldsmith has seen this effect when a pallion of solder draws up into a ball instead of flowing into a seam.

Siegfried Meyer of Freiberg has been experimenting with granulation in Au 858 (14k). Granules are made as described above. The thickness of the sheet used as a base should be the same thickness as the size of the granules. Lines are scribed lightly into the sheet to keep the balls from rolling off, then the sheet is sanded with a fine paper and degreased. The soldering/gluing solution is made of 1 part gum tragacanth and 4 parts ground borax. This mixture is applied to the sheet with a small watercolor brush, which is then used to position the granules.

The gold sheet is set onto a steel plate about 2 mm thick (12 gauge B&S) that conforms to the contours of the piece and is a little larger on all sides. The piece is allowed to dry for several hours to insure that all moisture has evaporated away. When the piece is dry the section of steel that projects around the piece is heated with a torch, allowing the heat to creep beneath the piece. When the gold is glowing red, the flame, (which should be large and bushy) is played over the top of the gold, which will "blink" and shine like a mirror at the moment of diffusion. The temperature is sustained for a few seconds, then the torch is removed. The time and temperature are critical –

Figure 8.26
Gold sphere pendant with linear and areas of granulation.

Figure 8.25
Soldering of filigree wire and granulation on brooch, overview and detail. "Gold Treasure from Hiddensee," latter part of the 10th century, Jutland. (Cultural Historical Museum, Stralsund)

difficult to describe in words and impossible to learn except through experimentation.

Granulation design
Having mastered the technique of bonding granules to a base, the larger questions of design come into play. Pieces from the historical record offer many dazzling examples but each goldsmith will need to develop his or her personal style. As a granulation master once said, "If granulation were such a simple thing that any clod could easily get the spheres onto a sheet,

the technique would only be a senseless game!"

The design possibilities include using granules across an entire surface, to outline specific shapes, to create geometric patterns, and to build up minuscule pyramids of spheres.

Because the technique has gathered an air of mystery, attention is usually focused on mastery of the process, which is incorrect. Granulation is primarily a matter of design – the vision and talent needed to paint across a golden sheet with tiny spheres.

8.4
Pinning and Riveting

Rivets and their close relatives, pins, fall under the broad category called cold connections. They use mechanical forces to join elements without the use of heat (like soldering) or chemicals (like glue). A fixed rivet is a short length of rod that holds two or more pieces together by trapping them between upset heads, or lumps on each end. An example would be rivets used to join a plastic handle to a coffeepot.

A free rivet is a similar device, but one that is permanently in place but allows the pieces to move against one another. The pin holding pliers together is an example of a free rivet. A pin is similar, as for

322

instance the pin of a hinge in a box, but has the distinction of being removable. If repair is needed on a silver box, the pin can be removed to take off the lid without damaging the hinge.

Pinning

After a hinge has been completely assembled it is tested with a temporary hinge pin, preferably made of steel. If the location and function of the hinge is acceptable, the piece can be completed, through the final finish. The proper fitting of the final pin, which is made of the same metal as the box, is achieved through a delicate taper, as is seen, for instance, on the glass stoppered bottles used for storing acids.

The interior of the hinge is shaped ever so slightly with tapered reamers, always working from the same end (figure 8.32). As a convention, it is recommended the tool is always inserted from the top down or from the right side. Consistency in this makes life a little easier for later repairs. The reamer is inserted and rotated by hand until it can be felt to make contact all along its length. At this point the reamer is removed, the top separated, and those hinge knuckles are reamed slightly more. This will allow them to rotate freely on the pin.

The hinge pin is filed and sanded to achieve the identical very gradual taper. It is then pressed into position, where it will make a snug contact all along its surface. It is pushed/screwed into place. If the small end projects enough to grip it in pliers, the pin can be pulled from there to cinch it in place. It is not necessary to hammer the pin! This arrangement will stand up to years of wear, but can be dissembled for repair by tapping smartly on the tiny end with the point of a scribe.

Riveting

The parts to be joined are drilled, with care taken that the bit is held exactly vertical. If several rivets are being made, drill all the holes in the top piece, but only one in the lower unit. No matter how careful you are, it's likely that pieces will shift slightly during drilling, leaving holes that do not line up. After the first rivet is completed the next hole is drilled and a second rivet set. Only then − when the pieces are locked together − can the remaining holes be drilled.

In order to guarantee that the rivet forms heads on the ends, it must be securely restrained within the holes. This means the rivet wire must make a very tight fit into the holes just drilled. Typically a wire slightly oversized is selected and sanded until it makes the perfect fit.

A way to make a head on one end of a rivet wire is by drawing a bead or enlarged lump by melting. Hold a wire vertically in tweezers, pointed downward. Direct a small flame at the tip and the wire will pull itself up into a ball. Quench the wire and slide it into a tight hole in a riveting stake block, a small piece of hardened steel with holes of various sizes. As shown in the top half of figure 8.31, the head is formed with blows of a light hammer. Resist the temptation to use a drawplate for this purpose, which risks damaging it.

Forming rivet heads

The process of completing a rivet is shown in figure 8.31. The rivet is slid into place, tapped to seat it, and cut off so that the projecting amount is roughly equal to half the diameter of the wire. The end of the wire is filed flat to allow a clean blow with the hammer. After a couple initial taps to flatten the rivet, a small punch or ball peen hammer is used to spread the rivet head. When the metal has been completely pressed down against the sheet, use burs, files and sandpaper to shape and smooth the rivet. Figure 8.30 shows a schematic drawing of several kinds of rivets. In practice they do not look quite as precise as those shown here, but with a little practice it is quite easy to make consistently solid and attractive rivets.

A variation, shown at 8.30d, is called a flush or disappearing rivet. The process is as just described with one alteration. Before the rivet wire is fed into place the outer edge of the hole is beveled outward with a bud burr or a large drill bit. This allows the head of the rivet to form below the surface of the sheet. The head can be filed flush with the sheet without undermining its holding capacity. In the case of different alloys this will appear as an inlayed dot; when the rivet is made of the same material as the sheet it will blend in completely, or "disappear."

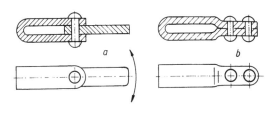

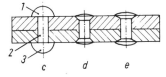

Figure 8.30
Riveting and types of rivets.
a) movable(or pivotal) rivet, b) fixed rivet, c) buttonhead rivet, (1) closing head, 2) rivet shank, 3) tail of rivet, d) countersunk, e) lens rivet (lentoid).

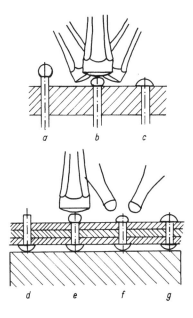

Figure 8.31
Riveting.
a) wire with rounded melted head,
b) forming, c) finsihed rivet head,
d) inserted rivet shank,
e) hammering the head,
f) forming the head,
g) finnished rivet with both heads.

8.5
Screws and Bolts

Everyone is familiar with the huge range of nuts and bolts available in our industrialized culture. Not even considering the exotic specialty shapes, bolts can be found in almost every material, diameter and length. Standardized sizes have long been in place for threads. In fact they were the subject of one of the first international standardization sheets, the DIN (Deutsche Industrie Normen) which has become an international standard. DIN 13 describes the metric standard thread, while DIN 244-247 details metric fine threads (figure 8.33). In the United States, these are supplemented with the National Coarse (NC) system and the National Fine (NF) system.

Most bolts can be identified by citing one of these systems and giving its diameter and length. A typical nomenclature, for example, would be 6NC32, meaning a size 6 diameter in the National Coarse system with 32 threads per inch. Metric threads use diameter: M10 refers to a metric thread with a 10 mm diameter. The finer thread version of this bolt would be written as M10 x 0.5.

As the scale moves down to the small sizes typically used in jewelry work the proportions of thread to diameter must change to create an effective thread.

Cutting threads
Special die cutting plates are manufactured to create threads at the small size needed by goldsmiths (figure 8.34). Most plates include two sets of holes for each thread size, a pre-cutting die to remove the bulk of the material, and a finishing die to make the threads precise.

Start with a wire, preferably unannealed, whose diameter is as large as the final diameter of the bolt. File a slight point on one end. Screw the wire into the pre-cutting hole, or alternately, grip the wire in a vise and turn the die plate around it. Use a slow steady motion, taking pains to keep the plate at a right angle to the wire. The chip formed in this operation will be pulled off into a hole drilled adjacent to the die in the plate. Facilitate clearing the chip by unscrewing a half turn periodically as cutting proceeds. Continue

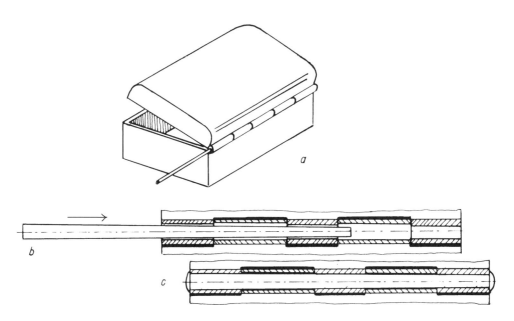

Figure 8.32
Five part hinge with inserted pin. Three knuckles on the box, two on the lid.
a) box mounted with completed hinge, b) insertion of the conically formed pin in the hinge, c) completely inserted pin.

screwing the wire into the plate until it can be felt to move easily.

The thread at this point is still trapezoid and coarse. Just below the pre-cutting die is another die that will alter the angle of the threads. Use this in the same way as the first die, screwing the wire through it until it runs freely.

Interior threads are cut with a tap, a tapered rod of hardened steel cut with threads along its length. It has two flat sides (or sometimes a pair of grooves) along its length to allow the chips to fall away.

Start by drilling a hole of the appropriate size. The drill hole should be the same as the inside minor diameter of the threads. This is often shown on a chart attached to the die, but as a rule of thumb add about ¾ of a millimeter to the inside diameter of the cutting die.

Taps are notoriously fragile, so care must be taken when threading a hole. Screw the tap a turn into the hole then unscrew it a half turn to clear the chips. Continue in this way – full rotation forward, half rotation back – avoiding jerky movements or abrupt force. Use soap or a light oil to facilitate the cutting.

Applications
Though the use of threaded connections has long been a part of the watchmakers art, goldsmiths seem reluctant to take advantage of the many advantages they offer. Bolts allow a piece to be assembled without heat or stress, and also permit a piece to be dismantled for repair or customizing. Silversmiths have traditionally used screws and threaded fasteners to attach elements.

8.6
Gluing

Adhesives have a long history in jewelry making, but have also become associated with poor craftsmanship. Of course when glue is used where a soldered joint would serve better, the disdain is deserved, but in many cases adhesives can be used professionally to good effect. There are many cases where nonmetal elements such as bone, stone, glass, ceramic, plastic or gem materials need to be attached. The point is not to avoid glues, but to use them with the care and understanding given to every other material.

325

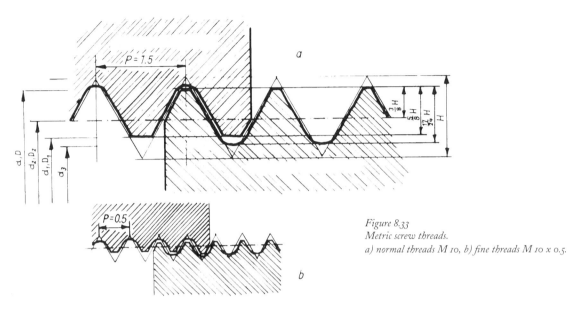

Figure 8.33
Metric screw threads.
a) normal threads M 10, b) fine threads M 10 x 0.5.

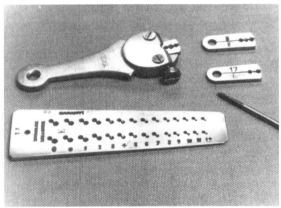

Figure 8.34
Tap and die.

8.6.1 GLUES

The strength of a glue joint depends on two factors:
  – adhesion (of the molecules and the glue to the surface being joined)
  – cohesion (the cohesiveness of the molecules witin the glue)

Naturally-based materials
  – animal protein products (bones, skin, leather)
  – carbohydrates (starch, dextrin)
  – plant saps and resins (gum Arabic, rubber, pine resin)

Synthetically-based materials
  – synthetic plastic resins
  – synthetic rubber
  – water glass (sodium silicate)

Whether they occur naturally or are synthetic, what makes all glues bond is their ability to form macro-molecules. The solidification of the glue occurs either through the evaporation of a solvent (drying) when a molten glue cools, or through the cross linking of large molecules achieved by a chemical reaction.

Tremendous advances have been made in the field of adhesives in the last several decades, yielding glues with increased strength, resistance to corrosion and flexibility. The good side of this is that jewelers can find a product for almost every need. The down side is that the many possibilities require research!

Before selecting a glue for a particular application, consider these factors.

• What materials are being joined?
• Should the surfaces be joined with a thin contact cement or are there gaps that need to be filled?
• Is a quick-drying or slow drying glue preferred?
• Should the glue be rigid or elastic?
• What mechanical and chemical stresses will the glue need to withstand?

8.6.2 CEMENTS

As defined in the context of goldsmithing and jewelry construction, cements are "reversible" in that they can be made fluid by heating them. This is unlike glues, which are difficult to remove once they have hardened. Two natural cements, mastic and shellac, have a long history in goldsmithing, not only in finished objects, but for their use in some processes.

Mastic

This is the resin of the mastic bush *(Pistacia leiutiscus L.)* which is found on the Greek island of Chios and on other Mediterranean islands. Mastic is available to the trade in the shape of small, light yellow, transparent beads. Decorative addition materials can be cemented in place with mastic.

Shellac

This adhesive and coating material comes from India and Thailand. This caramel-colored material is an extraction from the shellac beetle *(Tachardia lacca)* which stores up the basic material on the branches of certain trees as a resinous mass. In purified form, shellac is sold as brittle flakes. Shellac has been used for centuries to attach decorative elements and to secure pearls into end caps.

Stone cement

Equal parts shellac and mastic are dissolved in alcohol and stirred with glucose to a stiff paste. This mixture is suitable for cementing gem stones and pearls and for the fixing of pearl threads into the end caps. This glue hardens when the alcohol evaporates.

Pearl cement

To prepare a pearl cement, warm carpenters glue (e.g. Elmer's) and stir in fine ground plaster to a sticky paste. This glue hardens when it dries.

Coral cement

Equal parts shellac and mastic are melted together. This glue hardens when it cools.

Flatware cement

Two parts shellac are heated and prepared with 1 part whiting (ground chalk). This hardens when it cools.

Filling cement

Hollow objects (like flatware handles, candleholder bases, etc.) are filled with this to provide weight to support to thin metal that might otherwise be easily dented. Mix equal parts of carpenters glue with plaster or lime and powdered sulfur, stirring constantly until a sticky paste is formed. This glue hardens when it dries.

8.6.3 FIXING DECORATIVE MATERIALS IN PLACE

Though modern glues are remarkably strong, they are not particularly resistant to shearing or bending stresses. Gluing should not be mindlessly used to simply stick pieces together, but should be considered as a factor in design. It is always wise, for instance, to provide as much surface area as possible between sections being glued. It is also prudent to provide a mechanical attachment whenever possible, as for instance in setting a pearl onto a post.

In terms of design, elements that will be glued on should have a low curved profile. Avoid pieces that jut out abruptly from the form unless they can be attached with something more permanent than glue. Insure that glued elements are large or thick enough that they will not bend under stress: bending will cause a glued joint to fail. Here are a couple of standard examples of design used to accommodate cements.

Box frame

A piece being glued on is protected from sideways forces by being set into a box structure. This is made to fit the piece and soldered onto the base, using either sheet metal or square wire to make the frame. Unlike a bezel, this frame does not need to be as tall as the object being attached, though that of course provides extra protection.

Pearl cup with peg

The setting consists of two equally important parts – the cup which supports the pearl from below and the peg that secures it from its interior. While either one could be used alone, neither a peg nor a cup offers nearly the security of the two together. Obviously the following can be transferred to other materials such as gem beads and small carvings.

A small disk of metal is dapped to make the cup for the pearl, leaving it a little larger than the gem to allow room for glue. The height of the cup will be determined by the particular design, but it is generally from about one-half of the sphere (figure 8.35).

The peg is soldered on oversize (which makes it easier to hold during soldering), then cut off to equal about 2/3rds the diameter of the pearl. The peg should not be a plain round wire, which offers no purchase for the glue. Use a twist of wire, a square wire twisted a few times, or a wire that has been textured by squeezing it repeatedly with wire cutters.

Large pearls can be held in the hand for drilling, but small pearls will be easier to handle in a jig like the one shown at the top of figure 8.35. The folded strip of brass is secured with sliding hoops. It can be seen in use in figure 5.29.

Despite rumor to the contrary, pearls can be drilled with a flexible shaft machine. Examine the pearl to find any flaws, and position it so these will be out of sight near the hole. Run the drill at a very slow speed, withdrawing the bit frequently to check depth. This is made easy by the fact that the pearl dust clings to the bit. No lubricant is needed.

A special method, appropriate only for large pearls, is illustrated in figure 8.35d. Solder a small flag or tab onto the tip of a post as shown. Drill a hole in the pearl that is the same size as the post, then use a small bur to reach into the hole and carve a groove along the hole at one point. Do not make this groove come all the way to the outside: the hole at the surface of the pearl should be round.

Apply a small amount of cement or glue and angle the pearl onto the post. Press it on as far as it will go then rotate the pearl a half turn. The tab will scrape into the soft interior, firmly anchoring itself.

Traditional cementing method
If the pearl is to be fixed in place in the traditional way, pearl cement is heated to convert it to a sticky mass. Joining occurs when the cement cools, and can be reversed by heating the pieces. In this and all other joins, remember that the metal must be clean and roughened. In this case it will be necessary to preheat all the units being cemented.

Warm the cup and peg and smear on a small amount of cement. Roll a tiny piece of cement between your fingers and slide it into the pearl hole. Warm a small piece of sterling wire and push it into the hole to melt the glue there. Hold the pearl in your fingers (yes, your fingers) and pass it through a very small flame, warming the cup and post at the same time. The heat needed can be provided by the pilot light of a torch, which is to say, very little is needed. If your torch does not have a pilot light, you might use the heat of a desk lamp instead. As long as you can still hold the pearl in your fingers it is safe from damage, which is why you should resist the temptation to use tweezers. When both parts are hot enough they are pushed together with a slight twist. After cooling any excess cement can be cleaned off with tweezers or a scraper.

Removing a pearl
In normal cases a pearl can be removed by heating the jewelry piece lightly (even a hair dryer might do), then twisting the pearl free. A more demanding problem arises when the post has broken off and is lodged inside the pearl. As a first resort, attempt to heat the pearl and withdraw the peg, but if this fails, use the method shown in figure 8.35e.

Obtain a tube of a hard material like stainless steel or 14k gold (au 585). The ideal tube will be thin-walled and will have an inside diameter just larger than the peg. Cut tiny saw teeth on the end of the tube and chuck it into the flexible shaft machine. Running at slow speed, ease into the pearl until the peg has been cut free. It might be necessary to use tweezers to grip the end of the peg and pull it out.

Gluing of pearls and additional elements
Because of their great reliability, modern synthetic glues are used much more often than cements, even for pearls. Glues like epoxies and cyanoacrylates (Super Glue) are stronger, easier to use, can be colored with dyes and eliminate the risks of heating nonmetal elements – and burning your fingers!

8.6.4 BONDING OF METAL PARTS
In the last several decades glues have been invented that raise the integrity of adhesives and earn them a

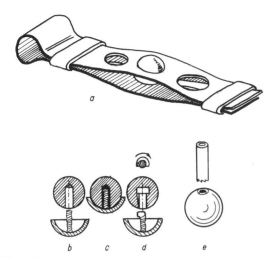

Figure 8.35
Mounting and removing pearls.
*a) pearl holder, b) pre drilled pearl, cup with pin, glued pearl, c) secu-
rity pin and pearl with roughened hole, d) security pin is screwed in,
e) removal of broken pin.*

new place in the arsenal of jewelry techniques. It
must be noted, however, that the truly remarkable
results that can be achieved with glues often refer to
extremely expensive industrial adhesives with elaborate procedures. The glues commonly available,
though very good, are generally weaker than soft solder and significantly weaker than silver solder.

Figure 8.36 illustrates the various stresses that can
be applied to a joint. As the drawing makes clear, glue
joints will be significantly stronger when the design
provides for mechanical extension of the surface area.

The illustrations in figure 8.37a & b show a sensitive adjustment to the use of glue in displaying two
ways to attach a standing cylinder to a base. The first
example, which would be appropriate for hard soldering, is not recommended for adhesives: it's an accident waiting to happen. The second drawing, in
which a hole has been drilled in the base to anchor
the post, has a much better chance of staying
attached. If the height of the post can be reduced, the
potential torque against the column would be less-
ened, further adding to the life span of the joint.

Certainly soldering, the centuries-old method of
fabricating jewelry, is the most effective method and
will always be preferred. But adhesives offer valuable
potential for specific uses. Consider for a moment the
advantages of glue.

- The parts being bonded can be finished before
  construction, by polishing, electroplating,
  enameling, etc.
- Gluing can be faster than soldering.
- The risks connected with heat treatment disappear;
  parts are not automatically annealed when joined.
- Cleanup and finishing work are unnecessary.
- The parts being joined, and this is particularly
  interesting with hollowware, cannot distort or
  warp, a common problem when soldering.

Examples
The two rings shown in figures 8.39 and 8.40 were
completely glued together. The requirements men-

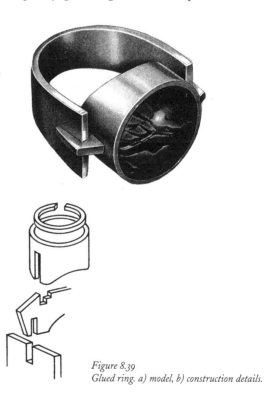

Figure 8.39
Glued ring. a) model, b) construction details.

tioned above for increased surface contact and
mechanically assisted structures led in these examples
to a new way of considering form. The stones were
also glued in place, resulting in new options for settings. After practical testing, these rings have proven
themselves to stand up to the stresses normally
incurred by jewelry.

Exciting possibilities come to mind when we consider the option of combining soldering and gluing as a way of assembling jewelry.

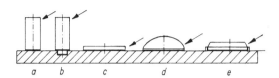

Figure 8.37
Diagonally stressed constructed forms.
a) rod glued simply to the surface, b) rod with sunk tenon,
c) glued on disk, d) arched plate, e) plate with secured frame

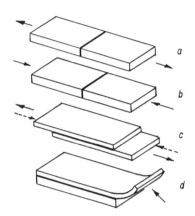

Figure 8.36
Possible stress areas on glued parts.
a) & b) stress transverse to the glue.
c) stress longitudinal to the glued surfaces,
d) stress diagonal to the glued area.

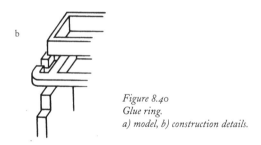

Figure 8.40
Glue ring.
a) model, b) construction details.

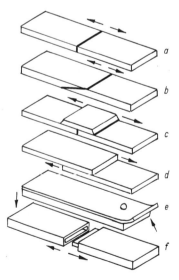

Figure 8.38
Arrangement for glued surfaces.
a) butt connection, b) scarf joint, c) glued on flap, d) overlapping,
e) glued with axillary rivet, f) tenons or telescoping tubes.

CHAPTER NINE

Finishing Techniques

9.1 Sanding and Polishing

The concept of abrasives is simple: Hard grains are bonded into or onto a carrier of some sort in order to be applied with pressure against a surface. There the particles shear bits of the material away, sometimes being broken or pulled off in the process. Coarse particles are used to remove relatively large amounts of material (as in shaping) and smaller or more fragile particles are used for smoothing.

As the particles become smaller it is difficult to bond them without having the glue get in the way of the cutting process. This can be illustrated, for instance, in the case of sandpaper, where fine particles would become lost in a layer of adhesive applied to the paper. At this point the particles are suspended in a waxy material and applied to the carrier as work progresses. A typical arrangement uses a fabric wheel spinning on a machine that is coated ("charged") with abrasive every few minutes as work proceeds.

Though the two processes, sanding and buffing, appear to be very different at first glance, in both cases an abrasive particle is forcibly dragged against a surface through the agency of a carrier, so they are essentially the same. Transitions from coarse to medium to fine sandpaper and then into grades of polishing compounds are fluid. There should be an even progression from each level to the next. Proper finishing requires that each stage of the process receive its full treatment. Skipping a step or moving on to the next prematurely will almost guarantee a flawed surface. Correcting this will involved backtracking to earlier stages. It is a waste of time and often has the effect of eroding details. Because of this, it is most efficient to take whatever time is necessary to progress deliberately through each stage of the sequence.

9.1.1 PROCESSES IN
ABRASIVE WORK AND POLISHING

One of the coarsest abrasive tools in the metalsmith's shop is a grinding wheel, typically a thick disk of abrasive particles mixed into a ceramic matrix that has been fired to make it hard. These are mounted on the spindles of machines that are anchored onto a benchtop or pedestal.

SAFETY NOTE: Never use a tapered spindle with a grinding wheel. Pressure against the wheel can force it along the taper which will act like a wedge and split the wheel, causing it shatter into dangerous projectiles!

The coarseness of grinding wheels is determined by the size and hardness of the particles, and the condition of the ceramic binder (figure 9.1). Because the particles are randomly distributed in the wheel, the cutting is geometrically indeterminate. The cutting angle is normally negative, so the chip is scraped off. The depth of the attack and therefore the condition of the worked surface depends upon the size of the abrasive grains. In addition, these grains project at different heights from the binding material and therefore have different working depths. The clearance is formed by the porosity of the binding agent.

The pressure of the workpiece against the wheel wears off the sharp edges of the grains as grinding progresses. In proper grinding, the dulled grains fall out of the wheel to expose a fresh layer of sharp-edged particles. If the ceramic binder is too strong, the dulled particles are not released; if the binder is too fragile the particles drop off before they are worn and the wheel is used up prematurely. Other factors that come into play are the type of metal being cut and the speed of rotation. Soft metals (aluminum, copper, silver) tend to "smear" or clog the pores of a wheel, quickly reducing the cutting effectiveness. Such metals require very coarse wheels and slow speeds, and even then the wheels will need frequent dressing to expose fresh abrasive. Brittle metals on the other hand, tend to wrench the grains out of the matrix before they are dulled.

The same process plays itself out when polishing with polishing compounds on felt wheels, but of course in a reduced form. Even fine compounds abrade metal away. This is proven by the observation that the lint and dust from polishing is sent to a refiner to retrieve the precious metal it contains. Where does this metal come from if not polishing!

The final stage of buffing uses rouge (powdered iron oxide) which under a microscope reveals its shape as tiny flat disks. These burnish the surface, rubbing against it to press the high spots into the low ones. This is exactly the process we can observe when using a steel burnisher, but of course the rouge process is happening on a much smaller scale. Unlike all the other stages in finishing, burnishing does not remove material. This is true of all burnishing, which includes hand rubbing, tumbling and the use of rouge.

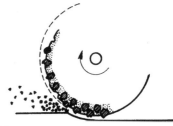

Figure 9.1
Grinding process.

9.1.2 EQUIPMENT AND TOOLS

Grinding and buffing motors are available from many sources, including jewelry supply companies, industrial suppliers and local small motor repair firms. They are available in many sizes and with either one or two spindles. A typical size is ¼ horsepower, but ⅓ or even ½ can be used. The most common speeds in the United States are 1725 or 3450 RPM (revolutions per minute). Either one can be used for grinding and polishing.

As mentioned above, grinding wheels must be permanently mounted directly on the shaft where they are held between steel disks that look like large washers. Also for safety, grinding wheels should only be used in conjunction with a support table (tool rest) that is adjusted to sit very close to the wheel. As the grinding wheel wears down the support should be moved so the space between wheel and platen is never more than 3 mm (⅛").

On buffing machines it is typical to fix tapered threaded spindles onto the cylindrical axles of the motor to facilitate quick change of wheels. Tapered spindles can be purchased from tool suppliers: you will need to know the size of the axle and the side of the motor, left or right, where the spindle will be mounted. Remember that rotation must be downward, away from the worker.

Figure 9.2
Double axle polishing machine with exhaust. (J. Schmalz Company, Pforzheim)

Ventilation equipment is used to catch the dust from grinding and buffing, first to prevent it entering the lungs of the worker, and also because the precious metal particles it contains can be retrieved by a refiner. A simple dust collector is a container mounted behind the wheel to catch the dust where it is thrown by the machine. A much better system involves an active motor-driven exhaust system that pulls air through a filter that catches the lint and other debris. Figure 9.2 shows a popular unit in which the dust collector is contained in the bench that supports the machine.

9.1.3 ABRASIVE AND POLISHING MEDIA

Diamond, C. Diamond powder forms the absolutely hardest abrasive material. Because natural diamond is very expensive, synthetic diamond powder is used almost exclusively.

Aluminum oxide, Al_2O_3. Corundum occurs in nature in the purest forms as ruby and sapphire. Additionally, natural corundum is found in the form of grainy inclusions in host rock. Its hardness is 9.

Emery, a gray to black mineral consists of about 65% Al_2O_3; it is mixed with magnetite, hematite and quartz. Depending upon purity its hardness ranges between 6 and 8. Large deposits of emery are found on the island Naxos in the Aegean Sea. The natural pieces are ground up to a fine grain to produce the well known abrasive. This historically important abrasive has been largely superseded in modern times by the aluminous abrasives described below.

Aluminous abrasives are a synthetic product. Bauxite and carbon are heated in an electrical arc at 2200°C, a very high temperature that reduces the bauxite to aluminum oxide (alumina). The end product contains about 94–99% Al_2O_3 and impurities of iron, titanium and silicon.

335

Pure electro corundum, one of the aluminous abrasives. Heating pure bauxite with sodium hydroxide in a pressure vessel and subsequent precipitation yields a very pure Al_2O_3 that is harder than natural corundum.

Silicon dioxide, SiO_2. Quartz is the purest form of the crystallized silicon dioxide and occurs in many forms in nature, where its hardness is 7. It is used in sandpaper, scouring powder, abrasive pastes and in sand blasting machines. Siliceous earth is a decomposition product formed by algae. The yellowish earth is washed out and purified, heated and pulverized. The end product, called *tripoli* (after the city in Libya where it is found) is used as the basis for different abrasive media. Synthetic tripoli is a fine-grained mixture of the different states of silicon dioxide: anhydrous siliceous acid, powdered quartz crystals and quartz sand.

Silicon carbide, SiC (Carborundum) is made at over 2200°C by melting together coke and quartz sand with additions of sawdust and ordinary salt in the electric furnace. The usually black crystals have a hardness of 9.5. The brittleness of the material limits its use primarily for soft metals and brittle materials.

Iron Oxide, Fe_2O_3. Hematite is a natural occurrence of this form of iron oxide. The steel-gray stone is used with pressure for burnishing by hand. Polishing rouge, (also called Paris Rouge) is usually made from ground and liquid red hematite or by the synthetic oxidation of iron filings. The darker the red color, the harder is the polishing compound.

Chromium oxide, Cr_2O_3. This is green rouge which is particularly suited for hard metals. Chromium oxide is only made synthetically.

Tin oxide, SnO_2. This gray powder is made through the combustion of tin. Because of its limited hardness the fine grained powder is particularly well suited for fine polishing and refinishing.

Zinc oxide, ZnO. In appearance and in use this is the same as tin oxide and like it, it is produced by the combustion of the metal in the air.

Magnesium oxide, MgO. This white, flaky powder, also called magnesia, is a particularly mild polishing medium. Together with aluminum oxide, *Viennese Chalk* and other additions it makes white polishing compound.

Calcium carbonate, $CaCO_3$ (chalk). Chalk slurry is derived from natural chalk which was formed by the layering of tiny sea creatures. Weathered chalk is mixed into a thin paste with water to form slurry, which then settles, is dried and if necessary is ground up again. This method is used to create a basic ingredient of various cleaning powders and polishing pastes.

Viennese Chalk, burnt lime, is made of the mineral dolomite, in which the calcium and magnesium is removed from the carbonate to form oxide compounds. Because Viennese Chalk is not stable in air it must be stored in a sealed container.

Grit size
The grain size of the abrasive medium is determined according to the mesh count of a sieve; i.e. how many holes there are in a square inch. The standardized grit sizes are shown in Table 9.1.

In a general way, the actions of the various sizes can be described like this:
• preliminary abrasion   20–36
• finish abrasion   46–80
• fine abrasion   100–200
• finest abrasion   220–600

Bonding media
As shown in Table 9.2, the material used to secure the grit to the paper or other carrier is an important factor in the effectiveness of the abrasive. As described above, the bonding media must be firm enough to hold the particle until it wears out, but light enough to shed the dull particle and replace it with another.

9.1.4 WORKING METHODS

Sanding

SANDPAPER

The fineness of sandpaper is determined by the size of the grains in the abrasive compound. When a waterproof glue is used the paper can be worked wet. This is especially useful for non-metallic materials (e.g. enamel) in that the particles are carried away with the water, leaving the worked surface free of disturbing scratches.

SANDING STICKS

These simple tools are important to all goldsmiths because they make sandpaper more effective. Strips of wood roughly the size and shape of files (rectangular, triangular, half round and round cross sections) are wrapped with sandpaper, glued or secured with tape. These provide increased leverage and, because they resemble the files used in preceding steps, they bring consistency and control to the process (figure 9.3).

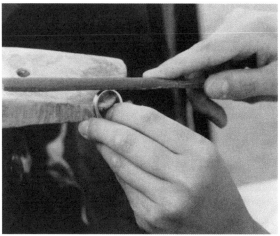

Figure 9.3
Working with a file using the benchpin for support.

Table 9.1
Standardized grit of grinding compounds.

Composition	Surface Application	Grit	
		Number	μm
coarse	pregrinding	20...36	1000...500
medium	finishing grinding	48...80	400...200
fine	fine grinding	100...200	125...60
very fine	very fine grinding	220...600	63...28

Table 9.2
Binding material for grinding wheels.

Characteristics	Ceramic Binder	Organic Binder
main feature	non-elastic	elastic
material	clay, feldspar, quartz; processed in a manner similar to porcelain	rubber, shellac, hardened synthetic (phenol) resin
processing	mix binder material with water and grinding grit; press in molds and fire at 1400 to 1600°C	synthetic resin mixed with grit and poured into heated molds; hardened under pressure
advantages	resistent to water and oil; high porosity; hardness can be calibrated	elastic, not sensitive to shock
disadvantages	sensitive to pressure and shock	the connective binder burns at 300°C

337

As described earlier, proper finishing requires a systematic progression from coarse to finer tools. This sequence usually starts with files then moves to coarse sandpaper. Each grit is used until it completely removes the marks of the preceding abrasive. This is made easier to see by altering the direction of the stroke when each new paper is employed. An exception to this practice is called for when creating a sandpaper finish, in which case the marks all go in the same direction.

In some cases, for instance when sanding a flat area like the side of a box, it is useful to set the sandpaper onto a flat surface like a tabletop and stroke the workpiece along it. A permanent version of this, called a sanding board, is made by gluing a sheet of sandpaper to a panel of Plexiglas or Masonite.

Abrasion with bonded abrasive media
GRINDING WHEEL
As mentioned above, grinding wheels are usually the coarsest tool in a metalsmithing studio. While they are almost never used on gold, silver, copper or brass, they are handy for reshaping hammers and stakes and preparing other tools. Figure 9.4 shows a ceramic grinding wheel and the proper way to mount it on a machine. It is very important to follow these guidelines exactly – the risk of an exploding wheel is very real and very dangerous!

Before mounting a wheel it should be checked for cracks. In addition to a visual inspection, hold the wheel without touching it by sliding a pencil through its center hole and tap it lightly as if ringing a bell. Remembering that this is a ceramic object (despite appearances) it should produce a ringing noise, just like a teacup will when similarly struck. If it doesn't make a ringing sound, discard the wheel!

It is important that the wheel fits snugly onto the axle. Plastic insets are made to accommodate this difference if the hole in the wheel is too large. Do not proceed without one.

The wheel is set into place and securely held with a threaded nut. This is in turn locked into position with a second nut which is finger-tightened against the first. Even after all these precautions it is still best to stand to one side of the machine when turning it on.

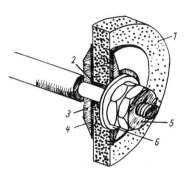

Figure 9.4
Mounting the grinding wheel axle.
1) grinding wheel, 2) bush (or liner), 3) flange, 4) back plate, 5) nut, 6) washer.

Check to see that the wheel runs true without wobbling from side to side. Here again, if the wheel is not running smoothly, avoid risk and possible injury by discarding it.

The grinding wheel should be covered as much as possible with a protective guard. The adjustable tool rest, a small steel plate in front of the wheel, should be adjusted so there is only a small gap between the grinding wheel and the plate. The idea is to make it impossible to accidentally catch the workpiece in the gap there. Remember to adjust the tool rest as the wheel wears away.

Protective goggles must always be worn when using a grinding wheel. Only use the outer (circumference) portion of the wheel; the side surfaces should never be used. Because of the friction heat produced in grinding, either use gloves or a ring clamp to hold work when grinding. Even then you will want to dip the work into water to cool it periodically.

Figure 9.6 shows a few of the dozens of shapes of grinding wheels. Miniature versions of these, called mounted abrasives (figure 9.8), are made for the flexible shaft machine, and consist of ceramic/abrasive forms fired permanently onto steel mandrels. When the abrasive unit is ground away the mandrel is discarded.

GRINDING STONE
This simple and versatile tool is usually considered only in the context of sharpening knives and stoning enamels, but should be remembered whenever coarse

338

abrasive work is needed. A popular version is a flat rectangular stone of about 20-30 cm long, often consisting of a coarse and a fine grit cemented back to back. The stone can be laid flat on the bench (figure 9.5) or used like a file to stroke across the piece.

SILICON CARBIDE STICKS (CARBORUNDUM FILES)

These tools are about 15 cm long, come in different grits, and have the familiar square, rectangular, triangular, half round or round cross sections of files (figure 9.7). When used on glass, enamel, or precious gems the stone is kept wet, often working under a trickle of water at the sink.

When working at the bench, stones are kept moist in a container of water, and dipped periodically to keep them moist. The workpiece should be rinsed with water between grits to flush away all residue.

PUMICE

Though lump pumice is used more for soldering than as an abrasive today, it has a long history in that context, particularly in silversmithing. A lump of the lightweight volcanic stone is given a desired shape with an old file then rubbed against the workpiece to remove fine scratches. The use of powdered pumice is described below.

SLATE

Slate is an indispensable natural fine abrasive material. Like the silicon carbide files mentioned above, slate stones are available in familiar cross sections. In addition they can be filed to any desired special shape, including pointed slates that reach into otherwise impossible areas. These are similar to the silicon carbide files but produce a finer surface.

POLISHING CHARCOAL

While not mineral, charcoal is included here because its use mimics abrasive stones so closely. A lump of charcoal is made wet with water and rubbed over a surface to scour out very fine scratches and leave a matte finish. It is both mild and messy and therefore almost never used today.

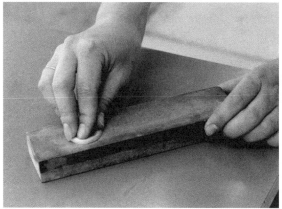

Figure 9.5
Using a grinding stone to grind the work piece flat.

Figure 9.6
Various shaped grinding wheels for finishing jewelry pieces.

Figure 9.7
Grinding with slate and silicone carbide sticks.

Handwork with grinding stones has largely been replaced by motorized grinding and buffing using bench mounted motors and the flexible shaft machine. Nevertheless, these ancient methods deserve our attention, not only for historical interest, but because in some cases they still offer the best, if not the quickest, finishing technique. This is made clear when polishing a flat surface. No matter how sophisticated the equipment, grinding and buffing wheels do not lend themselves to flat surfaces!

Abrasion with loose media

Some abrasives are available as a powder that is rubbed against the workpiece to remove scratches or create a shine. The two most common materials in this category are pumice and tripoli, both of which were described in the previous section. Of the two, pumice is the more aggressive, though it is still considerably finer than silicon carbide or emery.

Pumice powder is supplied in several sizes of particles, which all of course have the same hardness. In addition to jewelry suppliers, pumice can often be purchased at a hardware or paint store because it is used in furniture refinishing.

Either tripoli powder or pumice grains can be used dry, though they tend to fall off the work too quickly this way. More typically they are mixed with water or a light oil or grease to make a paste. The water makes the particles cut a little faster. The grease version is so widely used that generally the only way to buy tripoli is in a solid bar in which the compound is premixed with grease.

HAND ABRASION

Of all the devices conceived to press the grit against a piece, nothing is as versatile as the human hand. Depending upon the kind of object, pumice is gathered on a fingertip or the ball of the hand and then scoured across the object. This method is particularly useful for selectively polishing off a liver of sulfur patina. Because the process is mild it is unlikely to go too far, and because the process is happening literally at your fingertips it is easy to judge when the desired finish has been achieved.

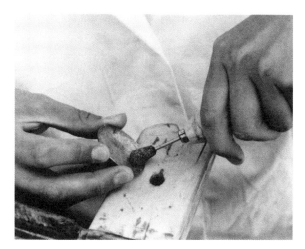

Figure 9.8
A grinding wheel is used in the flex shaft to remove burs.

ABRASIVE STICKS

There are occasions when the pumice or tripoli must be worked into tight spots that cannot be reached by fingers. In this case small wooden sticks are cut to shape, dampened with abrasive slurry, and wiggled into place. A close-grained wood is preferred for this; the species called "priest's hat" is traditional, but any dense hardwood will work (figure 9.9).

THRUMMING STRING

This bundle of strings is attached to the bench and used to reach into tight areas, for instance in piercings, settings, and chains. One or several threads can be used at a time depending on the need (figure 9.10). The bundle hangs on a hook at the edge of the workbench and tripoli compound is applied to the threads by rubbing the cake along them. Thread the strands through the area needing polish and strop the work back and forth, holding the strings loose or taut depending on whether the corners of the work should be crisp or rounded.

Abrasion with machine tools

FELT WHEELS

Felt wheels and circular brushes are available in different shapes and sizes to accommodate a range of possibilities (figure 9.11). They are screwed onto the tapered spindle of the polishing machine and coated

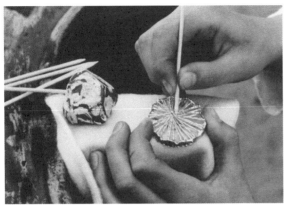

Figure 9.9
Finishing with polishing sticks.

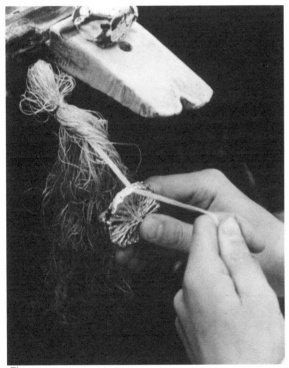

Figure 9.10
Finishing with polishing strings, a process called "thrumming".

or charged with an abrasive media such as tripoli. Each wheel can only be used for a single compound. Mixing them would undermine the effectiveness of both abrasives. The two most common materials for machine buffs are felt and muslin. The felt wheel is used for finishing flat surfaces and in cases where the cutting action needs to be localized or directed at a particular spot.

Figure 9.11
Finishing wheels for polishing machine.

Felt wheels can be shaped somewhat by scraping them with an old file while they are on the polishing machine. Be certain to wear a respirator because the process makes a lot of dust! It might be useful, for instance, to carve grooves of several contours to polish half round wedding bands, ring shanks and bracelets.

The wheel is screwed onto the tapered spindle with the machine turned off, then charged with abrasive compound as the wheel turns. Avoid the temptation to overload the wheel. Simply touching the lump of tripoli against the wheel for a second is sufficient to deposit a thick layer. The process is repeated every several minutes as the wheel is used.

ROUND BRISTLE BRUSHES
Brushes used for abrasive work have harder bristles than those sold for polishing. As bristles get shorter through wear they become less flexible, making them especially useful for some purposes. In contrast to the felt wheel, bristle brushes fit into even complicated shapes. This makes them especially useful for wire constructions. Because the bristles do not press hard against the metal, brushes can never deliver the same aggressive grinding action that can be achieved with felt. The circular brush is completely unsuitable for straight, smooth surfaces and sharp edges.

Abrasion with the flexible shaft machine
Not all parts of the a jewelry piece can be reached with the relatively large felts and brushes of the polishing machine; for detailed finishing we use the same shaped buffs on the flexible shaft (figures 9.12 and 9.13). These are identical but smaller and avail-

341

able in a dizzying variety of shapes. The advantage of the flex shaft is in its variable speed and the way the tool can be moved around the piece to reach into every area.

9.1.5 POLISHING

The work of polishing to create a highly reflective surface depends more than anything else on what has gone on before. If the metal has been properly abraded; that is, if the appropriate sandpapers and abrasives were used in their proper sequence and to the correct degree, then the polish phase is both quick and easy. Unfortunately, if the abrasive stage was rushed, polishing will simply make a flawed surface into a bright flawed surface. Polished metal in fact shows scratches, pits and dents more than any other finish, so literally no polish is better than a poor polish.

As described above, finishing can be described as a process of reducing raised or projecting areas until

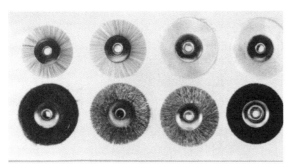

Figure 9.12
Wheels for the flex shaft. (J. Schmalz Co.)

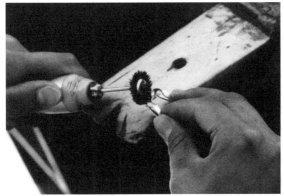

Figure 9.13
Polishing with the flex shaft.

they blend in with the flat of the sheet. The flatter the metal, the more light is reflected back, ending with a mirror-like finish. If all abrasive work has been done well, a microscopic view of the metal would reveal a surface that has only very slight furrows, the minor tracks left by the last fine abrasive used. From here it is an easy step to burnish the high spots down to create the characteristic warm shine of gold and silver.

Pressure polishing.
This is probably the oldest polishing method and consists of forcibly rubbing soft metal with a stone or steel burnisher. A modern variation is called tumbling, in which work is set loose along with small pieces of steel or some other hard media in a drum that is mechanically rotated.

Electrolytic polishing.
This is the most modern polishing procedure, a sort of reverse of electroplating in which a surface is stripped off with the use of electric current.

Mechanical Polishing.
This method is an extension of the abrasive process just described and is by far the most common used by goldsmiths. Much of the equipment and methods used for abrasive grinding are duplicated in polishing.

9.1.6 POLISHING MEDIA

As with abrasives, these are most commonly sold premixed with grease in the form of bars, cakes, or cylinders. A glance at a jewelry supply catalog will quickly reveal the wealth of options. Some of the more traditional materials are red rouge (iron oxide), white rouge (tin oxide), and green rouge (chromium oxide). Every goldsmith has a personal favorite. Beginning workers are encouraged to experiment to decide their own preferences.

It is absolutely essential that all the abrasive residues be completely washed off the metal before moving on to the polishing compounds.

Polishing by hand
One of the most effective hand polishing tools is also one of the most simple. Polishing sticks are flat strips

of wood onto which have been glued pieces of leather. These resemble sanding sticks, which in turn resemble files. It is useful to have several of these and of course they must be carefully marked. The compounds are rubbed into the leather and refreshed as often as necessary.

Thrumming strings, described above for abrasives, work very well for polishing as well. Again, a separate cluster of string is needed for rouge, which is rubbed onto the strings as they hang from a hook on the bench.

Polishing with machine tools

The same machines used for abrasive work can be used for polishing, but a separate set of buffing wheels must be used for every compound. The wheels themselves can be the same, though a soft muslin is often preferred. A special version of a fabric wheel is called the *swabbing* or unstitched *muslin wheel*. In Britain it is called a *loose mop*. Whatever its name, this wheel falls lightly on the metal surface, making it a milder tool. In addition, it is usually used with only sparing amounts of compound.

The final and highest polish is achieved with a woolen buff. In this tool a pierced wooden hub is covered all around densely with threads of white or gray sheep's wool. The woolen wheel works like a rapidly rotating polishing cloth. Use as little polishing medium as possible. The residue left on the workpiece from the last step is sufficient.

Burnishing

This ancient method, though little used today, has several benefits and should not be immediately dismissed. For one thing, the technique is as versatile as it is simple: tools can be made to suit any need and used in any context. Because the surface is compacted, burnishing tends to strengthen a piece; because no metal is removed, it is not wasteful. Burnishing lends itself particularly to situations in which a shiny area occurs next to a matte one: the burnisher makes it very easy to reach specific areas.

On the negative side, burnishing is time consuming and requires practice, particularly to achieve a uniform surface on a flat area. The technique does not do well in a heavily contoured piece such as an object covered with chasing or repoussé. In the case of thin metal, the pressure of burnishing can make dents or distortions.

STEEL BURNISHER

This is made of a high quality, hardened steel. Shapes are made for whatever needs are at hand, but generally avoid sharp edges that will scratch the metal. The steel must be polished to a flawless shine, and kept that way. Burnishers are securely fitted into wooden handles to provide leverage.

BURNISHING STONE

Some burnishers are made of quartz, but the best use hematite. A smooth, rounded shape is attached to a wooden handle by a brass bezel, and as with steel burnishers, several shapes are needed. Burnishing stones are capable of achieving an even better polish than with steel.

HANDLING THE TOOLS

Both stone and steel burnishers must be refinished from time to time by polishing them with a leather polishing stick treated with tin oxide. If there are deep scratches, they should be removed with corundum powder on a similar stick.

METHOD

Before burnishing, the metal should be thoroughly cleaned. Because pressure is so important to burnishing, the work must be supported well. This is often done by laying it on a bench pin cushioned with a towel. To reduce friction of the tool as it presses across the surface, the burnisher is typically moistened, often with spit, though a light mix of soap and water will also do. Remembering that steel will rust, be certain to dry off the tool before putting it away.

Rub the burnisher across the surface in firm strokes, starting lightly and increasing pressure as you become confident of control. Cover the entire surface with parallel strokes, then turn the piece and make right angles to the first pattern. When the surface is uniformly polished, rub it with a leather polishing stick or a soft woolen cloth impregnated with compound to remove the subtle tool marks.

STORING THE TOOLS

Steel burnishers are traditionally stored in a box with sawdust so they do not rust and cannot get scratched. Stone burnishers are wrapped in soft cloths to prevent damage.

Matte surfaces

As attractive as it is, there are cases where a high polish is not recommended. A highly reflective shine will show irregularities, fingerprints and stains with unfortunate clarity. In those cases one of the following methods should be used to convert the smooth surface to a slightly fine-grained one. In every case the metal should be made smooth and uniform first then given its matte finish. These techniques are not shortcuts to avoid doing work, though some people treat them that way!

MATTING PUNCHES

These texture-faced chasing punches are used to strike a stippled texture into a surface. Of all the options this is the most dramatic, durable and time consuming.

WIRE TEXTURING BRUSHES

These tools, two versions of which are shown in figures 9.16 and 9.17, consists of rows or bundles of swinging steel wires arranged around a wooden hub. When used in an electric hand drill, the wires fly out radially where they stay through centrifugal force. The workpiece is held lightly against the tips of the wire, which leave a roughed finish. The actual texture will vary depending on the particular tool, the metal being brushed, and the pressure of the wires against the surface. Parts of the surface can be covered up with a stout tape for special effects.

SANDBLASTING

The concept of sandblasting is very basic and in fact something nature has been doing in the desert for eons. Loose particles of sand or some other abrasives are propelled against a piece. At the moment of impact each particle makes a tiny crater before falling away. In the jewelry studio it is caught and often reused; when sandblasting buildings the grit is gener-

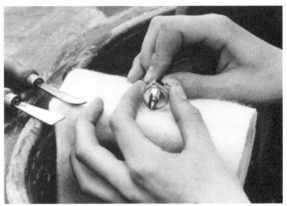

Figure 9.14
Hand polishing with hematite.

Figure 9.15
Hand polishing with a burnisher.

ally used only once.

Figure 9.18 shows a basic sandblasting unit that can be constructed in the studio. Make or find a cylinder about 60 cm (23") high and 30 cm (12") in diameter and outfit it with a funnel shaped bottom to which you can attach a hose. Holes are cut and fitted with rubber gloves to hold the work and a window to be able to see inside. The hose is connected to a powerful air compressor and sandblasting media is put into the container.

The work piece is set into the box which is covered, then the compressor is turned on. The blast of air from the hose will shoot the media up like a geyser.

Figure 9.16
Texturing wheels with movable single and double rows of wire; pumice stone. (J. Schmalz Co.)

Figure 9.17
Texturing wheel with fixed wire bundles.

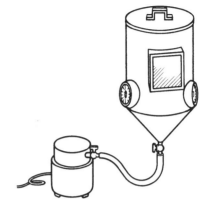

Figure 9.18
Simple sandblaster.

The worker simply holds the piece in front of it to achieve a sandblasted surface.

Several kinds of media are available for sandblasters. Like other abrasives, they are differentiated by the material of which they are made and the size of the particles. Of particular interest to jewelers are round glass beads that leave a delicate surface and run no risk of seriously eroding the precious metal. Some sands are very aggressive and can leave a piece half its original thickness in a matter of minutes. Experimentation is recommended!

As a footnote it is worth mentioning that sandblasting is also being used to remove investment from castings, particularly in high volume commercial operations. In those cases a filter is used to separate the used investment from the sand so the latter can be reused.

A fairly recent addition to the goldsmithing studio is the small cabinet sandblasters shown in figure 9.19. These operate as the unit described above, but are smaller in every way. They take up less space in the studio and operate with a smaller compressor. The air supply is attached to a gun that directs the spray of sand. This allows the grit to be aimed and offers convenience and control.

SCRATCHBRUSHING

The surface created by a very fine brass brush is not exactly a matte surface, but because it is not a high shine we will consider it in this section. The name is misleading because no scratches should come from this process, but because the name is well established, we'll continue the misnomer.

Scratchbrushes, whether used with a machine or by hand, are made of very fine brass wires – 30 gauge or finer. When used with a soapy lubricant the wires burnish silver or gold to create a lustrous glow that is less reflective than a rouge polish but much warmer than other matte finishes.

SCRATCHBRUSHING TOOLS

This finish can be achieved with a handbrush that resembles a large toothbrush having brass bristles and a wooden or plastic handle. The brush is lubricated with soap and scrubbed across the piece in alternating directions. Work is typically done over a sink where the resulting soapsuds are rinsed off as work progresses to examine the results. If the metal has been properly prepared with careful sanding, scratchbrushing should take only a few minutes. The longer one works at it, the more glowing the results.

Many studios find scratchbrushing so valuable they set up electric motors to make the job more efficient. These can either be self contained like the example shown in figure 9.20, or are set beside a sink so the water drains naturally into existing plumbing. The rotation of this machine must be a lot slower than buffing machines; usually around 700-800 RPM. There is a danger in having an electric motor close to a water source, so a typical solution is to use a free-standing mandrel driven by a motor that is mounted slightly away from the sink. The beauty of this arrangement is that it allows the motor to be at a safe distance and simultaneously makes it easy to use a reduction pulley to slow down the RPM.

Brushes for the machine consist of wooden hubs mounted with nickel silver or brass wires that are, again, in the neighborhood of 0.15 to 0.25 mm thick. Here again it is important that the action be lubricated with soapy water. Without this, the yellow color of the brass is smeared across the surface. Work is rotated under the brush at a medium pressure until the desired finish is obtained, which usually takes only a minute.

9.1.7 BARREL TUMBLING WORK

Though tumbling is not a new process, its use as a finishing method has seen rapid growth recently. The traditional polishing media of steel shot has been supplemented by alternate media, extending the range of what can be accomplished and the materials suitable for the technique.

Tumbling is best suited to mass finishing at an industrial level, but small machines have recently made the process equally well suited to small workshops. Tumbling is at its best when identical or similar objects are being produced in quantity. Shops that concentrate on repairs or one-of-a-kind work might

Figure 9.19
Pencil bead blasters with one and two blasters. (Fenfert GmbH and Co., Hilzingen)

Figure 9.20
Texturing machine, stainless steel and synthetic coating. (J. Schmalz Co., Pforzheim)

not find a tumbler very useful, but many other situations will benefit from its hands-off efficiency.

In traditional tumbling a wooden barrel was filled about half full with steel shot immersed in soapy water. Several pieces of jewelry were added to the mix, the barrel lid sealed and the barrel was rotated, usually through the action of an electric motor. The pieces of steel would then cascade onto the jewelry to create a momentary burnishing action (figure 9.21). This was repeated hundreds or thousands of times as the barrel turned, leaving the jewelry piece bright and shiny. Rotational speeds are slow because if the barrel moves too rapidly the contents no longer slip and slide but instead are thrown about in the direction of rotation.

Wooden barrels have been replaced with rubber or plastic containers. These have a hexagonal interior cross section that "drops" the shot most effectively. In some machines water is flushed continuously through the barrel, cleaning the mix and contributing to the action.

9.1.8 TUMBLING MEDIA
Abrasive tumbling media
Various abrasives are mixed into plastic or ceramic to create variously shaped pieces that are used in a tumbler to smooth away roughness (figure 9.22a). These pieces are relatively large, averaging 6-9 mm (⅜") in size. These are used in a lubricant formulated just for this purpose, and require research and experimentation to determine the correct media for a specific project. Particularly in the case of ceramic media, the tumbling action breaks down the forms so they must be replaced periodically.

It is also possible to achieve a cutting action with small dice-like wooden media. A slurry is made of water and an abrasive paste, which is poured into the tumbler and run for a few minutes to allow it to coat the wooden forms. The jewelry is then added and further tumbling takes place, sometimes as long as 5 hours.

The contents of the barrel should be roughly ⅓ articles and ⅔ wooden tumbling media. This method has been largely replaced by the use of plastic media. These are less messy because the abrasive is build into the plastic, and faster because the greater weight of the media acts in the same way as pressing down harder when using sandpaper.

Polishing shot
Polishing is usually done with shot made of carbon steel or stainless steel, again lubricated with soapy water or a proprietary liquid sold for this purpose. Shot is available in several shapes (figure 9.22) that include spheres, chevrons, bits of wire, cones and ellipses. It is most typical to combine several shapes to insure that all areas of a piece will be properly polished. In certain jewelry pieces care needs to be taken to avoid using balls that are so small they get stuck in depressions or pierced areas.

It is important that the shot has a highly polished, pit-free surface to obtain a perfect polish. The shot is kept immersed in liquid between uses to prevent exposure to air that would cause rust. When no tumbling is expected for a length of time, the shot is drained in a sieve and poured out on a towel. Use a hair dryer or lamp to dry the shot completely before putting it into a sealed jar.

Even with this the surfaces can become matte and porous from corrosion because the aqueous polishing solution acts like an electrolyte. The movement between the base metal spheres and the precious metal articles creates an electrochemical reaction that has the potential to dissolve particles from the steel metal shot that go into the solution as ions. Commercial tumbling solutions contain chemicals that reduce the electrolytic potential enough to prevent corrosion and extend the useful life of the polishing shot.

Tumbling equipment
The range of machines available is large and increasing all the time. Readers are advised to consult catalogs to determine which tumbler is best suited to their needs. Catalogs (or a phone call to the supplier) will supply information about the capacity of the machine and its relevant features. Some companies are willing to review your needs and recommend a tumbling system.

The two styles being used currently are called vibratory or rotary (drum) style. In the latter case a

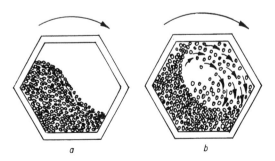

Figure 9.21
Movement in the tumbler. a) rotary movement at normal speed, b) disarray of contents from too rapid rotation.

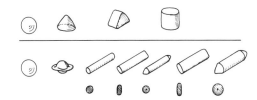

Figure 9.22
Grinding and polishing pieces. top: grinding pieces out of hard
ceramic, bottom: steel polishing (burnishing) pieces.

sealed drum is rolled on its axis, usually by being set upon rubber coated rods turned by an electric motor. The weight of the barrel pressing down on the drive shafts is sufficient to provide the necessary friction.

A vibratory tumbler consists of a plastic bowl or tub that is mounted on an eccentric shaft. When the motor is turned on, the bowl wiggles like an out-of-balance washing machine. These units are especially recommended for larger applications. In commercial situations it is common to have a series of machines that handle the sequence from coarse to fine media. Works are collected from each unit in turn, rinsed and dropped into the next drum.

The working procedure
Experimentation is needed to determine the optimum tumbling arrangements for each piece. This explains why tumbling is best suited to volume productions, where more or less identical pieces are being turned out in volume.

The variables that need to be adjusted include:
– the shape and material of the tumbling media
– the proportion of articles to media
– the type and quantity of lubricant
– the duration of the tumbling

As mentioned, it is vital that steel shot have a smooth shiny surface. The lubricant must be clean, as will be evidenced by white foam. If impurities are present the solution should be discarded and replaced. If the contents have not been used for a long time, run the tumbler for at least a half hour without jewelry articles to insure that the shot and solution are clean.

The length of time needed for abrasive tumbling will of course depend on the original condition of the

metal, the aggressiveness of the media and the power of the machine: it is not unusual for the process to take as long as 10 hours. Burnishing, by contrast, is usually faster, typically taking 30 minutes to two hours.

It is easy to check the progress of tumbling: simply retrieve a piece from the shot and examine it! Because some vibratory tumblers are open bowls it's possible to reach in without interrupting the process. When the correct finish has been achieved the work is separated from the media by passing it through a sieve that will catch the jewelry but allow the shot to fall through. It is caught in a convenient bucket and returned immediately to the tumbler. An exception is steel shot that is going to sit unused for a time: in that case the shot is dried as mentioned above.

The polished jewelry items are rinsed in clean water to remove soap residue then dried to prevent water spotting. This is traditionally done by placing the work in a box of fine sawdust (not pine or oak). After a few seconds the work can be pulled out and dusted with a soft brush.

For a particularly high shine, tumble again, dry, in a small piece of chamois leather.

Centrifugal force tumbling procedure
In normal tumbling, increased speed has the effect of holding the work against the outside wall by centrifugal force. This means the work is not tumbling against the media and is therefore usually avoided. It is possible, however, to arrange the drum so that it is electrically driven in the reverse direction of the centrifugal force. This has the effect of doubling the force with which the work is driven into the media, making it a useful technique for the deburring and smoothing of rough castings. The process is also used on some gemstones, but care must be taken because not all stones can withstand the significant pressure. For the same reason the procedure is unsuitable for final polishing.

9.1.9 CLEANING
As simple as it sounds, there is more to the issue of cleaning than meets the eye. For starters, the chemicals and debris that must be removed come from two

Figure 9.23
Polishing and grinding tumbler. This unit features an exchangeable
tumbler filter and a collecting tank.

sources – the fabrication of the work and the handling of the piece as it is worn. In the first category we could place investment, abrasive and polishing compounds and chemicals like flux or pickle.

In the other category we find jewelry cleaner, perfume, finger oils and the myriad chemicals of everyday life. These are of course most likely to be encountered in objects brought in for repair, but even a "new" object has often been exposed to a diverse collection of contaminants.

To further confuse the situation we need to be aware of two kinds of clean. In some cases we can be content when work looks clean, but in others, as for instance when applying lacquer, the metal must be carefully degreased, which is something a little different. This will be achieved with two chemicals: a grease solvent that will dissolve the grease so it can be wiped away, and a degreasing compound that will remove the last trace of grease from the already cleaned surface.

Annealing

The temperatures of annealing burn all traces of grease off a piece. Submersion in clean pickle will dissolve the oxides formed by heating while leaving the surface grease free. This is effective but of course has its limitations. If a piece has been polished, this treatment will reduce the finish to matte, and of course it

cannot be worked where the issue of heat would damage the work, for instance where gemstones, adhesives, enamels or tempered elements are in place.

Even when these concerns are taken into consideration, this process is worth remembering, particularly for large silver objects where other surface treatments could be time consuming.

Degreasing solutions

Recent and ongoing developments in this field are yielding compounds that attack grease without the health and environmental dangers of their recent predecessors. Not only jewelry supply companies, but industrial suppliers and custodials distributors can supply degreasing agents suitable for studio use. While this book has endeavored to present an historical perspective wherever possible, we've decided to omit references to chemicals that are flammable or known to have health risk.

Each reader is encouraged to purchase a locally available solvent and follow manufacturer's directions carefully. Avoid the temptation to mix solutions to higher than recommended concentrations, and use ventilation as required.

USING GREASE SOLVENTS

Place the work in a solution of cleanser, following directions concerning its temperature; some solutions work faster when warm. The effect can be dramatic, particularly when the piece is very dirty, for instance after machine buffing. Simply sitting in a dish of solution is enough to free a cloud of dirty particles.

Allow the work to sit for several minutes or longer depending on the degree of dirtiness. Agitate the piece slightly, perhaps using a soft brush (e.g. a toothbrush) to wiggle debris from pockets. The piece is then soaked briefly in a water/ammonia solution, then rinsed under running water. In these final steps care should be taken to hold the work only by its edges with rubber-tipped tweezers.

USING DEGREASING SOLUTIONS

Most degreasing solutions are strongly alkaline. In a process called saponification, greases are split into fatty acids and glycerin. These are then absorbed into the fluid where they form a foam, and can be easily removed. This leaves only mineral greases, which do not saponify.

The more strongly alkaline the solvent, the more effective it is at removing grease, but it must be remembered that strong bases are just as corrosive as strong acids. Use of too strong a solution not only risks damaging the jewelry piece but might involve danger to the goldsmith too.

DEGREASING AGENTS

Sodium hydroxide, NaOH (lye) and *potassium hydroxide*, KOH (caustic potash) are similar to each other and deserve the same caution. Both are particularly strong agents that can attack the skin and can also damage the metal. Needless to say, they should be avoided.

Ammonium hydroxide, NH_4OH (aqueous ammonia) is the aqueous solution of ammonia. This is the common grocery store variety of household cleanser, often available with a sudsing agent (and even a modified scent!). This is an effective cleanser that is relatively harmless on the skin, making it a good choice for workshops. Care must be taken that ammonia is not splashed in the eyes or allowed to get into open cuts, so gloves and goggles are recommended. Ammonia does not hurt metal, but prolonged exposure (more than an hour) will turn brass dark gray.

Potassium cyanide, KCN and *sodium cyanide*, NaCN are very effective alkaline degreasers, but they are not recommended because both are extremely poisonous.

Sodium carbonate, Na_2CO_3 (baking soda) and *potassium carbonate*, K_2CO_3 (potash) are weakly alkaline and therefore belong in this list of cleansers. Both are non-poisonous and safe for metals, but unfortunately they are not particularly effective cleaners.

As with the grease solvents mentioned above, follow manufacture's directions to ensure safe and effective cleaning. Many solutions are sold in concentrated form to be mixed with water. If possible the solutions

are used hot, sometimes even boiling, because the grease solubility is increased when warm.

As described above, the usual sequence is to remove most grease with a solvent, then move to the degreasing agent to remove the final film. Even though the piece appears clean it should be left in the solution for several minutes to ensure that every trace of grease is lifted off. Test a piece by holding it under running water. If the water beads up, the piece is still greasy even though it might look perfectly clean. When all grease has been removed the water forms a uniform sheet over the surface.

The piece is handled with a minimum of hand contact, perhaps by hanging from a wire or using some kind of jig. Degreasing is followed by a rinse in water, except in the case of electroplating, where the piece can go directly into its first solution.

It is sometimes possible to use only this second step, degreasing compounds, to clean work. Experimentation and the use of the "sheeting test" will soon tell you the most efficient method.

The ultrasonic cleaner

This relatively recent device provides efficient and thorough cleaning through the use of sound waves. No workshop, even the smallest, should be without it. Jewelers who continue to wash with toothbrushes are subject to a false economy. Not only are they spending time but such manual techniques can never duplicate the microscopic cleaning of the ultrasonic machine.

Ultrasonic wavelengths are outside the range of human hearing, typically operating at 16 kHz. They oscillate back and forth more than 16,000 times per second. This is barely imaginable yet technically possible. Household currant of 60Hz is converted to the required high frequency with a specially constructed generator. These electrical oscillations are then transformed into mechanical ones. This is achieved through the use of the piezoelectric effect with a sound generator, a process first observed with quartz. When a quartz crystal is compressed at a right angle to its main axis, its internal potential is polarized so that a measurable current can occur in an external electrical circuit. This process is reversible and is known as the reciprocal piezoelectric effect. When external current is shut off, the crystal resumes its original shape. This change in shape occurs at an extremely small size.

Original oscillators were made with natural quartz that have today been replaced with synthetically made piezoceramic oscillators. The particles are distributed in an electrical field on the polycrystalline ceramic body.

Modern ultrasonic cleaners have this oscillator permanently attached to the outside floor of the bath container. In this way the container becomes a resonating body and the bath liquid is uniformly agitated by miniature oscillations.

A commercial preparation is usually used as a bath liquid. Degreasing and grease dissolving agents cut the dirt which is then "wiggled" free by the ultrasonic vibrations. Liquid soap and water can also be used. The particles of the fluid are excited about $1/1000$ of a millimeter at least 16,000 times per second. Because of their mass moment of inertia they are physically unable to move that fast. Backward flowing particles strike against forward moving ones creating a pulsing effect that "tears apart" the liquid in a process called cavitation. The fluid breaks against the surface of the article with great agitation and tears off a particle of dirt. A second result of this process is the breaking down of each dirt particle to a smaller size. If the solution is warm, the process is accelerated and for this reason some machines include a small heating unit. The smallest equipment holds about one liter with larger units holding at least 16 liters (figure 9.24).

The work to be cleaned is suspended in the bath generally from hooks draped over the edge or hung from rods that span the unit. It is important that nothing touch the walls or floor of the container because that would dampen the vibrations. An immersion of 20 to 60 seconds is sufficient for almost all cleaning. The pieces can then be removed, rinsed in running water, and if necessary, clinging particles can be removed with the brush or a jet of high pressure steam.

Drying after cleaning
In order to prevent water spots, pieces must be dried immediately after their final rinse. This can be as simple as wiping them with a soft cloth. In cases where more than a single piece needs to be dried, a traditional method is to drop the work in a box of sawdust. The water is absorbed by the wood chips almost instantly. The pieces can then be lifted out, blown free of any chips, and packaged. In some situations a plastic sieve is used to recover the pieces after drying. Drying can be accelerated by using a lamp to warm the sawdust. This arrangement should never be left unattended because of the fire hazard. In industrial situations, a version of this that resembles a cement mixer is used to dry hundreds or thousands of pieces. An angled, rotating drum tumbles the objects in sawdust or a similar absorbent material. When dry the bell is tilted and emptied into a basket.

9.2
Pickling, Coloring, and Cleaning

9.2.1 SULFURIC ACID PICKLES
By definition, a pickle is a chemical solution that will attack surface films. In ancient times, vinegar and salt were used and it is from this origin that we derive the name. In more recent history strong acids, diluted with water, have traditionally been used. Today these have been largely replaced by proprietary solutions that are less caustic but equally effective. In the interest of historical foundation, this section will describe traditional acid pickles.

Pickle containers
The size and shape of a pickle container will vary depending on the needs of each studio. It must obviously be large enough to accommodate the biggest pieces being made, but having too much is not only wasteful but can be frustrating when small pieces need to be recovered from the bottom of a deep vat. It is not unusual, therefore, for a studio that works in both large scale and small scale to have several sizes

Figure 9.24
Different capacity ultrasound cleaners. (Heraeus Co., Pforzheim)

of pickle containers. They can be made of glass, porcelain, glazed stoneware, and most hard plastics. Photographic trays made from PVC can be useful for large flat objects and in certain cases (rods, tubes, wires) a bottle might be useful.

The action of the pickle is accelerated with heat. In cases where the solution will be made warm, glass must be Pyrex and plastic is of course no longer acceptable. Suppliers of jewelry equipment sell a small heated container made specifically for pickle. A popular alternative is a household crockpot. Before use, the crockpot seams must be sealed with caulking to prevent the pickle from attacking the heating element. The temperature of pickle should be about 50 to 65°C (125–150°F), uncomfortably hot to the touch but not quite boiling. Pieces can be simply dropped into the pickle pot, though sometimes a plastic sieve is used when pickling many small units.

Preparing the pickle
SAFETY NOTE: Protective clothing, gloves and goggles must be worn when handling acid.

The appropriate container is filled with water and sulfuric acid is poured into it in a thin stream. This activity generates a significant amount of heat energy which is why the sequence is important. If one were to do the reverse, that is pour the water into the acid, the water droplets would be immediately heated to the boiling point and, turning into steam, would

Figure 9.25
Hot air drying centrifuge. (Heraeus Co., Pforzheim)

explosively spray out along with the acid. Even with care taken, workers should wear gloves, goggles, and an acid proof apron.

For most applications, a typical mix is one part sulfuric acid to twenty parts water. Or to say it another way, the solution is about 5% acid. When the solution will only be used at room temperature, a greater concentration is recommended; as much as 10% acid (one part acid to ten parts water).

Using sulfuric acid pickle
When fabrication is complete the piece is either allowed to cool or quenched in water. On no account should it be thrown into the pickle while hot. Not only is there a danger of splashing acid, but the expanded air in hollow spaces compacts when quenched and will suck the quenching liquid inside.

Figure 9.26
Pickling pot (J. Schmalz, Pforzheim)

This affects not only perceivable interior spaces, like the inside of a bead, but also fine cracks and microscopic pores. Acid residues will be unretrievably retained in these spaces. Because sulfuric acid is hygroscopic, moisture in the air will continually refresh the chemical activity of these residues. The results of this process include skin irritation for a wearer, decomposition phenomena of the metal, and a bluish green copper sulfate efflorescence.

If the object is first quenched in water, the same reaction occurs: the spaces fill with water which prevents pickle from entering.

Work is left in pickle only as long as necessary to clean the surface. Prolonged exposure can weaken silver soldered joints.

Safety
Sulfuric acid is a dangerous material, even in a low concentration solution such as 5% pickle. Exposure to skin will result in irritation; exposure to open cuts can lead to painful inflammation. Plastic tweezers are used to remove work from cold pickle. For hot pickle copper or brass tongs are preferred.

Steel tools should never be introduced into the pickle because the tiny electrical charge created in the reaction between ferrous metal and silver-copper alloy will trigger a plating reaction that deposits a small amount of copper on the articles in the pickle at that time. It is for this reason that only copper, brass, or plastic tongs are used.

Organic materials are oxidized by sulfuric acid.

This means that holes can be eaten in clothing by acid splashes. When using a strong pickle like this, baking soda should always be close at hand to neutralize a spill. Even small splashes can later yield holes in clothing. This is an example of the hygroscopic effect that allows the acid to continue its corrosive action with a later addition of water.

9.2.2 SILVER AND SILVER ALLOYS
Pickling
Fine silver (Ag 1000) retains its white color even when heated. As copper is added to create traditional alloys like sterling the metal becomes subject to the formation of black copper (II) oxide on the surface as oxygen combines with the copper. At room temperature this tarnish develops slowly and is easily removed.

When silver/copper alloys are heated for annealing or soldering, the film grows faster and is more tenacious. Though it can be mechanically removed with abrasives, a far more common and efficient practice is to dissolve the oxide in pickle.

Pickle dissolves flux residues while it also transforms the black copper (II) oxide into copper sulfate which goes into solution. Note that copper (I) oxide is not attacked.

The main reaction is:

$$CuO + H_2SO_4 \rightarrow$$
copper (II) oxide   sulfuric acid
$$CuSO_4 + H_2O$$
copper sulfate   water

Depletion silvering
If the copper is leached from the surface of a silver/copper alloy it stands to reason that the resulting "skin" is pure silver. This process, which can be used effectively as an alternative to plating is called depletion gilding. Though this can be achieved in the proprietary pickle used in most studios (Sparex) it is most efficient to use the traditional sulfuric acid pickle. This assumes ventilation and safety equipment. Because the process is the same for either method, the information below will suffice for either situation.

In the case of a sodium bisulfate pickle (like Sparex), the copper in the alloy must be converted to copper oxide in order to be dissolved. The process is to heat the work until it turns gray then quench it in water and warm it in pickle until it is white. The process is repeated several times until the color is uniformly white. It will also be noticed that at this point the metal is slower to oxidize when under the flame.

A 10% solution of sulfuric acid is strong enough to attack not only the black copper (II) oxide but metallic copper particles within the metal. On the positive side this means the work does not have to be heated to darken it before the pickle will take effect. On the other hand this acid is so strong it will etch away the surface and joints if the work is submerged too long. Usually a dip of a few seconds is sufficient to pickle a sterling object.

The reaction is:

$$Cu \quad + \quad H_2SO_4 \quad \rightarrow$$
copper \quad sulfuric acid
$$CuSO_4 \quad + \quad H_2$$
copper sulfate \quad hydrogen

If red copper (I) oxide is present it can also be dissolved out.

$$CuO_2 \quad + \quad H_2SO_4 \quad \rightarrow$$
copper (I) oxide \quad sulfuric acid
$$CuSO_4 \quad + \quad H_2O \quad + \quad Cu$$
copper sulfate \quad water \quad copper

Note the release of copper into the solution. This explains why the pickle takes on a blue-green color as it is used. This is the characteristic color of copper compounds. Note also that even this aggressive etching does not dissolve the zone of deep oxidation that forms under the surface by the diffusion of oxygen called firescale.

The efficiency of a sulfuric acid pickle is significantly improved by the addition of potassium permanganate, Mn_2O_7 which reacts to form manganese heptoxide, and anhydrite of permanganic acid:

$$2\ KMnO_4 \quad + \quad H_2SO_4 \quad \rightarrow$$
$$Mn_2O_7 \quad + \quad K_2SO_4 \quad + \quad H_2O$$

Because potassium permanganate decomposes quickly in air it must be added to pickle before each use. This nuisance is compensated for by the extremely good results obtained through the addition.

It often happens that a thin flashing of copper remains behind on a silver alloy, a pinkish plating that cannot be dissolved even in hot pickle. In addition to abrasion, this can be removed in two ways.

1) Immerse the work in a strong solution of nitric acid, typically 50-60% with water. This process, called bright dipping, involves strong acids and so certainly requires ventilation and protective clothing. The work is strung on a copper or stainless wire and dipped only for a few seconds. The copper flashing will be instantly converted to a dark gray film that can be rinsed off with water. If the pink is not completely removed in one dipping, repeat the dip-and-rinse process, never leaving the piece immersed for more than 10 seconds.

2) Heat the piece to convert the copper flashing to copper oxide (a gray layer) that can then be dissolved in pickle.

In most cases a single pickling cycle is not sufficient to create a bright white layer of fine silver so the process is repeated several times – heat, quench, pickle, rinse, scratchbrush, rinse – through four or five repetitions to obtain the desired effect.

Particularly in large pieces with broad flat surfaces this can lead to detrimental changes in the structure and to deep oxidation (firescale). In such cases the procedure can be shortened with this alternate method. After the first pickling, coat the work with a paste of water and potassium carbonate, K_2CO_3 (potash). Allow the covering to dry then heat the piece as if annealing. The potash changes the copper oxide into an easily soluble carbonate:

$$K_2CO_3 \quad + \quad CuO \quad \rightarrow$$
potassium carbonate   copper (II) oxide

$$CuCO_3 \quad + \quad K_2O$$
copper carbonate   potassium oxide

As water evaporates from a sulfuric acid pickle the strength of the solution is increased, eventually reaching as high as 49%. This will quickly attack silver alloys and is dangerous to handle, so care should be taken to replenish water as necessary so that the degree of dilution remains the same. Sparex evaporates and should be refreshed with water periodically but it does not increase in corrosive action as it becomes more concentrated, another reason it is preferred by most shops.

Pickle is colorless when first mixed but takes on a blue-green color as it absorbs copper sulfate. The presence of this compound eventually reduces the efficiency of the pickle, though it can be quite effective even when clearly blue. It is possible to remove the free copper ions in the solution by plating them onto an insoluble anode but this is generally deemed an inefficient process. Instead the solution is neutralized by adding baking soda and discarded.

Room temperature procedures

There are some cases where heat must be avoided, for instance when gems or tempered metals are involved. For those situations the following recipes are recommended.

Dissolve 100 grams potassium hydrogen sulfide, $KHSO_4$ in 1 liter of water. Immerse the work at room temperature until the oxide is dissolved. The solution works like this:

Light oxidation can also be removed in this traditional cold pickle, a favorite kitchen recipe for removing tarnish from silver flatware:

1 part baking soda (sodium hydrogen carbonate)
2 parts table salt (sodium chloride)
1 liter water

Line a pot with aluminum foil, pour in the solution and immerse the pieces. The oxide will dissolve and the Cu^{2+} ions will migrate to the aluminum, leaving the work white.

Blackening silver

As has been discussed above, silver/copper alloys oxidize to produce gray and black films when heated. The different reaction occurs in air as the metal reacts with sulfur and sulfur compounds like hydrogen sulfide, the principle tarnishing agent in silver sulfide Ag_2S.

$$2\ KHSO_4 \quad + \quad CuO \quad \rightarrow$$
potassium   copper (II)
hydrogen sulfate   oxide

$$CuSO_4 \quad + \quad K_2SO_4 \quad + \quad H_2O$$
copper   potassium   water
sulfate   sulfate

Knowing that this process will happen naturally in the course of time, some jewelers prefer to darken their work in the studio so customers are seeing the piece as it will appear for most of its life rather than in the bright white version that will require polishing to stay shiny. This process, called oxidizing or antiquing, often uses sulfur compounds and, in many cases, heat. In addition to rendering a work in its "natural state" the process increases contrast and makes relief work more dramatic.

Making liver of sulfur

Liver of sulfur is the most common preparation used to darken silver alloys. It is generally purchased from suppliers in the form of lumps ready to be dissolved in water to make a patina solution, but here is the recipe for those who wish to make their own in the traditional manner.

Combine equal parts of potassium carbonate (potash) K_2CO_3 and sulfur flowers (pure sulfur) in a melting ladle with a small bit of water. Heat the mix over a medium flame to make a brown paste. When the ingredients are blended, lower the ladle into a container of water where the paste will go into solution to make a deep amber liquid. This is ready to use and can be diluted with more water if necessary.

$$4 K_2CO_3 + 6 S + O_2 \rightarrow$$

potash   sulfur   oxygen

$$2 K_2S + 2 K_2S_2 + 4 CO_2$$

potassium   potassium   carbon
sulfide   thiosulfate   dioxide

Potassium sulfide easily adds sulfur in a chain-like bond forming potassium polysulfide:

$$K_2S + 3S \rightarrow K_2S_4$$

potassium   sulfur   potassium
sulfide   polysulfide

Liver of sulfur, then, is formed by a mixture of potassium polysulfides with potassium thiosulfate.

The principle drawback of liver of sulfur (beyond its odor) is the fact that it is unstable in air and light. This means it is broken down by both of those and quickly looses its effectiveness. For this reason liver of sulfur is always stored in airtight, darkened containers. Mix up only what can be used immediately, and recap the supply jar as quickly as possible.

Note that if liver of sulfur is accidentally mixed with an acid it releases the toxic gas hydrogen sulfide.

Using liver of sulfur

Though it can be used at room temperature, the solution is more effective when used warm. It should never be heated to a boil. The object is degreased and suspended on a wire or held in tweezers for immersion into the liver of sulfur bath.

In a matter of a few seconds the silver will start to turn black; agitating the work helps to insure even distribution. If spots resist the coloring it is probably the result of insufficient degreasing. Rinse the piece, re-clean and try again. The finished article is rinsed off under cold running water then dried in cold sawdust. Hot water and warm wood chips could lead to spots on the blackening.

To achieve a lustrous blue-black shine, first finish the piece with a brass brush, degrease, patina with liver of sulfur and follow this with a light treatment with the brass brush. A separate scratchbrush should be reserved just for this use.

It is typical to contrast darkened areas with the bright shine of polished silver. The result, as when placing black and white next to each other, is to make each element appear in its best light – the darks are richer and the brights seem brighter. This is traditionally achieved by darkening the entire piece then relieving the raised areas by rubbing them with fine pumice or chalk dust. The vehicle used (fingertips, linen, leather sticks) will depend on the shape of the piece and the amount of sulfide layer to be removed.

In some designs there might be a problem removing the dark film from certain areas. In these cases the liver of sulfur can be painted on with a brush to avoid having to color an area that is to remain bright. This sounds easier than it looks. The liver of sulfur solution is so thin and watery that it flows wherever gravity takes it. With this in mind, position the piece so that the areas to remain bright are above the darkened area. It is also smart to warm the object. This allows the sulfide to work faster and so minimizes the time of exposure. Be careful when flushing the liver of sulfur away that you don't accidentally flush it into the very area you've been protecting!

An alternative is to protect selected areas by coating them with a thin layer of rubber cement. This is allowed to dry, the work is patinated and rinsed, then the rubber coating is pulled away.

Cleaning of silver alloys

Both jewelry items and hollowware frequently come to a metalsmith for repair and in all cases the first thing to do is clean the piece. At its most immediate level this refers to the removal of grease, oil, makeup, polishing compound and the dozens of other kinds of gunk that stick to a piece. Use soapy water and a stiff brush or an ultrasonic machine to remove this sort of dirt.

That process will not remove tarnish, which is a different sort of "dirt" altogether. We should distinguish it by using the term patina, in this case a black sulfide that is unwanted.

DEPLETION GILDING

As mentioned above, this direct method has the advantage of efficiency and ease. Simply warm the piece to burn away grease then immerse it in pickle to remove the oxide films created by heating. The drawback is that the process cannot be used on heat-sensitive objects like those set with stones, amber, pearls, ivory, enamel, wood, plastic and so on. Also pieces with springy parts (clasps, catches, hinges, etc.) must not be heated at the risk of losing their temper.

CHEMICAL CLEANING

Proprietary cleaners

Most jewelry shops and all suppliers to the trade will sell a non-poisonous anti-tarnish solution formulated to break down sulfide products through simple immersion. These are most useful for thin films, but even thick layers of tarnish can be loosened by prolonged exposure to these liquids.

The drawback of these solutions is that objects treated this way tend to tarnish again more quickly than they would otherwise and after several uses a gray deposit forms that must be removed by polishing or scratchbrushing.

Cleaning pastes

Commercial cleaning pastes that combine the chemical action of the anti-tarnish solution with a mild abrasive like chalk or pumice are slightly more aggressive. These are familiar from the grocery store where they are sold to clean pots and plumbing fixtures.

To use these, wet the tarnished surface and sprinkle the powder over it. Allow the paste to sit for several minutes as the chemical reactions proceed. Follow this by rubbing with a damp cloth or sponge. The combination of mechanical action and chemical cleaning produces a dramatic result.

To create your own cleanser (again this is more for historical perspective than practical advice) mix household ammonia with fine chalk dust to form a paste. Spread this on the tarnished object, allow a few minutes for it to work, then scrub it off. The sulfides are converted to soluble complex compounds that are easy to remove:

$$4 \, [NH_4]OH \; + \; Ag_2S \; \rightarrow$$
ammonium silver
hydroxide sulfide

$$2 \, [Ag(NH_3)_2]OH \; + \; H_2S \; + \; 2H_2O$$
ammonium silver hydrogen water
hydroxide sulfide

If the chalk dust is too coarse it will slightly abrade the silver, which clearly diminishes the desirability of the process!

Household stripping bath

A chemical stripping solution can be made from simple household ingredients. Combine a tablespoon of table salt (sodium chloride) $NaCl$ with a tablespoon of baking soda (sodium bicarbonate) $NaHCO_3$ and a liter of warm water. Line a bowl with aluminum foil, place the tarnished object in the center of it and pour the mixed solution over it, extending the recipe as needed to completely cover the object.

Having the copper or silver in contact with the aluminum creates an electrical potential (in essence a battery) that triggers a reaction. The aluminum is the anode and is "plated" with the metal ions of the sulfides as they are pulled off the silver. The process can be accelerated by wrapping aluminum wire around the work or by warming the solution slightly, or both. When the object is cleaned it is removed, rinsed and dried.

Sodium thiosulfate solution

This recipe makes a cleaning solution appropriate for polished heavily tarnished objects. Mix one part sodium thiosulfate $Na_2S_2O_3$ with two parts water to make a paste. Spread this onto the article and allow it to work for at least several minutes then rub it off with a chamois cloth.

Borax solution

Dissolve borax in cold water and slowly heat to a boil, stirring until the solution can absorb no more borax. Reduce to just below boiling and lower the piece into the bath on a sieve.

Potassium cyanide ("bombing")
SAFETY NOTE: This process uses a poisonous solid and creates a poisonous gas therefore it requires active ventilation.

Potassium cyanide KCN is very effective for cleaning silver and has been widely used in the trade for generations. Mix up a solution with a concentration of 100 grams per liter of water and add a little table salt. The tarnished object is suspended in the bath by a silver or brass wire. The chemical reaction transforms the sulfides into soluble complex compounds that can be easily rinsed away.

$$4 \text{ KCN} \quad + \quad \text{Ag}_2\text{S} \quad \rightarrow$$
potassium cyanide   silver sulfide

$$2 \text{ K}[\text{Ag(CN)}_2] \quad + \quad \text{K}_2\text{S}$$
potassium silver cyanide   potassium sulfide

9.2.3 GOLD AND GOLD ALLOYS

As in the case of silver, the pure or fine version of gold has no need of pickling because it does not oxidize. And again as is the case with silver, when an alloy includes copper (as many gold alloys do) the copper combines with oxygen to form an unattractive gray film when heated.

Most gold alloys contain both silver and copper. Understanding that it is the copper that is oxidized and then removed, it becomes clear that a mixture of silver and gold will be left at the surface. This is green gold, so depending on the proportions the color of the object will appear green or paler than it really is.

Depletion gilding and related coloring techniques have been replaced by electroplating, particularly in large shops, but the traditional methods will be described here not only for their historical value but because independent goldsmiths will continue to find them useful. This material has been gathered from the classic texts of the last century.

Pickling
When fabrication and abrasive finishing is complete, the article is placed in the same sulfuric acid pickle as was mentioned above for silver. A 5% solution is used warm and a 10% solution if used at room temperature.

This will dissolve the copper oxide portion of the surface, leaving a green or gray-green matte surface of silver-enriched gold alloy at the surface.

This layer must be removed to reveal the actual color of the alloy, a process that can be done by mechanical abrasives and polishing. This is not an ideal solution because it takes time, wastes material and often results in uneven color since not all areas can be reached. A better solution is to use electrolytic stripping or bright dipping to remove the unwanted silver from the surface layer.

Depletion gilding ("yellow etching"")
The work must be thoroughly degreased, if possible by annealing. If that foolproof method is not possible, a strong chemical degreaser is used and allowed sufficient time to insure that it is effective.

In a general way this process parallels the depletion gilding of silver described above but in the case of karat golds there are several more color options. These variables are determined by the composition of the solution, the temperature at which it is used and the length of time the article is immersed. Only objects of identical alloy composition should be placed in the bath at the same time. When treating matching articles such as earrings, it is best if they can be immersed at the same time to insure the same color.

The process and its results will vary considerably depending on the composition of the original alloy. The method is effective for alloys containing gold and silver, gold and copper, and gold/silver/copper, but the relative amounts of each will affect the time needed and the colors that result. The work is first dipped into a strong sulfuric pickle made by mixing equal parts of sulfuric acid and water.

SAFETY NOTE:It bears repeating yet again that acid must be added to water, not the reverse, and protective clothing and ventilation are mandatory. This is a very strong pickle!

The solution is used at a temperature of about 80°C (176°F). It attacks not only the copper oxides but the metallic copper as well. Sulfuric acid does not dissolve silver however.

Red golds (gold/copper alloys) will return to their

natural color in this solution. Gold/silver/copper alloys will be left with a pale green color the exact shade of which depends on the proportion of elements in the alloy and the length of the immersion in the pickle.

The work is placed in a second pickle made of equal parts of nitric acid and water, and yes, the same cautions apply. This pickle is also used slightly warm, but this one has the capability of leaching out metallic silver. Depending on the exposure time this will result in a yellow or deep yellow color.

Because there are so many variables it is impossible to give precise values to the immersion times or the expected results. Instead, work is withdrawn from the bath after a brief dip, rinsed well in water and examined in natural light. Continue until the metal develops an attractive color.

It is also possible to obtain a rich yellow color in pure hydrochloric acid or in aqua regia, but these frequently cause spotting and are therefore not recommended. In addition, hydrochloric acid fosters stress corrosion, even in an annealed piece, so objects that have been significantly deformed cannot be treated that way.

Coloring gold alloys
This process differs from depletion gilding because it involves the deposition of a layer of gold onto an object. In this regard it would appear to be more like electroplating, but the results from this time-honored method are perceivably different, especially in the warm golden matte surface that is seen in antique work.

The process described below can be made to work on almost any gold alloy, but will have diminishing results as the proportion of gold goes down. That is to say it will yield rich results with high karat alloys and only qualified results with very low karats.

Here is an old recipe for a coloring solution.

2 parts concentrated hydrochloric acid
1 part nitric acid
2 parts table salt
40 parts water

The mixture must be made up fresh for each use. The salt allows the solution to precipitate out silver as it dissolves which is necessary so it doesn't deposit back onto the article. This is a strong solution so work is dipped only for a few seconds at a time, removed, rinsed and examined.

The following solution is used in the same way but it is less intense and therefore a little easier to control.

115 g sodium chloride (NaCl)
230 g potassium nitrate (KNO$_3$)
150 g water
170 g hydrochloric acid (HCl)

The sodium chloride and potassium nitrate are mixed together and ground up in a mortar, then mixed with water. This is heated to a boil, stirring constantly, then the hydrochloric acid is added, still with constant stirring. Allow the mix to boil for one minute then solution is ready to use.

Coloring process
The article to be colored is completed, polished and given a pure surface through depletion gilding. When the object has a uniformly clean surface, the work is hung on a thin wire and heated slightly until it turns gray. It is then dipped into the boiling coloring solution and moved back and forth through the solution for about three minutes.

The effectiveness depends upon nitrosylchloride and free chlorine as well as aqua regia forming

KNO$_3$ + HCl + NaCl →
potassium   hydrochloric   sodium
nitrate   acid   chloride

NOCl + Cl$_2$ + NaOH + KOH
nitrosyl-   chlorine sodium   potassium
chloride   hydroxide hydroxide

It is possible for the gold to be dissolved in the solution. The silver chloride developed is precipitated by the sodium chloride and cannot disturb anything further. If the solution is enriched with sufficient chlorauric acid H[AuCl$_4$] an ionic exchange ensues between the precious gold ions and the non-precious copper ions. This is why the red gold alloys color best.

The surface of the article is covered by newly deposited gold crystals because of this ion exchange. As the silver and copper in the alloy are being dissolved, gold particles are simultaneously being deposited on the surface, leaving a matte yellow-brown appearance. When this is scratchbrushed the gold is smoothed to a more reflective structure that better shows its rich color.

If the color is not correct the work is returned to the boiling solution for another minute then tested again. If the color is correct, the article is neutralized by immersing it in aqueous ammonia then rinsed in water and scratchbrushed.

9.2.4. COPPER AND COPPER ALLOYS
Pickling
Copper and brass can be cleaned of flux residue and black oxides by dipping them in the same pickle mentioned above for silver, a 5% solution of sulfuric acid mixed with water. Since the development of the safer proprietary pickles like Sparex, these have been substituted for the sulfuric solution in most studios, and will substitute in this case as well.

Pickling is done as desired throughout the fabrication process, and certainly when all assembly is complete. As with other metals, the piece is quenched in water then immersed in pickle until the oxides are dissolved. If the pickle is kept warm this will take a few minutes; at room temperature it will require as long as an hour.

In the case of copper and brass, even the best pickle will leave an uneven surface, especially on brass where a pinkish flash plating of copper will remain. Even so this amount of pickling is preferred to none at all. To achieve a more uniform color the work can be dipped in stronger pickles in a process called burning or bright dipping. These are included for scientific and historical but are not recommended because of their dangerous corrosive nature.

SAFETY NOTE: The following recipes all involve strong acids and require ventilation, rubber gloves, goggles and a plastic apron. In every case acid is added to water.

Bright Dip A
    1 liter nitric acid
    10 g sodium chloride (table salt)
    5 g lamp black (also called shining soot)
    200 ml water

Mix the soot and table salt together, then dilute the nitric acid with the water and pour it over the dry ingredients. Allow the solution to sit for several hours before use.

Because of the strength of this acid the piece can only be exposed for a very short time. To ensure that the work is easily removed, hang it securely from a wire or grip it in locking tweezers. Dip it for a few seconds and rinse in running water. If the surface is not yet shiny the process can be repeated. Be careful not to leave the article in the solution for too long or the surface will be etched matte.

Bright Dip B
    1 liter sulfuric acid
    1 liter nitric acid
    10 ml hydrochloric acid
    20 g sodium chloride (table salt)
    10 g lamp black (shining soot)

The sulfuric and nitric acids are poured into each other, then the hydrochloric acid and the table salt is added, all this being accomplished under approved ventilation hoods and with careful attention to safety. Simply mixing these chemicals together will generate heat, so vessels must be approved for acid use. When the solution has cooled to room temperature, the soot is mixed in and allowed to mingle with the acids for 12 hours. The dip is then ready to use. The piece is immersed for a count of only a few seconds then immediately rinsed in water and examined. The process is repeated as necessary until a bright copper or yellow brass color is achieved.

Patina
When copper is left exposed to air it will quickly discolor to a mottled brown. Given longer, or in certain

environments, the copper will progress to a uniform dark gray or black. In different situations and given enough time, copper will naturally form a green patina, as witnessed in the roofs, gutters and ornaments of buildings.

This is the result of a copper carbonate layer that forms because of the carbonic acid content of the air. It requires the action of sun, rain, dust and other ingredients to grow into the richly colored and strongly adhesive layer that makes it so valuable as a surface patina. The proof of the delicate nature of this mix can be found in buildings with copper embellishments at different levels: trim at the top of the building is green while the same metal closer to the ground is left black by the interaction of other pollutants.

We might therefore conclude that the best way to achieve a rich patina is to leave an article exposed to the weather in a high place for several generations. While this would work, few metalsmiths have the luxury or patience for this long a wait! The following section describes some studio techniques that mimic the natural process of chemical reaction.

Copper is available in many grades of purity, and the word brass describes a large family of alloys that have widely differing proportions of copper. These variables, impurities in water and chemicals and variations in temperature and humidity in the studio will all affect the colors achieved with the following solutions. Experimentation and a flexible attitude are both valuable assets when working with patinas.

Preparation

It is vital that surfaces be properly prepared in order to achieve an attractive result. After all fabrication and finishing is completed the work is thoroughly degreased and thereafter handled only by the edges.

Failure to make the metal perfectly clean will be revealed as a spotty color that does not bind properly to the surface, often being so fragile it is brushed away with a light touch. The surface should be slightly matte rather than taken to a high polish. This can be achieved with pumice, fine sandpaper, an etching bright dip or sandblasting.

A slight oxidation with hydrogen peroxide pro-

motes adhesion of the patina to the metal. The standard 30% hydrogen peroxide solution is diluted with four times as much water, then dabbed on with a brush until a slight oxidation of the metal appears.

BLACK ON COPPER AND BRASS

A consistent result can be found with proprietary coloring solutions that can be purchased from jewelry supply companies. These are generally applied with a small brush (synthetic bristles preferred), but in some cases it is easiest to spray the solution from a bottle.

The color appears faster if the metal is slightly warmed but care should be taken that it doesn't get too hot since this makes the solution decompose and undermines its effectiveness. A hairdryer or lamp is recommended as a heat source. When the color appears dark enough the article is rinsed and dried.

Here is a recipe for those who wish to mix up their own version of the commercial darkening agents:

30 g sodium sulfide (Na_2S)
4 g flowers of sulfur (sulfur powder)
50 ml water

These materials are boiled together and then diluted with 1 liter of water. The article is dipped into this hot solution until it has taken on a black coloring.

A second option is:
5% potassium hydroxide solution KOH
1% potassium persulfate solution $K_2S_2O_8$

The ingredients are mixed and heated to boiling then the article is dipped into the hot solution. The copper surface becomes brown, violet or black depending upon the length of the exposure.

Green on copper and brass
This traditional solution requires ventilation and protective clothing, especially when used warm or applied to hot metal.

300 g copper (II) nitrate Cu $(NO_3)_2$ [cupric nitrate)]
1000 ml water

Degrease the metal well, give it a slightly roughened surface and apply an undercoating of oxide with hydrogen peroxide as described above. All of this will work together to insure proper adhesion of the patina to the article.

The piece is warmed slightly with a bushy flame or a hair dryer. Avoid getting the metal too hot because this will break down the solution and slow down rather than speed the process. The solution is applied by spraying or with a soft brush and allowed to dry. The drying process can be slightly accelerated by setting the work in a warm spot, but here again, trying too hard to speed the process has a reverse affect. If the patina is rushed it fails to bond onto the metal and will brush away when touched.

After the surface is dry a fresh layer of solution is applied over the first. This is allowed to dry and the process is repeated until the patina is thick and richly colored. The color is usually lichen-green, with other shades running to yellow-green or blue-green. To increase the blueness, spray the piece (or immerse it briefly) in a baking soda/water solution.

Heated varnish
To develop a deep brown varnish layer on copper sheet, a thin film of linseed oil is spread onto the metal and evaporated off at a very low heat. This process might be repeated as many as 20 times to create a dark brown shiny layer that looks very rich and offers good protection from further oxidation.

The process was described by the monk Theophilus in the Middle Ages so precisely that it can be quoted directly here.

Chapter 71
In what manner copper is colored brown. Let yourself make sheet of the required length and breadth from the copper described above, that is called "red copper." If you have cut this to shape and prepared your workpiece accordingly draw on it ornaments, animals or whatever you wish and engrave these in with a narrow engraving tool. Then take oil which is made from linseed, rub it thinly over the entire surface with the finger, dis-

tribute it uniformly with a goose feather and hold [the sheet] with a pair of tongs over glowing coals, do this so long that the oil is dried out. If you see that it is overall smooth bring it onto lively burning coals and leave it lying on them so long that it completely stops smoking.

And if it is dark enough then it is good. If not, paint on just a little bit of oil in this manner with the goose feather onto the heated sheet, paint that oil uniformly and lay the sheet again onto the blown upon coals and proceed as before. If it is cooled off, not in water but by itself, then carefully scrape the ornament out with a sharp scraper so that the area [between] fields remain dark brown. If it is however dealing with lettering it lies with your common sense whether you desire them dark brown or gilded.

As Theophilus hints, a particularly striking effect can be made by contrasting the rich dark brown copper with gilded portions. To achieve this the entire surface would by darkened with the oil patina then sections would be scraped bare and gilded. A contemporary approach would be to selectively electroplate some areas then apply the patina over the rest.

Japanese colored metal design
Precious metals were always scarce in China and Japan; perhaps this is why those cultures developed such a high degree of expertise in manipulating copper and its alloys and in using small amounts of gold and silver with such powerful effect. Nonprecious alloys like copper and bronze were used to make vessels, containers, weapons, sculpture and jewelry to such an extent that even today when one thinks of Asian metalwork, bronze is usually the first material that comes to mind.

Investigation and development took two separate but related paths: the invention of new alloys and chemical treatments for coloring those alloys. For centuries goldsmiths of the West showed little interest in Japanese and Chinese techniques outside their presentation in museum collections. Today all metal-

Figure 9.27
Copper plate with brown patina ornamentation. Base plate of portable altar of the cardinal virtues. Cologne, approximately 1150 – 1160 A.D. (Staatl. Museum, Berlin)

one liter of water to a boil and dissolve in it:

> 20 g copper (II) sulfate (copper vitriol)
> $CuSO_4 \cdot 5\ H_2O$
> 20 g potassium aluminum sulfate (alum)
> $KAl\ (SO_4)_2 \cdot 12\ H_2O$
> 20 g copper acetate (verdigris)
> $Cu(CH_3COO)_2 \cdot CuO \cdot 6H_2O$

Drop the pickled and cleaned article into the boiling mixture. The color is modified by the relationship between working time, temperature and concentration. The following approximate colors can be expected:

Nigurome	Enamel-like red	
Sin-chu	Brown	
Shakudo	(1–2% Au)	Bronze colored
Ginshibuichi	Pearly gray	

VARIATIONS

The effect can be altered by changing the proportions of the chemicals. As the amount of copper sulfate goes up, the copper is made increasingly brown. To add green tones to shinchu, add acetic acid to the solution.

workers are encouraged to add the valuable palette of those cultures to their own repertoire, not to copy the Asian work but to expand the range of what can be accomplished (figures 9.28 to 9.30).

CHEMICALS

In general, Japanese coloring solutions work through corrosion of the surface. This means that instead of acids and oxidizing chemicals they are more likely to use relatively gentle salts. For the basic mixture, bring

METALS

Name	Added Metals	Type of Alloy
Nigurome	small amounts of tin, arsenic, nickel, iron, etc.	Impure copper, also known as copper bloom
Kara-kane	4–20% lead, 2–8% tin, balance copper	A complex bronze which is also used for bells.
Art bronze	4–15% tin, 1–10% zinc, 1–3% lead, balance copper	Statue bronze comparable to gun metal
Sin-chu	33.3% zinc balance copper	This is the same as our malleable brass.
Ginshibuichi	Approximately 25% silver, balance copper	In Japanese, gin = silver, bu = ¼, and ichi = one: one/fourth silver
Shakudo	1–7% gold, balance copper	

Other salts can be mixed with water and added to the basic recipe above to experiment with other colors. Try adding copper chlorides, sulfates, nitrates and carbonates.

USES
Inlay
In many instances, pieces made from the copper alloys listed above are colored then set into a base sheet using cold joining techniques. Outstanding examples can be seen in museums of the sword furniture of Japanese weapons that take this process to a high degree of mastery.

Mokume
In this ancient technique, layers of sheet metal of various alloys are fused or soldered together to create a thick block or billet that somewhat resembles plywood. In the case of mokume the original stack is rolled, cut and restacked to create a piece with as many as several hundred layers. This can then be manipulated to reveal the layers either randomly or in patterns. In one style, incised holes or trenches can be cut part way through the stack, which is then rolled flush, exposing the layers as different colors laying side by side. In another technique, depressions are hammered up from the back leaving bumps on the front. These are filed off to reveal concentric circles of the alloys in a pattern that resembles woodgrain. The bonded metals are colored to exaggerate the contrast between alloys.

Lamination inlay
In this process contrasting metals are soldered or fused one on top of another then passed through the rolling mill to create a flush surface (figures 9.31 and 9.32). It appears as if the decorative elements were inlayed (a time-consuming process) but in fact they are simply layered and pressed into a single plane.

The effect is difficult to see when the metals are polished because they have about the same reflective properties, but when patinated the contrast reveals a dramatic graphic effect. Because the metals and alloys react differently to various chemicals it is possible to immerse the entire piece and have only certain areas take the color.

9.2.5. COLORING OF STEEL (BLUING)

Steel is often patinated with a brown, blue or black oxide layer, a process that can be done with heat or chemicals. When silver or gold ornaments are used with the steel, the result is to enhance the contrast with the lighter colored metals. In addition, the patina film retards the formation of rust.

Coloring with heat takes the same form as the tempering process, though in this case there is no need to harden the work first. The steel is cleaned by abrasion and warmed either with a torch or in a kiln. To achieve a uniform color the piece can be buried in clean sand and heated to about 315°C (600°F).

Here is a recipe for chemical coloring of steel:

400 g sodium hydroxide NaOH (lye) is mixed with
10 g of potassium nitrate KNO_3 (saltpeter)
10 g of sodium nitrite $NaNO_2$ then dissolved in
600 g of water

Mix the dry ingredients into the water and bring it to a boil, stirring well. Attach the article to a wire and submerge it in the boiling solution until the desired color develops. The effect is the result of the release of oxygen from the solution to form iron (II, III) oxide Fe_3O_4 on the surface of the steel.

9.3
Fire Gilding

In the twentieth century there can be little doubt that electroplating is the best way to develop a gold coating on a metal object. It provides successful results in many colors and can be adapted to one-of-a-kind or mass production. Knowing this, it might seem peculiar to devote the following section to the ancient art of fire gilding. It is more time consuming than modern methods, it requires more material, there is a greater risk of failure, and it is a health risk unless performed under ventilation. Why then should it be included?

For one thing, it is vital that the field of goldsmithing remember its origins in order to keep the sense of history alive. For another, when antique work

Figure 9.31
Bracelets. Alpaca and pure silver, milled together, heat patina. Alpaca is an alloy of 58-65% Cu, 12-28% Zn, 10-25% Ni. (Renata Ahrens, Bad Doberan)

Figure 9.32
Necklace. Alpaca and pure silver, milled together, heat patina. (Renata Ahrens, Bad Doberan)

is to be repaired or an exact replica made, modern techniques simply will not do. There is a clearly visible difference between the intense saturated layer of gold created in this process and the mechanically different layer that results from electroplating.

SAFETY NOTE: Mercury evolves poisonous, invisible vapors even at room temperature. As mercury is heated the vapors are even more aggressively released.

These vapors are absorbed through the lungs and stored in the body; they cannot be cast off and therefore accumulate. This means that even minor exposure will result in a health risk eventually. The first signs of mercury poisoning are gum and throat inflammations, nervous disturbances, irritability, general aches and pains, muscle tremors, and fainting.

Mercury should be stored in sealed containers under water. Because mercury can be absorbed through the skin, direct contact should be avoided; always were thick rubber gloves and tight protective clothing. Because the vapors are so dangerous only ventilation systems with the highest rating will allow safe use of mercury. If any symptoms appear, stop work and see a doctor immediately.

Making the amalgam
The first step in the process is to make a paste or amalgam of gold in a vehicle that will later be driven off. The amalgam will be made by joining fine gold and mercury. It is widely known that the phrase "mad as a hatter" comes from the brain damage that was common among tradesmen who made hats because of the use of mercury in that process. Though goldsmiths seem to have avoided the bad press, they are just as susceptible to the neurological damage of mercury. Industrial strength ventilation is mandatory for this process.

In order to provide the maximum amount of surface area, a sheet of fine gold is rolled as thin as possible and then cut into tiny pieces. The process resembles the cutting of solder chips but the pieces should be much smaller. If the pieces curl this has the advantage of preventing them from lying flat on the floor of the crucible.

It is impossible to mix mercury and gold by melting them together because the mercury vaporizes at a relatively low temperature. Instead the two metals are put into a mortar and pestle and ground together. The process will be assisted a little if the gold and mercury are first put together into a closed container and allowed to diffuse into each other. In order to reduce the danger of exposure to toxic mercury fumes the grinding is done underwater.

The process is among those that was well documented by Theophilus, Pliny and other early writers about metalworking. The proportions given in those ancient sources, still relevant today, are 1 part gold to 8 parts mercury, or 11.1% Au/88.9% Hg.

A phase diagram of the Au-Hg system shows that the amalgam of this composition has a liquidus temperature of about 290°C (550°F). As the amalgam cools to temperatures approaching 124°C, mixed crystals of the concentration of about 22% Au, 78% Hg precipitate out of the melt. At 124°C these mixed crystals have a proportion of the entire mass of only about 17%, which is to say that despite these crystals, the greatest part of the amalgam is still fluid.

Upon further cooling a structural change occurs: the β-mixed crystals transform themselves and there develop crystals of the intermetallic phase Au_2Hg_3 (a concentration of about 39% Au; 61% Hg), which swim in the mercur-rich remnant.

At room temperature the mixture is about 37% solid Au_2Hg_3 and 63% fluid mercury. The gold may be described as "floating" in the mercury in the same way that crushed ice floats in water. This yields a spreadable, pasty gilding material.

Even if the proportions are changed somewhat because of the burning off of mercury, the mix will still work. If the proportion of gold were to drop below 39% the mixture would start to harden, but this is very unlikely as long as you start with initial mixture of 1 part gold; 8 parts mercury.

Working under a fume hood, the mercury and gold is heated to the boiling point of the mercury (357°C; 675°F). More gold can be introduced into the crucible at this point and the whole mass is stirred with an iron or titanium wire until solid pieces of gold can no longer be felt.

The mix is poured into a basin of clear cold water at this point to force a crystallization of the amalgam. Because of the rapid cooling the transformation of the β-mixed crystals into the intermetallic phase Au_2Hg_3 is repressed and the condition of the temperature zone between 290–1240° C is "frozen in." It is this process that leaves the β-mixed crystals floating in fluid mercury.

To remove excess mercury the mass is collected and set onto a square of chamois leather that is then pulled up into a pouch and twisted tight at the neck. Small drops of mercury will be wrung from the mass and should be scraped off the leather. This is a very dangerous process because mercury can be taken in through the skin. Wear heavy rubber gloves and work in a fume hood! The finished amalgam should be pale yellow and as spreadable as butter.

Metals able to be gilded
Mercury gilding works very well on silver/copper alloys like sterling and it is no surprise that this was its most common use. These objects – a layer of gold applied to sterling – are still called *vermeil* (ver-MAY), after the French term for fire gilding. It is also possible to deposit a layer of gold onto copper, iron and bronze, but the surface must be specially prepared first. In principle brass can also be gilded, but the results are often spotty. To prepare iron and brass, a layer of copper is deposited, either by electroplating or by immersing the work in a saturated pickle. In the case of bronze, steel wire is wrapped around the piece to hasten the plating reaction.

Preparing the article
The article to be gilded must be perfectly clean, a state that is best achieved with a bright dip of diluted nitric acid. The precise mix will depend on the alloy being used but something in the range of a 50-50 mix is typical.

Immersion of a few seconds is usually sufficient to remove all grease, dirt and oxidation. Longer dips are not recommended because they eat away from the surface and leave it matte. The microscopic craters that result from this etching will require extra gilding to fill in and are therefore something to be avoided.

Quicking the surface
Amalgam will adhere well to alloys that contain over ¾ths silver. For metals of lower silver content, including copper and copper alloys like brass, a preparatory step called quicking is required. The preparation of this chemical is described in Chapter 11, Section 2. In

this process a layer of mercury is laid onto the article first to provide a better adhesion of the gold amalgam.

Applying the amalgam
The amalgam paste is spread onto large objects with a brass brush. For smaller objects it can be more convenient to use a spatula-shaped steel rod. Quick the end of the rod and pick up a mass of amalgam then spread it onto the piece as you might spread butter.

It is wise to work over a dish that will catch the excess as it falls off, and of course it is worth repeating that this process can only take place under ventilation. Remember that mercury is always releasing harmful fumes!

Evaporating (literally, "smoking off ")
The traditional way to drive off the mercury is to warm the piece over a charcoal fire. This will of course still work and has the advantage of creating a gentle uniform heat. It would be possible, for instance, to build a fire in an outdoor hearth, to set the work on a steel grill and in this way remove the mercury. It would be unsafe to use this grill for cooking food after this use.

In the case of ventilation systems, mercury causes a special problem because it often precipitates onto the walls of the ventilation pipes after it has been removed from the immediate vicinity. Even a properly functioning ventilation system can be contaminated by mercury in this way unless special filters are used. As mentioned at the outset, it is no wonder that this process has been superseded by electroplating!

Over the fire the amalgam gives up the mercury, possibly turning into a fluid coating if the heat is high enough. This is not required for the process to work, nor does it cause a problem, but in large pieces like vessels the work must be rotated to prevent the fluid from flowing down the sides of the form.

When the mercury has been completely dissipated the surface will be left with a pale yellow matte covering. If the coating does not appear complete, additional amalgam can be added at this stage. The area is re-quicked, fresh amalgam is applied, and the piece is heated. When the covering seems adequate the piece is allowed to cool.

It is normal for 5–15% of the mercury to remain behind permanently bound up with the gold, but if more than this remains the result is a pale color. To avoid this the amalgam is heated further, but care must be taken not to go so far that the gold fuses into the surface where it will make an alloy with the silver of the article.

Finishing treatment
A soft golden color can be obtained through scratch-brushing, but it is more common in fire gilding to seek a bright gold. This can be achieved by depletion gilding; that is, by heating the article and immersing it in pickle.

A more uniform coating can be achieved by mixing the following:

40% potassium nitrate
35% table salt
25% alum

Mix the three ingredients together with enough water to make a paste, heating the whole to a boil to complete the blending. Apply the paste to the gilded surface and suspend the work over a fire (or set it on a screen and heat it with a bushy flame) until the paste has solidified into a salty crust. The piece is then quenched in water, which will cause the crust to break away and dissolve. The piece is then cleaned in a dilute nitric acid bright dip and rinsed.

Specialty Techniques

10.1
Niello Work

Niello is a deep black metal mixture that is fused onto metal for decorative effect. Though worked on three-dimensional objects, the effect might be considered graphic because it relies primarily on shape and pattern. The contrast of the lustrous black inlay against either matte or polished metal is striking and has earned niello a special place in the arsenal of decorative techniques.

The process can be thought of as having two parts – making the niello material and fusing it into position. The latter is generally a matter of filling depressions or incised lines made by engraving, etching, stamping, rolling or layering (figures 10.1 to 10.3).

This technique can be traced all the way back to ancient times. Theophilus, a monk in the Middle Ages, has given a description of the procedure which is so accurate that it could be used here. Unfortunately niello is rarely used today, almost forgotten, perhaps because goldsmiths have forgotten how to work with engraving tools and chisels. There is no reason why niello can not be used in contemporary design and achieve again the high regard in which it was once held.

Figure 10.1
Communion chalice. Silver. Religious motifs and inscriptions, treated with niello and engraved. Nodus with engraved representation of the rivers of paradise, Second half of 12th century. (Monastery church, Trezemeszno, Poland)

Figure 10.2
Silver bracelet, overlay, niello work. (Student piece, School for Applied Art, Heiligendamm)

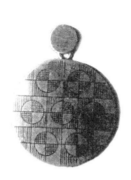

Figure 10.3
Silver pendants, sawed and engraved with niello. (Student work, School for Applied Art, Heiligendamm)

10.1.1 THE BASE METAL AND ITS PREPARATION

Niello fuses well onto silver and sterling, and can also be used on gold alloys. It does not bond onto copper, brass or nickel silver. As mentioned, niello is generally used to fill recesses which can be made by any mechanical process (engraving, machining, etc.) or by the fabrication process called overlay in which layers of sheet are soldered together to create chambers to hold the niello. All soldering is completed on the piece, which is then pickled, scratchbrushed, and thoroughly rinsed.

10.1.2 MAKING NIELLO

A survey of the historical literature of metalworking will turn up several recipes for making niello, but for our purposes here only one will be presented. It has the benefit of being simple, reliable and proven in the studio by the author.

1. In a conventional crucible, melt together 2 parts silver and 1 part copper, adding a small amount of borax as a flux. Have an assistant keep this metal molten.
2. At the same time, melt 1 part lead in a steel ladle.
3. Working under a fume hood with active ventilation, add powdered sulfur to the molten lead in generous amounts. Stir vigorously, the intention being to saturate the lead with sulfur as quickly as possible. Much of the sulfur is immediately burned

away, so it is impossible and useless to specify the amount of sulfur needed. Instead, stir sulfur into the lead until is seems to take no more. The fumes that result from this activity have a strong odor and constricting effect on the throat. Do not attempt this unless there is a way to draw these fumes away!

4. Pour the lead/sulfur mixture into the molten copper/silver alloy, stirring well with a steel or carbon rod. Failure to mix thoroughly will yield a mottled niello with flowers of sulfur.

5. Preheat another crucible, preferably a tall narrow vessel, and add another generous supply of sulfur. As before, this will immediately release clouds of noxious smoke. Pour the copper/silver/lead mixture into this crucible, keeping it fluid all the while and again stirring with rod. The intention at this point is to further saturate the alloy with sulfur.

6. Make a flux by dissolving ammonium chloride in hot water to make a thin paste; add to the niello.

   a. Pour this mixture into water which will break the niello into granules. Grind the niello in a mortar and pestle, adding flux to create a paste.

   b. Alternately, the niello can be cast into a sheet or wire ingot mold to make a solid bar and used to directly apply the niello to the work.

The two-to-one proportion of silver and copper in the recipe yields an alloy (Ag 667) that is close to the eutectic proportion for those two metals (Ag 720). This means the niello has a low melt interval, or goes from solid-to-liquid quickly.

Only a certain portion of the metal reacts with the sulfur, forming metal sulfides in the sequence of each metal's affinity to sulfur according to their atomic ranking:

1. PbS 93 kJ/mol
2. Cu2S 79 kJ/mol
3. Ag2S 29 kJ/mol

The mass of niello consists of the copper/silver alloy with lead and with the sulfides of the composite metals. The mixture forms a number of complicated eutectic mixtures and intermetallic compounds.

Test the niello by striking a lump with a hammer. The piece should shatter like glass and reveal a fracture surface that is uniformly black. If the niello does not show both of these properties, remelt it, using more sulfur and stirring the mass more completely.

10.1.3 APPLYING AND FIRING THE NIELLO

After all soldering is completed the work is pickled, scratchbrushed and degreased. After this thorough cleaning it should be handled only by the edges. Grind and mix with flux just as much niello as will be used on the current project.

The niello paste is packed into the recesses with care typically sliding it off a small carrier such as a fine brush (a goosequill is specified in the ancient texts). Pack the paste as firmly as possible with a small spatula to create a dense filling. Even with this the niello will occupy less space as it fuses and should therefore be mounded up higher than the level of the piece being filled. When the piece is "loaded" it is set into a warm spot to dry, for instance under a lamp or on a heater. If the piece is fired when wet, the expanding steam tends to throw the niello particles aside.

Goldsmiths of the Middle Ages melted their niello over a charcoal fire; today an electric kiln is preferred because of its uniform, controllable heat. The dried piece can be set directly into the kiln, or laid onto a tile or piece of firebrick to make it easier to withdraw from the kiln. First the ammonium chloride spreads over the niello as a white covering layer. As the heat approaches 500°C (930°F) the black metal powder will glow red and spread to fill up the depression into which it was packed.

In flat objects gravity will pull the taffy-like molten niello into place. When working on curved surfaces, particularly something a fully round as a sphere, gravity of course has the opposite effect, pulling the niello out of place. Rounded objects must be kept turning, a process made easier if they are attached somehow to a long rod. The piece can be withdrawn for brief times from the kiln and the niello troweled back into place with a lightly oiled steel spatula. Prolonged heating will allow the sulfur portion to burn away, leaving a porous brittle surface.

It is also possible to fuse niello into place with a torch. Because of the danger of overheating the niello, the flame is played on the work in such a way that the heat travels from there to the niello. If possible the work should be heated from below, for instance by placing it on a tripod and screen.

If there are voids or bubbles, apply additional niello paste and repeat the process, using the spatula to press the fresh melt into the first layer.

In some cases, particularly those where an engraved or stamped line is being filled with niello, the paste process just described is less successful than the following adaptation. Pour the niello into an ingot mold or similar arrangement to make rods of the raw material. Prepare the metal as described above, brush on a coat of the ammonium chloride flux and warm it with a torch. Keeping the metal warm, melt the tip of the niello rod and smear it into the prepared grooves, adding as much as necessary to fill the groove.

10.1.4 FINISHING WORK

Remove excess niello with a scraper or coarse file. Particularly in cases where the original depression is shallow, it is important to work carefully so that you don't remove the pattern entirely. As soon as the general outline of the niello-filled area is clear, shift to the conventional sequence of finishing–files, coarse sandpaper and polishing compounds.

The niello is relatively soft and will therefore respond well to burnishing. Be careful when using a flex shaft or polishing machine for the same reason: the niello will be removed twice as quickly as silver or gold. Stiff polishing equipment such as a leather stick or a felt wheel are preferred.

Niello takes a rich black shine, but also looks good in its matte version. To achieve this, polish it first with sandpaper and compounds, then give it a quick rubbing with pumice powder.

SAFETY NOTE: Because of its lead content, it is important that all traces of niello and any tools used with it are kept separate in the studio. Lead will migrate through skin, so wear gloves when finishing the niello. In addition it will contaminate all jewelry metals and must be rigorously kept away from them.

Use a separate file and discard all sandpaper that has come into contact with lead or niello. Scraps can be returned to a refiner for reclamation but should not be reused in the studio.

10.2
Enameling

For more than two thousand years, goldsmiths have fused glass onto their work for color enrichment. Wonderful enameled work can be found from many ancient cultures, providing familiar icons of the technical skill and aesthetic sensibilities of their makers.

In our own century enameling has benefitted from scientific and industrial research and because of this it has grown from being just one element of the goldsmith's art to a position of prominence on its own. One need only think of enameled housewares, architectural trim and utilitarian objects to understand the importance of enameling in our society.

For a complete description to enameling the reader is referred to books specifically on that topic such as *Kunsthandwerkliches Emaillieren* by Erhard Brepohl, third edition, VEB Fachbuchverlag, Leipzig, 1983. But even those who do not intend to incorporate enamels in their work as a primary element should have an understanding of the historical importance of enameling and a general idea of the process. It is for those people that the following pages are included here.

Enameling is a simple process that uses very little specialized equipment. The electric kiln in which the metal is brought up to temperature is the single most expensive piece of equipment, and even this has the advantage of lending itself to several other uses in the studio. Of far more importance and requiring greater skill is the preparation of a piece preliminary to enameling. Without intelligent design and proper goldsmithing work, enameled pieces are simply colored bits of metal.

IO.2.I ENAMEL APPLICATIONS

Cloisonné

In this popular process, thin flattened wires, usually of fine silver, are bent into specific shapes and set on edge to create a pattern. The wires appear as silver lines in the finished piece and further serve to create small compartments (in French, *cloisons)* to contain the enamel. The strips are sometimes soldered into position, but more commonly they are anchored into a layer of clear enamel called flux until the finish layer of enamel can secure them. The cloisons are filled, fired and refilled as necessary, then ground flush after firing to create a flat surface.

Champlevé

Depressions are cut into thick metal plate by engraving, chiseling, etching, turning, filing or burring; these areas are then filled with enamel powder that is fired to fuse it into place. Though less common, it is possible to make the recesses by soldering together pierced layers in the process known as overlay.

Sunken enamel

This process is a combination of champlevé and cloisonné. A relatively thin sheet of precious metal is formed into a recess. Cloisonné wires are bent according to the design and placed into this area, then filled with enamel powder and fired in the usual way. This is also called false champlevé.

Plique-à-jour enamel

In this rather specialized technique, enamel is made to fill openings that are exposed on both sides, causing it to resemble a stained glass window. The structure is cut from sheet, fabricated from wire or cast, then given a temporary backing of foil or placed on mica to contain the enamel powder during firing. Once the chambers are filled the backing is removed and the surfaces are ground flush. Like stained glass windows, such work becomes particularly striking when light falls through it.

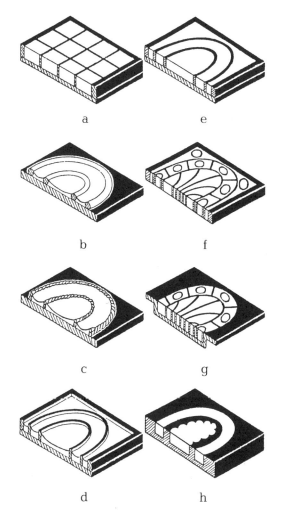

a   e

b   f

c   g

d   h

Figure 10.4
Overview of enameling technique in goldsmithing.
a) Flat wires are bent, placed on edge and soldered. Small strips are glued and cloisons formed.
b) Wire-enameling contours are formed by bent and soldered round wire; colored enamel is fused in by the recesses.
c) Filigree enameling-walls are formed by twisted filigree wire, procedure otherwise similar to wire enameling.
d) Enameling using straight cloisonné wire which is bent and soldered; enamel is fused into the depressions.
e) Cloisonne enameling similar to d) but the cloisons are filled to the top and stoned flat.
f) Pliqué-à-jour-bent and mounted cloisonné wire, the holes filled and fused with enamel, stoned smooth.
g) Recessed enameling on a thin base sheet which has been depressed, cloisonné wire is arranged and the cells filled with enamel.
h) Basse taille recesses in a thick sheet are made and filled with enamel which is fused and stoned smooth.

Basse taille enamel

In this process recesses are made by engraving, milling or cutting with chisels. The depth and textures of the recesses are given careful attention, then the piece is filled with transparent enamel. The relative depths will be revealed through varying shades of color, just as the water in a pool or lake will appear differently as the bottom slopes away. Deeper spots appear darker because of the thicker enamel, the raised ones brighter because they lie close to the surface of the enamel.

Enameling en rond bosse (3D enameling)

This term refers to the use of enamel to cover metal sculpture on all sides. It can be a solid cast miniature sculpture or a hollow one formed from sheet metal.

Limoges enamel

In the 15th and 16th centuries, an enameling technique was taken to a high degree of refinement in the city of Limoges, France. Since that time the process has taken the name of the city. In the Limoges process a base of black enamel is fired over an object. White enamel is then painted over the base, creating a range of grays and whites depending on their thickness. and fired to create an image. A variation called *grisaille* starts with a layer of black enamel to be covered with powdered white enamel. The white is drawn aside with a brush to reveal the black line.

Enamel painting

Portrait miniatures are painted in the same way a potter paints on porcelain. Metal oxide colors are applied to a base coat of white opaque enamel. These are laid down with a fine brush and can equal the precision and detail of oil paint. After the enamels are fused they are covered with transparent enamel called the *fondant*.

10.2.2 MATERIALS AND EQUIPMENT

Enamels

Enamels are purchased either as powders or lumps that are ground to particles as needed. They consist principally of frit, oxides and, in some cases, opacifiers. Frit makes up the body of the enamel and con-

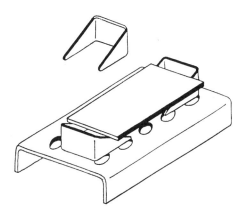

Figure 10.5
Simple set-up with enamel piece for firing in the kiln.

sist of quartz, feldspar, boric acid, soda, potash, and lead oxide. Color is achieved through the addition of metal oxides; other ingredients might be added to create special effects.

Enamels are available from specialized distributors; a glance at a catalog will dazzle the beginning enamelist with the wide range of colors available. The number needed will of course depend on the work being done, but it is wise for a first time enamelist to limit his or her selection to about ten colors. This will guaranty an understanding of these enamels and provide a foundation upon which additional colors may be acquired. The enamels should be stored in wide-mouthed clear glass jars.

Because the color of the enamel powder is different from the effect when fired, it is necessary to create a sample of each color, preferably showing what it will look like in several different applications. Clean a piece of copper about 6 x 15 cm (3 x 6 inches) and apply vertical strips of equal width of white, ivory and transparent high firing flux. Also include a band of flux into which you have fused a panel of fine silver foil.

Apply each of your colors across these stripes at right angles. This will show the effect of each color on these various backgrounds. Keep the test panel handy for reference as you select enamels for particular projects, and make new test panels as your selection of enamels increases.

Kiln

Enameling can be done in a flame and was in ancient times done on a hearth, but nowadays it is considered standard practice to work in an electric kiln. You will need a unit that can achieve and sustain temperatures of 1000°C (1830°F). A kiln with a small chamber is suitable for most jewelry work; but of course larger units will be needed for other applications. The kiln should be fitted with a thermostat, a device that will regulate temperatures to sustain a constant level. Accuracy is important, but it does not need to be as precise (or expensive) as those used in scientific laboratories.

Firing supports

Objects being enameled must be supported off the floor of the kiln while the enamel is melting. This is achieved by resting the work in a metal structure called a trivet. These are available in a variety of shapes and can be made of steel, stainless, titanium, or several other exotic alloys. The requirements of a firing support is that it withstand heat without shrinking, that it not create oxides (they might pop off and contaminate the enamel), that it make only limited contact with the workpiece. Asbestos should not be used because of health and safety concerns.

The point of contact where the piece touches the support will not have a smooth coating of enamel, so these points should be minimized and arranged to fall in places where they will not ruin the design. Figure 10.5 shows a simple but reliable support that achieves this goal, but keep in mind that conventional supports might need to be altered for specific pieces.

10.2.3 THE WORKPLACE

Cleanliness is critical to successful enameling. Dirt, dust, grease, and impurities of any kind will affect enamels, and can turn a rich transparent into a cloudy film or render a brilliant hue as a muddy tone. The area used for grinding and polishing must be removed from the place where the enamel is applied, with proper ventilation in place to keep airborne dust away. A goldsmith who sweeps his tools to one side with the thought of applying the enameling at his bench has clearly not understood the importance of this warning.

It is best to designate a specific work area for enameling. A clean, well-lit, waterproof tabletop is ideal. Tools will include a clean cloth, several watercolor brushes, and a dish of clean water. Wires are bent with delicate pliers and placed with tweezers. A porcelain mortar and pestle is used to grind glass lumps into a powder, a process that will ideally be done at a sink. Powders are poured into porcelain or plastic containers from which they are applied to the work. Gum tragacanth powder is mixed with water to make a paste that is used to adhere cloisonné wires to their base. Small sieves are used to dust the powder onto the metal.

Supports are needed for firing and a long handled fork or similar tool is used to place the work into the kiln and withdraw it when done. The area around the kiln should be equipped with firebrick or a similar surface that will provide a place to set the hot work. You will need heat-resistant gloves and apron, and dark glasses to protect your eyes when looking into the glowing chamber. Finishing work requires silicon carbide stones and rods and the usual range of abrasive papers.

10.2.4 METALS FOR ENAMELING

Because enameling requires a minimum temperature of 800°C (1470°F), the metal base may be made of high karat gold, fine silver, copper, and brass alloys that have a minimum of 5% zinc. Gold expands only slightly when heated, a factor that helps secure the glass layer to the metal base. In addition, the rich color of golds provide a suitable visual environment for colored glass. It is hardly a coincidence that we are able to find so many beautiful examples of enameling on gold in our museums.

Fine silver is a good base for enamels, but alloys of less than 950 Ag purity are not recommended, particularly for transparent enamels where the oxides will cause cloudiness. Sterling, at 925 Ag is not recommended. When applying enamels to silver it is helpful to roughen the surface. This improved mechanical grip will help secure the enamels to the metal.

375

Copper is especially good for enameling, not only because of its low cost, but its rates of expansion and shrinkage and high melting point also make it reliable for virtually every enamel. Of course copper forms oxides easily and because of this colors will not be as bright, especially with transparent enamels.

Brass alloys with less than 5% zinc make excellent surfaces for enameling. They have the advantages of copper and in addition offer a somewhat higher tensile strength. Brasses with higher zinc contents are absolutely unsuitable for enameling because the fired enamels pop off as the metal cools.

Champlevé

Recesses that will contain the enamel are cut into relatively thick sheet with gravers, chisels or mechanical equipment. The technique is particularly suited to transparent enamels because differing depths show up as darker shades of color. This aspect of champlevé cannot be used well on copper since transparent enamels cannot tolerate the oxides given off by that metal. Recesses can be etched, a process in which mechanical effort is replaced with chemical corrosion.

The bottom surface of the recess is roughened to increase the grip of the enamel on the metal. The walls of the cut should be vertical or may lean slightly outward. Undercutting, which would be preferred in the case of metal inlay should be avoided here because it will create stress cracking. When fabricating a layered piece for enameling, the metal partitions that separate each section can easily be made of different and variable width, a distinguishing feature that instantly identifies this process as different from cloisonné (figure 10.8).

Cloisonné

Because cloisonné wires are thin, it is important to build the work within a stout metal frame to ensure its strength. Remember that not only must the enamel be supported in its final state, but before then it must withstand the stress of firing and of being ground flush. This frame is soldered to a piece of sheet metal with IT solder and should be thick enough to resist warping in firing and cooling.

Figure 10.8
Plique à jour. Yellow and white gold, pierced out sections with no base, filled with enamel. (Ralf Bender, Hanau)

Perhaps more than other enameling techniques, cloisonné may be thought of as a graphic process because of the importance of lines. Each piece of wire is a line, and like a pencil drawing, each can add to the character of the piece. Place the drawing under glass or plastic to protect it while working. It is typical to draw the design carefully and at the correct size on paper, and to bend wires directly upon the drawing to insure their accuracy.

Though it is occasionally necessary to use a single straight piece of wire, it is far more common to break the design into units that can be bent in such a way that they will stand up by themselves. Consider setting a "V" into position as contrasted with setting two single lengths of wire and you'll perceive the point.

It is typical (though not mandatory) to start by coating the sheet metal with a layer of clear flux, a material that is in essence a colorless enamel. Wires are then glued into place on top of this with gum tragacanth, a temporary support that will keep them from being pushed out of place as the enamel powder is laid into place with a brush. When the piece is fired the fused glass will bond to the lower layer and to the wires and hold everything together.

10.2.5 METAL PREPARATION

Enamel can only stick to metal that has been cleaned and degreased. Sometimes it is possible heat the metal in the enameling kiln to a temperature at which grease residues burn off, but care must be taken that you do not reach a temperature at which oxides are formed.

10.2.6 PREPARING THE ENAMEL

The best enamels are sold as gravel shaped lumps that need to be ground up in preparation for use. The first step in this is to use a steel mortar and pestle arrangement like the one shown in figure 10.10. In this case the pestle makes a snug fit into the cylinder which prevents the pieces from sliding away. Though not absolutely necessary, this device provides quick reduction of large pieces and prevents undue wear and tear on a more delicate mortar.

The small pieces are transferred to a porcelain mortar and pestle where they are ground into a finer powder. Add a small amount of water to keep the grains from jumping out of the bowl. If your water supply is laden with chemicals use bottled or distilled water. Opaque enamels are ground to a fine powder, but transparents will produce their brightest color if left slightly larger.

After grinding, the enamel powder is washed by placing it in a shallow dish and swirling it in clean water. Pour off the cloudy water and add fresh, repeating the process several times. In the case of opaques you may quit after a couple of rinsings, but transparents require that they be rinsed until the runoff water is clear. Though the author's experience has been fine with tap water, enamelists working in other environments might find it necessary to use distilled or bottled water to prevent mineral contamination of the enamels.

The cleaned enamel is transferred to small glass dishes that are in turn marked with the number of the color. These are kept under a bell jar during the course of the work day to minimize their drying out and to protect them from dust. Powders left over at the end of the session are put back in a jar and mixed with a generous supply of water to keep them fresh.

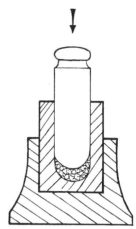

Figure 10.10
Mortar and pestle (cross section).

When starting up next time the water is poured off and the enamel is rinsed a few times.

10.2.7 APPLYING THE ENAMEL

Glass shrinks as it cools, which means that a panel having enamel on only one side will curl up when is it taken from the kiln. To prevent this and equalize stresses throughout the piece it is vital to apply enamel to both sides of a work. The reverse side, called counter-enamel, is often nothing more than an unpatterned layer of a single color but its importance cannot be understated. Applying the counter enamel is the first step to be undertaken.

After cleaning and roughening the metal, paint on a thin layer of gum tragacanth. It is also possible to add some gum tragacanth powder in with the enamel. Sprinkle this onto the sheet in an even distribution by using a brass sieve. Put enamel into the spoonlike tool and shake it several inches above the plate. Allow the enamel to dry, invert it carefully and set it into a firing support, and apply enamels with a brush into the cloisons.

Pick up a dollop of damp enamel with a moistened brush and deposit it onto the prepared workpiece. The degree of dampness depends upon the kind of work being done. If the enamel is too wet it will run out of place and can mix with previously applied colors. If it is too dry it will not flow into the chambers.

In the case of cloisonné and champlevé it is usually best to build up the enamel in several layers because some enamels become milky if applied too thickly all at once. The full height is typically achieved with two to four firings.

10.2.8 FIRING THE ENAMEL

As mentioned above, the enamel powder is mixed with water to help it flow into the cavity that is meant to contain it. Once the powdered glass is in place, however, the water becomes unnecessary and so must be allowed to evaporate away. Place the work on top of the enameling kiln, which by this time is preheating in preparation for use. In most cases this will only take a few minutes.

If some of the enamel drops off during drying or as the piece is being set into the kiln, do not apply fresh wet enamel. It will appear cloudy. Instead either fill the area with dry powder, repair the loss in the next firing, or remove all the enamel from that section and refill it with fresh damp powder.

When the kiln has reached the intended temperature, the firing support that holds the work is set into the kiln. Manufacturers will often provide information with their colors about ideal firing temperatures and while these should be heeded, no amount of reading or planning can take the place of intuitive understanding of what constitutes a correct firing. Each situation depends to some degree on the thickness and size of the metal object, the other enamels present, the thickness of the enamel, the accuracy of the kiln and other subjective factors.

Generally, there are three phases in the fusing operation. First, the enamel powder sinters into a pasty mass. If you could touch it (don't – it's hot!) it seems like it would be crumbly. This then melts into a sticky mass, still uneven on its surface. The mass usually looks red at this point. With continued heat the enamel mass will glow a bright red and even itself out to a smooth level surface. This indicates that the piece is ready to be removed. Avoid overheating because this might change the color of the enamel.

The work is removed and set onto a firebrick or similar heat proof surface near the kiln. If the piece has warped it should be flattened immediately, while still red hot. Lift the work from the firing support and set it onto a steel surface plate. Press down on it with a stiff spatula – a mason's trowel is useful.

10.2.9 FINISHING ENAMEL

Grinding

It is traditional, particularly in the case of champlevé and cloisonné to finish the piece to a flush surface. This accentuates the graphic nature of the design and allows the wires to show well. This is done with bars and rods of silicon carbide in a process called *stoning*.

After the firing is complete and the work has cooled to room temperature, it is set on a board in or across a sink in such a way that a trickle of water can be run constantly across it. A stone of the appropriate shape is rubbed with firm pressure back and forth across the piece until the surface is completely flush. While it is possible to achieve this with a wet sander, in most studio situations enamels continue to be stoned by hand.

Washing

After grinding the enamel surface has many pores, the result of air bubbles in the molten glass. In the stoning process these bubbles are cut open and remain in the surface as tiny pits. Remnants of the abrasives become stuck in these openings and can mar the finished piece as gray flecks if they are not removed. Scrub the finished work aggressively with a glass brush under running water, then follow this with another scrubbing with soap and a toothbrush. Examine the surface with a loupe to insure that all traces of debris have been flushed away. Large pits are cleaned with a needle, filled with fresh enamel and refired.

Flash firing

If the piece is to have a matte finish, stoning is the last process. When the enamel is intended to be shiny, the work is returned to the kiln for one last firing after the surface has been ground flat and cleaned. The kiln is brought up to a high temperature and the piece set into it for a few seconds, just long enough that the surface will melt and become smooth. The hotter the kiln at this point, the brighter the resulting colors, but care must be taken to insure that the work is not over-heated.

Polishing

The metal around an enameled area can be polished with the usual compounds as long as you are careful to avoid keeping the buff too long at any one spot. The compounds will not wear down the glass, so prolonged exposure risks creating an uneven surface as metal is removed. This is generally easy to avoid. A light touch with the buff should be enough to bring the metal to a bright shine.

Table 10.1 shows some possibilities for errors when enameling.

10.3
Inlay work

There are many techniques in which contrasting metals are placed side by side. Those that can properly be called inlay require a mechanical attachment to secure a soft material into a harder one. Examples can be seen in figures 10.12 through 10.16.

10.3.1 MATERIALS

Proper inlay requires materials of contrasting hardness to hold well, and contrasting color to look good. A combination that does well on both counts is the use of pure silver or gold into blackened steel. Another popular combination has fine silver pressed into copper or brass. Examples can be found in museums, particularly in weapons and decorative objects from Asia.

10.3.2 CREATING THE CAVITIES

The principal behind metal inlays is that wire or pieces of sheet are forced into cavities or hollowed out areas. These are cut so their walls slope inward, or are undercut. This insures that a piece of metal will get stuck there once it is forcibly rammed in. It is a simple process and judging from the fact that we can find inlays that are many hundreds of years old, an

Figure 10.12
Gunlock. Steel with silver inlay, some losses. Middle 19th century. (State Museum, Schwerin)

Figure 10.13
Flintlock rifle. Steel with gold inlay.
a)top view, b) underside. (Michele Nauttista, Nepal 1774. State Museum, Schwerin)

effective one. While the pressing in requires sensitive hammering, the most important part of inlay work lies in cutting the cavity in the first place. There are several methods available to a metalsmith.

Etching

The process is worked as described in Chapter 10, section 7, with nitric acid being the preferred mordant in this case. As the acid works its way deeper into the metal it has a natural tendency to also work outward, creating exactly the undercut that is needed. Unfortunately this is not the natural tendency of ferric chloride, which has the usually agreeable tendency to leave a vertical wall.

Burring or milling

In a miniature milling operation, a bur can be used in the flexible shaft machine to remove metal. Once the cavity has been excavated with a ball, barrel, or similar bur, the walls are given the necessary undercut with an inverted cone bur or with a narrow graver.

Each piece will present unique approaches, so it is best to let your instincts guide you. The point is to create a cavity with sharp edges, a uniform depth, and undercut walls. A tube or other curved surface can sometimes be decorated with a sawblade, a chisel or a bur, or a combination of tools.

Engraving

An ideal approach for delicate linear designs is to make a pair of cuts with a narrow onglette graver. This tool is driven along a drawn line at a steep angle, as shown in figure 10.18b. The same tool is then passed along the same line at the opposite slant, creating a cavity with a swallowtailed cross section.

In cases where the desired inlay is larger than a wire, sheet material is used. In these cases, a square graver is used to excavate the area, then the onglette is used around the edges to create the undercut. This is shown in figure 10.10c.

Chiseling

Using chisels to cut away sections of metal sheet is an effective technique that has the advantage of being relatively easy to learn. The metal is secured on pitch as for repoussé, or in some similar way clamped onto a sturdy work surface. Chisels of several sizes will probably be needed, each taking the shape shown in figure 10.19b. The tool is held between the thumb and

Figure 10.14
Patinated steel brooch with gold, silver and copper inlay. (Rolf Lindner, Erfurt)

Figure 10.15
Patinated steel brooch with silver and copper inlay. (Rolf Lindner, Erfurt)

Figure 10.16
Patinated steel bracelet with silver inlay. (Wolfgang Schluter, Hirschburg)

Problem	Cause	Remedy
Metal parts melted	kiln was too hot …	reduce kiln temperature
Cloisonné wire sinks in the enamel	wire is alloying with solder …	use less solder
White becomes spotted with green	enamel is reacting with copper …	use a thicker layer of enamel
White becomes spotted with yellow	enamel is reacting with silver …	avoid contact with silver
Black spots on the enamel	iron dust or filings may have fallen on the enamel …	clean the elements and kiln chamber
Gray spots on the enamel	could be residue of polishing compounds …	clean the work thoroughly after stoning or polishing
Porous enamel	the enamel might have been over-heated; use of inappropriate metal as a base for the enamel …	reduce the kiln temperature; use a different metal
Discoloring film on the enamel	gas deposits …	avoid gas formation
Enamel is gray and cloudy	enamel was insuffiently cleaned …	clean the enamel more thoroughly
Bubbles in the enamel	enamel has been contaminated …	clean the enamel more thoroughly
Cloudy spots and edges	water might have run in to the dry enamel powder …	moisten the enamel uniformly
Enamel shows cracks	uneven heat expansion of adjacent enameled areas; uneven heating between enamel and metal; wrong thickness of metal; not enough counter-enamel …	change to enamels with similar properties; use more counter-enamel
Clear enamel becomes cloudy	too finely ground; not sufficiently cleaned; spread too thick, kiln temperature too high …	use frit that is more coarsely ground; wash well; fire at a more moderate temperature
Metal warps	incorrect firing base; insufficient counter-enamel …	Select a different metal as the base; use more counter-enamel

Table 10.1
Possible mistakes when enameling.

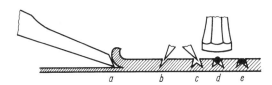

Figure 10.18
Inlay with engraved recesses.
a) raising a bead, side view, b) first cut, c) second cut to insert wire,
e) inserted wire hammered into place.

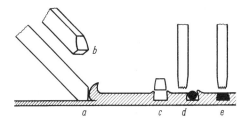

Figure 10.19
Inlay with chiseled groove.
a) chisel cut side view, b) chisel cut, c) chiseled groove, d) tapping down
the ridge, e) hammered inlay completed.

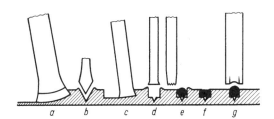

Figure 10.20
Inlay with punched grooves.
a) punch side view, b) incised groove, c) flat punches side view,
d) enlarging the channel, e) hitting down the edge, f) finished inlaid
wire, g) rounding off the inlaid wire for relief inlay.

the two first fingers and struck lightly with a small hammer. Particularly when first learning, avoid the mistake of gouging out too much at a time. Think of shaving off layers of metal until the proper depth is reached. The cavity should have smooth walls and a flat bottom and attain a uniform depth throughout.

It is usually best to first make the cavity walls straight, focusing on the correct shape for the cut. When this is achieved, use another chisel and go around the inside of the form to undercut the walls slightly. Where small wires are to be inlaid, an alternate method is to use a chisel to pull up a bur along the edge as shown in figure 10.20d.

Using punches

This method is similar to chiseling except that no metal is removed. Because of this it is not recommended for large inlays, though it can be very efficient for small wires. Select a sharp liner that will cast up a bur on both sides of its mark. Use magnification to check the results of the too (figure 10.20b).

Follow the first cut with another punch, this one a flat-ended punch that will widen the groove to accept the inlay (figure 10.20d). Only a small amount of metal is needed to secure the wire but it must stand up above the surface as shown. It is important to select tools of the proper size and strike each blow cleanly so the tiny bur is not accidentally pressed down.

10.3.3 FIXING THE INLAY IN PLACE
Wire inlay into undercuts

Use an annealed wire that is a proper fit for the groove. A wire that is too small will not be securely held while an oversize wire risks distorting the inlay (as well as requiring tedious extra finishing). Start at one end of the groove, tapping the wire lightly into place for a short distance, than proceed to the next area. The idea, seen in figure 10.18d and e, is to press the wire outward into the swallowtail or undercut area, locking it into place. The action has the added advantage of work hardening the inlay.

Once the wire is firmly pressed into place, use a smooth-faced planishing punch to even the surface and refine the inlay. Make a series of light passes over the wire and surrounding area, feathering the surface until it is flush.

In the case of a groove cut with a chisel or punch, in which the edge of the cavity has been thrown up in a delicate bur, the process is a little different. The wire is set into position and a slightly roughened matting punch is used to gather the material immediately adjacent to the groove and press it onto the wire, figure 10.20e. A variation on this is to create a roughened punch with a slight arc in its center, shown at figure 10.20g. This tool spans the wire and presses down on the inlay to lock it in place. Once it is secure, planishing hammers, files and sandpapers are used to make the surface flush.

Sheet inlays

A cavity is made as described above, using either chisels, gravers or through acid etching. The walls of the cavity are undercut, causing them to slope inward. A piece of sheet metal a little thicker than the depth of the cavity is cut out and filed so its edges are beveled to resemble the slope of the walls. The piece is domed slightly, which will allow it to drop into the cavity. Measurement and close tolerances are clearly very important.

Once it is in place the sheet is flattened with a mallet or punches, which causes it to press against the undercut walls, locking it into place. The surface is planished then refined with sandpaper.

Relief inlays

While most inlays are flush, it is also possible to create an inlay that stands above the surface of the base. In the case of sheet inlays, the piece might be formed through repoussé or casting. The inlay process is the same as described above but of course the inlay panel must not be planished. Instead it is pressed flat with carefully located punches that will not damage the shape on the panel.

In the case of wires, the round wire mentioned above is replaced with a flattened wire, the smaller dimension of which fits snugly into a groove that has had a bur thrown up along both sides. A matting punch is used along the side of the wire to press the bur against it, alternating from one side to the other. To cinch the inlay use a flat-faced punch that has a groove the width and height of the projecting element cut into it. This punch, called a veining tool, travels along the metal, tapping the base piece against the sides of the wire and trapping it into position.

10.4
Engraving

Many industries have need of specialized engravers, for instance those who make dies, who cut stones and glass, and others who carve reliefs. Though a goldsmith might call on a specialist for certain jobs, it is useful to have a general understanding of the technique and sufficient skills to use gravers for simple everyday tasks at the bench.

10.4.1 HOW THE ENGRAVING TOOL WORKS

Engraving tools are miniature chisels made of hardened steel. They are chip forming tools and subject to the same forces described in Chapter 5. In proper engraving a sharpened tool is set against the metal at a specific angle and pressure applied both downward and forward. The tool buries itself into the sheet, forms a chip, and pushes that curl of metal ahead of it as it cuts.

The angle of attack is important to achieve a controlled and uniform cut. If the angle is too steep the tool digs itself into the sheet making it impossible to push it forward. The effort to overpower a buried tool can result in a loss of control and a broken tip. If the angle is too shallow the point never gains purchase on the sheet. There is no chip formed and no cut made. Because the tip of the tool is not caught by the metal, the tool easily slips, creating a nasty scratch.

The proper angle will depend on the shape of the graver, the quality of the desired line and the metal being cut. Understanding and responding to these factors requires a sensitive touch and considerable experience.

10.4.2 ENGRAVING TOOL SHAPES

Engraving tools, called gravers, are precise instruments. They must be made from top quality steel, shaped and sharpened to specific angles, and fitted into handles that provide comfort and control. Commercially available gravers are made from a highly refined fine grained tool steel. A high speed steel is to be recommended for working harder materials and to have the greatest possible durability; there are even engraving tools with carbide cutting tips.

Gravers are usually sold with preshaped tips, but these angles will need to be reworked before the tool is used. Gravers can be purchased from jewelry supply companies in the shapes shown in figure 10.21.

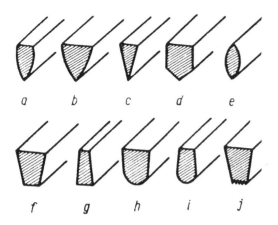

Figure 10.21
Graver forms.
a) small pointed (onglette) graver, b) wider pointed graver, c) knife graver, d) facet graver, e) oval graver, f) flat graver with wide rib, g) flat graver with small rib, h) rounded grave, i) rounded graver with small rib, j) line graver.

Onglette

This popular shape is shown in two sizes in 10.21a and 10.21b. The sides curve slightly outward from a top edge that is flat and can range from one to four millimeters wide. This tool offers great versatility, cutting a thin line with a light stroke and widening as it is rolled on its side or pressed more deeply into the sheet. It is preferred for cutting letters because of the ease with which it cuts a line of increasing width.

Knife graver

Illustrated at 10.21c, this graver is a slim, straight-walled version of the onglette. It is difficult to control on curves and rarely used by itself, but it cuts deep hair-thin lines. It is often used to add delicate embellishments to figures cut with other tools.

Beveled graver

This is the stout sibling of the wide onglette, figure 10.21d, used to make bold cuts in tough metal. The side surfaces form an angle of 100°, with the upper sides being parallel. The width of the back can be between 1.5–3 mm.

Oval graver

This tool, shown at 10.21e can be considered a slim version of the onglette, but in this case the pointed oval is not truncated with a flat spine along the top. In practice this shape offers a blank that is ground as needed to create a tool to shave metal from within tight enclosures. This is the tool, for instance, that is used to carve a seat for a stone inside a bezel wall.

Flat graver

This tool has a flat base, or "belly" that can be used to carve away unwanted metal, as for instance when removing excess solder. The cross section can be trapezoidal (figure 10.21f and g) or a rectangle (not shown). This is also the tool used to make decorative wiggle cuts. It is the practical workhorse of the graver family, being used less for ornamentation than shaving, scraping, and cutting textures. Flat gravers are available in widths from 0.2 mm to 5 mm.

Round graver

This name is deceiving because the tool itself, pictured in two sizes at 10.21h and 10.21j, is not round. Nevertheless, the groove it cuts is a round-bottomed trench and it is from this the name is derived. As shown, the side walls can be either parallel or sloped. This tool is among the easiest to control and is therefore useful for all kinds of decorative work.

Florentine finish graver

This tool looks at first glance like a flat graver, but closer examination will reveal delicate lines cut lengthwise into the belly. These cut fine parallel lines into the surface, an effect that is used to ornament an otherwise plain surface while simultaneously protecting it from wear and fingerprints.

Preparation of the engraving tool

It is customary that graver blanks are furnished in a length sufficient to accommodate the largest hand. This means that the rest of us must start by shortening them. Grasp the tool vertically in a vise with the unwanted portion of the tang projecting up. Strike a vigorous blow with a steel hammer sideways against the tang and it will snap off cleanly. To prevent the tip from shooting across the room, catch the broken off part in a towel or rag held against the vise.

Reshape the tang by grinding, either with a bench grinder, sanding machine, or appropriate wheels on a flexible shaft machine. The graver is secured by friction into a handle in the same manner as a file; secure it into a vise and tap the handle into place with a mallet. As the tool becomes shorter through numerous sharpenings, a long handle is replaced by a shorter one. Though the grip might feel a little awkward at first, it will become more comfortable with experience. If your hand muscles get cramped during engraving the tool is too short and should be replaced.

Proper shaping and sharpening of gravers is as important as it is difficult to describe on the printed page. The following description should be supplemented with practice and experimentation. Refer to figure 10.22, an onglette graver, for the following instructions. In general these same steps will be used for other shapes, though the angles of each tool differ slightly.

Gravers are sold in their hardened state and any grinding should be done in such a way that this temper is preserved. Touch the tool lightly to the grinding wheel, dipping it frequently into water throughout the process to prevent it from overheating. If the steel starts to show color the temper has been compromised.

The first step is to narrow the area adjacent to the tip for 1–2 centimeters (½ – ¾ inch). This will allow better viewing of the working tip of the tool and facilitate sharpening since there is less metal to be removed. Use a stone to cut away at least half of the top section at the tip, creating a gentle arc as shown. This edge should be made smooth because your fingers will be resting on it while cutting. Do not go too far back because this will weaken the tool.

The belly or underside of the graver is ground so it shows two symmetrical facets. If the tool was turned over, these might be said to resemble the roof of a house. The angle between these two facets will be between 30 and 60° depending upon the hardness of the material to be cut. A narrow tip cuts a finer line but is more fragile.

The face of the tool is then ground to a slope, typically around 45°, again depending on the material being cut; the finer the slope, the more delicate the tool. It might help to visualize a pencil point. If it is made very long and pointy it makes a fine line but often breaks in use.

Both belly and face surfaces should be perfectly flat like the facets on a gem. This will insure that the angles where the faces meet are straight and crisp, which in turn is what makes the tool sharp. Grinding is usually done on an oilstone, working in a circular stroke, first on a coarse stone and then on a finer one. When the surfaces are correct – check with magnification – shift to a polishing stone like Arkansas or a fine abrasive paper. Follow this with a few strokes on a hard leather with a polishing powder to create a mirror bright finish.

Test the sharpening by sliding the tip of the graver along your thumb nail. A properly sharpened tool will stick immediately while an improperly shaped tool will slide off. There is no point in going to the metal until the tool passes this test. Cutting with a dull graver is tedious, uncontrolled and almost certain to ruin the work.

10.4.3 HOLDING EQUIPMENT

As important as the gravers are, it is hard to understate the importance of the devices used to secure work while engraving. Or to say it another way, even a properly sharpened graver in experienced hands will be difficult to use if the workpiece is sliding across the bench. Knowing this it is not surprising to find that several tools have been developed to hold onto the work for cutting.

The simplest and cheapest tool is a pitch stick, described earlier in the section on filing. This is nothing more than a convenient length of wood that has a layer of pitch smeared on one end. The work is set into the softened pitch and pressed down to insure a grip, then the pitch is allowed to cool and solidify. The stick is held against the bench pin as the graver is moved against it. When cutting is complete the pitch is warmed slightly and the piece is removed. Alternate adhesive media include flake shellac and hot glue.

Figure 10.23 shows a top-of-the-line holding device, a weighty steel ball called an *engravers block*. This steel sphere is divided at its equator and mounted on a greased bearing to allow it to rotate easily. The top element is fitted with a vise that has many holes to receive holding pins. One side of the holding plate swivels, so by placing pins strategically and turning the plate as needed it is possible to hold almost any shape in the block. Tiny pieces can be secured with pitch onto a strip of wood that is then clamped into the device.

The gravers block is set into a felt or leather ring that allows it to be tilted at any angle. In conjunction with its free rotation, this makes the tool extremely responsive to even subtle movements as work is being moved under the cutting action of a graver. The gravers block is also a useful tool for chasing, stone setting and other "two-handed" tasks.

10.4.4 WORKING WITH THE GRAVER

Elaborate designs or lengthy panels of text will almost certainly be given over to professional engravers, but it is useful to be able to cut a monogram or decorative line at the bench. In addition, goldsmiths who have confidence in their engraving skills will find themselves reaching for a graver to assist in clean up, to sharpen a detail, and to cut seats for stones. It is worth noting that every culture that has worked precious metals has invented a graver or similar cutting tool.

Imagine learning to play a sport or to dance only by reading about it and you will have a sense of the importance of practice when it comes to learning how to engrave. The following passage attempts to describe the cutting process, but no amount of reading or observation can take the place of sitting down with the tools to practice. Regular work with gravers, however, will teach subtle factors such as angle, force and roll if you keep at it. It is better to practice for 15 minutes every day than to labor for a couple hours once a month.

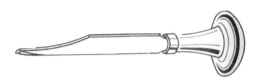

Figure 10.22
Graver with small rib partially ground back.

Figure 10.23
Engraver's block with universal adjustments.

The proper stroke will involve a delicate ballet between tool and object as each is moved into the other. Dozens of muscles in the hands are constantly receiving information and reacting to it in the form of subtle adjustments of pressure and tilt. Attempt to remain relaxed as you cut, keeping your shoulder and arm muscles loose.

If the graver is properly sharpened it will slide through even tough metal relatively easily. If you are driving the tool with brute force something is wrong and the tool probably needs to be resharpened.

Recognize this as a necessary part of the process and stop as soon as it is needed. Again think of a pencil – if the point has gone dull there is nothing for it but to stop and sharpen it!

To learn engraving, prepare many panels of copper or aluminum roughly 40 x 40 mm (1.5 x 1.5 inches) and 1.5 to 2 mm thick (16–12 gauge B&S). Secure a piece to a pitch stick or in a gravers block and practice making straight parallel lines such as shown in the top row of samples in figure 10.24. Avoid the temptation to "scoop" with the tool, allowing it instead to glide along its path. Stop when you get weary and return fresh another day.

Next test your skills at making curved lines, following the patterns shown in the second row of the illustration. Strive for smooth curves and consistent line width. You will find this easiest if the metal plate is

moving into the graver as the tool is sliding across the metal.

Finally, train yourself to create a cut line that goes from narrow to broad and back to narrow again. This "line of beauty" is a staple of engraving and will justify whatever time it takes to learn it. Some people make the cut in two stages, cutting a thin line first, then recutting over the same line, this time rolling the graver over slightly onto its side to broaden the line. The tool is rolled and pressed forward in a smooth motion, then straightened gradually to return to a narrow line. The samples in the bottom row of figure 10.24 offer some examples of patterns to be cut.

Having mastered these strokes you will be able to assemble them into almost any pattern. Figures 10.25 and 10.26 show some examples of decorative engraving intended to inspire your practice.

Figure 10.24
Suggestions for engraving excersises.

10.4.5 ENGINE TURNING

This technique can be thought of as an extension of engraving in that a sharpened steel tool is used to cut away small bits of metal to create decorative patterns. The principal difference is that the work is guided under the tool by a machine set up in such a way that it produces regular, often repetitious strokes. The results, seen in figures 10.27 and 10.28, are hypnotically rich. Though rarely seen today outside of museums, the elaborate machines, called rose engines, that were developed in the heyday of engine turning are testimonials to ingenuity and inventive play.

The technique can be used to carve forms, for instance in plastic or ivory, but our focus here will be on its decorative use on flat surfaces. The technique is especially appropriate for decorative boxes, watch cases, writing implements, medallions, and similar objects that will be handled because the decorated surfaces disguise wear better than smooth surfaces. Transparent enamels appear very precious indeed upon engine turned surfaces.

Engine turning was developed in the middle of the last century in the context of the industrialization of jewelry production, but today it has been superseded by other more expedient methods. Still the process is intriguing and continues to offer rich possibilities for experimentation. It is included here for the interest of aficionados and with the hope that this lovely and intriguing process will not be forgotten. Goldsmiths wanting to pursue this process will need to research further and undertake personal experiments, but it is hoped that the following introduction will at least guide goldsmiths as they get started.

The concept of the machine can be seen in figure 10.29. As this shows, the basic elements are a sliding mount that holds a graver rigid against the metal and a bed on which the panel is mounted. This bed is moved in accordance with a template (here the corrugated strip along the left edge). A spring on the right side maintains pressure against the bed, forcing it to press against the template and in this case slide back and forth as it travels vertically. From this example one can see that by altering the tools, templates and

Figure 10.25
Heraldic engraving. Silver. 1938 (Ernst Brepohl, Anstadt).

Figure 10.26
Engraved medallion. Silver. 1877 (Private collection, London).

Figure 10.27
Designs for machine engraving.
a) straight line method, b) circular combined with straight lines.

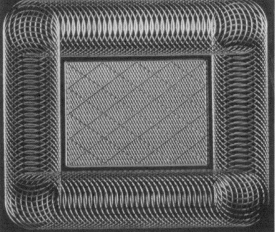

Figure 10.28
Examples of machine engraving.
a) chalice, b) box lid. Walter Zeiss, Pforzheim. (Technical Museum Pforzheim).

direction of travel an endless variety of patterns can be cut.

The machine can be driven by hand or motor power, though most rely on electric motors today. One can imagine how this might be arranged when looking at figure 10.30 in which the templates are rotated on an axis. The rotating axle is mounted on springs so it can respond to the action of the feeler pin against the template profile, driving the template (and the workpiece, which is attached to the same axle) back and forth as it rotates. By having several templates mounted side by side as shown, a variety of patterns can be cut on the same machine.

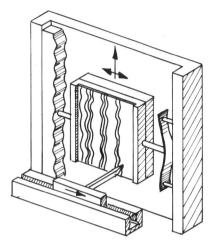

Figure 10.29
Working principles of the linear engraving machine.

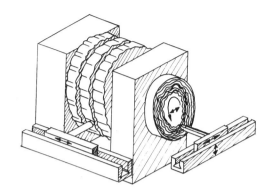

Figure 10.30
Working principles of the circular engraving machine.

10.4.6 MACHINE ENGRAVING

We are all familiar (too familiar!) with objects like those shown in figure 10.31, the results of a device incorrectly called a pantograph. A pantograph is a mechanical device (figure 10.32) through which an existing pattern can be duplicated. By altering the points of pivot, the pattern can be enlarged or reduced in perfect proportion as shown. When a pantograph arm is connected to a miniature milling tool mounted in a small powerful motor, the result is a popular device shown in figures 10.33 and 10.34 called a *pantograph engraving machine*.

Because the actual cutting is done with a rotating bur the cut is very different from an engraved line, a distinction that is clear to goldsmiths but perhaps less obvious to others. The advantage of the machine is its great regularity. No particular hand skills or experience are required to use the machine. A worker secures the piece into position and guides the feeler along a template. This in turn passes the rotating bur against the metal where a line is cut. The advantage is that the letter or image is cut identically every time; the disadvantage is that there is no room for subtlety or nuance. A pantograph engraving machine is like a typewriter in this way, efficient but visually boring.

With the aid of additional attachments it is possible to work on other than flat surfaces, as is seen in

Figure 10.31
Examples of machine engraving.

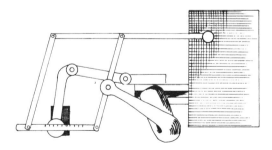

Figure 10.32
Working principle of the pantograph.

Figure 10.33
Ebener Pantograph. Firm Gravograph, Umkirch-Freiburg.

figure 10.34 where a goblet is being engraved. In this way the pantograph machine can be adapted for use on concave or convex curved surfaces (the surface of a button), tubular shapes both outside and inside (micrometer collars, inside wedding band engraving), and conical metal surfaces like the goblet shown. It is also possible to mill completely through a piece of sheet metal, a process used for instance, to create brass stencils for spray painting letters.

Though little energy is given to traditional engraving in recent time, considerable effort has been devoted to developments along the lines of pantograph engraving. In the process called CAD/CAM (computer-aided design/computer-aided manufacturing), a tool is guided in the x, y, and z axis by a computer, making possible the development of forms from an image created on a computer screen.

10.5
Repoussé

10.5.1 DEFINITION

The terms repoussé and chasing are often confused and not without good reason since the two techniques are often worked together. One might as well think of "slipping and sliding" to realize how difficult to establish a clear definition particular to each pro-

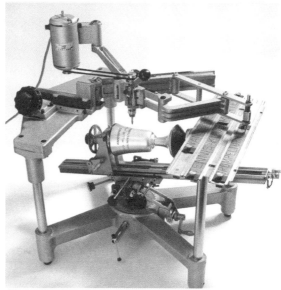

Figure 10.34
3D pantograph.

cess. In general we might think of repoussé as primarily a relief process (3-dimensionally oriented) and chasing as more often a intaglio (2-D or linear) technique.

Another useful division is to think of repoussé as a process that creates relief without significantly altering the thickness of the starting sheet. The metal is pushed and pulled but, as shown in figure 10.35, its thickness remains the same. This differs from chasing where the ability of metal to compress is used to create relief. Some areas are allowed to remain at their original height while adjacent areas are compacted with tools to make them lower. It must be remembered, however, that the two techniques are often used together.

Chasing has a long history of use in conjunction with cast forms, where steel punches were used to refine the form of a cast object. It is still an important part of that process. Repoussé was probably developed not simply as a decorative technique but because a contoured or corrugated form is considerably stronger than a flat one. This meant that a thinner gauge metal could be used, allowing larger objects or greater profit.

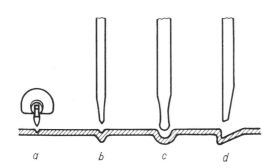

Figure 10.35
Stressed and unstressed metal forming.
a) engraving, b) punching, c) modeling, d) tracing.

These techniques share several properties, among them the fact that they can be worked on tiny jewelry pieces or large architectural or sculptural work. In both cases hammers are used to press pencil-like steel tools against metal, forming or compressing it, or both. Both repoussé and chasing can be worked on all the conventional jewelry metals with ease, of course suggesting the more malleable metals as the best candidates. High karat gold, fine silver and copper respond very well, while pale brass, nickel silver and steel require greater effort.

10.5.2 TOOLS

Punches

Tools called punches are used in both repoussé and chasing, with a few of the tools being used in both techniques. They are steel rods of various thicknesses about 10–15 cm long (4–6 inches), hardened and tempered to retain their shape through years of work. The top end where the hammer strikes, is slightly beveled to create a truncated pyramid or cone at that point. This serves to focus the force of the hammer blow.

Tool steel, typically W1 or O1, is cut to length, shaped with files and sandpaper, then hardened and tempered at the tip to a straw yellow color. The shank of the tool is left annealed, which reduces shock to the holding hand. The working tip can assume many shapes. A collection of 100 punches is not unusual, given that several sizes of each shape are often needed in a single project. A few of the general styles are shown in figure 10.36, but bear in mind that each of

these has variations, and each might be needed in several sizes. Tools can be purchased from suppliers but goldsmiths who spend much time with these techniques will soon find the need to create special shapes for their unique requirements. Each new project seems to require a shape that is somehow missing so your collection of punches is perpetually growing.

When a wide flat blade is needed, the tool blank might be hot forged first to achieve a blank of the proper dimensions, then is finished with a file. The shape is then worked to sandpaper to insure there are no sharp edges or corners that might tear through the sheet, and finally given a polish.

Tools with square or rectangular shanks are easier to steer across the metal and more comfortable to grip. The proper length of a tool is a personal matter, but it can be said that if they are so small they are lost in one's hand they are difficult to hammer with confidence. If they are too long they tend to wobble about, making accuracy difficult.

The general shapes of punches fall into the following families, illustrated in figure 10.36.

Liners (also draw or marking out punches)
These versatile punches are used to draw lines, form letters and outline shapes that are later given more dimension with other tools (figure 10.36a and b). The tip of the tool is shaped like a wedge but it is "softened" or rounded with sandpaper so it won't cut through. Wide tools are preferred for making long straight lines because they tend to stay straight. Narrow tools are needed in cases when working on a small design. A variation on this tool is a liner with a gentle arc which is used to draw curved lines. Again several sizes will be needed.

Modeling punches (forming punches)
This is perhaps the largest category because it includes any punch used to push metal around (figure 10.36c, d and e). These might be thought of as the fingers and thumbs that a metal relief sculptor uses to shape his or her material. Most tools are polished, but larger shapes might be left with a sandpaper finish because the slightly roughened surface will get a better grip on the metal being formed.

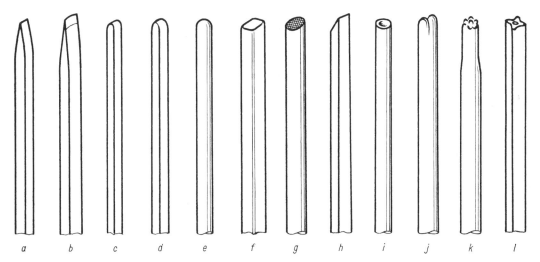

Figure 10.36
Various punch forms and sharp punches.
a) and b) lining tools, c to e) modeling punches, f) planishing punch, g) matting punch, h) setting punch, i) hollow or ring punch,
j) jig punch, k) and l) texturing or design punches.

Planishing punches

As the name suggests, these punches are used to smooth the relief (or background) just as planishing hammers are used to smooth forms when raising. These punches (figure 10.36f) are always highly polished and generally have a straight wall in order to reach neatly into the area where a raised section joins the floor or base of the relief. The top view of planishing punches would reveal them as square, rectangular, round, triangular and so on; again with the idea of reaching cleanly into the nooks that surround the relief image.

Matting punches

These useful tools (figure 10.36g) resemble planishing punches in shape but have a different surface, being inscribed with textures or lines that will leave behind a characteristic non-reflective or matte surface. They are used to create contrasting areas of shadow, to camouflage marks left by other tools, and to create a surface that will stand up well to handling.

Matting punches can be made by engraving, carving, sawing or filing a pattern of marks into the end of an annealed tool blank. Another effective means is to strike the soft tool blank hard on an old file – the

steel will pick up an impression of the file. This makes a useful tool after it has been hardened and tempered.

Setting punches

This specialized family of punches (figure 10.36h) are similar to planishers except that the face is set at an angle, though not necessarily one as steep as that shown. When used along the edge of a design the point of transition between relief and floor is made very clear, somewhat like outlining a drawing with a dark black line.

Hollow punches

These too can be made or purchased (figure 10.36i). They produce a rounded bead and are most effective when used repeatedly in close proximity to create an overall pattern. A version of this is used in Japanese metalwork and it is known as the fish roe pattern.

Jig punch (also called chain tool)

This is shown in figure 10.36j and illustrates not only a specific tool but a means for insuring even spacing. In the case of the tool shown (which would make a shallow round crater) the first blow will create a pair of indentations. To make the second blow, one "foot" of the tool is placed in an existing crater, thus guaranteeing the even spacing of the new impression made. This process is continued to make a decorative line or border.

Stamps

This is a separate category of tools that are not really chasing or repoussé tools, but will be listed here because in general form they resemble the punches, (10.36l). And as mentioned before, it is not impossible for stamping to be used in conjunction with the other relief techniques.

Where chasing and repoussé punches create a range of shapes depending on how they are used, stamps have a particular shape and press it into the metal when struck. In this regard they might be seen as a relation to children's rubber stamps. A picture of a cow can be used here or there, right side up or upside down, once or in series, but it will always be a picture of a cow.

Wooden punches

As you might guess, these are nothing more than alternate punches made from lengths of hardwood. They have the triple advantage of being inexpensive, easy to form and incapable of making damaging marks on the work. They are used at any time, but are particularly handy when unusual shapes are needed, when the work is being formed off the pitch bowl, or when only subtle adjustments are needed.

Chasing hammer

Even the best punches will be ineffective if they are not properly struck with a hammer. Any small hammer can be used but the process is greatly facilitated by using a tool whose design has evolved since the 18th century to become not only the best tool for this job, but a symbol of goldsmithing hand work with its typical shape which stems from (figure 10.37).

The proper hammer is light enough to be used for hours without strain, but heavy enough to accomplish its task. It is mounted on a thin springy handle made of a long-grained wood like hickory or apple. This allows the hammer to whiplash almost imperceptibly in the users hand, lending increased force to each

blow. The handle is carved to fit comfortably in the hand, sanded smooth and given a coat of linseed oil to make it comfortable.

The face of the hammer is unhardened, allowing the punch to make a microscopic indentation there at the moment of contact. A hardened hammer would resist the tool; an angled blow would deflect the punch sideways. The face of the hammer is significantly larger than would be expected for its weight, typically measuring at least 28 mm across (1 ¼").

10.5.3 PITCH

Repoussé and chasing both require that the metal be well anchored on a reasonably resistant surface for working. In both cases a material called jewelers pitch does the job. It consists of three principle ingredients or categories of ingredients.

- pitch – originally a residue derived from tree resins, but now also seen as a petroleum product.
- binder – brick dust or dry plaster are added to give the pitch more body.
- lubricant – linseed oil, beeswax, or tallow are added to make the pitch softer.

Pitch can be purchased ready to use or made from the raw materials listed above, following the recipe of 3 parts pitch, 2 parts binder and 1 part lubricant. These ingredients are blended in a discardable pot at a low heat and stirred with a stick until well blended. It is possible for pitch to catch fire if it gets too hot so do not leave the pot unattended. (Remember those torches in Frankenstein movies? They were made of pitch.)

Even when purchasing pitch from a reputable supplier it will probably be necessary to adjust the pitch to suit your personal working style and the climate in your area. Add more lubricant or binder to give the pitch the consistency you need. In a good pitch a blow with a ball peen produces a slight indentation without the pitch cracking away.

Pitch is poured into a shallow sheet metal box (e.g. a cake pan) for working on flat objects like trays, and into a heavy steel pot when working on smaller

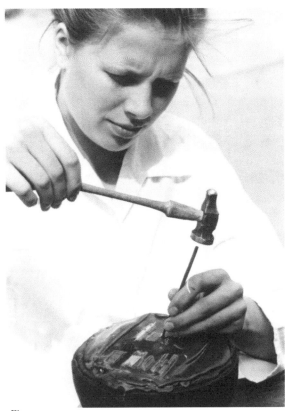

Figure 10.37
Chasing with punches and hammer on pitch bowl.

objects. The pot is traditionally made of cast iron, giving it a weight that keeps it stable on the bench. In order to conserve pitch, the pot is filled at least half full with plaster, cement, lead or pieces of brick, this layer being covered with fresh pitch at a depth sufficient to hold the work. The pot sits on a leather pad or rubber wagon tire in such a way that it can be tilted in any direction during work. This allows the tool to be kept vertical even when the angle of impact on the metal is at a slope.

Though not nearly so functional, it is also possible to do a modified repoussé on other semi-yielding surfaces. Soft wood, felt, rubber and leather have all been found to work. In these cases the work cannot be attached to the surface so it is helpful to have an assistant standing by to hold the metal as work proceeds.

Despite the range of tools described above, we can divide the actions of repoussé into as few as three categories: lining, modeling, and setting down.

Lining
Lining, also called tracing, uses chisel-shaped punches to outline a form for repoussé, to draw letters, and to make a linear pattern or ornamentation. The tools used look like blunt chisels. When worked on a hard surface it is possible to cut a line that closely resembles an engraved line, though chasing does not easily permit the graceful broad-to-narrow stroke. When worked on a slightly yielding surface like pitch, the liner creates a ghost image on the reverse side. This is especially useful as a starting point for repoussé.

The punches are held comfortably between the thumb, index and middle finger as shown in figure 10.38. The little finger rests on the pitch to support the tool and steady the holding hand. The tool is held not quite vertically, but rather at a slight tilt. This will propel the tool along its path effortlessly – as long as the tilt is correct. If the tool is too vertical it will fail to move; if it tilts too much it will hop along leaving spaces between points of contact and making a dotted line. Trial and error are used to discover the correct angle. When you achieve it the tool seems to drive ahead by itself.

The hammer blows should also come easily, the arm and shoulder being relaxed enough that you can continue for hours without fatigue. The movement of the hammer should come from the hand itself rather than from the wrist or forearm. This stroke will deliver tiny focused blows consistently to the end of the tool. If you'd like to try everything wrong, grip the handle tightly, tense your arm muscles, allow your wrist to wiggle from side to side, and lay your index finger along the handle. The results will be frustration and fatigue!

Compared to engraving, chasing is relatively easy to master. This does not mean, however, that practice is not necessary. It is suggested that a beginner devote several hours to cutting the linear patterns shown in

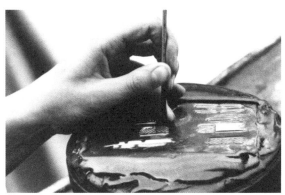

Figure 10.38
Correct position for holding the punch.

figure 10.24. With experience you will feel the almost magical effect of tools, process and intent coming together seamlessly. It's worth the effort!

Repoussé

This relief process, sometimes called modeling, makes full use of the malleability of metal to push and pull it into relief. The first step is to draw the intended outline on the annealed metal sheet with permanent ink. This is then gone over, or traced, with a liner as the metal sits on pitch. This has the effect of starting the relief in that the sheet is no longer perfectly flat, but rather has a shallow contour. Perhaps more important, when the sheet if heated and removed from the pitch, it will be seen that the image has been transferred to the back.

Do not anneal the metal at this stage. The work-hardened lines will anchor the form as the areas in between are worked aggressively with pitch to give them dimension. Set the piece back into the pitch upside down, pulling the warm pitch over the edges of the metal here and there to lock it into place.

Rounded repoussé punches or dapping punches are used to push the metal down to its maximum depth. Depending on the design, this step can involve large tools and heavy hammers to move the metal rapidly. While attention is paid to the form, refinement will come later. The intention now is to generate enough

height to provide material for the modeling from the front that will come later.

It is possible to use modeling clay to take an impression from the back that will give an idea of how the form is developing. When it seems you are approaching sufficient depth, or when the metal has work hardened enough to pull itself out of the pitch, remove the metal, dissolve excess pitch in kerosene, and anneal the work. It might be necessary at this point to also warm the pitch slightly to allow it to flow back into a level surface. Be careful that you do not heat the pitch to the point where it smokes or bubbles. This indicates that the oil is being evaporated and will result in a brittle pitch.

The annealed and cleaned piece is set back onto the pitch, right side up this time, and work continues with punches to refine the form. Though we usually think of metal as a rigid material, repoussé teaches us about its great plasticity. It is possible to model and "erase" forms as you feel your way into the design, a process that takes some getting used to.

Work continues in this way, flipping the sheet over and working alternately from front and back as the relief develops. Anneal as necessary and use whatever punches are required to give the intended form.

It is unavoidable that the flat sheet surrounding the repoussé image is distorted and slightly contoured. To flatten it, set the panel on a hard flat surface like an anvil and work the background down with wooden punches. Having this area, the floor of the relief, perfectly flat will provide a visual contrast that highlights the relief. It is also possible to saw the modeled section out of the sheet, in which case the edges are hammered over slightly and filed smooth.

An alternative treatment in which the transition between flat background and repoussé relief is softened is also attractive. In this case rounded wooden tools are used to smooth the sheet without striking exactly at the point where the relief meets the floor. In the case of a shallow relief, all the forming can be done from the back, leaving a form that is softened like a figure draped under a billowy cloth.

10.5.5 EXAMPLES OF REPOUSSÉ

Example 1

The brooch shown in figure 10.39 shows a combination of repoussé and chasing as used on a small object. The first step is to cut a piece of metal a little larger than the intended brooch and fold up the sides about 5 mm all around, figure 10.40a. These will lend stability to the form during modeling. The little box is filled with pitch, care being taken that there are no voids or air bubbles and the piece is allowed to cool.

The flat surface of a pitch pot is warmed to soften it, then the box is set into place, pitch side down, where it will bond securely with the warm pitch in the bowl. This method guarantees that the sheet of metal is fully supported by pitch. From here the steps are as follows:

1. The outer grooves are drawn onto the top surface of the box, which is in fact the front of the brooch, with a liner (figure 10.39a and b).

2. The pitch is then warmed enough to allow the box to be lifted free. It is held over the pitch bowl and warmed just enough to allow the pitch left in the box to drip back onto the bowl. The piece is cleaned and its edges are bent in the opposite direction, forming a similar box but this time such that the surface that was just on top is now the inside floor of the box. It is again filled with pitch and again secured in the heated pitch of the bowl.

3. While the pitch is still soft the of the front side of the brooch is hammered with a crowned planishing hammer to become a shallow dish (figure 10.40c).

4. The design, in this case a pair of stylized animals, is traced with a liner on the inside of this dish shape, as illustrated in figure 10.40d.

5. The piece is pulled from the pitch, cleaned, and worked from the back with small rounded punches to press up the volume needed for the animals.

6. After being cleaned and annealed. The piece is returned to the pitch, this time right side up. The front is now finished using whatever punches are necessary to create the details, textures and contrasts that best serve the design. As a final step the excess sheet is sawn away and the edges are smoothed with files.

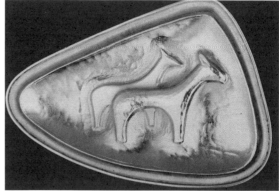

Figure 10.39
Silver brooch. Chased and repoussé design. (Gerhard Herbst, Weimar)

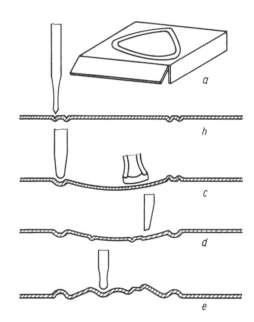

Figure 10.40
Steps involved in chasing the brooch.

Example 2

1. A piece of sheet metal is worked over stakes with hammers or mallets to achieve a spoon-like shape.

2. A terminating deck is soldered on in the region of the forehead.

3. The "blank" is pressed into warm pitch upside down. The eyebrows and folds of the cheeks are marked out with traced lines; the nose area is pushed out using rounded punches.

4. The piece is removed, cleaned and set back into the pitch, this time right side up. The hollows of the eyes and parts between the nose and chin are set back with forming punches from the front side. The nose is shaped and modeled; the lined contours are hammered out and refined.

5. The piece is again lifted free, cleaned and returned to the pitch where the eyelids and lips are worked in from the back side. If needed the nose is finished further.

6. To complete the piece the eyes and mouth are sawn out, the form is cut free from its flange and a back plate is attached.

Example 3

The two plates shown in figures 10.42 and 10.43 illustrate the kind of lively reliefs that can be made through the simple steps of lining, modeling and setting down. Note that the piece in figure 10.42 is shown from the back side, but still makes a stimulating visual effect.

Practice is needed to achieve these kinds of strongly plastic images. They also take time, even for a professional worker, which probably explains why repoussé is one of those traditional techniques relegated to the Endangered List. In addition to the fact that there is no better way of teaching the plastic limits of metal, and not even mentioning the delightful

Figure 10.41
Silver mask. (Gerhard Herbst, Weimar)

Figure 10.42
Richly decorated heraldry, done as a chasing exercise. (Johannes Kretzschmar, Dresden)

Figure 10.43
Rococo ornamental forms. (Johannes Kretzschmar, Dresden)

Figure 10.45
Traveling shaving kit. Chased silver. German work about 1870.
(Private collection)

Figure 10.44
Silver pendant,
free form chasing.
German work, 16th century.
(Craft Museum, Leipzig)

Figure 10.46
Chased silver stick handle (detail). Chinese work, 2nd half of the 19th
century. (Private collection)

effects that can be achieved, it is worth noting that time spent working in repoussé is particularly rewarding to the goldsmith. The process is a synthesis of design, sensibilities, technique and manual dexterity. There is nothing quite like seeing an image come to life out of a sheet of metal. It is a thrill every student is invited to share!

10.6
Fusing

10.6.1 DEFINITION

When precious metal is heated to temperatures approaching its melting point there is a short span during which the outer layer or skin begins to melt while the interior remains solid. Or, to say the same thing technically, the interior remains in the solidus zone while the surface regions enter the liquidus range. The effects are to create an uneven reticulated

Figure 10.54
Silver and gold brooch. Chased fields with soldering and granulation. (Gabriele Putz, Magdeburg)

Figure 10.55
Silver brooch, chased areas with textured and soldered designs.

surface and to allow pieces to join by welding. Every goldsmith discovers fusing, usually by accident and usually as a mistake, when pieces being soldered are overheated.

For years it was accepted in the field that fusing was the result of poor craftsmanship and had no place in the jewelry world. In the 1950's intentionally fused pieces were first shown, pieces that used the rich textures and spontaneous compositions that are part of the process. There was considerable resistance to this "technique" but it has now become adopted as yet another tool in the goldsmith's bag of tricks.

The results of fusing are to some degree dependent upon chance but with some experience the creative effects can be anticipated and controlled. It is easy to distinguish work in which fusing is used for legitimate design purposes from pseudoartistic "works" in which handwork and design inabilities are masked by fusing.

10.6.2 THE PROCEDURE

Because the process depends on localized heating it must be done with a torch, preferably one with a small hot flame. In the case of copper and brass an oxy-acetylene welding torch might be needed. The metal is placed on a clean soldering block, fluxed, and preheated overall. The flame is them played on the area to be joined or textured, typically with a gentle back and forth motion. The metal is brought through red to the flash point; the moment when the surface

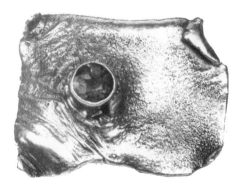

Figure 10.56
Silver cufflinks with fused surface. (Erhard Brepohl, Bad Doberan)

becomes fluid and shiny. At that moment the torch is abruptly taken away. This instant chilling causes the metal to contract and draw itself up into ridges.

If several pieces reach the liquidus point at the same moment, they flow together just as several beads of mercury rolling on a table will merge if they come into contact. When the flame is removed these pieces are joined permanently. Edges tend to draw up on themselves, thickening and making a soft shape. Because of this it is necessary to start with a piece of metal slightly larger than the desired result.

As with other dramatic textures, the effect is often enhanced by using it selectively alongside smooth polished sections or when ornamented with gemstones. It is useful to bear in mind that fused elements can be soldered like any other metal. Because of the inherently chancy aspect of the process, it is sometimes prudent to switch from fusing to soldering when a particularly appealing texture or shape has been created.

10.6.3 EXAMPLES

In the cuff link shown in figure 10.56 a simple rectangle of silver sheet has been cut out with shears and heated with the flame until the edges rolled in and the surface drew itself up into folds. As can be seen with the brooch in figure 10.57, the same texture forms on gold sheet when fusing. The pin in figure 10.58 shows the effect of fusing metal filings onto sheet. Naturally the filings must be completely clean and free from impurities. Depending on the application of the torch, the filings can be made to draw themselves up into tiny granules (heat from above) or to fuse in their irregular shapes (heat from below). The process can be facilitated by coating the sheet metal with a layer of solder before applying the filings, and while this is strictly speaking no longer fusing, the effect is closer to the spontaneous nature being discussed here than it is to traditional soldering. Figure 10.59 is another example of this technique, here used on a panel that is then soldered into a fabricated brooch.

Instead of filings other pieces of sheet and wire parts in any desired shapes can be fused on. A pre-

Figure 10.57
Gold brooch with fused surface. (Herman Junger, Poring)

Figure 10.58
Silver brooch with fused filings. (Student work, School for Applied Art Heiligendam)

Figure 10.59
Silver brooch with fused filings. (Student work, School for Applied Art Heiligendamm)

401

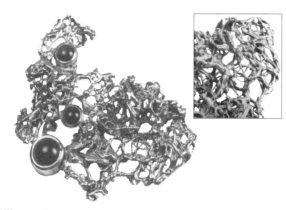

Figure 10.60
Silver brooch with fused wire elements.
a)overview, b)detail. (Rainer Schumann, Dresden).

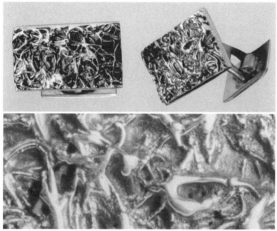

Figure 10.61
Silver cufflinks. Wire elements fused with one another and the base
plate. a) overview, b)close-up. (Rainer Schumann, Dresden).

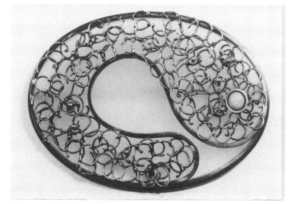

Figure 10.62
Brooch. Silver on piacrylic plate. Wire rings soldered and fused.
(Erhard Brepohl, Bad Doberan).

condition is always that a concrete plan of design is realized and one does not depend upon just any old accidental shapes.

Lovely effects can be produced when pieces of wire or bits of sheet are fused to themselves and to each other. To make the pin shown in figure 10.60, a mesh of wire was crumpled together and fused with a mini-torch; the richness that is achieved is clear in the close-up photograph.

A similar result can be seen in the cuff links in Figure 10.61, but in this case the underlying sheet plays a more active role. By comparing this last example with the first (figure 10.56) it is possible to see the depth and complexity of form possible with fusing when it is studied with the same intensity as any other process.

10.7
Etching

Etching uses chemical corrosion rather than mechanical force to selectively remove metal. Simply put, the idea is to cloak parts of an object with an acid-proof paint then submerge the piece in acid. The caustic liquid eats away at exposed areas to create a relief, figure 10.64. When the proper depth is reached the piece is withdrawn, rinsed and cleaned to reveal a pattern of raised and lowered sections.

The process can be used for delicate linear drawings (fine art prints), for bold reliefs (armor), for letters (plaques on buildings), and as a preliminary step for enameling, niello, or inlay.

The technique of etching has a long history, and can be glimpsed in the richly decorated beaker in figure 10.65. After a period in which etching was used primarily to mimic other techniques, principally engraving, in more recent times etching has been used as a vibrant graphic technique with its own specific look, as can be seen in the examples in figures 10.66 to 10.68.

The process itself if quite simple, though there are details of acid concentration and exposure time that will require some experimentation. Far more urgent is

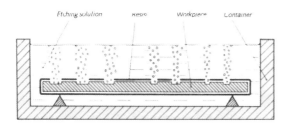

Figure 10.64
Prepared piece in the etching solution.

Figure 10.65
Silver goblet, etched ornamentation. About 1500. (Craft Museum, Leipzig).

the need for safety cautions. The following section discusses strong dangerous chemicals that must be used with care. Any handling of acids requires the use of protective clothing, goggles, and adequate ventilation. Metalsmiths unwilling or unable to meet those demands should not pursue etching.

10.7.1 PREPARING THE ARTICLES

Though each case is unique, etching is usually done in the late stages of construction, typically after all soldering has been completed. The metal is finished at least to a light sandpaper stage; because the etched surface will be matte, there is the potential for dramatic contrast if the pre-etched surface is polished to a high shine. Whatever the finish, the piece is pickled and washed to insure a grease-free surface. It is then handled only by the edges, or outfitted with a wire handle to make it easier to hold in the next steps.

All areas that are not to be attacked by acid must be completely covered with resist, by which we mean any substance that will protect it. This includes the back, all edges, and interior areas in some cases. Remember: the acid is not discriminating and will go everywhere it can!

Black asphaltum, a mixture of asphalt and turpentine, is the most common resist. It can be purchased from art supply and hobby shops. Other resists might include varnish, paint and wax, but these are not as easy to apply or remove, and cannot be guaranteed to stand up to all acids.

Applying the resist
Use a brush to paint the resist onto the metal in a layer that is thick enough to insure complete coverage but not so thick it will chip when a design is scratched

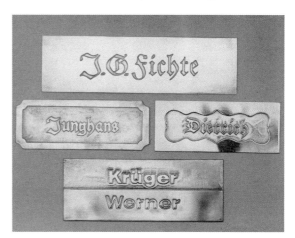

403

Figure 10.66
Door signs. Brass and copper; negative and positive etching. (H. Schoene, Seftenberg).

through it. The metal piece might be slightly warmed to assist in this, but too much heat will cause the asphaltum to drip off and slow down its rate of drying, which is already quit slow. It is also possible to mix asphaltum with beeswax to create a solid form called hard ground. This is formed into a lump that is rubbed over warm metal to build up the resist layer.

In some designs the etched portion is a relatively small part of the surface. In those cases the object is entirely covered with resist which is then scraped away to reveal bared metal in the places where an incised line is desired. Use a needle or similar small tool to scrape away the resist, taking care to lift off the curls of asphaltum so they don't accidentally fall back onto the piece where they might be cover up a scratched line.

In cases where large areas are to be exposed it is still possible to scrape away resist (use a knife or scraper) but often more efficient to paint the asphaltum selectively in the first place. It is still possible, after the resist has dried, to come back into the design with a needle to refine lines or add details.

Photographic resists

It is possible to use photographic rather than drawn images, a somewhat technical process that we will not pursue here. It is worth noting, however, that the technique is a straightforward extension of traditional etching, the only difference being the way in which resist is applied to selected areas of a sheet. Interested artists are encouraged to seek additional information through books or by visiting a local shop that does such work.

Mordants

The proper mordant, or etching fluid, must be used for each metal, see Table 10.2. In addition it is important that the acid be mixed to its proper concentration, which generally means that it is diluted with water. Ferric (III) chloride $FeCl_3$ is an exception to this in that a diluted solution etches more intensely than a concentrated one.

It is usually best to foster a slow etch. If the process goes too quickly the artist misses the chance to check depth frequently and make sensitive decisions. Also, a rapid bite tends to undercut or eat outward. In places where there is a thin line of asphaltum, the acid can cut it off from below, ruining the design. And finally, a concentrated acid solution might attack and lift a resist that is otherwise sufficient for the mordant being used. Follow the information in Table 10.2 carefully to avoid these problems.

10.7.2 THE ETCHING PROCESS

SAFETY NOTE: The acid is used in a container approved for this purpose, generally of thick glass or a special plastic. Because of the danger of accidents, use only approved vessels, which can be purchased through a chemical or scientific supply house. You might find it helpful to consult with the chemistry department of a local high school or college to locate a supplier. Work is done at room temperature in a well ventilated environment. It should go without saying that strong chemicals like acids should never be used in unguarded areas where children, pets or others might wander. Even then it is important to clearly mark the mordant as a dangerous substance!

The prepared piece is set into sufficient acid for it to be completely covered. The exposed areas will immediately appear matte, the effect of a layer of microscopic bubbles that forms on the surface. Most etchings will require several hours to achieve a reasonable depth, but the work must be checked periodically to be certain it doesn't go too fast.

It is possible to lift the work from the acid, rinse it and check it, but even a careful viewing in strong light is insufficient to really determine how deeply the acid has etched. To really tell you need to scrape away a bit of the resist so you can see the line itself, but this is of course a problem if the piece needs to go back into the acid – the scraped section will now be etched. To solve this, prepare a test plate of the same metal, scratch several lines into it and set it beside the piece in the acid. This can be checked periodically, always returning it to the bath so it reflects the same exposure as the work.

As etching continues, the metal forms a layer of bubbles that will limit the ability of fresh acid to

Figure 10.67
Student practice plates with etched textures, copper. Technical School of Applied Art, Helligendamm.

reach the surface of the metal. Brush the bubbles away every few minutes with a goose feather, the best tool for the job.

Etching copper in hydrochloric acid

A special case should be mentioned here, the use of hydrochloric acid on copper. Though the acid will work on copper by itself, the action is speeded up through the addition of hydrogen peroxide, through which oxygen is introduced to the chlorine atoms. This addition will stimulate the acid to etch more rapidly and to create straight-walled cavities. Unfortunately this advantage is unique to copper and hydrochloric acid. No similar situation exists for other metals or mordants.

The solution dissipates constantly – the oxygen goes off as vapors – so it must be remixed as needed. The process is made more dramatic if the solution is

Figure 10.68
Aluminum brooch. Etched texture. (Student work, School for Applied Art, Heiligendamm)

intermittently applied to the metal, that is, if the piece is dipped and lifted repeatedly. In the case of round objects like bracelets and rings it is possible to contrive a sort of rotisserie that holds the work above the acid so that just a small portion dips into the bath. In this situation a standard etch can be achieved in 2-4 hours (according to information from Dr. Walter Lachmann, Hamburg).

Finishing treatments

When the desired depth is reached, the work is removed from the acid and thoroughly rinsed under running water. It is important to guarantee that all trace of acid has been removed, a process that can be difficult in hollow or intricate pieces. After rinsing, the work is submerged in a solution of baking soda and water where it is agitated to insure that every surface is exposed to the neutralizing solution.

Before removing the resist it should be noted that a selective electroplating can be done at this stage. The gold or silver plating will only adhere to the recently etched, exposed areas.

Table 10.2
Etching solutions.

	Constituents in 1 liter of etching solution		
Material	Etching Acid	Concentration	Water Addition
Gold	concentrated niteic acid HNO_3 & concentrated hydrochloric acid HCl	167 ml 500 ml	333 ml
Silver	concentrated nitric acid HNO_3 & concentrated hydrochloric acid HCl	500 ml 500ml	—
Silver, Copper, Brass	concentrated nitric acid HNO_3	250 ml	750 ml
Copper	concentrated hydrochloric acid HCl & hydrogen peroxide (10%) H_2O_2	200 ml 140 ml	660 ml
Copper, Brass	ferric chloride $FeCl_3$	200 g	800 ml
Aluminum	Ferric cloride $FeCl_3$	200 g	800 ml
Iron, Steel	concentrated nitricacid HNO_3	150 ml	850 ml
Glass	concentrated hydrofluoric acid HF	1000 ml	—

The resist is then removed with turpentine or lacquer thinner, again observing the important rules of ventilation and fire safety. Remember to dispose of solvent-filled rags properly, and to store the acid in approved and well marked containers.

The object can be handled like any other in terms of soldering, patination and buffing, but care should be taken to minimize the use of mechanical buffing because it risks erasing the etch!

10.8
Working Titanium

Because titanium behaves somewhat differently than the standard metals in the goldsmith's workshop some special attention to its working is in order here. When sawing, begin the cut with a very light stroke, and increase the pressure only when the blade has securely caught. The sawblade can be protected with a lubricating grease, but even with this precaution it will dull quickly. Titanium can be worked with standard files, but a light pressure is recommended. The file has a tendency to clog, loading itself with particles of titanium that will "smear" the workpiece. Because of this, the file must be cleaned frequently. When drilling, use sharp bits and a lubricant. You will notice that even quality bits will dull after a few holes are made. If a drill bit is broken off in the metal, it can be etched out with nitric acid. When using a rotating bur, cool the action with oil and work at a slow rotational speed (RPM). Titanium responds well to diamond and ceramic abrasive points.

Titanium can be plastically deformed, but it must be annealed often because it becomes hard quickly. When rolling, considerable pressure is required. To draw wire, anneal it first; the lubricant sticks better to the oxide layer. Instead of the usual drawing wax, oil or soap are recommended as lubricants. The metal toughens quickly so you can expect to anneal after about three passes through the drawplate. It's possible to hot forge titanium at temperatures between 650–950°C (1200–1740°F), but the metal can also be worked cold. You will find that it is more amenable to stretching than compressing. Titanium cannot be sol-

dered with either soft or hard solders; welding can only be done under a protective gas.

SAFETY NOTE: There is a hazard of spontaneous combustion when titanium is heated at its surface, as might be the case in turning a sample on a lathe.

Because of the difficulty of welding, titanium is frequently joined with mechanical methods such as riveting or setting. Relatively low-cost spot welders (one brand is called Sparkie®) have made heat joins possible, particularly for attaching findings. It is generally impractical for the goldsmith to create a seam in the conventional sense. Titanium can be glued like any other metal if the connecting surface is large enough.

Titanium has established itself as a jewelry metal because of the beautiful colors that can be predictably achieved. When the metal is heated it shows the same colors associated with the tempering of steel, plus a few others. Unlike the fleeting effects on steel however, titanium colors are completely stable. When created by heat they are difficult to locate, but when the colors are achieved through the use of electricity, both the location and color can be precisely controlled.

The color phenomenon is caused by the development of an oxide layer in which a certain part of the light is absorbed and only the remainder is reflected to be perceived by a viewer. As the temperature increases, the oxide layer becomes thicker and absorbs more light. There is a clear series of these colors, beginning with a bright yellow, which is created by an oxide layer of sufficient thickness to cause constructive interference to give this appearance. As the oxide layer grows thicker, other colors are produced because the interference removes various parts of the white light striking the surface. The colors run through green, violet, bright blue to a dark blue. If heat is continued, a second yellow color will result as the interference causes the same effect as in the first yellow.

10.8.1 SURFACE PREPARATION
As mentioned, titanium is a tough, wear-resistant metal. To clean the surface in preparation for coloring, it is first sanded with various grits of abrasive paper. Standard abrasive compounds cannot be used for polishing on the machine. The best shine seems to

come with nickel oxide paste or with compounds intended for polishing steel. To prepare the surface for color treatment, lightly etch the surface to create a matte texture.

SAFETY NOTE: It is imperative to use great care when dealing with hydrofluoric acid. Because the skin will be attacked instantly upon exposure, rubber gloves and air-tight goggles are an absolute must.

Method 1
To prepare the surface, dip the object in a 2% hydrofluoric acid solution, then rinse it well in running water. A commercially available proprietary enamel or glass etching paste will also achieve the desired matte surface and, because of its consistency, it is safer. To prevent spotting while the piece is waiting to be colored, leave it submerged in a standard pickle such as Sparex®.

Method 2
Wearing rubber gloves, splashproof goggles and a rubber apron, and using an extremely well-ventilated workspace, combine the following ingredients:
   20% concentrated nitric acid
   20% hydrochloric acid
   20% lactic acid
   40% distilled water

Only a plastic container may be used, and care should be taken that the environment is not too warm because hydrofluoric acid evaporates at 16°C (60°F, room temperature).

Dip the object into the solution with plastic tweezers, then immediately dip it, without rinsing, into concentrated nitric acid. To avoid grease spots, from this point on the titanium is no longer touched with the fingers.

10.8.2 COLORING PROCESS

A welding torch is particularly well suited to achieving color effects on titanium because of its high temperature and focused flame. The torch can also be used to melt into the metal, throwing the surface up into relief, thickening the edges and generally developing organic textures like those associated with reticulation. The opportunity for contrasting smooth and textured areas offers immediate and intriguing design possibilities. Only generalized colors and effects can be created with a torch. Because titanium is a poor conductor of heat, colors crawl slowly and it is difficult to achieve a specific uniform color on a large surface.

Because of the exactly defined relationship between the applied current and the thickness of the oxide layer that is created, titanium coloring is most precise with a process called electrolytic anodizing. In this technique, household electrical current is passed through a rectifier to reduce its voltage. An anodizing unit with a voltmeter can then be used to control the specific amounts of electrical current that are relayed to the titanium. This current will create the growth of a layer of oxidation of a specific thickness, which in turn translates to the perception of a specific color.

SAFETY NOTE: Because a dangerously high current is used, all connections and contacts outside the bath must be well insulated. Always wear rubber gloves and, because hydrogen gas is evolved in the process, ensure sufficient ventilation.

The piece being colored is submerged in a bath to evenly conduct the electrical current. This bath is called the *electrolyte*, and may be made of a wide range of solutions. A 10% solution of sodium sulfide is used commercially, but solutions as disparate as a weak liver of sulfur solution, sodium carbonate, ammonium sulfate, cyanide salt baths and Sparex® (sodium bisulfate) have also been used.

The workpiece is held with stainless steel clamps and attached to stainless steel cathodes with an insulated copper wire. Use a current density of 5A/dm². As the current in the bath increases, thicker layers of oxide are formed. These in turn create the various color tones:

16V - yellow
22V - dark blue
27V - bright blue
58V - violet
70V - bluish-green

To create several colors on the same piece, the plate is first treated with the lowest voltage. The area on which this color is to be retained is then covered up (insulated) and the piece is taken to the next voltage. It is also possible to proceed in the reverse manner: first the highest voltage is used, then this region is covered up and all the remaining color everywhere else is removed by sandblasting. A lower voltage is applied to the metallic surface and a thinner oxide layer is formed, creating another color. To make specific areas metallically blank (white) use resists with sandblasting or cover the colored areas and etch selectively with hydrofluoric acid.

10.8.3 SPECIAL EFFECTS

The fact that colors are considerably more pronounced on an etched surface opens the possibility for a special effect. If the unprepared metal is covered with a resist and a pattern is scraped away then etched, the exposed metal will take the color in a vibrant hue, which will contrast with a duller color in the adjacent area. Again, use hydrofluoric acid to achieve this, and again, only when proper safety precautions have been followed meticulously. Another interesting effect is created by leaving the resist in place while the metal is electrolytically colored. In this way it is possible to decorate the colored surface with a gray design.

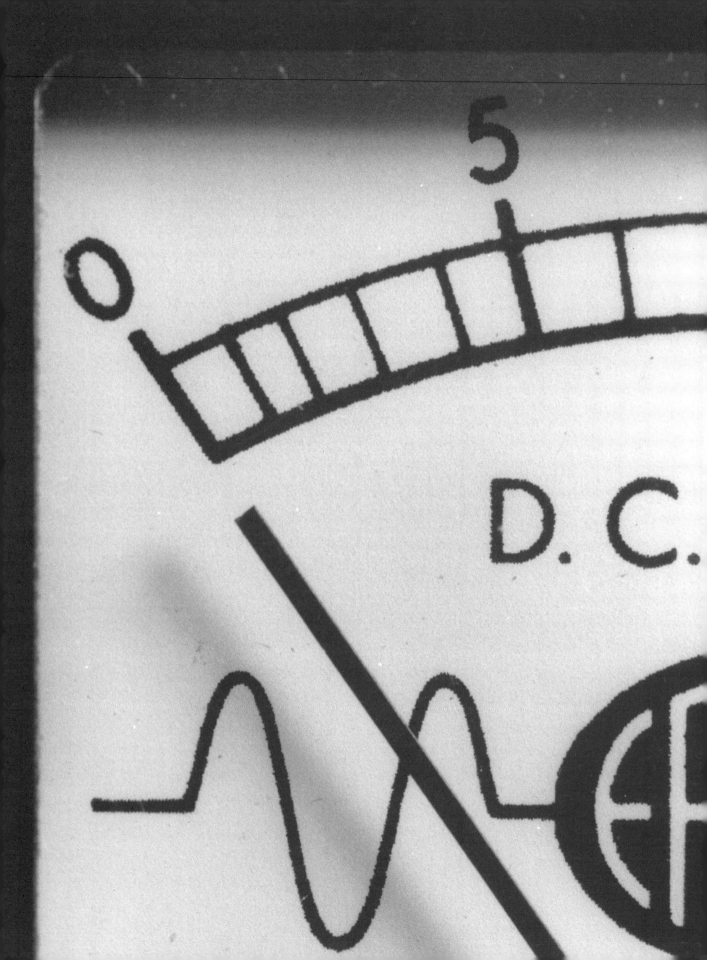

CHAPTER ELEVEN

Plating Technology

In the past few years, inexpensive and simple electroplating devices have become available, making it possible for even small shops to do their own plating. While this basic apparatus is useful, it is sometimes necessary for goldsmiths to work outside their range. For this reason, as well as the value of general knowledge when dealing with jobbers, it is useful to understand the principles of electrochemical processes and, if necessary, to be able to correct mistakes. It is for that reason that a theoretical description of galvanic processes is given here. This introduction can be augmented by consultations with professional platers as your questions become more complex.

11.1
Ionic Theory and Dissociation

Atomic structure

Each atom has a balance of positive and negative electrical forces. The number of positively charged particles (protons) determines the atomic number of the element, which in turn assigns its location in the periodic table. Because the atom is in balance, this number also represents the negatively charged particles (electrons) in orbit around the nucleus. These particles are located in individual orbits that accommodate only a definite number of electrons; the first can hold only two, the second holds 8 and so forth.

Molecular structure

Only a few gases have their outer ring filled with electrons. These are called inert gases and include helium, argon, neon, and others. Because their outer ring is filled, they generally do not combine with other elements, hence their common designation as "inert." Most other elements have fewer electrons in their outer rings than the orbits can contain – they have an "opening" that they can fill by combining with other elements.

Metals and hydrogen groups will release as many electrons as are expressed by their valences. Non-metals, oxygen and acid radicals can accept electrons in their incompletely filled outer orbits according to their valences. An atom in which the electrical charge is no longer in equilibrium is characterized as an ion.

When atoms unite into molecules, chemical bonds occur that alter the charge inside every atom. When electrons are given up, the positive charge in the nucleus predominates because the number of protons does not change. For those atoms in which electrons are gained, the negative charge increases. Throughout the entire molecule, the sum of the charges is equalized.

When an electron (which has a negative charge) is given up, the remaining atom is called an ion and because it is out of equilibrium in favor of the positive, it is written with a $^+$ sign, such as H^+, Na^+, Ca^{2+}, Al^{3+} and so on. When an atom takes on an extra electron it loses equilibrium in favor of the neg-

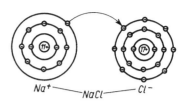

Figure 11.1
Ionic bond using the example of a sodium chloride NaCl.

ative: negative ions are written with a $^-$ sign: Cl^-, OH^-, SO_4^{2-} and so on.

Example

When sodium and chlorine are brought together, the sodium releases an electron and becomes Na^+. This electron occupies a vacancy in the outer orbit of the chlorine, creating a Cl^- ion. In this way both ions have completely occupied outer orbits, as shown in picture 11.1. Through the attraction of the electron charges, the Na^+ and Cl^- ions are united into a common ionic bond.

Dissociation

In aqueous solutions, molecules of acids, salts and bases break down into their constituent ions in such a way that the molecular particles separate from one another without releasing the exchanged electrons. This phenomenon, called dissociation, results in a solution that has electrical conducting properties. It is called an electrolytic solution.

Some dissociated ions are more likely to bind again into their molecular state than others, a phenomenon expressed as the degree of dissociation. The higher the dissociation, the larger the proportion of highly mobile, or free ions. Strong acids and bases reach almost a 100% dissociation, while complex salts attain only a small percentage of freely mobile ions.

Example

Copper sulfate dissociates in aqueous solution. In a 0.1 N solution of this salt, the degree of dissociation is 39%. The dissociation increases with dilution to the point that extreme dilution could result in a solution with only freely mobile ions present. As the solution is heated, the degree of dissociation decreases.

Figure 11.2
Electromotive Force Series

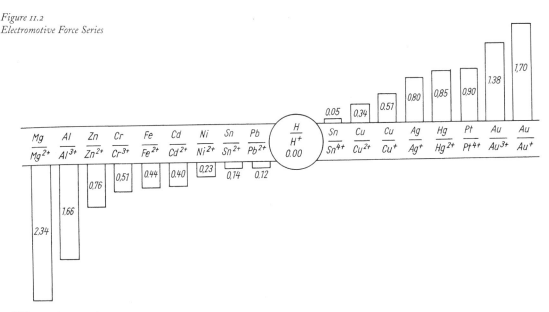

When electrical current is applied to electrolytic solutions, the negative ions (called anions) migrate to the positive pole (called the anode) The positive ions (cations) react at the negative pole, which is called the cathode.

11.2
Metal Deposition Without External Current

Electrons, which are necessary for the reduction of metal ions, are produced through electrochemical reactions in the solution. The following differentiation is made.

Immersion method:	The osmotic pressure is greater than the pressure of the solution.
Contact method:	The base metal is directly touching a contact metal.
Reduction method:	The deposition of the plating metal occurs through an added means of reduction.

11.2.1 OSMOTIC THEORY

When metal is put into an electrolyte it has a tendency to release atoms as ions into the solution in a phenomenon called solution pressure. The metal ions of the electrolyte, on the other hand, want to deposit themselves onto the surface of the immersed metal (osmotic pressure). Whether the solution pressure or the osmotic pressure predominates depends on the particular characteristics of the respective metal.

The metals of interest to metalsmiths can be categorized according to their voltage differences, electromotive series (figure 11.2). The voltage difference of the atom-ion is measured against a hydrogen anode which is set at 0.00 V. The given values are related to the metal, not the ion; the conditions are a 1 N solution of the respective salt at room temperature. If the concentration or temperature is changed, the given values will change accordingly. If a metal is immersed in another solution, for example a cyanide electrolyte, a completely new set of values are obtained and even the sequence of the voltages may change − for example in a cyanide electrolyte, silver can appear to be more noble (i.e. less reactive) than gold.

The metals to the right of hydrogen in figure 11.2 exhibit osmotic pressure greater than solution pressure. This means the natural tendency is for ions to be drawn out of the electrolyte to be deposited onto an immersed metal. These are the electrochemical noble metals.

Example
A copper rod is immersed in a copper sulfate solution. At the outer surface of the metal, a positive tension difference of +0.345 V arises; this means that the osmotic pressure of the ions of the solution is greater than the solution pressure of the immersed metal. An excess of electrons in the solution gives it a negative charge (figure 11.3).

Copper ions react with the immersed metal by attracting the electrons. When these attach to the ions (which were "missing" an electron) they are converted from ions to "complete" copper atoms.

The copper rod becomes positively charged. The number of positively charged ions is reduced in the bath solution, the osmotic pressure becomes weaker and the solution becomes negatively charged. The process is terminated when the equilibrium between the osmotic pressure and the solution pressure is reestablished.

All the non-precious metals seen to the left of hydrogen in figure 11.2 react exactly to the situation just described. That is, the solution pressure is greater than the osmotic pressure, so the direction of flow is from the immersed metal into the solution, a process that is evident in the technique called electrostripping.

An example is presented in figure 11.3b, in which a zinc rod is immersed in a zinc sulfate solution. The potential difference shifts to the negative, specifically to -0.76 volts. The dissolution pressure of zinc is greater than the osmotic pressure of zinc-ions in the solution. The immersed rod has a deficit of electrons so zinc atoms are given into the solution as ions.

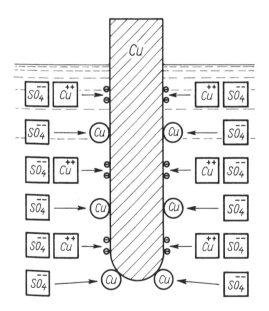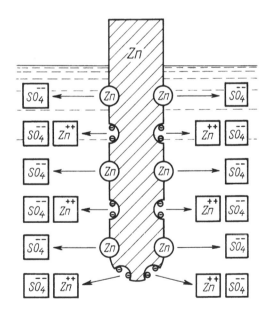

Figure 11.3
Osmotic pressure and anodic dissolution pressure.
a) osmotic pressure > dissolution pressure (copper rod immersed in copper sulfate solution),
b) dissolution pressure > osmotic pressure (zinc rod immersed in zinc sulfate solution).

This causes the rod to become negatively charged. Simultaneously the number of positively charged ions in the electrolyte increases and it thus becomes positively charged. This process of exchange will end when an equilibrium condition has been reached on the outer layer of the metal in solution. Because the zinc ions are rapidly carried into solution, the process often continues until the metal is completely dissolved.

11.2.2 IMMERSION (CEMENTATION) TECHNIQUE

In this process a non-precious metal is immersed in the salt solution of a precious metal. The farther the metals are from one another in the electromotive series, the stronger the reaction. The non-precious metal component goes into solution and displaces the precious metal out of its alloy. An example is given in figure 11.4 in which an iron rod is immersed in a copper sulfate solution where it becomes coated with copper. Iron has a higher dissolution pressure and it sends ions into the solution as shown. Because this kind of plating is spongy, it doesn't adhere well to the surface.

Cementation in silver plating electrolyte

When an object that is to be galvanically silver plated is put in the electrolyte there is a danger that a silver coating may occur even before the current has been turned on. This is a version of cementation in that the higher dissolution pressure of the non-precious metals go into solution as ions while simultaneously the silver ions from the electrolyte are deposited onto the base object due to their high osmotic pressure. This type of passive silver plating is porous (spongy) and cannot be improved through later treatment plating. Deposition of silver through cementation, therefore, must be prevented.

Mercury plating

In order to reduce the difference or potential between base metal and precious metal, the object is coated (quicked) with mercury before electroplating. This is carried over from the ancient process of fire gilding, where the same preliminary process was used for the

same reason – to allow the next layer to adhere well. Modern high efficiency baths make these preparations no longer necessary, but a short description of the procedure is included here for historical consideration.

The acidic mercury solution can be made by dissolving mercury in nitric acid to a saturation that results in mercury (II) nitrate $Hg(NO_3)_2 \cdot H_2O$. Obviously this would not be undertaken without proper ventilation and safety equipment! This is combined with water to make a solution of approximately 5–10g/liter. Copper, brass and nickel silver objects are briefly immersed in this bath, where they will pick up a shiny mercury coating.

11.2.3 BOILING METHOD FOR GOLD AND SILVER

Before electrical current was as readily available as it is today, goldsmiths needed to find a way to plate without current, at least sufficient well to recoat works that had been repaired. Though little used today (at least in industrialized nations) the method is included here in the interest of providing a full understanding to all workers in the field.

The technique is based on the principle described above; that atoms of non-precious metals release ions into the bath solution that displace precious metal ions from the solution and deposits them onto the object as a plating. As mentioned, this process is necessarily short-lived, winding down naturally as the solution reaches electrical equilibrium. When the potential difference no longer exists the ion exchange ends, leaving a very thin precious metal coating behind.

Cyanide solutions were traditionally used for this, heated to 80–90°C to stimulate the ionic movement. Objects to be plated were hung on a wire for a few seconds in the bath solution until a uniform coating was created.

415

11.3
Electrochemical Galvanic Techniques

11.3.1 THEORETICAL BASIS

Ohms Law: Current = $\dfrac{\text{voltage}}{\text{resistance}}$

$$A = \frac{V}{\Omega}$$

By rearranging the equation we get:

voltage = current $\cdot$ resistance
or: $V = A \cdot \Omega$

When determining the ideal voltage for a plating bath, the polarization voltage of the electrodes and the resistance in the bath must be considered. That is to say, the difference in voltage that exists between the metal electrode and the bath ions without outside current being applied and which needs to be overcome by an applied current:

$$V_{K} = \Delta V_{\Omega} + \Delta V_{pA} + \Delta V_{pK}$$

V_{K} - terminal voltage
ΔV_{Ω} - voltage according to Ohm's Law
ΔV_{pA} - polarization voltage at anode
ΔV_{pK} - polarization voltage at cathode

Current density
In electroplating the current density must be considered as a function of the size of the electrode surface in order to insure comparable current density. Density of current is measured in A/dm², (area divided by decimeters squared; 1 dm² = 100 cm²). For every bath a definite cathode and anode current density is prescribed. If the current density cannot be regulated through the controls of the plating apparatus, then the size of the surface of the object needs to be adjusted in line with the constant intensity of the current of the setup.

$$i = \frac{I}{A}$$

i - current density in A/dm²
I - current strength in A
A_{K} - surface of the object in dm²
A_{A} - anode surface area in dm²

Of particular importance is the cathode current density, which is related to the A_{K} at the surface area of the object.

Example 1
At the silver plating electrode i = 2 A/dm². The apparatus yields I = 1.5 A. How large can the surface area of the object be?

$$A = \frac{I}{i_{K}} = \frac{1.5\ A}{2\ A/dm^2} = 0.75\ dm^2$$

Example 2
At the strong silver plating electrode i_{K} = 0.3 A/dm². The set-up yields a constant I = 1.5 A. How large can the surface area of the object be?

$$\frac{1.5\ A}{0.3\ A/dm^2} = 5\ dm^2$$

Current yield
This is an expression of the degree of efficiency of the electrodes. The current yield is calculated from the ratio of the actual to the theoretically calculated amount of deposited material. The difference is the result of the loss through gases and through secondary reactions in the electrodes.

With a soluble anode the current yield at the anode and cathode must be approximately of the same magnitude. This limits the fluctuation of the metal content in the electrolyte. The yield of the cathode current amounts to 100% if the deposited amount of metal corresponds to the electrochemical deposition equivalent. Only a few metals achieve practical results near to the ideal, silver being among the best at 99%.

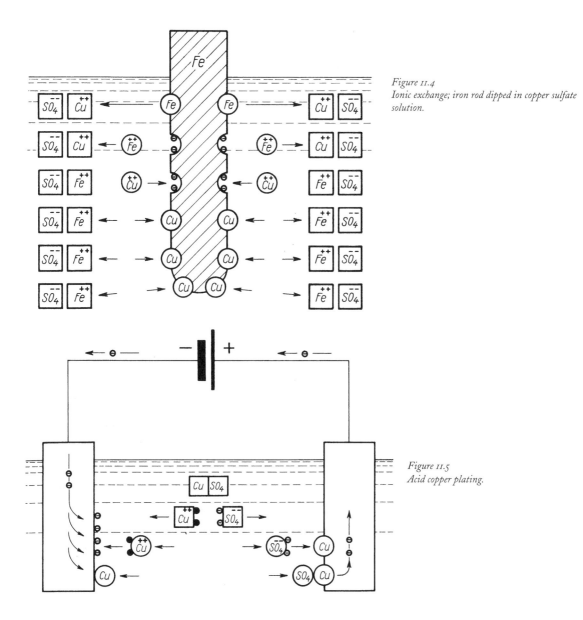

Figure 11.4
Ionic exchange; iron rod dipped in copper sulfate solution.

Figure 11.5
Acid copper plating.

The anode current yield is 100% if the number of metal particles that go into solution are the same as can be calculated by Faraday's Law. If the anode current yield is smaller than that of the cathode, the metal particles in the electrolyte are depleted.

$$\eta = \frac{A e_{pr}}{A e_{theo}} \cdot 100\%$$

η = current yield (electrolytic efficiency) in %

$A e_{pr}$ = the practical (actual) electrochemical precipitation equivalent

$A e_{theo}$ = theoretical electrochemical precipitation equivalent

11.3.2 GALVANIC METAL DEPOSITION
Acid copper plating

Copper sulfate	$CuSO_4 \cdot 5\,H_2O$	220 g
Sulfuric acid	H_2SO_4	30 g
Water	H_2O	1 liter

Two electrodes (for example two copper sheets, figure 11.6) are hung in the electrolyte solution and connected to an electric current, one as a positive and the other as the negative pole. The most important constituent of the electrolyte is the copper sulfate which dissociates in water.

$$CuSO_4 \rightarrow Cu^{2+} + SO_4^{2-}$$

The role of the sulfuric acid in the electrolyte is to prevent the formation of copper oxide (Cu_2O) at the cathode. It will also increase the conductivity of the solution and encourage a fine grained deposit by reducing the degree of dissociation of the $CuSO_4$.

When current is applied to the copper sheets, the cathode (electrically negative) triggers an increase in the osmotic pressure in the solution immediately around it as an excess of electrons are generated at the surface of the cathode. These "extra" electrons may

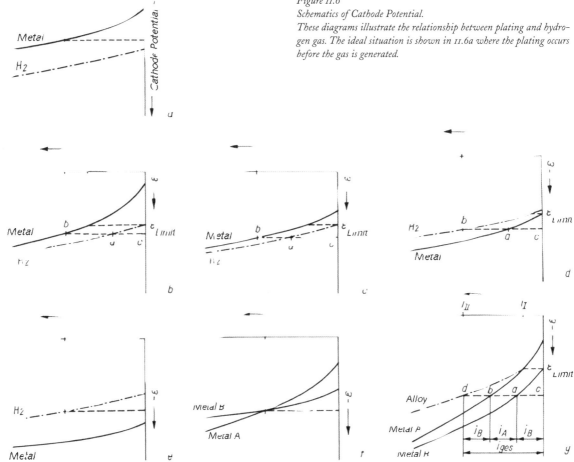

Figure 11.6
Schematics of Cathode Potential.
These diagrams illustrate the relationship between plating and hydrogen gas. The ideal situation is shown in 11.6a where the plating occurs before the gas is generated.

join with Cu^{2+} atoms to become neutralized copper atoms.

The positive electrical current at the other copper sheet (the anode) causes the osmotic pressure to fall to the point where the solution pressure of the electrolyte becomes strong enough to pull metal from the sheet into solution. At this point the negative sulfate ion SO_4^{2-} gives up both its excess electrons to the anode.

$$SO_4^{2-} \rightarrow SO_4\text{-radical} + 2e^-$$

The neutral state in the electrolyte is achieved again though the charge neutralization of both electrolyte ions Cu^{2+} and SO_4^{2-}. The neutral SO_4-radical is not capable of existing independently and immediately takes a copper atom from the anode to complete itself. The initial conditions are created again by dissociation.

$$CuSO_4 \rightarrow Cu^{2+} + SO_4^{2-}$$

The metal content of the electrolyte should theoretically remain unchanged.

The cathodic potential current density curves
A precondition for the continual process of deposition is continual ion availability at the surface of the work. If the cathodic current density is increased (in a given unit of time) then an ever greater quantity of metal is deposited on the work, and the concentration of metal ions of the electrolyte is reduced at the surface of the work. This pushes the potential toward the negative, or less noble values, also described as the difference in current between the metal and the electrolyte.

The difference in potential that results between the potential at rest and the potential created by the external current is called concentration polarization. With cyanide electrolytes there is also a chemical polarization caused by the destruction of the complex metallic-cyanide ions and this causes a chemical polarization.

It should be stressed that the equivalence values that are grouped in the electromotive series are greatly influenced by applied external current. This becomes so strongly negative at the cathode that the precious silver in the cyanide electrolyte takes on a non-precious, negative potential termed less noble.

The relationship between the shift of the cathode potential into the non-precious region and the current density of the applied current is shown in the accompanying diagram (figure 11.6). This is particularly important for electroplating procedures.

Hydrogen has a great influence on the course of the electrolytic process. In addition to the metal ions, every aqueous electrolyte contains hydrogen ions that are released at the cathode where they can be seen as bubbles of hydrogen gas. The dissociation potential of the hydrogen is shifted to negative values under the influence of the external current. This allows for the following possibilities:

a) The potential of the metal is significantly higher than hydrogen. The potential curve is shifted to less noble (base) values when the external current is applied, but the potential of the hydrogen is also shifted so the metal ions can be deposited as atoms (figure 11.6a). If the current density reaches a certain boundary limit value this causes concentration polarization at the cathode because the supply of metal ions at the boundary zone between the work and the electrolyte is no longer sufficient. Because of this the cathode potential at this boundary current density becomes increasingly negative until the deposition potential of the hydrogen is reached (figure 11.6b).

If the current density is increased over this boundary value, hydrogen is set free at the cathode. Because of the excess amount of current (ac), only the portion (ab) is available for metal deposition.

Because the transformation of the hydrogen ions occurs directly at the cathode surface it can damage the metal layers deposited. The deposit can become spongy, brittle and even crack off completely. To prevent this the electrolyte should be used only in the region below the boundary current density.

b) The potential of the metal is near to the hydrogen potential. This is the most common case in electroplating practice. It is unavoidable that a portion of the current is used for the simultaneous electrolysis (figure 11.6c). If the metal has the more noble potential, hydrogen is set free during the metal deposition even at low current densities. This reduces the current yield (electrolytic efficiency). Only the (ab) portion of the current density is used for metal deposition, while (ac) is used for the hydrogen evolution. Electrolytes are designed so that no damage occurs to the metal deposit because of the evolution of hydrogen.

This situation can be seen in chromium, nickel, zinc, cadmium, and rhodium electrolytes. If the potential of the hydrogen is more noble, metal deposition occurs first at higher current densities because the portion (ab) is used for the hydrogen and the (ac) portion for the metal (figure 11.6d).

c) The metal potential is significantly lower than with hydrogen. In this case only the electrochemically more noble hydrogen is evolved and even with an increase of current density the deposition potential of the less noble metal cannot be reached (figure 11.6e).

Alloy deposition
It is possible to deposit alloys (as opposed to pure metals) under carefully controlled circumstances. A precondition for the simultaneous deposition of several metals, (i.e. an alloy deposit) is the position of the current density potential curves. The ideal case is if both curves intersect so that the proportions of the mixture can be determined by regulation of the current density (figure 11.6f).

Often the potential curves are further apart. In these cases it is possible to bring the more noble metal closer to the less noble one by reducing the ion concentration (figure 11.6g). If the current density remains in the region between o and i , only the more noble metal A will be deposited. With a further increase of the current density, ions of the B metal are also layered on the cathode and thus make possible alloy deposition. When the current strength is iII both metals are deposited in equal amounts. The alloy curves are constructed because (ac)=(bd)-¹B.

The tricky part of plating alloys is not so much in creating the correct balance but in sustaining it over a period of time. The reaction requires the use of a nonsoluble anode, which means that the metal ion concentration of the electrolyte is steadily decreased during the working time because there is no replenishment coming from the anode.

The quality of the deposit can also be influenced by:
  – further addition agents in the electrolyte, such as conductive salts and brighteners
  – deposition conditions such as temperature and movement in the electrolyte
  – the pH values

Alloy deposition is therefore only possible with specialized modern equipment that can be automatically monitored and regulated.

Structure of electrolytic deposits
If viewed under extreme magnification it will become clear that cathodically deposited metal has a crystalline structure. As was described in the context of melting metal for ingots or casting, crystal formation and grain growth are subject to specific laws and in turn contribute to the nature of the final result. In the case of electrodeposition, other factors that come into play include the nature of the electrolyte and the deposition conditions, in particular the temperature and the agitation of the bath.

The intended objective of plating is to create a well-adhered deposit of sufficient thickness that is smooth and shiny and forms in the shortest possible time. While easy to theorize, in practice all these conditions cannot be achieved simultaneously. It is possible, for instance, to achieve a shiny surface quickly, but the resulting coating will be thin. To create a smooth surface that is relatively thick requires a longer deposition process.

Adhesion is strongest when the deposit continues the crystal structure of the metal being plated. By adding like to like, the two structures make the optimum bond. Unfortunately, this is only rarely possible. Normally the crystal structure of the base metal at the surface is so deformed that the grains of the deposit cannot attach themselves to it and they form their own lattice structure. A microscopic cross section of the interface between the base and the plated layer will show a clear separation between the layers. The adhesion in these cases comes only from the cohesive forces of the atoms.

A high current density is required at the start to obtain good adhesion. The speed of a fast plating insures good adhesion but generally faster plating creates rough surfaces. To create a smooth layer the process must be slowed down as soon as the first layer of atoms has been deposited. As was seen in the hardening of melts in casting, a fine grained deposit results if the most possible seed crystals form the most grains possible. Such a deposit has a dense, pore-free structure and a smooth surface.

It is one of the special advantages of cyanide electrolytes that because of the chemical polarization during the transformation of the complex ion such a retardation occurs. This allows for the rate of deposition to be reduced intentionally in order to create a fine-grained deposit.

Inhibitors have an important influences upon the quality of the deposit. These are materials that are added to the electrolyte so that they can be incorporated into the structure of the deposit during the plating. These can be organic substances and colloids that limit grain growth and foster fine grain formation, which is especially important for plating bright deposits. It is particularly useful if polarization phenomena are working together with the inhibitors. With an increase of the electrolyte temperature, the mobility of the ions increases, the concentrations polarization is reduced, and the deposition of the inhibitors is reduced so that large grain growth ensues.

Agitating the electrolyte reduces the degree of concentration polarization and increases the delivery of ions. Agitation also brings the inhibitors to the article in greater proportions; this allows the formation of a fine grained deposit even at faster deposition rates, improving the efficiency of the plating process.

The fine grained deposit that results from polarization forms a matte finish that must be smoothed out by scratch brushing after plating. The use of inhibitors (which are also called "brighteners") form the brightest, shiniest deposits.

The effectiveness of brighteners requires that the grains are oriented so certain crystal faces in most of them lie parallel to the surface. It is also important that the grains be only so large that their diameter is smaller than the smallest wavelength of light; that is, smaller than 0.36 microns. This orientation of the grains is a result of the influence of the electric lines of force upon the crystal (grain) growth.

Thickness of the deposit
According to Faraday's well known law, the quantity of metal that is deposited electrolytically can be determined from the deposition conditions:

$$m = c \cdot I \cdot t \cdot \eta$$

m - mass of the deposited material in mg
c - the constant of the electrochemical equivalent in mg/A $\cdot$ s
I - current strength in A
t - working time
η - efficiency

Depending upon the actual density it is possible to determine the thickness of the deposited layer from the amount deposited and the surface of the article being plated.

$$h = \frac{m}{A \cdot \rho}$$

h = the layer thickness in cm
m = the weight in g
A = the surface of the work in cm²
ρ = the layer density in g/cm³

Readers are advised to consult specialized literature for further information about the applications of Faraday's Law and the calculations that can be derived from it.

Table 11.1
Silver content of familiar tableware.

Quantity	Type	Silver Alloy		Silverplate
		Weight of Ag 800, in g	Proportion of Ag	Plating material, in g
12	Tablespoons	800	640	45
12	Forks	800	640	45
12	Knives	280	224	30
12	Dessert spoons	520	416	30
12	Dessert forks	520	416	30
12	Dessert knives	165	132	21
12	Teaspoons	230	184	18
12	Cake forks	160	128	16
1 pair	Salad servers	100	80	6
1	Punch ladle	240	192	12
1	Gravy ladle	75	60	4
1	Serving spoon	110	88	6
1	Serving fork	25	20	4

The layer thickness is a significant indicator of the quality and wearability of a plated deposition; the thicker the layer, the longer it will last. In accord with the legal system of measuring the layer thickness is today measured and given in microns:

1 micron (μ) = $\frac{1}{1000}$ mm

Though not technically a result of plating, this is perhaps the appropriate place to describe the nomenclature of other clad metals. The quality of a gold-filled material is not described by measured thickness but in terms of the relationship of the weight of the gold layer to the entire weight of the object. This is expressed in "millième" (French: thousandth parts). For instance, German doublè holds 20 millième, or 20 parts per thousand gold.

In the case of silver plated flatware, the normal values are determined by the quality of the applied layer.

Before it was possible to measure the thickness of the applied layer, it was described in terms of the method by which it was deposited. As an example to illustrate the method, we will determine how much silver has been deposited upon 12 spoons and 12 forks (table 11.1)

According to this system the "90" that is stamped on the work indicates that 90 grams of silver have been deposited upon the 24 pieces described. In the case of objects that were traditionally sold in sets of (such as desert forks, dessert spoons etc.) the stamp refers to the amount of silver upon the 12 pieces of flatware. As if this isn't confusing enough, in the case of single pieces such as a ladle, a stamp of "90" means that the silver layer on this piece of flatware is exactly as thick as on the rest of the set, in this example $\frac{1}{24}$ of 90 grams. Often there was a further stamp given that showed how many grams were actually applied to the individual piece.

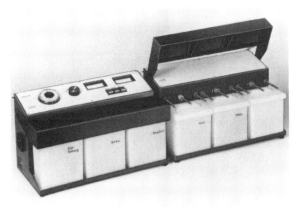

Figure 11.7
Small galvanic equipment. Compact casing with direct current gauge and 3 containers for liquid.

Figure 11.8
Small galvanic plating equipment. Compact housing with direct current gauge and 3 containers.

Figure 11.9
Galvanic table for industrial plating.

11.3.3 ELECTROPLATING EQUIPMENT

A significant development for small workshops has occurred in the last few years in exactly this part of the field. Plating units have become more compact, more dependable and less expensive in recent years. This makes it increasingly popular for small studios to handle their own plating needs rather than to rely on specialty plating jobbers. The small electroplating set up (figure 11.7) is seen frequently in even small goldsmithing studios.

The two most important components for electroplating are the transformer and rectifier. The former draws normal alternating current from a wall outlet and transforms it to low tension direct current. The rectifier controls the amperage and voltage of the current, generally regulating it from 0 to 10V/10 A.

The three tanks are made of polyethylene and each contain 1.5 liters. Over each of the tanks are two stainless steel busbars to which the anodes are connected. Between these is another busbar that is

423

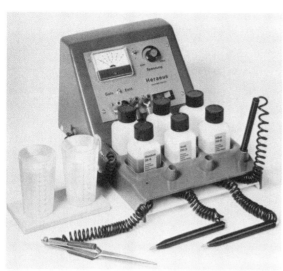

Figure 11.10
Example of a miniature plating machine.

hooked up to the cathode. This particular set up has a bath agitator in two of the baths and a thermostatically controlled immersion heater to warm the electrolyte. While this basic set up is adequate, it might be found useful to add other additional tanks. It is also helpful to have degreasing baths and other electrolytes readily available and next to each other.

The somewhat larger electroplating equipment (figure 11.8) has three electrolyte tanks which each contain 8 liters and three 4 liter rinse tanks. This is big enough to deal with mass production jewelry or even hollowware. As long as the rectifier delivers up to 10V/20A even large surfaces can be plated. The larger set up shown here allows for bath agitation and heating and also provides vents to remove potentially harmful fumes.

Modular electroplating tables (figure 11.9) can be combined to create a versatile installation that can be tailored to the requirements of a workshop. Tanks of various sizes are set into the table, while anodes and busbars, wiring, motors, ventilation equipment, heating and so on are installed under the table surface to keep them safely away and simultaneously provide more work space. The switches, meters, regulators and so on are housed in the instrument panel behind the table.

The pen plating unit (figure 11.10) offers a useful addition to electroplating equipment because very small surface areas can be plated with it. This allows individual components or even specific ornament shapes to be plated with various metals, a process that would normally require time consuming resist procedures. The disadvantage of pen plating is that the layer is quite thin and not recommended for areas of high wear.

The article being plated is connected to the cathode wire with alligator clips and a felt nib soaked with the electrolyte serves as the anode. The pen is rubbed across the surface for several seconds (or longer) to develop the desired plating.

11.3.4 ELECTROLYTIC SILVER PLATING

The purpose of plating a bright silver layer is to yield a uniform, attractive coating of a precious metal. When plating over base metals (which is usually the case) the plated layer hides solder, improves tarnish resistance, and yields a more precious looking object.

Until recently the only means of plating silver involved the use of a cyanide-base electrolyte. That method was used for over 100 years, a testament to its popularity, but it had drawbacks. The deposit was always matte and therefore had to be satin finished or polished in a separate finishing step. Because of the low current density, it took a long time to obtain a usably thick layer. The process is confined to the deposition of fine silver (which is fairly soft) and therefore plated work had limited resistance to wear.

Traditional high performance baths can only be run in specialized electroplating work stations in factories because the deposition conditions have to be held within very narrow parameters.

In the last decade the plating industry has developed a new generation of technology called hard and bright baths that are significantly easier to operate. As mentioned above, it is now practical for midsize and even small shops to apply their own highly reflective, hard silver platings. The important characteristic data for the old and new silver baths are given in table 11.2. Though the improvement in the new baths are major, both old and new style baths contain the same basic

Bath Constituency	First Silver Plating (strike solution)	Silver Plating (second immersion)	Silver Plating, Bright White
potassium silver cyanide K[Ag(CN)$_2$] (54% Ag)	8 g/l	50 g/l	67
free potassium cyanide KCN	80...100 g/l	25 g/l (parts) 35...70 g/l (mass parts)	140
potassium carbonate K$_2$CO$_3$	—	20 g/l	—
Deposition Conditions			
anode	stainless steel	fine silver	fine silver
bath temperature	18...20°C	18...20°C	15...25°C
cathode current density	0.5...2 A/dm²	0.1...0.5 A/dm²	max 2 A/dm²
bath voltage 15cm anode distance	4...6 V	0.7...1 V	0.4...0.8 V
amount of deposit	—	14 mg/(m · n)	65 mg/(A · min)
density of deposit	—	0.15 µm/min	0.5 µm/min
Estimated Values			
silver in electrolyte	3...4 g/l	15...30 g/l	34...38 g/l
free potassium cyanide	6...10 g/l	20...30 g/l	130...150 g/l
potassium carbonate	—	20..100 g	—

Table 11.2
Silver plating electrolyte.

ingredients. In order to better understand the electrolytic process, the function of these main constituents will be discussed in more detail.

Function of potassium cyanide
The decisive component of the electrolyte is the complex salt potassium silver cyanide $K[Ag(CN)_2]$ which dissociates in water to form:

$$K[Ag(CN)_2]^- \rightarrow K^+ + [Ag(CN)_2]^-$$

To draw the picture of the electrolytic process as simply as possible, secondary reactions such as the temporary formation of KOH have been omitted from these descriptions. At the cathode, the positive potassium ion, K^+, is neutralized to form an atom.

$$K^+ + e^- \rightarrow K \text{ atom}$$

At the anode the positive silver ion, Ag+, and both the CN^- ions are set free from the complex ion.

$$Ag(CN)_2 \rightarrow Ag^+ + 2 CN^-$$

Back at the cathode, the positive silver ion reacts with the metal of the cathode, takes an electron from it, is thereby completed to become a silver atom that is deposited onto the work.

$$Ag^+ + e^- \rightarrow Ag \text{ atom}$$

At the anode the CN^- ion gives up a free electron to the anode and thereby becomes a CN radical.

$$2 CN^- - 2 e^- \rightarrow 2 CN \text{ radical}$$

One cyanide radical bonds to the potassium atom formed at the cathode ($CN + K \rightarrow KCN$), while the other dissolves a silver atom out of the metal of the anode, $CN + Ag \rightarrow AgCN$. This forms a complex salt from both the cyanides:

$$KCN + AgCN \rightarrow K[Ag(CN)_2]$$

The initial state occurs again through dissociation and the whole process repeats itself.

It would appear that the silver is transported from the anode to the article by the electric current, without changing the composition of the bath. For many years people explained the electrolytic process in the same way. In fact what happens is that an atom of silver is dissolved out of the metal of the anode and simultaneously a silver ion is deposited out of the bath onto the article. The electrolyte regenerates itself almost completely by being replenished by the metal of the anode. This means the bath can be used for a long time without having to add silver salts. Note that the equilibrium can be thrown off if the current density is too high; in this instance the anode is passivated and the electrolyte can no longer regenerate itself.

The speed of the reaction can be altered by changing the potential of the cathode. This slows the release of silver from the complex ion, which in turn retards the secondary reactions of the potassium (K^+) ions at the cathode. This slows down silver deposition enough that the deposit develops the desired dense, fine-grained structure.

Hard and bright silver plating
Refiners deliver the electrolyte either as prepared solutions packed up in plastic canisters or as salts that must be dissolved in distilled water according to the accompanying instructions. Because of the sensitivity of the chemistry involved, never use tap water. Unknown trace elements can severely affect the plating solution!

Normally the salts are stirred into the predetermined amount of water at about 400°C, until they are completely mixed, then the solution is allowed to stand for about ten hours to completely dissolve the ingredients. Brighteners are added according to the instructions for use. It is worth mentioning that all cyanide-based electrolytes have a limited shelf life, and can decompose even when not being used. They should be mixed only as needed and labeled carefully with the date the solution was mixed.

Preparing the article

GRINDING AND POLISHING

A shiny silver plating can only be achieved on a properly prepared surface – proper finishing of the article must be very carefully completed before the electroplating procedure can begin. It is tempting to think of plating as a layer that will cover up small grinding marks, scratches and file marks. Not true! In fact the opposite applies: irregularities in the surface become more evident in the final bright silver layer. Abrasive and polishing material residues should be meticulously removed, if possible using an ultrasonic cleaner with the appropriate solutions.

ATTACHING THE LEADS

Optimum plating depends on consistent electrical contact between the work and the transformer. Jewelry items are hung on hooks that are in contact with the busbar or grasped in metal alligator clips. Chains are stretched out for plating and hollowware objects are wound about with the contact wires.

DEGREASING

To say that the metal must be clean is understating the point. Proper plating can only occur when the surface is free of oils and grease that do not show up to the naked eye. The first step in electroplating, then, is electro-cleaning, a process that uses alkaline hydroxides and a stainless steel anode.

The degreasing salts are dissolved in water as described by the manufacturer of the salts and the metal objects are connected to wires (also called leads). The article is then immersed in the solution and subjected to a sudden powerful application of current, typically:

- current 6–8 V
- current density 5–15 A/dm²
- time: about 30 seconds

If the immersion is too long, a tenacious tarnish film develops on the work. The bath can usually be used for several weeks before being discarded. Exhausted baths must be neutralized before disposing of them.

After degreasing, the articles are rinsed immediately under running water then, without drying them, they are neutralized in a solution of 5 g/l sulfuric acid. When the piece is rinsed once more in water it is ready for electroplating. It should go without saying that the piece should be protected from dust and fingerprints at this stage!

PREVENTING CEMENTATION

This special form of ion exchange was discussed earlier in this chapter. Cementation can be diminished or strongly reduced in several ways. In bygone times, the unhealthy practice called "quicking" used mercury or a mercuric nitrate solution to deposit a first layer on base metal before plating. This method is now outdated and, thankfully, no longer necessary.

Objects of iron and steel are pre-coppered by electroplating in order to reduce the charge difference in the Cu - Ag area. Zinc, tin, lead, copper and copper alloys such as brass, bronze, nickel silver are pre-silvered-plated with a "silver strike."

SILVER STRIKE

In order to allow a flash coating of silver to deposit onto base metal it is necessary to lower the "nobility" or silver content of the solution. This is achieved by adding free potassium cyanide to the bath, a process that lowers the current potential. To ensure that the deposit is not the result of simple ion exchange, the current is first turned on and then the work is lowered into the bath. It is left there just long enough to form a uniform covering of silver.

If the layer appears matte white the work is scratch brushed, rinsed again and immediately immersed into the bright silver bath. Modern high performance baths create deposition conditions that are so good they have eliminated the need for silver strike in most situations.

Advantages

As mentioned above, modern electroplating has seen important advances that make it possible to deposit a layer of metal that is both brighter and harder than was possible in the past. These effects are achieved

427

through the addition of proprietary solutions that are added to the electrolyte bath in prescribed proportions. The exact composition of the additions are secrets that remain with the manufacturers, but in general we can say that they contain compounds of the following:

– sulfur, particularly with carbon
– selenium and tellurium from the same 6th main group of the periodic table
– arsenic, antimony, bismuth from the 5th main group of the table

The precise mechanism that allows these additions to alter the plating is not fully understood, but it is clear that they leave a coating that is visibly brighter and testably harder than the original surface. Because the particular material is not always evident in the structure of the silver layer we can deduce that the effect is a result of a catalytic effect.

Because of the special structure of the metal lattice created in plating, the deposited layer is significantly tougher than annealed fine silver, achieving a Vickers Hardness (HV) in the range of 60 to 90. Values up to 180 HV can be achieved with special solutions. Even though hardness and resistance to abrasion are not necessarily related, this is the case for hard silver plating. When we consider that a plated layer as thick as 100 microns can be deposited, the importance and value of this technology becomes clear.

The procedure
Use only fine silver anodes for this plating, using two or curving the anode around the work if possible to insure that the article will be uniformly affected. The entire surface of the anode should not be smaller than the surface area of the work in order to sustain the regeneration of the bath.

The item is prepared as described above: Polished, cleaned, degreased, rinsed, neutralized in acid, and rinsed. At this point it is ready for the plating bath.

Problem	Cause	Remedy
Deposit doesn't adhere	surface not clean, difference in potential betwen object and electrolyte is too large, cementation	clean, remove grease, pre-copper plate, put in current
Deposit has bubbles	Surface is not clean	degrease
Deposit is streaky	Electrolylte is too cold or too viscous	heat, dilute with distilled water
"Burned" edges	insufficient metal content	replenish
Deposit is grey with H formation	cathode current is too high	decrease the current or put in more pieces
Poor dissemination in depth	cathode current is too low	increase the current
Irregular deposition, "burned" edges	object is too close to anode	minimal distance is 10 cm
Anode passive	anode resistance is too large	scratch anode
Anode has white metallic look	too much KCN	replenish
Dark spots on the anode; deposit is blue or yellowish	not enough KCN	add 1 – 3 g/l KCN

Table 11.3 Possible complications when silver plating with cyanide.

Follow the directions given with the plating solutions and those that came with the equipment. Note that the current strength (in A) is determined by the approximate surface area of the work (in dm²). In this way the current density (in A/dm²) is maintained. The time in the bath depends on the desired thickness – here again the reader is advised to consult the manufacturer's information.

The theoretical values of silver and free potassium cyanide must be maintained to achieve consistent results. After some time the brighteners will need to be refreshed, information that should also be available from the manufacturer.

Possible mistakes and suggestions for eliminating them are given in table 11.3.

11.3.5 GOLD ELECTROPLATING

As mentioned above, silver is often plated onto objects made of base metal to make them appear more precious. It's not hard to see that gold plating has the same effect, only more so! Because of its resistance to tarnish and inherent hardness, gold plating offers several benefits simultaneously. And because gold offers several possible colors, it brings the advantage of a wider range of hues than can be achieved with silver plating.

From the development of plating in 1850 until about 1950, the only method of plating gold was a basic standard method that, like silver plating, had some drawbacks.:

• Only pure gold was plated, leaving a layer that was soft and had limited wear resistance.
• The deposit thickness was a maximum of one micron.
• The plating process required a low current density (about 0.1A/dm²) so the procedure took a fairly long time.
• The deposit was so large grained that the layer appeared as a matte brown color; the true gold color was obtained only by subsequent polishing.
• Because the process only worked with pure gold there was no choice of color.

Before electroplating the preferred method of creating a layer of precious metal on a metallic object was fire gilding (see chapter 9) a mechanical deposition process known in ancient times and widely used until the last century. The results were better than with electrolytic gilding – the deposited layer was significantly thicker (and therefore more durable), and had a lovely, warm gold color. Because of the great health hazard involved in mercury gilding, the procedure has been completely replaced by electroplating.

As far back as the Middle Ages, thin layers of gold were soldered onto silver or base metals to create a material with the look of gold at a lower cost. This doubleè or clad material evolved into rolled gold fill in the last century. It could only be made and worked by specialized factories because a complicated technology was required, especially while soldering. A limitation of clad metal is the fact that cut edges reveal the cheaper metal. Despite this, gold-filled jewelry was widely used and has been appreciated up to the present time because its relatively thick gold layer has proven to last a long time in use. In Germany the following designations have been used:

– American doublé 10 millième,
  $^{10}/_{1000}$ Au (0.01mm)
– German doublé 20 millième,
  $^{20}/_{1000}$ Au (0.02 mm)
– Union doublé 50 millième,
  $^{50}/_{1000}$ Au (0.05 mm)

While of historical interest, the older methods have completely given way to the modern procedures of bright and hard gold plating which has these benefits:

• The plating operation is efficient, its rapid deposit made possible by relatively high current densities.
• The process can continue without interruptions for brass brushing, again adding to its efficiency.
• The layer can be made as thick as a clad doublé layer.
• Pre-polished articles yield a highly reflective surface, so almost no further polishing is needed.
• Because of the addition of hardeners the gold layer is significantly harder and more resistant to abrasion than traditional gold plating.

Designation	Type of Plating	Thickness in μm	Hardness in HV	Surface
Traditional cyanide gold plating	thin fine gold deposit	1	80	matte
Fine gold plating	thick fine gold deposit	5 … 20	up to 100	shiny
Hard gold plating	thick gold alloy deposit	5 … 20	up to 400	shiny
Colored gold plating	thick gold alloy deposit	0.1 … 0.5	up to 400	high shine

Table 11.4
Classification of galvanic gold plating.

Process Data	Unit	Crownclad	Crownclad Mix 'n' Match	Engold HSD
Gold	g/l	18-8C	2…6	15…20
Cobalt	g/l	2…10	0.5…1.0	–
Nickel	g/l	1…2.5	0.5…2.5	–
Indium	g/l		1…3	–
pH-value		1…1.15	3.5…4.0	6.3…7.0
Temperature	°C	30…50	25…40	50…70
Current density	A/dm²	1…5	0.75…1.5	0.55…3.5
Rate of precipitation 1 A/dm²	–	1μm in 10 min	variable	1μm in 100's
Hardness	HV	220	140…225	120

Table 11.5
Gold plating baths.

- Alloy metals can be deposited making possible a palette of different gold colors.

High performance baths

As described above for silver plating, modern methods have improved the technology of gold plating to a higher standard of coating both in finish and durability. The modern methods are also safer and cheaper and have therefore completely replaced the traditional methods.

Precise instructions for preparing, running and maintaining electrolytes are provided by the individual manufacturers and should be followed meticulously. Specific information about the ingredients of each electrolyte are proprietary and covered by patents. This level of information is not needed to use the baths – those readers who have a curiosity about the chemistry will need to research the patent literature. For a general overview of the basic electrochemical relationships see table 11.5.

Usually the gold, even in modern electrolytes, is bound as an alkaline gold cyanide. The addition metals (copper, silver and nickel) are also typically introduced as cyanide compounds. They influence both the color of the plated alloy and its hardness. The addition of very small amounts of other metals such as antimony, arsenic, bismuth, tin, and cadmium is also used to influence the nature of the deposited layer. Organic and inorganic substances are also included to create particular deposition conditions.

Electrolytes are described as acid, neutral and alkaline depending on their pH values. The modern acid electrolytes are made acidic using weak, usually organic acids or altered with a mixture of organic and mineral acids. The pH values lie near 3.4–5. At less than pH 3.2 the gold electrolyte decomposes. When a neutral electrolyte is needed, the pH is usually changed by the addition of phosphorous compounds. Alkaline baths are run in the 11–12 pH region. They have a high free cyanide content, can contain up to 20g/l gold and work with a high speed of deposition.

The components that were important to the traditional baths remain important in the modern high performance baths. These are:

- potassium gold cyanide $K[Au(CN)_2]$
- "free" alkaline cyanides
- alkaline phosphate as a "conductive salt" as well as to control the pH values

POTASSIUM GOLD CYANIDE

This is the metal carrier of the electrolyte. The gold is basically deposited in the monovalent condition. In principle the same processes occur in the gold plating electrolyte as in the silver plating bath. Because the complex ion is more stable than the respective silver compound, cementation rarely occurs. Insoluble anodes are used for the high performance baths so the deposited gold portion cannot be replaced from the anode metal. This of course causes the electrolyte to become impoverished of gold ions as it is used. The solution must be periodically rejuvenated through additions as specified by the manufacturer.

FREE POTASSIUM CYANIDE

Even though gold is the most noble metal in the electromotive series it is less noble than silver in the cyanide solution. The gold portion is reduced in comparison to the entire ion concentration because of the free potassium cyanide. This forces a further shift of the electrical potential towards less noble values causing a reduction in the difference in potential between the gold portion of the bath and the non-precious cathode metal.

ALKALINE PHOSPHATE

This ingredient improves the conductivity of the electrolyte, (the throwing power of the precious metal ions) and influences the color of the gold.

Preparing the work

Preparation methods for gold plating are the same as those for silver plating and will therefore not be repeated here; see above for details. Objects of iron and steel first get a covering layer in a gold strike bath. If this fails to hold, pre-plate the work with

Problem	Cause	Remedy
Spots on the plating deposit	remnants of chemical; porous base metal	clean the object
Plating is coarse	bath is contaminated; too much K_2CO_3	filter and/or replenish
Plating has bubbles	object is insuffiently degreased	degrease
Plating is discolored	anode is too large or too small	adjust the anode size
Plating is red	electrolyte contaminated with copper	add 2–3 g/l KCN
Hydrogen produced; slow action; plating is greenish-black	inadequate gold content	add gold salts
Hydrogen produced; edges are coarse and grey; deposti is green	cathode current density is too high	decrease current density or use fewer objects
Poor depth penetration	cathode current density is to small for the distance between object and anode	increase the current; minimum distance is 10 cm
Bath working slowly	electrolyte too viscous	dilute with distilled water
Anode has a metallic shine	too much KCN	replenish

Table 11.6
Sources of possible mistakes when cyanide gold plating.

copper before applying the gold plating. There are special electrolytes made for steel, (such as Crownclad 18–8 C gold plating bath, C. Hafner Company, Pforzheim) that allow gold to be directly plated onto steel or other hard-to-plate metals.

Zinc, tin and lead can be pre-plated with copper to reduce the difference in potential as a preliminary step to gold plating.

Copper and copper alloys can be directly gold plated but the surface is often improved by first plating a layer of nickel, but the possibility of an allergic reaction to the nickel generally makes this practice unwise except in cases where the object will not be in contact with skin.

The coating procedure
When the surface has been properly prepared, a thick layer of gold is applied. If a gold colored finish is desired it is applied over the fine gold base.

As mentioned above, the modern method uses insoluble anodes of platinum-coated titanium or niobium. This means the bath cannot regenerate itself from the anode metal and must therefore be regenerated from time to time by adding fresh solution. Table 11.6 illustrates the Engelhard program of the C. Hafner Company in Pforzheim.

CROWNCLAD 18–8 C
This solution has been developed to deposit a bonding layer of gold onto stainless steel and similar hard-to-plate metals. It is widely used for watchbands and

432

cases. The deposit has a significant hardness and sticks so well that even subsequent deformation is possible. The plating process develops a thick, shiny layer that can lose its shine somewhat when it becomes more than 5 microns thick.

CROWNCLAD 2000 – MIX 'N' MATCH
An acidic, variable gold bath used for colored gold plating (0.1–0.15 microns) and for heavy deposits (to 5 microns). Five basic colors can be applied from a constant color electrolyte base using a maximum of 6 components. The deposit has a fine content of 20–23.5 karat. The hardness of the plated layer can be increased through the addition of small amounts of other metals. When a nickel/cobalt addition is used the hardness can climb to a Vickers hardness of 185 HV. The inclusion of a nickel/indium alloy yields a Vickers hardness of 225 HV.

ENGOLD HSD
This is a rapidly depositing gold plating bath for thick fine gold deposits up to 300 microns. Note that in deposits up to 10 microns thick the gold layer is very bright, but after that the color fades. The thick layer sticks well onto precious and non-precious metals and is so ductile that plated stock can be rolled, bent and otherwise deformed. This plating is so thick that a bas relief can be created by selectively plating sections of an object. The deposition time depends on the current density.

0.5 A/dm2 produces 1 micron in 230 seconds.
1.1A/dm2 produces 1 micron in 100 seconds.
3.3A/dm2 produces 1 micron in 33 seconds.

Possible errors and their solutions are assembled in table 11.6.

11.3.6 RHODIUM PLATING
Rhodium is characterized by its high corrosion resistance and its resistance to wear. In other words, it's bright and shiny. Rhodium is often plated onto jewelry for two distinct purposes. In the case of white gold and platinum it is used to brighten the inherent color of the alloys and in the case of silver objects, rhodium plating is used to prevent tarnishing.

In the latter case it must be noted that the gain in protection comes at the cost of the traditional "warm" shine of silver and sterling. Rhodium, particularly to the trained eye, has a harder, "colder" blue-white color that lacks the depth of a silver shine.

The tarnish-preventing layer can be as thin as 0.2-0.3 microns. Thicker layers are not desirable because they tend to develop hairline cracks that expose the metal underneath to oxides and therefore no longer work as a tarnish preventer.

Silver and gold alloys (including white gold) can be directly rhodium plated. Brass and nickel silver must be pre-plated with a bright nickel coating. In all cases the surface must be very carefully prepared. The rhodium electrolyte is particularly sensitive, so the instructions for use should be followed to the letter.

When the bath is just made up it will have a reddish-brown color. This will turn to bright yellow as the solution is used, at which time it must be replaced. Rhodium plating electrolytes cannot usually be regenerated. This being the case, it's good to know that a liter of solution is usually enough to plate some 400–600 rings. The plating time is brief, usually achieving the desired thickness in just two or three minutes.

Proper plating depends on making solid, direct metal connections throughout the work. It is not sufficient, for instance, to hang chains in the solution; they must be stretched onto a conductive frame. Because of the unavoidable electrolysis of hydrogen, gas bubbles form on the surface of the work during plating. These must be removed by shaking or brushing to avoid the formation of spots on the surface.

11.3.7 PICKLING AND POLISHING
In addition to depositing a layer of metal onto a base, electroplating equipment can be used for two other kinds of finishing. In one, called electrolytic pickling or electrostripping, electric current is used to remove oxides from a metal surface. The other, called electropolishing, is used to smooth uneven surfaces.

Equipment

The electrolyte is prepared according to the manufacturer's instructions. The bath is warmed for use and therefore subject to evaporation. It must be replenished periodically with distilled water. When the shine being created is no longer bright, chemically rejuvenate the solution by adding 10–20 grams per liter of potassium cyanide. This reaction calls for a stainless steel cathode which should have twice the surface area of the work being cleaned.

Working conditions

The bath is heated to about 70°C (158°F) and the article is connected by leads to the positive pole of the transformer so it becomes the anode. Delicate objects can be cleaned with a power setting of about 8 volts (in the unloaded state) while larger thicker objects will require 12 volts. The work is hung in the electrolyte for only 32–5 seconds–several short exposures are better than one longer one. When dipped into the solution, a current density of 100–120 A/dm² develops. This means that about one amp is needed for every square centimeter of surface area on the work.

This relatively high current requirement means that if your equipment is capable of producing a current strength of only 10 A, the maximum surface of the jewelry pieces you can clean will be about 10 square centimeters.

Bear in mind that the contact wires will also be attacked so they should be thick enough to hold up to some loss. A wire of about 12 gauge B&S (2 mm) is recommended. In principle any gold alloy can be cleaned in this way but in practice the technique works well only on alloys of greater than 50% purity.

Because of the material loss, very delicate jewelry and thin chains cannot be treated by this process. A phenomenon called a "Faraday Cage" is created in objects that have an interior. The current is deflected in such a way that a non-conductive zone is created inside the object; this prevents the cleaning action from working in that area.

After electrostripping the work must be thoroughly rinsed in running water. In some operations an ultrasonic cleaner is used to remove the solution.

Table 11.7 shows some possible problems.

Problem	Possible Causes	Remedy
There is no shine; electrolyte discolored.	Immersion time in bath exceeded; bath temperature too low.	Redo the bath; warm the solution.
Dark grey spots on the object.	Use of water containing salt or calcium.	Use distilled water.
Brown spots on the object.	Inadequate preparation of the object; large amount of copper alloy.	Clean once again and degrease, repolish.
"Burnt" areas at the contact points.	Current concentration too high.	Change the position and repeat treatment.
Cloudy, almost white, circular spots at the contact points	Silver cementation.	Prepare the electrolyte again.

Table 11.7
Sources of possible mistakes when electroforming.

The technical explanation

When the current is first engaged against the oxide covered surface, the loosely attached layers are torn off the work. If the current continues, (a process called anodic polishing) microscopic irregularities are removed electrolytically because the "micro protrusions" have somewhat higher current strength than the depressions. This effect is heightened with a rapid on/off action of the current. This is why the usual procedure involves repeated dipping and lifting. Three exposures of one second each are better than one three second exposure.

11.3.8 CONVENTIONAL ELECTROFORMING

Electroforming is a process in which a layer of metal is deposited upon an object to increase its mass, as opposed to plating where the purpose of the deposited layer is generally to alter the surface color. Electroforming has been done for many years – bronzed childrens' booties come to mind – but it is relatively recently that the process has found a place in the arts.

Most commonly an original form is made in a nonmetal, a form that is called the matrix. This is either covered directly with a deposited layer or is used to make a mold whose interior surface is covered electrolytically.

Plaster objects

A plaster mold must be dried for 2 or 3 days at about 50–70°C (120–150°F), after which it is immersed in a pan of molten wax. The mold is completely covered in wax when no more bubbles appear. The plaster mold is then ready to receive a conductive layer.

Wax objects

Model parts of wax are washed off in an aqueous solution of 50g/l sodium carbonate (soda) Na_2CO_3, rinsed and dried, then covered with shellac.

ABS plastics

Certain thermoplastics based on acrylic-nitrile-buta-dine-styrene were specially developed as base materials for electroforming. For materials and plating instructions, consult a manufacturer.

Making the conductive layer

After the mold or matrix is properly prepared it must be made conductive in order to receive the electrodeposition. This can be achieved by coating it with carbon or a metal powder. Other metalizing procedures like vacuum deposition or the firing in of metal salts can only be carried out with specialized equipment and therefore are not described here.

APPLYING METAL POWDERS

Very fine graphite powder is sprinkled onto the work and distributed with brushes to create a cohesive, shiny black layer. This is capable of conducting electric current.

Copper powder (sometimes called ground copper or gold-bronze powder) is applied just like the graphite, dusted on and spread with a brush. The metal powder adheres to the surface because of its cohesive forces.

CHEMICAL SILVER PLATING

The procedure is particularly recommended for preparing parts of plants. Dip the object into an alcohol-based silver nitrate solution, allowing the excess to drip off. The piece is then dipped into a reducing media, typically a formalin solution such as formaldehyde. The standard 40% solution is diluted to 1%, a reduction sufficient to transform the silver nitrate into metallic silver.

SILVER CONDUCTIVE LACQUER

This is a ready-to-use commercial product consisting of metal powder mixed into a paint or lacquer. It is painted onto the non-metallic model and provides excellent conductivity.

ELECTROLYTIC METAL GROWTH

The metal layer should be smooth, usually shiny and applied as thickly as possible. Precious metal baths (in addition to their high cost) have the disadvantage of creating a texture when the thickness exceeds 30 microns. It is therefore the common practice to electroform by depositing a layer of copper onto the matrix. Copper deposits can easily achieve thicknesses of several millimeters. This structural layer can of course be plated in a second operation to color the object silver or gold.

An electrolytic covering of a metallic model – the situation, for instance, when a brass object is plated with silver – forms a cohesive union of the lattice structure of the base and the applied metals. In the case of electroforming onto a nonmetallic matrix, this bond is not created. The layer can peel away if it does not surround the object or is at least mechanically attached to a roughened surface.

Electroformed hollow jewelry
In recent years the technology of electroforming has developed to the point where a thin smooth layer of gold can be deposited on a nonmetal matrix to create hollow jewelry of consistent alloy purity and strength. Using computer controlled equipment, sophisticated plating systems monitor the many factors involved in electroforming to maintain high standards. The several methods currently in use are described below.

METALLIC CORE TECHNIQUE
A metallic core is plated with a sufficiently thick layer of gold to make a piece of jewelry that will stand up to wear. The core is made from a metal such as aluminum or zinc that can be removed from the gold form with chemicals or heat.

WAX CORE TECHNIQUE
A wax core or model is made electrically conductive and covered with a layer of copper about 80-100 microns thick. The wax is dissolved or melted out, the opening is closed and the copper shell is gold plated. In some cases the copper is then etched out.

Waxes for this process can be made individually or they can be mass produced through the use of rubber molds exactly as wax models are made in quantity for production casting. In the case of electroforming the waxes are covered with conductive paint, electroformed and plated, the wax core having been removed midway in the process.

11.3.9 TEXTURED ELECTROFORMING
As indicated through the above examples, electroforming was first developed as a way to create thin-walled hollow forms. Industrially this is still its most widespread use. In the 1960's the electroforming process developed in the USA as a new method of creating form and texturing metal. Since then electroforming has been taken up as a new option for designers working in metal.

As the boundaries of jewelry design shifted in the 1950s, designers and customers came to realize the wealth of processes that could be used to develop attractive surfaces. In addition to casting and reticulation, electroforming came to be viewed as a valuable addition to the jeweler's repertoire.

Unlike the industrial applications where smooth surfaces defined success, artists intentionally ran the baths at unusually high current density. This made the deposit form in large granular clusters. It is generally true that high densities create fragile deposition materials that do not adhere well to themselves or a conductive surface. Experimentation shows that copper plating baths run at high density with a powerful rectifier creates the best arrangement for stabile electroforming.

As described above, textured electroforming can be deposited on a wide range of matrices. Paper, plastic, natural objects, wax and combinations can be assembled and painted with a conductive paint in preparation for forming. Depending on the materials, it is also possible to incorporate metal wires and sheets as structural elements. This method is particularly useful in providing secure elements for the attachment of pin findings or bails.

Plating is done at high density in a copper bath with care taken to keep the supply of fresh copper sufficiently generous in order to preserve the balance of the electrolyte. Because of the crumbly nature of the large-grained deposit it is typical to finish the object by plating it with silver or gold.

The pleasure of electroforming (for a certain type of personality) lies in the random patterns created by the process. The technique lends itself to experimentation and surprise. It is hoped that the examples in figures 11.11 to 11.15 can serve as inspiration.

11.3.10 HANDLING EXHAUSTED ELECTROLYTES

In most silver baths a fine silver anode is used to perpetually introduce new silver ions into the bath as other ions are being pulled from solution for deposit onto the work. In this system the bath can be used for a relatively long time (assuming it is kept clean and pure). In the case of baths that use insoluble anodes, the baths are periodically renewed by adding fresh electrolyte purchased from a supplier.

Eventually however, all baths will need to be replaced. An old recipe for reclaiming precious metal from a spent bath through the addition of zinc powder was based on the ion exchange between the less noble zinc ions and the precious metal ions. Such procedures can no longer be practiced. The job took considerable time and energy for a meager reclamation and results in a highly poisonous cyanide solution.

Because they contain dangerous chemicals, often cyanide, the baths must under no conditions be allowed to enter the ground water. Disposal is strictly governed by law and is the responsibility of anyone who gets involved with an electrolytic process.

Settings & Findings

Portions of this chapter have been reworked from *Faceting and Finishing of Gemstones,* by Kuehne, Klaus and Erhard Brepohl, published in Leipzig, 1988. As presented here, settings for colored stones are described first, followed by descriptions of settings traditionally used for diamonds.

12.1
Settings

The pleasure and challenge of including gems in a jewelry object (beyond the intrinsic beauty of the gem, of course) is to resolve the various factors that come into play. A well designed setting must achieve several goals simultaneously – it must secure the stone, enhance both the gem and the metal object, it must stand up to wear while protecting the stone, and it should harmonize with the aesthetics of the piece.

One of the first decisions about incorporating a stone is to determine whether it is to be the focal point of a design or a component in service to some other more dominant aspect. Clear thinking on this fundamental question will assist in the many decisions that must follow, including proportion, style, texture, color, location and size.

12.1.1 BEZEL SETTING

This is the simplest of the basic settings. The stone sits on the base plate and is held by the perpendicular wall that surrounds the stone. This wall is pressed over the stone so that it leans against it, in this way securing it to the piece.

Bezels are most commonly used for cabochons, a gem shape that has a flat bottom. Because light does not usually enter a bezel set stone from behind, the setting is most commonly used for opaque stones.

The early steps in making a bezel are shown in figure 12.1. Cut a strip of metal, approximately .25 to .35 mm in thickness (27-30 gauge B&S), wide enough to extend over the curvature of the stone when set on its side. This dimension will vary considerably depending on the height of the stone; the taller the stone, the taller the bezel must be to properly secure it.

Form the strip around the stone so that it makes a close fit, then cut and prepare the ends to make a clean joint. In the case of rectilinear stones, use dividers to step off the various planes of the stone's perimeter, adding a little bit to allow for thickness, then use pliers to make sharp corners. For unusual shapes like the one in figure 12.1c it might be worth the time to saw out a silhouette (or footprint) of the stone from brass sheet, then use this as a form against which the bezel can be adjusted.

The bezel is soldered closed with hard solder and checked against the stone to be certain it makes a good fit. The stone should not rattle in the setting, but it should not need to be forced in either. If the setting is too large or too small, it must be fixed or discarded and a new attempt made. A poor fit at this stage will not improve later on!

The bezel is soldered onto a base plate, preferably from below as the arrangement sits on a soldering tripod and screen. Alternately, binding wire may be used to secure the pieces in their correct position. When the solder has flowed completely, the binding wire is cut off and the piece pickled. Avoid the temptation to check the fit of the stone at this point – because no further mechanical action has been taken, there is no reason why, if it fit before, it will not fit now. It often happens, however, that a lingering flux residue or

minor bending that occurs through normal handling will cause the stone to get stuck in the setting. For this reason, don't insert the stone until you are ready to set it. The excess sheet is cut off with a saw and the edges are filed (figure 12.1b). The base plate is usually cut flush with the bezel, but there is no reason why it cannot be cut ornamentally.

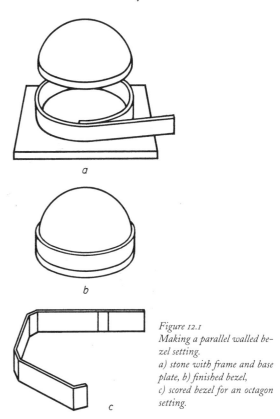

Figure 12.1
Making a parallel walled bezel setting.
a) stone with frame and base plate, b) finished bezel,
c) scored bezel for an octagon setting.

12.1.2 FRAME SETTING

This type of setting may be thought of as a backless bezel in that the holding aspect is a wall that completely surrounds the stone. As seen in the following illustrations, there are many variations on this setting – only the most basic are shown here!

Frame settings are particularly good for translucent and transparent gems because light can enter from the back side, but they can of course be used for opaque stones as well. In the case of parallel walled frames, an inner bearing is cut or added to support the stone; in the case of conical settings, the decreasing size of the form supports the stone from behind. In both cases there must be sufficient metal above the stone to press over it. This is what secures it in place. The thickness of the metal sheet must be determined for each case, and will depend on the size of the stone, the type of metal being used, and the nature of the jewelry item.

12.1.3 CONES AND PYRAMIDS

Figure 12.2 shows three different ways to make a conical setting; a fourth is presented in figure 12.3. As seen in figure 12.2a, a strip of sheet metal is scored, bent and soldered to make a parallel-walled square frame. Corners are cut from this, typically with a file, and are beveled so that they make a tidy joint when brought together. This frame is then soldered.

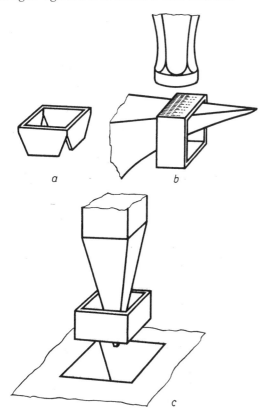

Figure 12.2
Constructing a conical setting from a parallel wall frame.
a) scoring, b) cutting, c) forging.

The advantages of this method lie in controlled measurements, even metal thickness, and the fact that this does not require special equipment. A disadvantage is that the corners are brittle because of the solder they contain; this makes them difficult to press down over a stone.

A parallel-walled frame is bent as before, by scoring the corners and folding up the form (figure 12.2b). This is then set on an anvil or similar steel form and planished at one end, making sure to strike each of the four surfaces equally. This will stretch the metal outward, forcing it into a pyramid shape.

Note that it is necessary to start with thick metal, not only to allow for the stretching, but because there will be hammer marks that must be filed out.

A Striking die made of hardened steel can be used to shape a cone or fabricated square frame into a pyramid. Start with a blank that is equivalent to the center dimension of the intended form. The lower part of this will be compressed and the upper section will be stretched. The annealed blank is set into position, the corresponding die is slid into it, and the punch struck with a hammer (figure 12.2c).

The disadvantage of this tool is its cost, but for some studios this will quickly be covered by the efficiency of the operation. Particularly once an ideal blank has been determined by trial and error, this stamping die is both easy and quick to use.

Perhaps the most universally useful method is to fabricate the frame from sheet metal, following patterns like those shown in figure 12.3. The dimensions and shapes are first laid out on stiff paper to insure the correct fit. This is then transferred to sheet metal that is cut out with a saw. If a number of similar mountings are to be made, it's a good idea to cut a copper or brass stencil of the form; this is more reliable and can be easily traced.

To layout a cone, first draw the intended shape in profile, or side view. Extend the lines of each side to locate the center point of a circle, seen in figure 12.3b. Set a compass point at this junction and strike an arc with the other point at the top of the cone. Repeat the process with the pencil end of the compass at the lower end of the cone – these two lines provide the

441

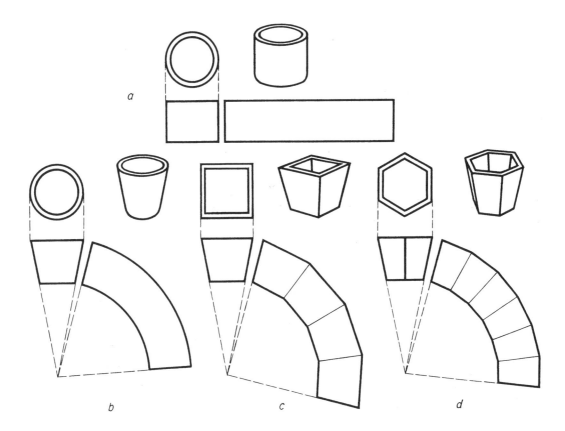

Figure 12.3
Diagrams of various constructed settings.

outer dimensions of the blank that will be needed.

To determine the length of the blank, calculate the circumference of the top of the intended cone by multiplying its radius times π (3.1416). Measure this distance with a curved ruler or a thread along the top of the arc, making marks at each end. Connect these marks with the center point that was used before and you will have laid out the exact pattern for the cone drawn in profile. In the case of metal (as opposed to paper, for instance) allowance should be made for the thickness of the sheet. While this can be calculated, on the scale of stone settings it is usually sufficient to simply add a small amount to the measurements made. This is especially possible in the case of a cone

because if the setting is too large at one point, the stone simply drops down a tiny bit to find the place where it fits.

Use a similar system to lay out patterns for the pyramid and sloping hexagon shown in figure 12.3. Repeat the first steps – draw actual side view, extend sides to locate a center point, and draw arcs at the top and bottom of the form using that center point. Take a measurement of the top of the pyramid with the compass and step it off across the arc. Connect these points to each other and to the center point with a ruler and you will have the patterns shown. These are transferred, sawn, scribed, and bent. Though it appears there is an extra step, these forms are even easier to make than the cone.

Figure 12.4
Creating a bearing by engraving (a) or adding an inner rim.

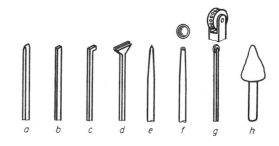

Figure. 12.5
Stone setting tools.
a, b, c, d) stone pushers, e) burnisher, f) beading tool, g) millegrain tool,
h) wax peg (for placing the stone).

12.1.4 MAKING A BEARING

To prevent the stone from falling out the back of the setting, and at the same time to keep it level, a frame style bezel needs a bearing, or ledge, on which the bottom edge of the stone can rest. This can be achieved by carving a portion of the bezel away or by adding a piece of material (figure 12.4).

In both cases the bearing needs to be sufficiently wide to secure the stone, and perfectly level within the setting. The amount of material above the bearing must be sufficient to press down onto the stone to hold it securely.

When fabricating a bearing, an inner unit (cone, pyramid or tube) is made in the same way as the outer one, though typically it is slightly thicker. Fit is everything, not only to allow a proper solder joint, but to hold the piece in position during soldering. In a proper construction the fit is so tight it must be forced into place. This will insure that it doesn't move as the solder flows. The solder chips are applied from the bottom and drawn up into the joint, the point being to avoid a build up of solder along the bearing.

When cutting a bearing, work can proceed with gravers, burs or a combination of both. In the case of a cylindrical mounting, a cylinder shaped rotary file is used to carve away a portion of the inside of the bezel. It will be obvious that the metal used to make the bezel must be thick enough to accommodate this. A flat or square graver is often used after the bur to even up the surfaces.

When cutting a bearing into a conical setting the outward leaning sides mean that very little material needs to be removed. The primary purpose of the bearing in this case is to level the stone and hold it in position as the stone is set. By thinning the wall at a specific band, the metal is made easier to bend over at that point, in this case leaving a top edge that is attractively thick. Of course it must be noted that the bearing cannot be cut too deeply for fear of breaking through the wall. This bearing can also be cut with a Hart bur in the flexible shaft machine, in which case a graver might be used only to even up the walls of the groove.

Cutting a bearing into an oval cone is slightly more difficult though the principle is the same. The different radii around the oval require a more sensitive handling of whichever tool is used.

12.1.5 SECURING STONES

When the bezel is made completely ready, it is wise to check the piece one last time to be certain that no further soldering will be necessary. When you are certain, pick up the stone with a bit of beeswax and set it into the bezel, making certain it is level.

The top edge of the bezel wall is then pressed over the stone to secure it in place. Any of the tools seen in figure 12.5 can be used for this – most goldsmiths develop a particular favorite, though all would agree there are times when the surrounding shape makes one choice better than another. These tools are usually made of unhardened steel, though brass or bronze can also be used. The surfaces are generally polished, but the fine tooth left by sandpaper has the advantage of gripping onto the metal slightly.

In order to avoid a pucker of metal at any one point, it is important to distribute the compression of the bezel around the stone. To accomplish this, press the bezel toward the stone, then move the tool to a point directly opposite and repeat the process, again pressing the bezel only part way down. Move to a point equidistant between these two points and press it, then go directly opposite that. If we imagine the points of a compass, the idea is to press the bezel at north, south, east and west.

Check to be certain the stone is level and seated as far into the mounting as it can go, then proceed to press the points in between those just bent over (NE, SW, NW, SE).

When setting a rectilinear stone, press the corners in first. When the stone is securely set – it feels stable and makes no sound when shaken – polish and harden the bezel by rubbing it with a burnisher. If the bezel is irregular after pressing, use a flat file or pumice wheel to make the surface flat before burnishing. When using a wheel, run it against an old file to sculpt exactly the correct shape.

The top edge of the bezel, (the small rim where the bezel contacts the stone), can be polished with a flat graver or a felt buff. It is also possible to leave it matte with the pumice wheel, or to ornament it with tiny beads using a millegrain tool.

12.1.6 HAMMER SETTING

In cases where a stone is very delicate or a bezel wall very thick, it is often easier to set a bezel using a hammer and punch. Though great care is needed, it is easier to arrest a hammer blow that is going wrong than it is to stop the muscular thrust of a hand-held bezel pusher.

The object is anchored by whatever method suits the studio and the stone setter: in the example shown in figure 12.6 it has been attached to a shellac (or pitch) stick. The first step is to secure the stone sufficiently that it won't jump about as the bezel is being pressed over. Though tempting, glue should not be used for this because it makes it impossible to know when the bezel has been properly secured. If an adhesive must be used, a tiny film of beeswax is applied to

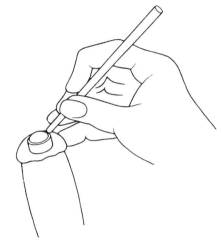

Figure. 12.6
Using punch to cinch the bezel.

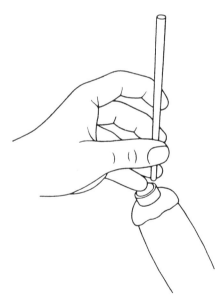

Figure. 12.7
Leading punch without the help of an assistant.

the underside of the gem. This will minimize its movement, but still allow a discerning worker to know when the wax is all that is keeping the piece in place. Use conventional bezel pushers to move the bezel enough to touch the stone, at least at the four cardinal points. It will then be possible to switch to the use of a small hammer.

It is often easiest if the goldsmith has an assistant

to strike the hammer blows, allowing the setter to hold the work and locate the tool. This is the situation shown here. Figure 12.7 shows the way a setter can use his or her little finger to press down on the stone while simultaneously holding onto the punch. In some cases a rubber band can also be used.

A motorized version of this process is made possible through a hammer handpiece, a specialty piece of equipment that converts the rotary motion of a flexible shaft machine to a back and forth stroke. In this case the operation is the same, but the machine is passed across the surface of the bezel, changing angles as the work proceeds to cinch the bezel down onto the stone.

A variation on this is called a mirror setting, so named because it presents a flat highly polished surface that surrounds the stone as if it was set into a mirror. This thick-walled bezel is particularly appropriate for stones with a large table, like the one shown in figure 12.8. A thick bezel is made and pressed over so that it completely covers the side facets of the stone. In practice it is best to provide a little excess metal, knowing it can be filed off later. When the metal is tightly pressed against the stone with a punch, the metal standing above the setting is taken away (do not use sandpaper!) and the surface is polished with pumice and a leather stick. After polishing, the stone will appear to have a shining mirror as its frame.

Another variation on a bezel is the "bowed setting" seen in figure 12.9. This is nothing more than a simple thin bezel in which the process stops after pressing in the first eight points. In a tall setting like the one shown, use a screwdriver or similar shaped punch to press the bezel wall at even intervals. When polished to a bright shine the convex shapes are highly reflective and make an eye-catching setting.

12.1.7 FRAMING AN IRREGULAR SHAPE
This variation on a bezel is less straightforward but sometimes the only solution, particularly when setting a panel of irregular contours. An example that will be used here is a shell cameo, and other uses include enamels, coins, found objects, etc.

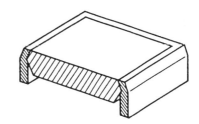

Figure. 12.8
Mirror setting.

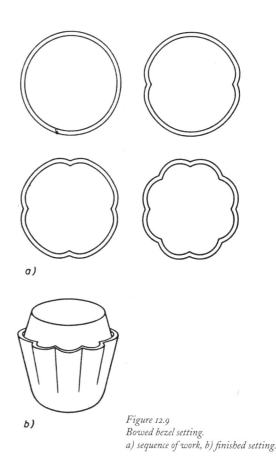

a)

b)

Figure 12.9
Bowed bezel setting.
a) sequence of work, b) finished setting.

Start by making a surrounding bezel in the usual way, making certain that the metal is thick enough to withstand the handling that is part of the process. When the fit is correct, solder the bezel closed and test the cameo in it, marking the orientation so it is repeated each time.

With the shell in place, scribe a line along the inside wall that follows the irregular contour of the piece. Remove the shell and cut away metal down to this line, using burs, shears and files. Make an inside bezel and slide it into the larger bezel, using the previously trimmed piece as a guide for filing the inner rim.

Make an oval of wire, solder it closed, and planish it out to make a flat rim. In the end, this is the element that will hold the stone from the front. Bend this as necessary to fit closely onto the top lip of the outer (larger) bezel. The detail at figure 12.10b might make the location of this piece more evident.

When all soldering and finishing is complete, the cameo is slid into the setting from the back and the internal bezel used to lock it into place. This tight fitting ring should make a friction fit all around the inside of the primary bezel. It is further held by rivets, engraved stitches, adhesive or tin solder.

12.1.8 PRONG SETTINGS

We might think of a prong setting as an open-backed bezel from which segments have been removed at equal spacing around the rim. The advantage of prongs is that they allow more of the stone to show; in this way a prong setting resemble the way you might hold a coin by its edges to show it to a friend. The disadvantage, not surprisingly, is that the fingers of metal are prone to snag on fabric, and can be bent back more easily than can a bezel.

Variations on prong constructions are as numerous as the shapes in which stones are cut. A few examples are shown in figure. 12.11, but these should be taken as only a glimpse of the many varieties that can be made. And keep in mind that each of these styles could be altered in proportion or metal to create several settings!

As mentioned above for frames, the bearing for a prong setting can either be added on or cut from the material itself. In those cases where an interior bezel is to be added, the upper edge must often be filed at an angle to properly fit the pavilion (underside) of a faceted stone. This situation is illustrated in the upper right corner of figure 12.11.

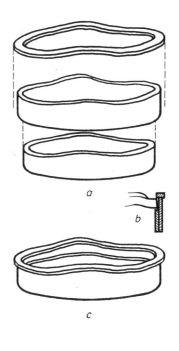

Figure 12.10
Framed setting.
a) separate pieces,
b) wall with inset
cameo (side view),
c) finished setting.

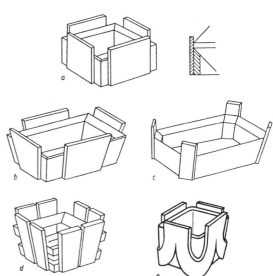

Figure. 12.11
Square prong setting.
a) vertical walled prong setting, b) and c) conical prong setting,
d) conical prong setting with split frame, e) special form of a square
prong setting.

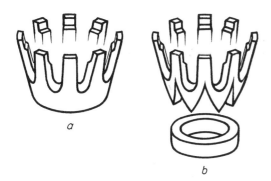

Figure. 12.12
Chaton.
a) file grooved prongs, b) prepared chaton with foot ring support.

Crown setting

This important setting, shown in figure 12.12, is a staple in the jewelry industry, and shows clearly how bezels are similar to prongs. If you can mentally "fill in" the scooped out openings in figure 12.12a, you will see how much it resembles the bezel shown at figure 12.4a. It would be a worthwhile exercise to set two identical stones in settings like these – the effort would show that while both are attractive, the effect of the bezel is to present a framed gem, while the prong presents the gem itself, ideally floating in the jewelry piece.

Though crown settings are commonly used today to set diamonds in ladies engagement rings, this is somewhat risky, given the ease with which prongs can wear down or be accidentally pried open. It is important to use metals and alloys known for their toughness when setting diamonds in prongs!

The construction of a crown setting starts with a cone of such a size that the stone fits part way into it. The cone is shaped on a mandrel and filed to uniform symmetry. It is possible to cut the bearing groove at this stage, though some goldsmiths prefer to wait until after the prongs have been cut out.

The upper edge is sanded smooth and divided with a compass or template into the chosen number of prongs, typically 4, 6 or 8. After drawing a guideline around the cone about one-third of the way up from the bottom, a saw or file is used to cut away material

from between the prongs. In a small setting, this is all that is required, seen in figure 12.12a. In larger settings, the cone is inverted and a knife-edged file is used to remove material in a position staggered from the location of the prongs as shown in 12.12b. This will visually lighten the setting. For strength the lower tips are soldered onto a ring made of flattened wire. Alternately, this piece may be made by soldering the prong onto sheet or by making the cone a little long, cutting the lower piece away, then reattaching it after the filing is complete.

The setting process is even easier than with a bezel because there is less metal to be moved. If the bearing has not yet been cut, it is made now, using a bur, a graver, a file, or some combination of all three. The particular action will depend on access to the setting, the number of prongs, the size of the setting, and the tools at hand.

After removing any last burs or flaws in the mounting, the stone is pressed into position and checked to see that it touches each prong. If not it is removed and the prongs adjusted accordingly. The prongs are next checked to be certain they are the proper height, and if necessary they are cut down and shaped with files. Each prong is then pressed over the stone part way, the stone is checked to be certain it is level, and the prongs are set down firmly onto the stone. The tips of each prong are hardened and burnished with a burnisher or a beading tool.

12.1.9 STONE REMOVAL

When doing repair work it is best to remove all stones from their settings. It is clearly most efficient if this can be done without harming the setting so it can be used again, but it often happens that a piece old enough to be brought in for repair is also sufficiently worn that the settings will need to be replaced. This can be a big job all by itself, so be certain to examine the settings while the customer is still on hand so you can inform them of this possibility.

In removing stones, remember that every stone, even those considered hard, should be treated with great care. Always work over a table, leather bag or sweeps drawer to catch the stone in case it is dropped.

447

Bezels

Use a sharp, pointed knife tip as a wedge, easing it in between the bezel wall and the stone. Always direct the force against the metal rather than the gem, and be patient, moving slowly around the bezel. For small stones, a steel needle or dental tool can be shaped to a narrow chisel shape for this purpose.

The hardest part seems to be in finding a starting point – it's possible to feel your way around the stone several times before the tip of the tool finds a point of entrance. Ease into this place and work from there around the bezel, always avoiding force and a levering motion. Pulling too hard on any given point not only endangers the stone but also pulls the bezel on the opposite side of the stone tighter. Continue going around the stone until the bezel is peeled back enough to allow the stone to be shaken out.

This method will not work for thick bezels; instead, use a saw to cut into through the bezel at one or perhaps two places. Insert the tool there and pull the metal outward. It is possible to repair these cuts by soldering a thin piece of metal into the cuts, but in some cases it might prove easier to make a new bezel from scratch.

Prongs

Lifting prongs is considerably easier than removing a stone from a bezel. Set the knife blade flat on the crown facet of the gem and slide it down to the girdle of the stone. The prong lifts quite easily. It is also possible to purchase a prong lifter, a rectangle of steel into which are cut into slots of various sizes. This can be used like a miniature crowbar to peel the prongs open.

12.2
Hunter's Jewelry

Grandeln

Grandeln are deer teeth, or more precisely, the two eyeteeth from the upper jaw of the red deer, which has no eyeteeth in the lower jaw. "Stag-grandeln" are those of the male red deer and are much larger than grandeln from the female. Both grandeln are referred to as "Tiergrandeln" by hunters. These eyeteeth have a base color of ivory and brown. These are valued according to their size, shape, whiteness, markings, and the color match of a pair.

These unusually formed teeth often show a very beautiful brown spot, and are sufficiently valued to be set in gold by many of their owners. Though grandeln are purchased in the same way as gemstones, their value comes as much from their importance as trophies as from their aesthetics. They remind a hunter of a particular hunt and, therefore, have a personal meaning for the hunter or his or her family. In this way, hunter's jewelry has found a place of its own. The valuable stag grandeln are usually paired, as one would with earrings. If single grandeln are used, they are usually from the female deer.

Grandeln can be found in virtually every type of jewelry – they are used in rings, pendants, necklaces, pins, bracelets, and earrings for women. In men's jewelry, grandeln have a tradition of use in rings, tie tacks, cufflinks, watchcases, and as pendants on a watch chain.

Though it is usually best to continually invent new designs, attempts to modernize the traditional settings for grendeln have been generally disappointing. The time-honored setting is the one shown in figure 12.13, in which a metal cap is added to create the appearance of a valuable acorn. These are often garnished with oak leaves and twigs cut from different colored gold, examples of which are shown at the top of figure 12.13.

CAP SETTING WITH TONGUE FASTENERS

When setting a pair of grandeln, they are trimmed by sawing and filing to achieve as good a match as possible. Material is removed from the brown root section if needed. The edges are filed smooth.

Form a sheet of gold as shown in 12.13d and e to make a cap that will cover part of the tip of each tooth. Bend and file this so it makes a snug fit over the tooth, then solder it onto a thin sheet of gold that will serve as the backing plate. The surface of this sheet is traditionally sawed, filed or engraved with criss-crossed lines to resemble the marks on an acorn

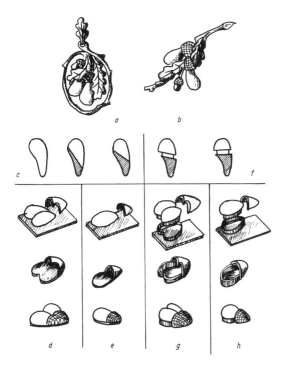

Figure. 12.13
Setting of Grandeln
a) Grandeln pendant, b) Grandeln pin, c) through e) cap setting with flat base, c) preparing the Grandeln, d) double setting, e) single setting, f) through h) cap setting with bezel, f) preparing the Grandeln, g) double setting, h) single setting.

cap. In examples like those shown at the left of the illustration, the tooth is cemented into place with a strong adhesive like epoxy. This is augmented with a pin that is driven into a predrilled hole, in essence nailing the mounting onto the tooth.

A better mounting is made so as to include a bezel, as shown in figure 12.13g & h. The back of each tooth is filed and sanded flat so it lays tight against the back plate, and a groove is filed around the tooth to provide a place for the bezel to gain purchase.

Caps are made as before and a bezel strip is bent to mate with the step filed into the tooth. Because the cap covers the ends of the bezel, it is usually sufficient to simply feed the ends of the bezel under the cap and end them there.

The cap and bezel are checked against the tooth – each situation will of course be unique – then soldered into place on a back plate. After pickling the

excess sheet is cut away. The piece is finished and cleaned and the grandeln are slid into position, typically with a dab of glue for security. When two teeth are being set side by side as in (g), they are pinned together with a length of wire inserted into drilled holes in each tooth. The bezel is set in the usual way, insuring a safe mounting.

Leaves
Make small oak leaves by a combination of repoussé and stamping, using a variety of tools to set out the veins and textures. It is traditional that these be made of green gold, though variations are possible. Light forming is done over small punches, with work alternating from front and back (figure 12.14).

Acorns
Little acorns are filed from half round wire. The sculpting is most easily done if the wire is kept long enough to hold onto while the form is developed, then cut off at the last stage. A fine wire can be soldered on to form a stem.

Branches
Thick round wire is laid on a steel block and forged to give it an irregular cross section and rough texture. Several pieces are made, each following the natural taper of tree branches. The ends of each twig are filed at a steep angle and soldered to the next larger branch, in each instance using a generous amount of

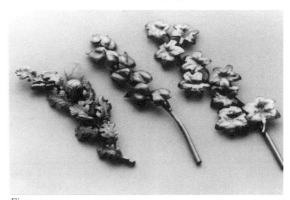

Figure. 12.14
Samples with formed leaves. Birgit Karsten, Firma Nothdurft, Schwerin.

solder to make a rounded transition. When the branch is completely assembled, it is worked over with a fine graver to heighten the bark texture and provide natural growth patterns at the points where the branches stem off.

ASSEMBLY

Leaves, acorns and branches are assembled and soldered together with the Grandeln setting. When soldering the cap to the main branch, it is advisable to drill a hole into the cap first to insure a proper positioning. The tips of the branches and leaves should be examined to make sure they will not get caught on a wearer's clothing, and soldered down wherever needed. It is sometimes useful to solder balls or ribs of wire onto the back to hold the pieces securely. Use binding wire or soldering investment to secure the many pieces during assembly.

Fox tooth

Fox teeth are sometimes set in jewelry, in which case a setting similar to the grandeln is used. The root of the tooth is shortened and glued into a cap. Because the teeth are round, no back plate is used. The tooth is secured with a strong cement like epoxy, perhaps assisted with a rivet.

12.3
Movable Connections

When a material as rigid as metal is used on a form as flexible as the human body, some method must be devised to make the one conform to the other. Over the centuries that goldsmiths have been applying their art, thousands of ways have been invented to allow metal parts to twist, slide, rotate, hinge and swivel. A complete list would be impossible to assemble, but it is useful to look at basic groups such as the following:

12.3.1 RING CONNECTIONS

This is perhaps the most basic of all movable connections. The examples in figure 12.15 show some of the ways that rings can be used to link two solid pieces in a way that allows them to move. Two rings are connected at right angles to each other (12.15a) or two stationary rings are linked by a third ring at right angles (12.15b and c). The connection illutrated in figure 12.15d shows a version of a hinge that is an extension of the preceding arrangement. In this case the travel or play of the movement is limited by the joining link. When compound or multiple units are assembled, a chain mail is formed (12.15e).

12.3.2 HINGES

As with every other family of movable parts, hinges exist in hundreds or perhaps thousands of variations. The concept and terminology will be introduced here by illustrating a basic version, but readers are advised to apply this information to their own explorations.

Hinges are usually made by soldering lengths of tubing, called knuckles, onto the parts to be joined. The tubing can be of any size relative to the rest of the piece, depending on design considerations.

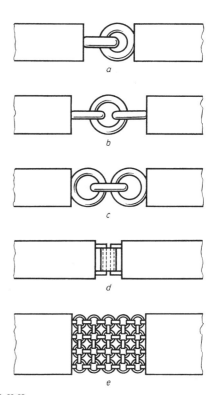

Figure. 12.15
Simple ring connections.
a) ring pair, b & c) three ring connection, d) hinge-joint catch, e) chain mail connection.

Generally the wall thickness should be about one-fourth the inside diameter, which is to say, relatively thick. Not only will a heavy tube be easier to solder, but the hinge will stand up to years of wear and tear.

Except for a few special cases, it is customary to make hinges with an uneven number of knuckles, (3, 5, 7, etc.). When making a three part hinge joint, the middle section can be larger than the outer two parts. The middle section is soldered to the lid, the outer pieces to the main piece, on a box for example.

In order to operate smoothly, the tolerances in a hinge must be tight. That is, the parts need to fit together closely in perfect alignment. One way to achieve this is to solder all the pieces into place on both base and lid in the same operation. This has the advantage of insuring correct fit but the disadvantage that elements that are supposed to move may become soldered fast to one another.

The alternate arrangement, in which parts are soldered onto the lid in an operation independent of a similar operation on the base has the advantage of low risk but makes it easier for pieces to be out of alignment. Both methods are widely used and both will be presented here with the thought that each goldsmith can choose a favorite method.

Method 1
Prepare a groove or bearing in the parts to be joined, for convenience here called lid and box. The groove should span the two units equally and should be a perfect fit for the tubing that will make the hinge.

A hinge or joint file is made just for this purpose: it looks at first glance like a flat needle file that has no teeth. In fact the broad surfaces are plain, but the

smaller edges are half round and cut with fine teeth. These will cut a parallel groove, unlike a tapered round file, which will of course cut an irregular groove depending on which part of the file actually does the cutting.

The tubing is cleaned and cut into the desired number of parts. It is critical that the ends of each knuckle are flat and at a right angle to the axis of the tube. A tube cutting jig is highly recommended because it insures a clean straight edge. Even when using a jig, be careful to use a small sawblade and to remove any bur that clings to the tube.

The tubing pieces are slid onto a lightly oiled piece of steel wire or a graphite rod (pencil lead), and the hinge unit is set into place in the fluxed groove, (figure 12.16a). A small clean piece of solder is set onto each knuckle, placed alternately so that if knuckles 1, 3 and 5 are attached to the box, numbers 2 and 4 are attached to the lid.

The piece is heated, concentrating first on one side, for instance the box. When the solder has flowed on those three knuckles, direct the heat to the lid and solder those pieces. If the solder only flows partially but is enough to tack the pieces into position, cool the piece, withdraw the wire and separate the two parts. Insert the wire through the knuckles in one unit to keep them in alignment and resolder to guarantee a solid joint. Repeat on the other unit if necessary.

Method 2
Prepare a groove (or bearing) as described above. Clean a length of tubing and mark it off into the desired number of knuckles as before, but this time do not saw each length off. Instead, use a saw to cut a line ⅞ of the way through at each mark. If the piece is to attach to the base, leave knuckles 1, 3 and 5, but turn the saw and cut away the pieces of tubing that fall between those three, leaving a small piece of the tube as a bridge that holds the three pieces at exactly the correct distance from each other.

This unit is then set into the groove on the box where it can be held in position with binding wire if necessary. Align the tube so that the bridging elements are facing out, away from the box. This will

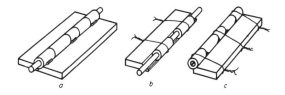

Figure. 12.16
Soldering the movable hinge-joints.
a) soldering of the entire joint, b) and c) soldering of the parts of both connection sides.

451

allow them to be easily reached at the next step. Apply a small piece of solder at the point of contact where each tube touches the box and heat until the solder flows.

When the soldering is completed and the work pickled, the thin strip of metal that previously held each knuckle is sawn away, using care to insure that the end of each knuckle remains square. Pieces of tubing are cut to fit snugly into the openings that remain, which are marked with a scribe onto the lid. The tubing pieces are slid onto a steel rod and fastened in place for soldering. Of course it is also possible to repeat the same trick and saw out the midsection of a length of tubing that includes the remaining two knuckles.

Spring loaded hinge

This type of hinge, shown in figure 12.17 is frequently seen in cigarette cases and novelty containers like pill boxes and compacts. The hinge is constructed of knuckles as described above, except in this case an even number is used. This means that one end knuckle is attached to the lid and the other end piece is attached to the base, a necessary arrangement for this hinge.

After assembly, the hinge is held together not with a conventional pin, but by inserting a flat strip of spring steel through the hinge. Depending on the purpose and scale of the piece, several pieces of spring can be laid on top of each other. The springs can often be retrieved from broken watches and clocks, though care must be used when pulling springs from those mechanism because they are under tremendous pressure.

The strip is cut a little longer than the hinge and slid into place where it is wedged into place at one end with a tapered plug; see figure 12.17. If the spring lays flat when attached (as in the upper illustration) the lid will be under tension when the hinge is opened and will snap closed. It is also possible to "load" the spring by grasping the projecting end with pliers and rotating the strip a full turn. In this case the lid will be under pressure to pop up, assuming you've rotated the correct direction. This is especially useful in a box fitted with a tight clasp. When the mechanism is proven to work correctly, saw the springs and plugs slightly oversize, tap them once more to insure a tight fit, and file them flush.

Cradle hinge

In this instance a thick bearing is soldered into position rather than cut from the existing material. It has several uses, but will be illustrated in a hollow hinged bracelet. Start by making two tubes that slide together, one into the other like a telescope. Both should be thick walled.

Set the smaller tubing aside and turn attention to the bracelet, preparing a hole that will fit the larger diameter tubing. This should be in contact with the outer wall of the bracelet – if the tubing diameter is smaller than the thickness of the bracelet, the resulting opening into the hollow center must be capped, both for strength and to make an attractive hinge. Fold over a piece of sheet metal and cut away enough metal to allow it to be put into position as shown in (figure 12.18a). Solder it there, being certain that no solder flows between the faces of the two sides.

File the seat, including the piece just inserted, so the larger tube makes a tight fit into position as shown in figure 12.18b. This tube, which will become the bearing for the hinge, is soldered into place.

The bracelet pieces are separated by sawing through the tubing in two places, at the top of the tube where it makes the tangent of the bracelet, and directly opposite that point, where the tube is closest to the center of the bracelet. The protruding parts of the U-shaped piece are cut off and trimmed neatly by filing. The result of all this is that the previously open ends of the bangle are each closed with a half section of tubing and a straight strip of metal, perhaps evident in figure 12.18b.

A knuckle equal to one-third the width of the bracelet is cut from the smaller diameter tube and soldered into place in the center of the bearing. Because the two tubes made a perfect fit originally, this knuckle has no where to go except to fall neatly into the bearing tube. It is soldered there, with a result that will look like the drawing at figure 12.18c.

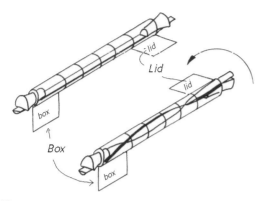

Figure. 12.17
Hinge with spring wire and wedge.
a) At rest, b) under tension.

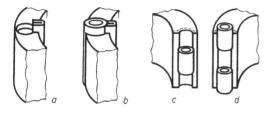

Figure. 12.18
Soldering of the counter hinge.
a) Inserting of the closing metal to adjust for the thickness of the ban
gle, b) soldering of the outer hinge, c) middle section – movable hinge
in its hinge shell, d) outer movable hinge.

Figure. 12.19
Bayonet linkage.

Lay the bracelet pieces together and mark the location of the soldered tubing onto the second bearing. Cut two additional knuckles from the smaller diameter tubing, apply flux, and solder them into position as indicated by the marks just made (figure 12.18d). Some people like to tack the pieces, lifting the torch just as the solder starts to flow. If the fit checks out, reflux the joint and heat it until the solder flows throughout. If necessary the protruding ends of the tubing are filed off flush with the side walls of the bracelet. A temporary pin can be inserted into the hinge to facilitate finishing.

12.3.3 BARRETTE LINKAGE

This linkage is seen most often in high end work. The possible radius of rotation is limited on one side of the shape by the wedge (which is inserted into the next unit) and by the size of the space between the units. The links can assume almost any shape, but usually they are closed four sided cross sections or have inner walls that are open as a U-shaped cross section (figure 12.19).

Create a square or rectangular tube by drawing a round tube through the appropriate drawplate while using a core of copper or steel. If possible, arrange that the seam lie on a corner. To make a bracelet, start by bending this stock around a bracelet mandrel or stake. The links are sawn apart and the core material is etched out.

If the links have a U-shaped cross section, a square or rectangular tube is made in the same way, but using a copper core. The seam is positioned on the side what will later be the inside of the bracelet; the form does not need to be soldered closed. Bend the square tubing around a bracelet mandrel then file away the inside surface until the core is laid bare. The individual links are sawn apart and the core pieces can be pulled out. This open back economizes on material but the links are not as comfortable against the skin.

File both ends of each link at a slight angle to allow flexibility between the links. Prepare sections of square wire (or rectangular stock) by filing each piece to the shape of a wedge. Solder a unit into one side of each link. This wedge is slid into the adjoining link and drilled through. After completing the links, a length of wire is fed through the holes and the links are riveted together as shown in figure 12.19.

12.3.4 STUD CONNECTIONS

This linkage system is a variation of the barrette joint described above. Because the links are designed for sideways movement their mobility in use is very good. The links are made as for the barrette linkage, using square, rectangular or U-shaped cross sections. Cut the links, leaving extra material for the joint.

One side of every link is filed half round and on the other side a matching indentation is filed out to create a matching shape (figure 12.20a). A square or rectangular wire that fits snugly into the link is used to create the center knuckle of each joint. When metal of the appropriate size has been prepared, it is curved around a stake to emulate the curve of the bracelet and cut into short pieces. A piece is slid into one end of each link and soldered in place. It is then filed to a round end as seen at the extreme left end of the illustration in figure 12.20a. The links are slid into position, drilled through, and connected with a hinge pin. If the linkage is not sufficiently flexible, additional filing might be needed.

In the case of wide bracelets, the internal bar method becomes heavy and expensive. This calls for a variation, seen in the lower drawings of figure 12.20. Begin by making two bands from rectangular material: these form the sides of the links. Solder the upper panels of each links onto this frame, allowing enough distance between each section to allow for the next step.

Saw the links apart, allowing the frame to extend on one end. This is filed into a round shape and at the same time the other end of each link is filed to the negative of this form. In this way, each link will fit into its neighbor.

Short, half-circle struts are prepared from the same material as the frame – they are shown in the lower left edge of figure 12.20b. These are soldered onto the inside of the frame at the filed end of each link. The round projections are drilled and the links are assembled with a hinge pin. Movement can be increased by careful filing and sawing.

12.3.5 PIN LINKAGE

As in the previous linkage, this system is somewhat time consuming to fabricate and is accordingly reserved for high end work in gold or platinum (figure 12.21).

A square wire (about 0.7 mm x 2.5 mm) is rolled flat to make a strip with a rectangular cross section. These are bent into three hoops whose inside diameter is the same as the desired bracelet – in effect, three simple bangle bracelets. Using careful measurement and a permanent marker, divide one of the bracelet blanks into identical sections, each between 10 and 13 millimeters long. Use a sharp divider to mark out the center line of the height of the wire, making a delicate mark near each end of each section. Use the dividers again to mark off a consistent dimension from the end of each link. The result will be the center marks shown in the top illustration of figure 12.21. Centerpunch and drill a small hole at each intersection.

Set a second bracelet directly under the first and drill a hole through the first band and into the second. Repeat this with another hole roughly opposite the first, then insert wires and temporarily rivet the two bands together. With the pieces locked in this way it is now possible to drill holes in the second bracelet that will align with those in the first. When the drilling is complete the temporary rivets are removed and the two bracelets can be sawn into sections. The ends of each link are filed to round off their corners.

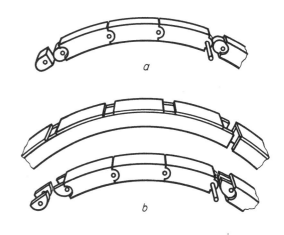

Figure 12.20
The connection of broad links.

The third blank is segmented with a marker into sections that are shorter than those made above. Mark and drill holes in the ends of each segment, then cut the sections out and file the corners. Note that if these sections are made too large the finished bracelet will be too big.

The bracelet is assembled as shown in the lower half of figure 12.21 with wire pins running through the segments. The ends of the pins can be soldered or riveted, depending on the metal and scale involved.

12.3.6 LINKED STONE SETTINGS

The flexible linkage described in this section is most commonly used to assemble a row of settings. The several methods shown allow movement in either vertical or horizontal direction; the choice of which style to use will depend on the size of the settings and the application. When properly constructed, the settings should touch as tightly as possible and only move in a sideways direction. When at rest they must hang exactly vertical.

The settings are made by cutting sections of a tube of the appropriate length. Seats for the stones are made by soldering a wire inside each tube. Care must be taken when deciding on the height of each tube to insure that there is sufficient material to make a bezel on the top and to protect the pavilion from poking out the bottom. In the case of flat-bottomed stones, it is possible to make these settings quite low.

Use a sharp divider to mark a uniform distance from the bottom of the tube with the goal of producing the two square openings shown in figure 12.22a. Drill two holes in each tube and use a saw or file to create the desired shape. It is particularly important that the post between the slots is the same on all the sections.

Make jump rings of the appropriate size and saw a piece out of each to create a three-quarters ring. This is slid through the slots in a tube and soldered onto the next link. Repeat the process, moving link by link up the chain.

A variation on this is to saw out what amounts to two large slots, opposite each other and each taking up most of the side of the tube. This will leave two posts, opposite each other. Use normal jump rings to connect the settings, soldering each closed for security. Though it is possible that the rings would be free moving, the chain will hang better if the rings are soldered to the posts on one side of each linkage.

Tube settings

In this version, as in the one just described, it is important that the distance between the settings be as small as possible. Start as before by cutting identical lengths of tubing. Solder a bearing into each to support the stone. To make the links, drill two small holes opposite each other and at the middle height of each link. Below each hole, use a round file to cut away a small scallop from the lower edge. These are shown in the left edge of the drawing in figure 12.22b.

Figure 12.21
Assembly of the pin linkage system.

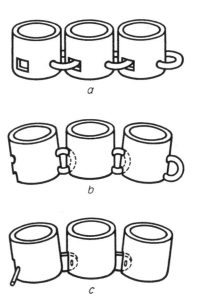

Figure 12.22
Tube settings linkage.

A three-quarters jump ring is fed through a hole in one link and fitted into place on its adjacent link where is it soldered. To allow proper movement, the unsoldered hole might need to be filed a little larger. The chain is assembled and soldered link by link.

Figure 12.22c shows a third variation on this linkage. Start as before, but this time use a flat file to create a facet on the lower edge of each tube. This is shown in the left-most tube in the drawing. Sheet material (or flattened wire) is soldered onto each tube section, then cut to size and drilled.

Slots are sawn into each tube opposite the projecting lug and of a width that the pieces can be fitted together. The links are assembled and holes drilled as shown. Pins are inserted and, ideally, soldered into place in each tubing.

12.4
Chain and Bracelet Catches

12.4.1 GENERAL CONSIDERATIONS
The first requirement of all catches is that they secure neckpieces and bracelets in such a way that they will not fall off the wearer. Once this is accomplished, there are other concerns that should be addressed.

- A catch is a component of the entire design of the piece of jewelry, and should relate to the rest of the work. In some cases this is a matter of making the catch unobtrusive and in others the catch may be emphasized as a decorative element.
- The catch must be designed and placed so the wearer can operate it without difficulty.
- The maker (whether goldsmith or factory) would like the catch to be simple to make, if possible. It is also an advantage if the design of the catch allows for easy adjustment.

It is unrealistic to expect a single "ideal" catch that can fulfill all these expectations. For this reason, the history of jewelry has several categories of catches with countless variations in each style.

Spring rings and box catches are the most common closures used for chains and bracelets, perhaps because they lend themselves to inexpensive mass production. These catches have become so familiar that they are often used without consideration to how they fit into the whole design of a piece. Some goldsmiths even use mass produced catches in their creations when competing in competitions! This is regrettable because failure to consider the catch as an integral part of the design can diminish an entire piece.

Making catches requires a high level of skill, but the rewards, in both technical and aesthetic satisfaction, make the effort worthwhile. The following examples should only serve for inspiration, and may need to be altered for your particular use. It is part of the creative process when designing and drawing the piece to create the most suitable catch and to incorporate it into the entire design of the work.

12.4.2 CROSSBAR CATCH
In this simple catch (figure 12.23), a cross bar on one end of a chain is free to pivot so it can be laid flat along the chain. This allows it to pass through a ring on the opposite end of the chain. When allowed to hang, the bar is pulled perpendicular and cannot pass back through the ring, thus securing the clasp.

The design is not complicated – the bar is nothing more than a short length of wire with a jump ring soldered onto the middle to provide the connection to the chain. The opposing jump ring should be just large enough that the bar with its jump ring barely fits through.

It is nearly impossible for the bar to slip out of its ring accidentally, but to be absolutely safe, solder another jump ring onto the opposing one (to create a "figure 8"). When the bar is passed through both, the effectiveness of the catch is doubled – even if it slides

Figure 12.23
Crossbar catch.

Type of Closure	Preferred Use	Functional Principle	Directon of Opening as related to direction of Pull	Required Flexibility of Chain or Bracelet
Toggle clasp	chain	tension	opposite	longitudinal
Hook	chain	tension	opposite	longitudinal
Spring Ring	chain	tension	opposite	longitudinal
Box clasp with	chain, bracelet	spring	opposite	not required
Spring	chain	spring	identical	transverse
Bayonet clasp	chain, bracelet	spring	identical	totational
Screw clasp	chain, bracelet	friction	identical	rotational
Box clasp	chain, bracelet	spring	identical	not required
Slide clasp	chain	friction	transverse	not required
U-form clasp	chain	spring	transverse	transverse
Open tube	chain	tension	transverse	transverse & longitudinal

Table 12.1
Overview of necklace and bracelet closures.

through one ring, the odds of it passing through both are extremely low. The bar looks more finished if the ends of the small rod are balled up into small spheres as shown.

The crossbar catch can only work if the section of chain to which the bar is attached can also fit through the opposing jump ring. In the case of a thick chain, it might be necessary to use a smaller loop in the section immediately adjacent to the catch, as seen in figure 12.23.

12.4.3 HOOK CATCH

It would be difficult to imagine a catch more basic than a hook. The basic shape is easily bent up from round wire (figure 12.24). The free end of the hook should if possible be long and bent around so that it sits tightly against the jump ring. The opposing jump ring should be large enough that the hook just fits through it.

The security of a hook depends on the tensile strength of the material used to make it. A hook made from thin annealed copper, for example, will simply not stand up to normal wear, no matter how beautifully fashioned it is.

Hooks also work best when they are under some tension. In the case of a necklace catch, the weight of the pendant will keep the chain pulled taut, making the hook secure. When a chain is hanging loosely, as is typically the case in bracelets, it is necessary that the hook and ring snap tightly together.

Variations on the hook clasp are too numerous to list. One possibility is to make the hook from sheet metal rather than wire, as shown in figure 12.25. This has obvious advantages for wide bracelets.

Also shown here are several possible interpretations that can be modified to meet specific needs. The catches shown in figure 12.26 illustrate a "fitted hook" that snaps into its housing. The wire neckpiece in fig-

457

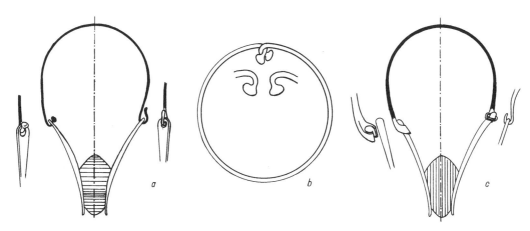

Figure 12.27
Hook catch on neck ring.
a) hook and eye clasp, b) double hook, c) ball and open socket (with hook on the right).

Figure 12.24
Hook catch.

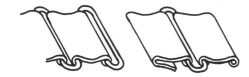

Figure 12.25
Sheet metal hook catch.

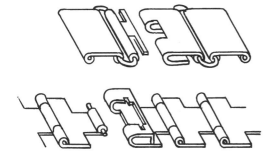

458

Figure 12.26
Variations on the sheet metal hook catch.

ure 12.27a is bent up from a simple round wire and hung onto the forged ends of the lower part. The joint is like a hook catch which is permanently locked in place because the end of the wire has been balled up after being inserted through the hole. The hook for the catch is bent up from round wire. Security in use comes from the springiness of the hoop and the weight of the front, lower portion of the neckpiece.

The hoop in figure 12.27b is closed with a double hook which is functional as well as decorative. A precondition for its effectiveness is the springiness of the hoop.

Two unusual solutions are shown in figure 12.27c. The ends of the thick wire that makes up the hoop that encircles the neck are forged out. On the left, the material is hammered into a claw-like sleeve that will catch the tapered arm of the pendant. This connection is used to hold microphones into their stands. On the right we see the neck wire bent into a hook that engages a loop cut into (or soldered onto) the arm of the pendant. Both variations require that the pendant be relatively heavy in order to keep the parts under tension.

12.4.4 LENTIL CATCH

The term comes from the lentil-like shape of this traditional catch, though in our modern age it might just as readily be called an "aspirin" shape (figure 12.28).

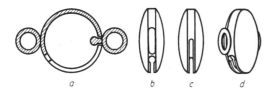

Figure 12.28
Lentoid closure.
a) cross-sectional view, b) side view, c) side view of opposite side,
d) perspective view.

The body of the catch consists of a flattened hollow bead that has a ring attached on one side. The side of the bead is pierced by a slot that ends directly opposite the fixed ring.

The other end of the slot has a round hole, creating a sort of elongated keyhole shape. A ring is fitted with a short length of wire, the end of which has a ball. To engage the catch, the ball is fitted into the hole and drawn around the circumference of the bead until it stops. Tension on the chain keeps the catch closed.

To make this catch, form a circular band from a strip of sheet material. Cut out two circles and dome them slightly. Solder one onto the strip, then drill a hole in the wall. The other dome can now be soldered on and the edges filed smooth.

Saw a slot the takes up at least one-third of the circumference and even it out with needle files. A jump ring can now be soldered onto the wall of the bead, directly opposite the end of the slot. Make a ball of the exact size of the hole and solder it onto the end of a short length of wire. This is fitted with a ring that will join it to the chain. As with any catch, minor adjustments might be needed to make the parts fit smoothly together.

There are many possible variations on this mechanism. If the links of a chain were spherical (or pearls or beads, for instance) an more appropriate shape would be a sphere. In this case omit the ring and make the clasp by soldering two deep domes together. The slot is cut along the seam between the two halves.

In the case of a round wire link, the better choice of clasps might be similar to the lentil but without the domes. For proper strength, use a slightly thicker metal to make the strip. The catch will blend nicely

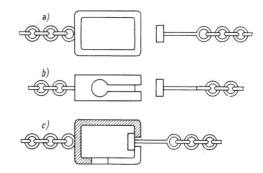

Figure 12.29
Open lentoid closure.
a) and b) opened, top veiw; c) closed, side view.

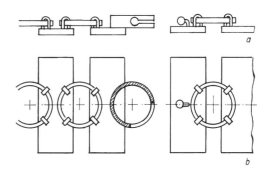

Figure 12.30
Ring-formed lentoid clasp on bracelet backside.

into the rhythm of the chain; the fact that the mechanism is visible adds interest.

In the variation shown in figure 12.29, the lentil shape has been replaced by an open rectangular frame. The ball has been changed into a flat disk that lays snugly against the inside of the frame when the catch is secured.

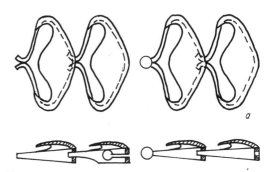

459

Figure 12.31
Ring-formed lentoid clasp enclosed in bracelet frame.

The principle of the lentil catch can be altered to make a hidden catch, an example of which is seen in figure 12.30. Narrow sheet metal links are connected with each other by round jump rings – the frame of the catch with its drilled hole and slit is soldered onto the last link of the chain.

The bracelet seen in figure 12.31 takes this catch to its extreme. The clam shell-shaped links are made of domed sheet metal portions soldered onto frames that are each bent up from flat strips. Holes are made into the frames through which the ends of the wire frame of the next link are placed. The links are joined to each other by inserting the ends of the frame of one unit into the hole on its neighbor. The ends are bent outward slightly (cotter pin style) to join the links. The frame is left somewhat wider on the catch unit to provide for the drilled hole and slot. The ball of the catch is soldered onto the next link, making a completely invisible catch.

Figure 12.32
Spring ring clasp.

12.4.5 SPRING RINGS

The spring ring clasp is perhaps the most familiar of all necklace closures (figure 12.32). They are commonly used on inexpensive chains though they are also seen on expensive pieces. Of course it is possible to make spring rings by hand, but the high quality and low cost of machine made versions make this unnecessary.

Every spring ring has a small jump ring by which it is attached to the chain. This is soldered onto the loop during manufacture, but arranged so its joint remains open. When the chain is connected this ring remains unsoldered because the heat of soldering would destroy the springiness of the catch. Where added security is needed – as in the case of a particularly expensive pendant – the connecting ring can be

sealed closed with a low-melting tin-based solder.

Wear on a spring ring usually occurs at the attaching jump ring. Though it is possible to remove the spring and repair the ring, this is usually not worth the bother. The rings are cheap enough that it is more efficient to remove the worn clasp and replace it with a new one.

Spring rings should never be placed into pickle because the steel spring causes an ion exchange that will cause copper flashing (plating) on the work. If the chain needs to be pickled it can be hung into the bath in such a way that the clasp is not immersed, or the clasp can be removed.

12.4.6 FISHHOOK CLASP

This traditional clasp, seen in figure 12.33, has long been associated with strands of pearls, though it is by no means limited to that application. The clasp is simple and lends itself to mass production which means, of course, that they are inexpensive. The specifications of the tongue are critical, so mass produced clasps of mediocre quality should be avoided. For consistent quality and long wear, the tongue (or hook) must be of precisely the right thickness and shape. It is possible to refine the shape of commercial hooks to improve their "snap."

To make the catch, draw the shape of the unit and plan the location of each of the struts. Draw in a strip of metal that extends at a right angle outward from the "floor" of the catch. Saw this shape from sheet metal approximately 0.5 mm thick. Use a needle file to score a V-groove at the point where each strut

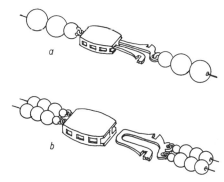

Figure 12.33
One-sided, flat clasp.
a) for single strand and, b) double-strand.

meets the floor. Bend these pieces upright and solder each of the bends to strengthen the scored area.

Cut the tongue from a hard springy alloy, typically 14K gold or nickel silver. Test the tongue in the catch and file both units as necessary until they slide together smoothly and lock securely. The idea is that the tongue first hooks around the end strut then slides into place between the struts on either side of the catch. To release, the sides of the catch are pinched together. This makes the tongue narrower and allows it to slip out of its position.

When the action is perfect (and not before!) the struts are filed to a low and uniform height and the roof of the clasp is soldered on. This is a piece of sheet metal sawn to the same shape as the floor. A jump ring is attached to one end to connect the catch to its chain.

Catches for multiple strand chains can be made using the same principle (figure 12.33b). This catch is not recommended for very heavy necklaces, such as multiple strands of glass beads.

Figure 12.35
The 2-sided horizontal tongue adapted for a link bracelet.

12.4.7 PINCH CLASP

This variation on the catch described above is shown in figure 12.34. It is more secure and therefore sometimes preferred for particularly expensive strands because it has two points of contact. This variation will be used to describe an alternate construction method, though either this or the one described above will work for either catch.

Start by sawing out two identical pieces to be the floor and roof of the catch. To simplify registration, fold a sheet in half and saw out both pieces at once, leaving the fold, of course, until last. Solder short pieces of square wire into position as shown in the diagram, noting that they can extend outside the dimensions of the floor – excess is easily trimmed off later. The jump ring that will connect the catch to the strand is soldered on to one end at this time.

Saw the tongue in the shape shown and test it against the catch before the roof is soldered on. This makes it much easier to see where refinements are needed. When the fit is tight and the action smooth, solder the roof into place and cut away any excess wire that projects from the catch.

A third variation, shown in figure 12.35, lends itself especially to bracelets. The frame of the catch is made from square or rectangular wire, bent into a "U" whose ends are bent inward to form short stops. This unit is soldered onto a rectangular floor plate. The tongue is sawn from sheet metal and embellished with spheres (or other shapes, including bezels) that will offer the pinch points. Assuming the bracelet is hinged, a tubing of the appropriate size and length is soldered to the end of the tongue.

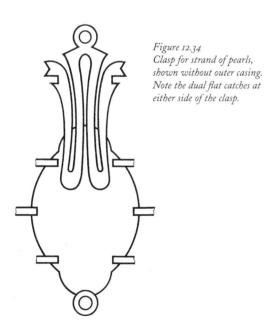

Figure 12.34
Clasp for strand of pearls, shown without outer casing. Note the dual flat catches at either side of the clasp.

461

The action and grasp of the tongue is tested and the pieces are filed as necessary to make a perfect catch. The roof is then soldered on, a tubing knuckle is attached to the back end of the catch and the seams are filed smooth.

12.4.8 BAYONET CATCH

This clutch mechanism, named after its application in securing a bayonet onto a rife, is shown in figure 12.36. The rod is inserted into a tube-like sleeve so that its small projecting pin enters a slot in the side of the tube. The rod is pressed against a spring, rotated, and recoils to seat the pin in the end of the track.

The inner rod can be made of solid wire or a tube that has been capped on both ends, depending on the size of the catch. It is matched with a sturdy tube into which it makes a snug fit. The tube is capped at one end and a jump ring is attached there to connect to the chain.

Use a saw to cut the track, following any of the examples shown in figure 12.37. The idea in every case is to guarantee that the pin "turns the corner" and is

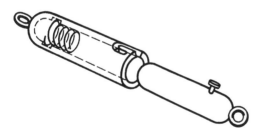

Figure 12.36
A bayonet catch showing the interior spring that keeps the closure under tension.

Figure 12.37
Possible "spring back" shapes for slots in a bayonet catch.

seated in the tip of the slot. In order to release the catch, the rod must be pressed against the spring and rotated – an action that probably won't happen by accident.

In order to lock the spring into position, curl the first coil outward so it has a larger diameter than the tube. When the spring is forced into the tube this tension will keep it in place. It is also possible to secure the spring into place with epoxy, but be certain to use only a tiny amount!

Figure 12.38 shows a sophisticated version of a bayonet clasp in which the mechanism is hidden. This version lends itself to silk cords or similar necklace materials that will need to be glued. The open tube on each side of the catch (#1 and #5) become caps into which a cord can be glued.

The catch is built on tubing in three sizes that slide together. Cut a section of the middle size (#2) and saw the J-shaped track into it. Cap a section of a smaller tube (#1) with a piece of sheet metal. When sawing off the excess metal allow a small tab to remain – this will become the pin that travels into the catch.

When #1 and #2 are working smoothly, solder the tube with the track into the largest sleeve. At the other end, insert a piece of the same tubing used in #1 and solder it into position. In order to ensure smooth action the end of the spring should have a face plate; a small disk that will slide easily along the inner walls of the tube. This is cut from sheet (or by slicing off a tiny section of a thick round wire) and tin-soldered to the spring. The wire is held in place by friction or glue as described above.

12.4.9 THREADED CATCH

This threaded mechanism can be modified to blend into the design of a piece unobtrusively. In traditional ivory and bone necklaces it is common to carve the catch from the same material. In the case of metal jewelry, the shapes of the beads can often be adapted to the form of the catch.

The most basic version is shown in figure 12.39 and consists of two identical sections of tubing. Both are capped on one end and drilled to accept a wire onto

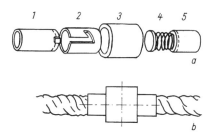

Figure 12.38
Assembly diagram for a hidden bayonet catch.

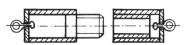

Figure 12.39
Cut-away diagram of a basic threaded catch.

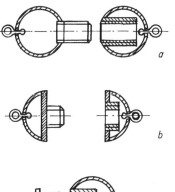

Figure 12.40
Examples of threaded catches hidden inside hollow forms.

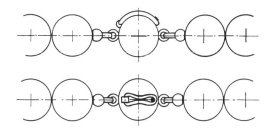

Figure 12.41
Side and top view of a practical but inelegant safety catch.

Figure 12.42
Safety catch on a single sphere.

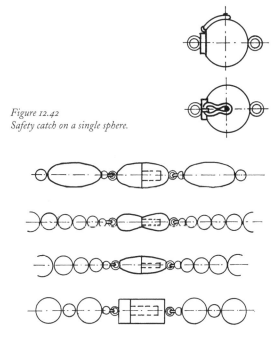

Figure 12.43
Threaded clasps can be designed to blend in to a wide range of shapes.

which a bead has been drawn. This wire will be bent up to make a jump ring and of course is free to rotate independent of the catch. A jump ring connection that was fixed to the catch would cause the necklace to wind up as the catch was being closed.

A thick-walled tube is threaded with a tap and die, cut to the correct length, and soldered into the outer tube. Obviously care must be taken in selecting these tubes to ensure a tight fit. A rod of the correct diameter is selected and tapped with matching threads. When the pieces are confirmed, a short length of the threaded section is sawn off and soldered into the

other piece of the catch. It is useful to bevel the tip of the threaded section slightly to make it easier to engage the threads.

Many variations can be worked on the threaded closure, a few of which are seen in figure 12.40. In the first example, two spheres are purchased or made by soldering together two dapped domes. A tube is threaded on its interior walls with a die and a matching rod is cut with threads to make a tight fit. These are then soldered into position as shown at (a).

In the case of 12.40b, a single sphere is made to enclose the catch. One dome is decked and a thread-

463

ed rod is soldered into its center. To make the other piece, start by soldering a section of tubing onto a piece of sheet. Drill a hole through the sheet and thread the interior of the tube, then solder the whole unit to a hemispherical dome. Note that the same kind of jump ring connection is used.

The variation shown in figure 12.40c might be seen as a hybrid of the first two. Like the first, it has a significant length of threads, which clearly contributes to its strength. Like (b), the clasp is a single sphere. As before, cut and shape all the pieces, but avoid soldering them all together until the threaded sections have been proved to work.

The familiar safety catch, shown here in figures 12.41 and 12.42, consists of a loop of wire that snaps into place on a small ball attached to the opposite half of the catch. As shown, either variation is possible,

but neither complements the sophisticated clean lines of the hidden catch.

Though difficult in the telling, threaded closures are easy to make if you have a tap and die. They lend themselves to a wide range of use, as shown briefly in figure 12.43, where the catch is "camouflaged" to work well in a variety of situations.

12.4.10 BOX CATCHES
Box catches lend themselves to a wide range of shapes and are frequently used on chains, bracelets and cuff bracelets. They combine security with ease of use and the ability to be adapted to the needs of each design. After mastering the basics, it becomes an appealing challenge to a goldsmith to design a box catch uniquely suited to each new piece. The basic ingredients – tongue, box, snag and trigger – will be introduced through the basic box shown here, and they will reappear in each permutation.

There are many ways to approach the construction of a box catch, each with its proponents and detractors. The following pages show several traditional procedures with the hope that each reader will take from them whatever tips and suggestions seem best suited to his or her individual working style.

First variation
Figure 12.44 shows a bracelet catch. Start by bending up a rectangular frame from strips of sheet metal, probably about 0.5 mm (24 gauge), leaving the wall high enough to allow a slight curve to be filed in. This will accommodate the curve of the wrist and allow the catch to blend in with the rest of the bracelet. The frame is decked with curved panels of the same gauge. In order to avoid the problem of soldering an enclosed form, cut a line (or drill a small hole) in the top panel at the place where the slot will be cut in the next step.

Fold a sheet of the same gauge metal in half and tap it with a mallet make it flat. This will become the two face plates of the catch. As seen in 12.44b and c, cut a slot in the box that will permit this folded sheet to slide snugly into place. Slide the folded piece into position and scribe a line onto this piece to indicate

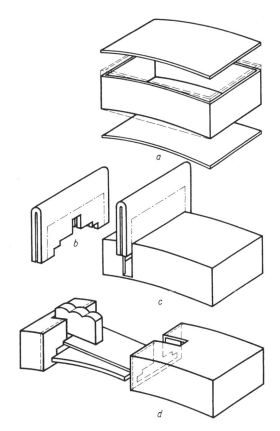

Figure 12.44
The constructions details of a box clasp, described here as the first variation.

its location in the box. This fine line shows up in the center illustration. Centered in this space, use a saw and files to create the silhouette shown in (b) to provide a space for the tongue, which will be attached to the shorter side of the catch. The shape and proportion of this cutout might seem odd at first, but will make sense after going through the process a few times. The face plates are centered in the slot using the scribed line drawn earlier and soldered. The projecting portions of the face plates and the floor of the original box are cut with a saw so the box comes apart in two pieces. The floor plate is separated with a sawblade between the two halves of the face plate.

Use a thin sawblade to cut a rectangular opening in the top of each half to accommodate the trigger, the vertical segment that is pressed down to release the catch. The size of this opening depends on the size of the trigger, which is in turn a function of the design and location of the catch.

The tongue can be made in several ways, but however it is constructed it must make a snug fit into the matching slot and be springy enough to recoil when it is depressed (figure 12.44d). One way to achieve this is to attach the trigger onto a strip of thin metal that is then folded, trimmed to size and checked against the slot. When the tongue fits well and the action is as desired, the tongue is soldered to the shorter section of the catch.

An alternate method is to construct the tongue from two pieces of metal that are riveted together at the tip. The trigger is attached to the top panel and the lower piece is soldered onto the box, then both pieces can be hammered to restore their hardness. Tiny rivets are set in the tip to bind the two pieces together. In either case it is useful to saw or file small notches in the top of the trigger to allow the user's fingernail to grip it.

In a proper box catch the pieces will not rattle against each other, but rather fit like a hand in a glove. A light push on the trigger should flex the tongue enough to allow it to clear the place where it is "hung up" on the inside of the face plate. When being closed, the tongue should be easily pinched as it slides into the box, then it should snap up to engage. The pressure needed to make this happen should be noticeable but not painful.

Second variation
Figure 12.45 shows a variation in which a single face plate is used. The box is prepared as before and the appropriate profile sawn into a single sheet. A slot is cut into the box as shown, wide enough that the plate attaches to just one side when soldered. Of course it is also possible to cut the box into its two halves then solder the face plate onto the larger unit.

Cut a strip of thin metal that will become the tongue and solder the trigger onto one end. Position this, trigger down, in the smaller box and solder it

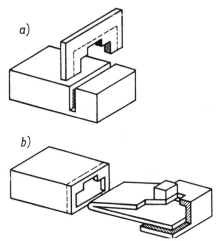

Figure 12.45
The construction details of an alternate style box catch, described in the text as second variation.

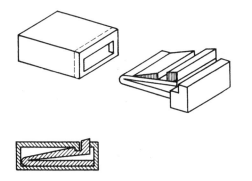

Figure 12.46
A third variation on the box catch.

there. Scribe a line and fold the tongue in half, striking it with a mallet or small hammer to crimp the fold and work harden the tongue. Use a knife blade or similar small tool to lift the tongue to its springy position.

Third variation
In the catch shown in figure 12.46 the box is the same as the previous types, but the tongue is different. The trigger is a bar the goes across the width of the tongue, made either by soldering on a section of square wire as shown here, or by bending the tip of the tongue up at a right angle.

The element of the tongue that engages the lip of the box is not the end of the tongue as before, but the leading edge of an applied piece of sheet soldered across the tongue. This must have a sharp corner at

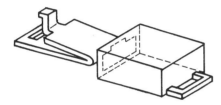

Figure 12.47
Box catch with tongue made from a single sheet of metal.

the edge closest to the trigger – this is what gets "stuck" on the inside lip of the face plate and makes the catch work. The appliqué sheet is filed to a wedge shape to allow it to slide easily into position.

Fourth variation
The tongue of a box catch can be as simple as a sin-

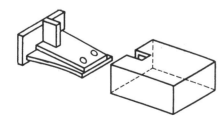

Figure 12.48
A box catch in which the tongue has been riveted on to the base plate.

gle piece of sheet metal, cut and bent as shown in figure 12.47. In this case no soldering is done to the tongue so it remains work hardened. The construction is so simple this kind of box catch is often used on inexpensive commercial chains. Though simple, this most basic version is rarely used for high end jewelry because it lacks the delicacy of the versions shown above.

Fifth variation
The tongue is sometimes made from a sheet riveted onto a single plate (figure 12.48). This is easy to make but the tongue can easily bend out of shape or break off at the point where it is soldered to the short plate that makes up the back of the catch.

As stated above, each situation will dictate the appropriate size and shape for a box catch. Nevertheless, it might be useful to have some general guidelines:

- To achieve the necessary springiness and tensile strength, the tongue should be about 10 mm long, 6 mm wide and made of metal that is 0.4 mm (24 gauge) thick.
- The height of the catch must be sufficient that the tongue can spring up inside it. Note that the end of the tongue must engage with the inside of the face plate, but that only a small lip is necessary.
- The slit in the face plate into which the tongue slides has to be high enough for the tongue (two pieces of sheet) can enter it when pressed together.

Box catch safeties
Box catches are very secure if they are well made and properly used. Because they're relatively easy to make and virtually foolproof to use, most of the time they are sufficient and reliable. The only way they can come undone by accident is if there is some force that unintentionally presses down on the trigger. Especially in the case of bracelets, where a wrist can easily bump against a surface, this is cause for some concern.

A simple solution is the addition of pieces of metal on either side of the trigger as shown in figure 12.49.

These can of course take a variety of shapes and offer an opportunity to embellish the design. They generally contribute to the look of a box clasp in that the trigger no longer projects abruptly from the flat surface of the box.

An alternative that can work with or without the addition of blocks is a safety clasp that is engaged after the box clasp is secured. A selection of this kind of attachment is shown in figure 12.50.

The safety in figure 12.50a consists of a flap with a pin projecting from it. This flat is made to hinge from the body of the box catch and is secured be pressing the pin into a hole in the same half of the clasp. With the pin in place the tongue of the box clasp cannot be depressed.

The most common style of safety is the figure 8 safety seen in figure 12.50b. The wire loop pivots in a section of tubing and snaps in place behind a ball which is soldered onto the tongue portion of the catch. The first benefit of this safety is that it guarantees that the tongue is pushed far enough into the box catch – the mechanism only works when the box catch is fully closed. In addition it also holds the box catch together if the trigger is accidentally depressed.

The safety device in figure 12.50c works just like the figure 8. In this version a strip of sheet cut to the shape shown in the drawing is used instead of a wire loop. Some variation on a hinge is used to allow a pivot on the end of the strip while the free end snaps tightly over a ball soldered onto the tongue-end of the clasp.

Yet another variation is shown at 12.50d. In this case the safety is loosely riveted on and rotates up or down to engage or release a pin from within a small loop. It is worth mentioning here again that each of these examples could be modified in many ways. In this case, for example, the loop could be a section of tubing or the rotating bar sawn from sheet.

Almost all of the mechanisms above can be applied to the top plate of a box catch as well as to the sides as shown. In some cases it is possible that the safety takes the role of the bars mentioned above in that the

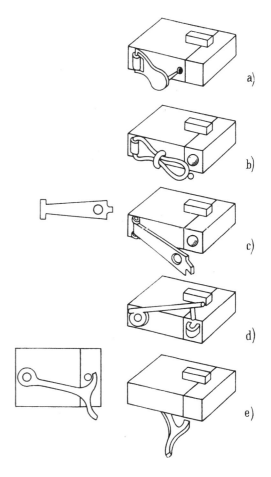

Figure 12.50
Various safety catches on box clasps.

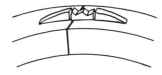

Figure 12.49
The trigger can be protected against accidental opening by placing ornamental ribs on either side.

mechanism shields the trigger from an accidental push. In addition it can sometimes be contrived that the loop like the figure 8 loop hooks directly onto the trigger, in which case the addition of a ball can be avoided.

The drawback of these ingenious variations is that they sometimes get too complex, visually and manually. Two important factors in evaluating a catch are its ease of use and its ability to blend into the overall design.

The safety shown in figure 12.50e illustrates a device that can be almost completely hidden beneath the box catch. In this case a horizontal action is used to hook or disconnect a loosely riveted hasp. The pivoting section can be sawn from sheet or made from wire and will probably require delicate adjustment to achieve a snap fit.

12.4.11 HINGE-STYLE CATCHES

The following catches are all based on a conventional hinge – that is, a series of tubes (knuckles) soldered alternately onto two elements in an alignment that permits a rod (hinge pin) to penetrate the entire series. In the case of a clasp, the pin is removable. The basic arrangement is shown in figure 12.51.

Though it has other uses, this style catch is most commonly seen on hinged bracelets. Among its advantages are the facts that it blends in with the rest of the piece and has the same range of movement as the other joints.

As with other catches, many variations are possible. As a general rule, each will have these requirements:

- The pin must be loose enough to be removed, but tight enough that it doesn't fall out by accident.
- The pin must have a knob or similar arrangement to provide a grip for ease of removal.
- The pin must be somehow permanently attached to the clasp so it is not lost.

The hinge-style catches illustrated here use three-part hinges, and though five or seven part hinges can be used, it is usually best to limit the number to three. More knuckles make closing the catch more difficult.

To make the clasp match other hinges that have more units, file grooves as needed to imitate a multiple knuckle hinge.

Pin catch with a friction fit
The simplest version of this style is depicted in figure 12.51a, a catch that has traditionally be used in filigree bracelets. In this case the tubes are exactly the same as the other hinges in the bracelet. A pin is made of a tapered rod onto which a ball has been soldered to serve as a knob. A small piece of chain is attached to the pin to prevent its being lost when removed and the pin is flattened slightly to make it a tight fit in the tubes.

A simple variation is shown in 12.51b. Here the chain length is contrived so the pin cannot be withdrawn from the last knuckle of the tubing. Obviously when this clasp is being assembled the pin must be in location before the chain is soldered to the knob.

If the chain is attached to both ends of the bracelet

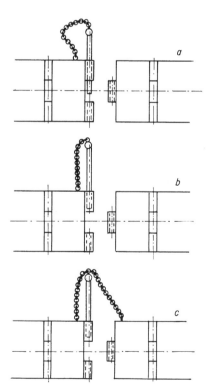

Figure 12.51
Variations on a hinge-style catch.

as well as to the pin (figure 12.51c) it also has the function of a safety chain. As with other uses of this safety chain, there is risk that the delicate chain will get caught on things as a wearer moves her arm, rendering the chain more of a liability than a safety. In the case of the example shown at (c) this means the safety chain would encourage removal of the pin rather than prevent it!

In the basic version shown here, the tubes are often of the same thin-walled construction as the hinges, though thicker material is preferred because it will stand up to the stresses of use associated with the catch. In the following variations, thicker tubing is assumed.

Figure 12.52 shows a variation of the hinge-style catch in which the pin is prevented from coming completely free by a stop that is attached to the end knuckle. In this version the pin is made of a length of tubing that makes a snug fit inside the knuckles. Cut a small slit at the top of the end knuckle (or, alternately, drill a hole there) and insert a tiny piece of sheet or wire so that it projects into the tubing. Cut a slot along the length of the tube equivalent to two knuckles and insert the pin, from the "bottom" into the catch. Contrive the length of the pin so that it can be withdrawn only far enough to disengage the knuckle on the other unit of the bracelet. With the tube in its fully extended position it is relatively easy to solder on some sort of knob that will prevent the pin from falling out. This sequence, in which soldering is done on the pin when extended will be used on the following examples as well.

The same catch principle can be seen again in figure 12.53 but here two catch hinge pins are used, one coming from each side. This makes the construction more complex but increases the safety factor because the bracelet can be lost only if both pins are opened simultaneously.

The variation shown in 12.54 uses a solid round wire as the hinge pin. This wire is filed to have a flat facet on its upper two-thirds as shown. A wire or tiny piece of sheet is soldered across the top opening of the end knuckle, the pin is insert (again, from the "bottom") and the knob is soldered on.

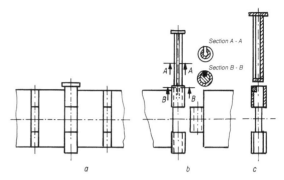

Figure 12.52
In this variation of the hinge-style clasp the pin is held into the top knuckle. This makes the attaching chain unnecessary.

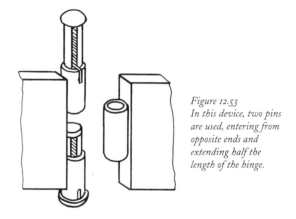

Figure 12.53
In this device, two pins are used, entering from opposite ends and extending half the length of the hinge.

469

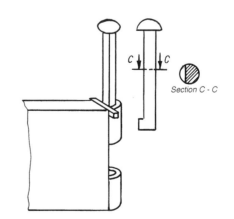

Figure 12.54
This catch shows yet another way to trap the sliding pin into the tubes.

Catch with a tension pin

The action of the pin will feel more secure if there is friction of the pin against the inner walls of the tubing. The catch shown in figure 12.55 illustrates a version that achieves this while also using a stop similar to the styles just shown.

The pin is made of two lengths of half-round wire. This can be purchased or made by folding over a flattened strip of wire and pulling it through a round drawplate. The tip of the two pieces is reinforced by soldering and they are rounded to make a tidy end. The top of the end knuckle is prepared as before by sawing a slit and inserting a small piece of thin sheet. This is soldered into position across the opening of the tube, shown here at E-E.

The split pin is inserted from below and slid up the tubes so that one leg goes on each side of the bar. A knob is soldered on, thereby locking the pin into place. The legs of the pin are pulled apart as needed to achieve a snug fit when the catch is closed.

The catch with a spring pin shown in figure 12.56 has no stop against falling out, but the degree of security is significantly higher because of the springiness of the pin wires. A knob is made by soldering a disk to a short length of tubing that makes a snug fit in the top knuckle of the catch. Half-round wire is prepared as before but left springy as a consequence of its being drawn down. Two pieces of this wire are laid flat-to-flat and attached inside the knob with tin solder. This will insure that the springiness is retained.

Make a jump ring of thin wire and solder it inside the opening of the end knuckle, then file small notches in the two wires that make the pin as shown. The wires are sprung outward so they make a tight friction along the walls of the tubing. Before the pin can be completely removed these filed notches will snag on the jump ring. The tips of the wires are filed round to make it easier to insert the pin.

Turning pin catch

This version of the hinge-style catch (figure 12.57) is somewhat elaborate, both to construct and to use, but the result is sophisticated and very secure. Start by making a pair of tubes that fit snugly together, one

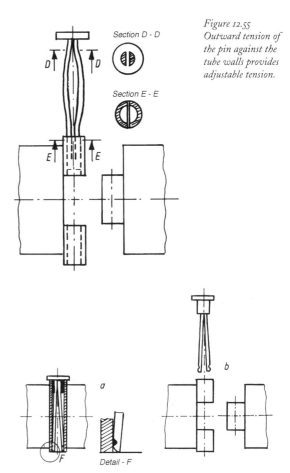

Figure 12.55
Outward tension of the pin against the tube walls provides adjustable tension.

Section D - D

Section E - E

Figure 12.56
A simple yet effective mechanism that protects against the pin sliding out.

Detail - F

inside the other. Cut a length of the smaller tube that is slightly shorter than the width of the catch and saw a slot along almost the entire length of this tube.

Prepare the hinge pin by creating a rod or tube that fits into the catch. Solder a short piece of sheet at one end as a key flag. The size will be such that this pin slides neatly along the track made by the slot in the inner tube. When all the pieces work together, slide the tubes together and solder them. This tubing is then cut into three sections and soldered to the bracelet units, with care taken that the slot matches up when the pieces are brought together.

Notice in figure 12.57b that the inner tube is slightly shorter than the catch itself. In this way the pin can be rotated when the bracelet is closed, considerably

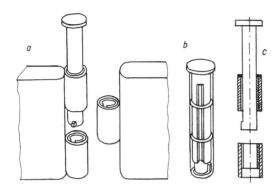

Figure 12.57
This challenging construction allows for the pin to lock into place by being rotated when closed.

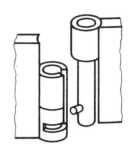

Figure 12.58
This catch has no moving parts, but instead depends on the stiffness of the bracelet to provide the tension needed to keep the clasp secure.

improving the security of the catch. To achieve this effect, slide the pin into place, rotate it to engage the flag on the lip of the inner tube, and trim the top of the pin flush. Rotate the pin enough to allow the flag to find the track, extend the pin, and solder the knob on the top.

Catch with a fixed hinge pin
This catch looks like a hinge-style catch, though in fact its mechanism is considerably different. In situations where there is flexibility, it makes an easy and intriguing alternative.

As seen in figure 12.58, the catch consists of two pieces of tubing, one twice as long as the other. A shallow line can be cut around the longer tube to give the appearance of a hinge. A piece of round wire is soldered into the shorter length tube and given a small projecting pin as shown.

The larger tube is slotted with a saw to create an opening whose width will allow the pin to travel easily along it. These two prepared tubes are soldered onto the bracelet in an orientation that requires the bracelet to be flexed at an extreme angle to engage the pin in the slot. The pieces are linked together and the short horizontal part of the track allows the bracelet to return to its normal, wearable position.

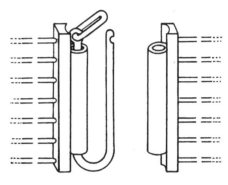

Figure 12.59
This simple catch is often appropriate for multiple strand necklaces and bracelets.

U-shaped link with a hook
Unlike the catches described above, this variation rarely blends into the design. It particularly lends itself to flexible bracelets and necklaces made up of beads, jump rings or wire elements. As shown in figure 12.59, the catch is built on two panels that will connect to the bracelet. These can vary considerably in shape, depending on the context of the work.

Onto these are soldered two identical lengths of tubing. A wire is prepared so it makes a snug fit inside this tube. Solder a small tube or jump ring at one end of this wire and through it feed a jump ring of thin gauge wire. This is soldered and bent to a long oval. Feed the wire through one of the tubes and bend it

471

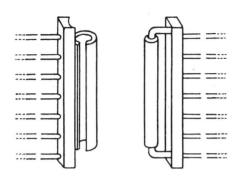

Figure 12.60
More a wide hook than a tube catch, this resembles a hinge catch but has no moving parts.

into a U-shape in which the two arms are parallel and an appropriate distance apart to make the clasp look good. Slide the other tube in place to close the catch, trim the wire to length and file a notch as shown to snap onto the oval ring. It should be clear that springiness in the U-shaped wire will add strength to the catch.

Figure 12.60 shows a less exotic catch that is included here only because it can be made to resemble a hinge. Solder a length of tubing onto one side of the bracelet and cut a slot along its entire length close to the point where it attaches to the bracelet. On the opposite side, bend a wire to make a wicket that will engage the open tube as a hook engages an eye. Of course it is possible that this is a simple wire, but the proportions are generally improved if the wicket is thickened with the addition of a tube as shown. In practice it is important that the slot is a tight fit for the wicket so the two elements snap together.

12.4.12 FUNCTIONAL ANALYSIS

By way of a summary it might be helpful to review several familiar catches in objective terms. This analysis will consider the use or application of a finding, the appropriate environment for the catch (i.e. the flexibility, weight, and access associated with it), its

direction of opening, security, and how well it lends itself to harmonizing with a design.

The illustrations on pages 473–475 show each of the clasps discussed in this section. The drawings and descriptions above are intended to present in a general way a few of the most common families of catches. For simplicity most have been presented in the context of a bracelet, but it must be emphasized that the relevance of these catches extends to necklaces, armbands, watch straps, and dozens of uses yet to be devised.

Designers must consider many factors as they decide which closure will best complete a given jewelry piece. In some catches the direction of tension is the same as the direction of opening. An example would be a box catch, in which the tongue slides into the box in the same axis as the chain it is closing. An example of the other category in which the direction of closing is at a right angle to the direction of tension is a hinge-style catch. Here the joining mechanism of the pin is 90° from the direction of opening of the bracelet.

This tells us that in the former cases, security depends on the tensile strength, springiness and wear resistance of the metal selected. In the second category, the closure is primarily a matter of mechanics. For maximum security it is best if the opening direction and the direction of stress on the catch are at right angles to each other because external forces are completely absorbed by the rigid parts of the catch.

One of the enjoyable challenges of goldsmithing is that of determining the ideal clasp for each situation. This will be aided by a thorough understanding of the traditional devices outlined here, but it must be more. A creative designer will modify findings to his or her particular need, going so far in some cases that the end result is an entirely new concept!

CROSSBAR CATCH

Application   A catch for single chains; preferred for chains with open links.

Function   The crossbar is fed through the opposing jump ring; this mandates flexibility or small links. The opposite jump ring must be large enough to permit entry by the crossbar and chain. The catch works by tension on it in use.

Opening   Right angles to the direction of stress.

Security   The catch holds securely even under low tension, as with light chains, particularly if the catch has been made with two opposing jump rings.

Design   This catch lends itself to chains with large open links and simple designs.

HOOK AND EYE

Application   The catch is preferred for single chains, particularly for open links and for neckpieces.

Function   In order to be able to hang the hook into the opposing jump ring the chain has to have a certain degree of flexibility. The catch requires some tension to be secure so it is not recommended for very light pieces.

Opening   In opposition to the direction of stress.

Security   Tension on the clasp must be large enough that the hook cannot come free by itself. Security is increased if the hook is long and the opening as small as possible.

Design   Open chain links with pendants and for neckpieces.

LENTIL CATCH

Application   Single chains as well as open link chains but also with strands of pearls and gems.

Function   The knob of the catch is inserted into the catch and revolved about 160° so the chain must have some flexibility. The catch is held under tension by the weight of a pendant or similar force pulling it taut.

Opening   In opposition to the direction of stress.

Security   If the chain is heavy enough the knob cannot slide back on itself in the slot.

Design   The shell of the catch can be lentil shaped, spherical or fitted to similar kinds of links; a pierced or open version is suitable for lighter designs.

SPRING RING

Application   It is a catch for all kinds of chains, even strands of beads as well as neck and arm jewelry. It is not suitable for wide link bracelets.

Function   The spring ring is similar to a hook but here it is closed by the movement of a spring-loaded element that closes the hook. Because of this the spring ring is secure even when there is no tension on the chain.

Opening   The spring ring coordinates pretty well with open chain links, particularly if its size is similar to the chain. Spring rings are not generally used for bracelets or bands with wide links because they disturb the visual rhythm.

FISH HOOK CLASPS

Application   Preferred for single and multiple strands of pearls.

Function   The tongue is pushed into the box catch and snaps into two notches. It functions independently of any tension on the piece, but if the stress is too large the tongue can accidentally open.

Opening   It is identical to the direction of tension.

Security   Under normal stresses the catch is trustworthy. In those designs that allow the tongue to hook around a strut of the box, the catch gains an additional degree of security.

Design   Often used with beaded strands, even though it interrupts the unity of the design. Because the workings are internal this catch offers a relatively broad surface for embellishment.

BAYONET CATCH

Application   A catch for narrow chains and bracelets.

Function   A pin or bolt is pushed into a tube, guided by the a small projection that travels along a slot. The insertion depresses a spring which pushes the bolt outward as it is rotated to lodge in a "backflow" section of the slot. The catch works independently from any tension on the object.

Opening   Identical to the direction of tension on the object.

Security   The catch is very trustworthy as long as the spring is sufficiently powerful.

Design   Because of its round cross section the bayonet catch is especially used for chains with cylindrical links, but it is also suitable for the decorative cords and strung beads.

THREADED CATCH

Application   A catch for narrow chains and bracelets, particularly if the links have a round cross section; also used for strands of beads.

Function   Because the catch is threaded and screws into place, it must rotate independently of the neighboring links.

Opening   The same as the direction of tension.

Security   Security depends on the precision of the threads, the wear resistance of the material, and the friction between parts that will prevent the pieces from unscrewing as worn. If these factors are handled well the catch if very secure.

Design   It can be used as an alternative to a bayonet catch, blending well with necklaces and narrow bracelets.

BOX CATCH

Application   Widely used for bracelets, necklaces and watch bracelets. With variations box catches can prove useful in other situations too.

Function   The tongue is pushed into the catch and snaps into place behind the face plate. The catch is independent of external tensions on the work.

Opening   Identical with the direction of tension on the piece.

Security   If the tongue has a full degree of springiness and snaps into place properly behind the face plate the catch has a high degree of security. It is important to insure that the trigger cannot be depressed accidentally.

Design   Because the box can be hidden on the underside of a decorative link the catch is not obtrusive. It is frequently possible to incorporate the box catch mechanism into the visual flow of a piece and in this way hide the catch.

HINGE-STYLE CATCH

Application   This catch is used most often for wide bracelets.

Function   The tube links are held in alignment, then a pin is pushed in to secure them.

Opening   At right angles to the direction of tension.

Security   If the pin cannot slip out by itself then the catch is very trustworthy.

Design   This catch is most appropriate for hinged bracelets.

U-BEND CATCH

Application   A catch for wide bracelets.

Function   The bracelet must be moveable sideways, so that the hinge tubing can be hooked over the U-bend. The closure flap along with the springiness of the U-bend ensures against lateral shifting.

Opening   At right angles to the direction of tension on the object.

Security   Because any weight or stress is carried by the U-bent wire, the catch is very trustworthy as long as the closing flap remains in place.

Design   Because a bracelet must have some side-to-side flexibility to engage the catch, jump rings and overlapping unit bracelets are especially well suited for it.

OPEN TUBE

Application   This is a catch for wide bracelets.

Function   The bracelet has to be flexible in both its length and cross section in order to be able to engage the clasp. It is then held in place by the tension on the bracelet.

Opening   At right angles to the direction of stress.

Security   Depends on the snap fit of the outer tube over the wicket. This is in turn largely determined by the tensile strength and thickness of the metal being used.

Design   This catch can be an alternative to the preceding two catches.

12.5
Brooches

12.5.1 FUNCTIONAL ELEMENTS
AND DECORATIVE FORMS

Centuries ago when humans were limited to relatively crude techniques for cutting and sewing garments, pins were used to gather and secure pieces onto the body. With the development of tailoring and fasteners, pins have evolved from functional to decorative accessories.

Our most basic understanding of a pin derives from its ancient origins and consists of a thin pointed shaft that easily penetrates fabric, but that has a "head" on the other end to prevent the pin from going all the way through (figure 12.62b). This simple configuration can still be seen today in the form of tie pins (stick pins) and still have the same shortcoming – because there is nothing on the tip, the pin can work itself loose and fall out.

One historically important style of simple pin is called the penannular brooch, shown in figure 12.62c. A section of fabric is gathered up and pulled through the ring where it is speared by the pin. The ring is rotated until the pin lines up with the opening – it is passed through to the top of the ring which is then rotated to cinch it in place. This is particularly effective on thick fabric, which explains its wide use among the Celts of Britain who used it to secure their tartan robes.

Another ancient device (figure 12.62d) is so familiar that it's easy to forget what an important advance it represented in its day. It has remained unchanged through thousands of years, which says a lot about the effectiveness of the design. Safety pins can be made of almost any size wire, though most fall between 1 and 2 millimeters. One end is filed to a point and the other is forged to widen it. This section is bent into a scoop as shown to contain the tip of the pin. The springiness is determined by the type of wire used and its degree of work hardening.

We will go on to discuss more elaborate catches, but it is worth noting that this simple pin has all the ingredients we will find in more sophisticated pins: a pointed stem, a hinged section, and an enclosing catch.

The last drawing in figure 12.62 shows an early variation of the safety pin called a fibula. The pin, spring and bow are typically forged from a single piece. In this case the catch has been soldered on.

Of course it is still possible to make fibula; a contemporary example is shown in figure 12.63. Far more common, however, are pins in which the holding apparatus is distinct from the piece of jewelry, generally created or purchased as a separate finding that is attached to the back in such a way that it is invisible when the pin is being worn.

As mentioned above, a pin back system consists of the pin, a hinge-like element called the joint, and a

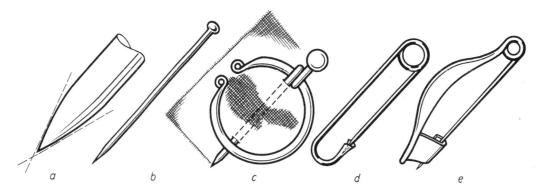

Figure 12.62
a) shows the ideal "bullet" point for a pinstem, c) shows a traditional penannular brooch, d) shows a classic fibula design in both its ancient and modern versions.

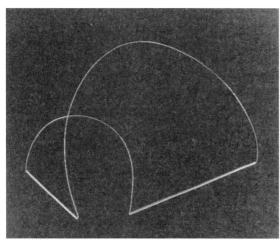

Figure 12.63
Pin made of steel wire and silver tubing.

catch. These components are manufactured in equal quality and far cheaper than it would be possible to make them by hand Accordingly they are used not just in mass produced jewelry but also with one-of-a-kind pieces. The decision to attach a manufactured pin back onto a hand made piece of jewelry it is always a judgment call as to whether it can be unified with the sensibility of the piece. In certain cases there will be the need to make the finding by hand so that it integrates in shape, size and proportion to the unique object. With this in mind, some traditional pin systems are described here.

There are some principles and obvious rules that arise from the function of a pin back system, and even though they should be part of a goldsmith's basic knowledge they are not always completely clear, particularly with younger colleagues (figure 12.64).

- Pins are made to be pushed into the material with the wearer's right hand. Therefore on the back of a brooch the joint should lie on the right and the hook on the left when they are soldered on.
- The opening of the hook should always face down. If the safety should open, the point is still held into the hook by the force of gravity upon the brooch.
- The joint and hook catch are positioned above the center axis of the pin. This will prevent the pin from tilting forward when being worn.

- The joint and hook catch should be just high enough off the pin to allow a gather of fabric to fit easily beneath. From this it follows that pins intended for heavy fabric like coats will need taller findings than pins intended to be worn on a sheer blouse.
- When the pinstem is engaged in the catch it should lie parallel to the back of the brooch (d).
- The pinstem should be able to open wide enough to make it easy to position, typically as much as 90°, as seen in (b).
- The pin is bent slightly at the joint to create tension when the tip is contained in the hook. Though subtle, this provides a surprising amount of security in even simple catches.

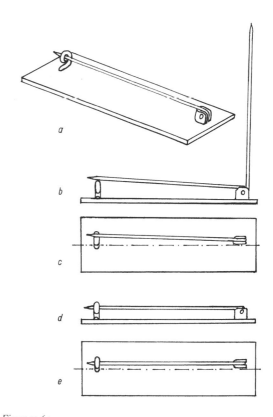

Figure 12.64
A basic pin mechanism.
b) illustrates that the pinstem is under tension at rest, c) shows the location of the stem above the midline of the brooch.

477

12.5.2 PINSTEMS AND JOINTS

Virtually all pinstems are made of round wire, often the same alloy as used to make the piece. An exception is the use of nickel silver on sterling objects, where the base metal provides increased toughness and spring. If the pin is attached by a mechanical means (like a rivet) it does not need to be taken into consideration when stamping the quality of the alloy.

Most pinstems will have a diameter of 1.2–1.5 mm (18–16 gauge) but of course each situation must be considered individually. Where the pinstem is longer or the pin heavier it might be wise to increase the diameter of wire being used.

The simplest attachment for a pinstem is to simply bend a loop at the end. More sophisticated arrangements will attach a piece of sheet or a section of tubing to provide the hinge pivot. When this is attached the pinstem is cut to the correct length and a point is filed at the tip. This is more demanding than it might seem at first. If the pin is overly tapered it becomes weak. If the point is too severe it will snag on threads as it penetrates the fabric and cause damage. The proper point (figure 12.62a) is a long cone that has been smoothed and then burnished to a bullet shape. It should be tested through fabric samples at the bench to insure that it can be pushed through without catching or jerking.

Tie pins (stick pins)

Though not widely used today, these ornamental pins contribute to the scarce range of men's jewelry and in fashions of a bygone era provided an elegant accent on a gentleman's tie. The pin stem is prepared as above, bent at a right angle and soldered to the ornament as shown in figure 12.65. It would be possible to stick the tip of the pin into a cork to hold it in position while soldering, but if many pieces are being made an jig like the one shown might be worthwhile.

In previous times in order to help fix the pin in place, the middle region would be forged flat and twisted. This increases the friction of pin against the fabric, but has the disadvantage of widening the hole and possibly damaging the cloth. A modern variation is the addition of a spring-loaded clutch that attach-

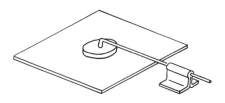

Figure 12.65
Soldering a stick pin finding in place with the aid of a holding jig.

es over the tip of the pin. This protects the point against accidentally poking the wearer and makes it impossible for the pin to fall out by accident.

U-shaped joints

The joint (or hinge component) is shown in its assembled side view at the top of figure 12.66a. This version is bent up from a single strip of sheet, filed and drilled to accept a small bit of wire that passes through the pinstem. As shown in the accompanying drawings, a flattened jump ring is soldered onto a wire to complete the pinstem. The finding can be lightened and made more graceful by cutting away a small section on the underside as shown.

The location of the hole should be such that when the units are temporarily assembled, the pin sticks dramatically upward. Use a round file to take material away from the bent section of the joint (the bottom of the U) until the pinstem lays down almost flat. Tension on the pin is created by forcing the stem to bend slightly as it is hooked into the catch. If the pin sticks up too far, this effort will bend the pin and defeat the purpose. In practice it is a simple matter to check the tension frequently during filing.

A simplified version of this joint is created by soldering a U-shaped piece so it is the bottom of the U that is in contact with the pin. This arrangement does not provide a surface against which the pin pushes, and therefore does not provide the upward tension just mentioned. To create this a short length of wire is soldered to the pinstem near the joint, coming off at a right angle. This is trimmed to a length at which it stops the pin at the appropriate height.

Ball-shaped joints

This joint looks nicer than a simple U-bend joint with its rounded sides and it fits better with the ball catch that is frequently used (figure 12.66b). Saw the basic shape from sheet that is one millimeter thick and bend it around a piece of stock that is slightly thicker. Drill a hole through both sides and round the piece with a file. File a flat facet on the bent area to create a soldering surface and attach the piece to the pin, again locating it above the center line.

Because this pin joint does not have a stop for the pin, a foot must be added to the pinstem itself. This can be as simple as a bend of wire, leaving what might be thought of as an "S" on the end of the pin. A more elegant solution involves soldering a piece of sheet metal to the stem and shaping it as shown in figure 12.66b.

Hinged joint

Measure a short piece of tube into three equal seg-ments and cut each line with a fine sawblade, stopping when the cut is about ¾ths of the way through. File away the middle segment, leaving only a bridging strut that connects to two end pieces (figure 12.66c). The "bridge" will hold the knuckles in alignment and prevent their sliding closer together or further apart.

Prepare a shallow groove to accept the knuckles, wire the piece into position and solder it in place, either directly onto the pin or onto a thick piece of stock that will then be attached to the pin. When the solder is complete and confirmed, saw away the connecting strut.

Take a small piece of the same tubing, slightly longer than the gap between the two knuckles, and solder it to the pinstem. The joint will be made stronger by first filing a groove into the tube. Allow the back end of the stem to project beyond the tube; this makes a useful handle in which to grasp the pinstem for hardening. Hold each end of the stem in pli-

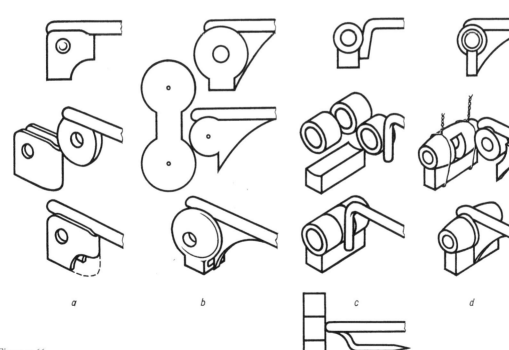

a   b   c   d

Figure 12.66
Today many jewelers use manufactured pin joints but any of these styles can be made at the bench as needed.

479

ers or a pin vise and rotate the wire to harden it. To complete the final fit, file the ends of the middle knuckle until it just fits between the outer two.

Barrel hinge (barley grain hinge)

This elegant variation of the hinged joint involves considerable work, so its use is reserved for the most expensive work (figure 12.66d). Start with a thick-walled tube or create your own by repeated drawing down. Cut off a section and file it to a barrel shape. Prepare a seat to accept this shape and solder the pieces on as described above. A foot is soldered to the wire that will become the pinstem and a length of the tubing is attached at a right angle. It is filed until it fits smoothly between the outer knuckles.

Hinge rivet and pin

The pin joint and catch are soldered on late in the assembly process, but the true completion of the pin is left until almost the last step. After all soldering is complete the piece is cleaned, polished, patinated and stones are set. Only when all these steps are done is the stem set into the joint and held there with a short hinge pin.

The wire that passes through the joint should be annealed and made to fit tightly into the drilled hole. It is snipped off on both sides of the joint so that only a little bit protrudes, then the ends of the wire are upset by careful blows with a small round peen hammer. The rivet head can be further shaped with a pumice wheel or a steel burnisher.

12.5.3 BROOCH CATCHES

Figure 12.67a

The simplest pin catch is a curl of wire, sometimes called a "pig's tail." It can be made from wire or sheet but generally offers very little room for embellishment or elaboration. To be secure the loop should curl around about ¾th of a circle and create a gap that the pinstem fits through only under some pressure; i.e. it should snap into place. Upward tension on the pinstem is also needed, as is the case with any brooch finding.

Figure 12.67b

From a thin sheet (0.3 mm or 28 ga.) cut out a shape like the one shown here, third shape from the top in the center column. This is bent to shape with a combination of work with pliers and dapping punches to create a bracket that will enclose the pinstem. The catch is then soldered on to the back of the brooch.

Solder a small section of tubing just in front of the catch as shown and insert through it a small wire that has had one end drawn to a bead. Bend the wire so its two legs cross – they will catch the pinstem and press it firmly into the catch area. To release, the crossed wire is flipped down flat on the brooch.

Figure 12.67c

This elegant catch captures the pinstem and protects it inside a tube that slides open for release. Start with a pair of tubes that slide one inside the other. Cut a slot in the larger diameter tube about ⅔rds of its length and attach the tube to a short leg of some sort to lift the finding up off the brooch. This can be ornamented as shown or designed in many other ways.

Solder a fine wire to the tip of the smaller diameter tube at a right angle to its axis. Cut most of this off, leaving only a short pin that will prevent the tube from coming out of the catch. Slide the tubes together and extend the smaller one as far out (open) as possible by sliding the pin along the pierced groove. Solder a jump ring or disk of metal on the top of the inner tube to serve as a knob when using the catch. In use the pinstem is fed into the catch and the narrower tube is slid over it.

Figure 12.67d

This is a classic safety catch that is relatively simple to make by hand. Cut the two pieces in the shapes shown here. The larger piece can be of thin stock, 0.3 mm / 28 ga., but the hook shape should be cut from sheet about 0.7 mm / 14 ga. thick.

Twist the legs of the catch so they stand parallel to each other and roll the top section in round-nose pliers to make the shape shown at the bottom of the drawing. Drill a hole through both sides of the catch

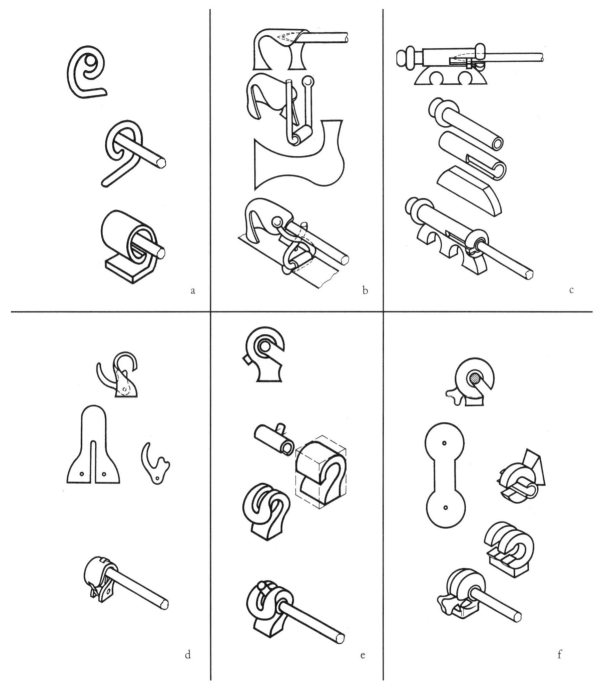

a

b

c

d

e

f

Figure 12.67
Variations on pin catches. See the text for assembly instructions.

as shown, then insert the hook and drill it. Remove the hook, solder the larger unit to the brooch, and clean up the piece. For final assembly, insert the hook and slide a wire through the holes to join the pieces together. When the action is correct, rivet the pin.

The catch works correctly if the pinstem just barely fits in when the safety is open. Small adjustments might be needed to make the two units conform neatly to each other.

Figure 12.67e

This variation on a popular commercial finding is carved from thick stock, a process that will be made simpler if the initial work is done on the end of a length of heavy wire. Alternately, the finding can be temporarily soldered onto a rod that will provide a comfortable grip.

Drill a hole through the rod and use a saw to open it to an outside edge. File an attractive shape as shown, then use a fine sawblade to cut a slot in the top of the catch. Select a tube that will fit over the pinstem and solder a short length of fine wire onto it. Trim until only a small tab remains. Cut away about a third of the tube to allow for the pinstem.

Solder the catch unit onto the brooch and complete the assembly by bending the hook open enough to allow the tube to be inserted. Bend the hook back to its original shape to hold the tube section in place. The catch is opened by rotating this smaller piece.

Figure 12.67f

This catch is similar to the two preceding styles and is probably familiar to most people because it is the catch most commonly mass produced. It is used in everyday jewelry but should be considered equally appropriate for high end handcrafted work. Machine made versions of these catches can be purchased or they can be made at the bench as shown.

From relatively heavy sheet (1 mm / 18 ga.) saw out the "barbell" shape shown in the illustration. File the connecting section thinner and bend the piece into a U shape with the two disks laying parallel. File the

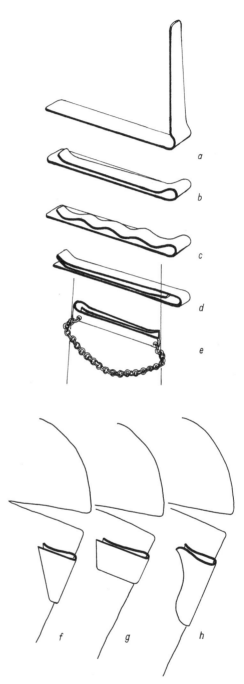

Figure 12.68
Tie and lapel clips.
a) bent spring clip, b) flat spring clip, c) rippled spring clip, d) double spring clip, e) double spring clip with decorative chain, f) to h) reverse side of lapel clips.

catch into a pleasing rounded form. The center unit, (the part that rotates) is made by soldering a tab onto a short length of tubing. Saw away a section of the tube and be certain it is large enough to fit over the tip of the pinstem.

Solder the catch unit onto the brooch and bend it open sufficiently that the rotating pin can be slid into place. Bend the catch back to its original shape, adjusting as necessary to allow the internal unit to rotate smoothly.

12.5.4 TIE CLIPS

This simple tension device has several uses, most commonly as a tie clip (figure 12.68). Like a tie tac (a.k.a. *tie pin*) the purpose is to prevent a necktie from falling forward and getting in the way. Though not essential, a tie bar offers a small opportunity for decoration in the limited world of men's jewelry.

The basic shape is bent up from a strip of work hardened sheet. The lower jaw of the clip is often made a little shorter and narrower than the upper leg. Bend the form with round nose pliers or over a small mandrel to create a form that will have parallel surfaces when slid on the fabric of the necktie and shirt.

To increase the grip, bend the lower leg in a series of ripples as shown in 12.68c. These points of contact have increased holding power. Even greater tension can be created through a three-layer arrangement as shown at 12.68d. One application of this is shown below, a design in which a chain is visible over the tie while the clip is entirely hidden behind it.

In many cases the ornamentation of the tie bar is done through cold techniques like engraving, chasing or etching. When soldering is needed it is best to start with thick metal. This allows for the bend area to be forged out slightly, a process that will harden it and make it springy.

Though not commonly seen, the same mechanism can be used to create clips for other places on garments such as shirt collars, jacket lapels and so on. These can be of almost any size and either quite plain or very fancy.

12.6
Earrings

In their original form earrings were probably exactly that: rings that passed through the lobe. Of course this is still a popular style, but the term has been expanded to include all nature of ornaments for the ear, including pendant forms that suspend from the ear and buttons that more of less cover the lobe. Particularly in recent times we have seen numerous variations on ear decoration, including ear cuffs, band of metal that curls around the outer rim of the ear and posts that pierce the upper sections.

In terms of attachment, earrings are often inserted through holes that have been pierced through the skin of the lobe. It is not uncommon for people to have more than one hole in each ear. Another style, called an ear clip, or clip-on mounting, uses tension to hold the ornament in place on the lobe, typically with a spring-mounted bar on the back of the earring. A post-style earring attaches by a short wire that goes through the pierced hole – it is capped from falling out either by a friction nut or with a threaded nut that screws onto the rod. Pendant-style earrings usually hang from a delicate wire that passes through the lobe. This can be a machine-made element that is linked into the earring or a more integrated component of the earring design.

Despite improvements in clip mechanisms, most people would agree that the most secure method of attaching an earring is through a pierced hole. While some people have a distinct aversion to this, the process is painless and only in very rare cases leads to problems. If a pierced hole is not used for several months, particularly in the first year or two after piercing, it will probably heal closed.

It has long fallen to goldsmiths to do the actual piercing, a process that is simple but should not be undertaken lightly. Though superficial, ear piercing is still a form of surgical intrusion and requires sterile tools and care. The old methods of using a sewing needle backed up with a cork for support have given way to compact "guns" that swiftly insert a specially-designed chemically inert surgical steel post earring through the ear. The earring is designed to be worn without removal until the area has healed into a tube or canal that passes through the lobe. These devices can be purchased through some jewelry suppliers, but it is most common for handcrafting goldsmiths to leave this part of the business to commercial establishments.

Should any complications appear a doctor must be consulted. Though not a matter of goldsmithing, it may be a jeweler that is consulted about a problem piercing. In rare cases bleeding does not stop or the wound becomes inflamed; in these cases the customer should be sent to a doctor or back to the place where the piercing was done.

Finally it should be noted that a hoop or post stuck through the ear lobe must be biologically inert. Copper, brass and nickel, for instance, will tarnish or corrode against the skin and result in inflammation. Gold and silver are usually acceptable, though some people have allergies to these metals. The reactive metals (titanium, niobium, etc.) and surgical stainless steel are also widely used. In the case of inexpensive fashion earrings that might be made of base metal, the small element that passes through the ear is still made of one of these inert alloys.

12.6.1 EARRINGS FOR PIERCED EARLOBES
Figure 12.69a
This is the most basic version of a hanging wire, sometimes called a French Loop or Shepherds Hook. The wire is bent up from round wire of about 0.8–1 mm thickness. They can be purchased in several forms or made in the studio as needed, either individually or with the use of a jig. Note the length of the free end of the wire – this is necessary to guaranty the security of the attachment. A shorter wire is at risk of falling out if the earring is lifted slightly, a movement that can result from turning the head, combing hair, putting on a scarf and so on.

In this case, and wherever a wire is being slid through a pierced hole, it is important that the end of the wire be smooth and rounded. It is even possible to draw a small bead on the end – this makes insertion slightly more difficult but also prevents the wire from coming out by accident. It is not a good idea to sharpen the wire to a point. Instead of the wire finding its way through the existing hole, this risks jabbing a new hole in the earlobe. Ouch!

The shepherd's hook is such a practical connection it is probably the most common style of earring wire. The only limitation with a simple hook is that it doesn't suit every earring design. The following earring mechanisms are derived from the shepherds hook. Because the wires are shorter, these styles call for some method of closing the loop.

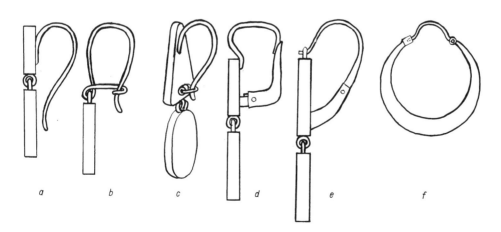

*Figure 12.69
Earring clasps.
a) open,
b) with safety hook,
c) with folding loop,
d) with spring clip,
e) leverback,
d) "creole" (hinged).*

a   b   c   d   e   f

484

Figure 12.69b

This popular mechanism, often called a kidney wire because of its shape, is bent up from just one piece of wire. The springy hoop is latched into a hook at the other end of the wire in a manner similar to a safety pin. This allows the earwire to be shorter than with the previous mechanism. This design usually permits use of a finer gauge wire because the loop locks on itself.

Figure 12.69c

The hoop is made from a length of round wire as above, but in this case it attached by means of a section of tubing soldered onto the back of the earring. This allows increased movement of the earring.

Figure 12.69d

This mechanism has a springy latch that does not lend itself to handmade production. The earwire in this case is relatively short and fixed in place on the back of the earring. The L-shaped closing unit is spring loaded and closes the loop to make this a reliable fastener. The latch contains a leaf spring that presses onto a stud, in such a way that the latch stops in the closed or open position. The latch is riveted onto the stud so that it can move.

In the course of use the leaf spring becomes fatigued and the sides of the stud wear away so the mechanism needs to be repaired. To do this the rivet holding the latch is removed so the mechanism can be taken apart. The leaf spring can be bent back into shape and the worn stud can be lightly forged to return it to its original shape. If the piece is seriously damaged it is usually not much work to remake a new stud from round wire. Because the spring will lose its strength when heated it absolutely must be removed before annealing or soldering the earring!

Figure 12.69e

In this interesting variation, the earwire if flattened on one end to allow it to be drilled and riveted into a bar that projects out from the lower area of the earring. This bar is often made of square wire – a slot is sawn into the end to allow a hinged joint. A jump ring on the top of the earring makes a tension closure for the earwire.

Figure 12.69f

The ring-shaped earring is closed with a short hoop that is drilled and riveted as a hinge at one end. At the other it snaps into place where it is locked by the tension created through the curve of the wire.

Figure 12.70 a, b, c

Posts for pierced ears must be made of a metal that will not react with skin, typically gold, sterling, or stainless steel. The size varies but will usually be between 0.7 and 1 mm or 18–20 gauge. In most cases the wire is notched near its end, either by filing a small groove or by gripping tightly with round nose pliers while rotating the work. A friction nut will "find" this groove and snap into it.

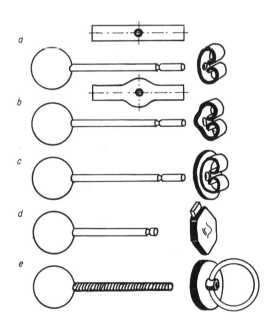

Figure 12.70
Earpost backings.
a) grooved post with simple back, b) widened back, c) back with disk,
d) spring-secured back, e) threaded post with nut.

The nut can be purchased through suppliers or made at the bench. In the latter case, the shapes shown in the illustration are sawn from sheet metal and drilled. The starting sheet should be cold rolled (work hardened) to insure proper springiness in the end result. The drill hole should fit tightly onto the post. Both ends of the sheet are curled with round nose pliers so that the gap between them is slightly smaller than the diameter of the post.

Figure 12.70d
This unusual variation on the spring loaded ear nut is an example of a device that is more easily created in a factory than at a goldsmith's bench. The advantage of this design is that the end of the wire does not project out from the nut, but the post must be exactly the right size for this earring to work properly.

Figure 12.70e
A coarse thread is cut onto the post of the earring and the earring is screwed on with a nut. This a simple and therefore trustworthy method of fastening, which has the advantage that the user can themselves set the position of the ear nut and therefore the pressure on the ear lobe. There are several different basic shapes for the nut, but it is always important that enough turns can be cut on the threaded portion so that the nut that lies against the ear lobe cannot accidentally come undone. The threaded ear nut for this has to be fairly thick – sometimes a short tube is soldered onto the nut to increase the length of the threading.

12.6.2 EAR CLIPS

Clip-on style earrings are less popular today than they once were, partly because they provide a less secure attachment than pierced styles and partly because they always involve a painful or at least annoying pinch. They are associated with fashion or costume jewelry – expensive jewelry is almost always fitted with the more reliable pierced style.

Clip-on findings (figure 12.71a) are most commonly seen in their mass produced base metal version, though there is no reason they could not be made at the bench. Though shapes may vary, the mechanism

Figure 12.71
Earring clips.
a) flat spring clip, b) bowed wire clip.

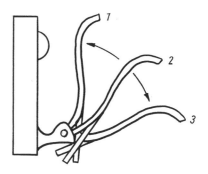

Figure 12.72
Clip mechanism.
a) closed, b) mid-point, c) open.

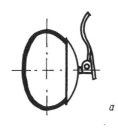

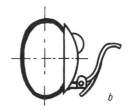

Figure 12.73
Cross-section of mounted clip.
a) incorrect, too high, b) correct.

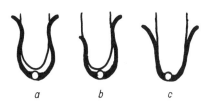

Figure 12.74
Pressure points of a clip earring.
a) correct, accross from each other, b) incorrect, offset, e) incorrect,
too deep.

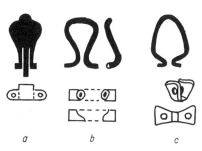

Figure 12.75
Components of the ear clip.
a) flat clip and hinge, b) bowed wire clip and hinge, c) bowed wire clip
folded hinge.

is almost always the same and depends on tension of a springy part of the paddle rubbing against the post that is attached to the earring. In order to correctly install and adjust the mechanism it is important to understand how the mechanism works (figure 12.72).

In its closed position the paddle snaps against the earring; at its open position, the paddle snaps open. At exactly the midpoint (i.e. 45°) the paddle is under even tension. A small push in either direction will cause it to either snap open or snap closed. To be most effective (and least painful) the mechanism should be fitted to the thickness of a wearer's lobe in order that the maximum tension is delivered just at the point where the paddle pinches. In its closed position, the paddle should be parallel to the back of the earring. This is typically adjusted by bending the paddle or angling the post.

Clip-on style earring findings can be made more secure by attaching a small projection onto the back of the earring at the place where the paddle touches, figure 12.73. As shown in the following diagram, even this simple modification requires care. In a proper mechanism (12.74a) the lobe is pinched symmetrically between the paddle and the earring. The white dot at the bottom of the mechanism shows the hinge while the area between is a cross section of the lobe. If the two points of contact are not opposite each other (12.74b), the earring is far less secure. This is also the case if the pinching action is concentrated on the lower part of the lobe, as seen in the third illustration. This earring is almost certain to fall off.

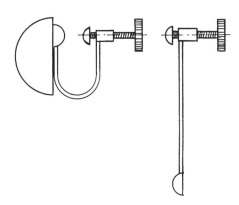

Figure 12.76
Cross-section of the hreaded post mechanism.

The maximum amount of pressure that can be created is determined by the pain sensitivity of the wearer – security has its limitations. There are limits to how much one should suffer for fashion!

Figure 12.75 shows the pieces needed to make a friction clip. Because the springiness depends almost entirely on the inherent quality of the metal, care must be taken to select an alloy that is tough. It should be work hardened and left sufficiently thick to remain springy – usually about 0.6 mm thick (22 ga.) The paddle and joint are sawn from sheet in the shapes shown in 12.75a. The arms of the joint are bent up at the dotted lines and this piece is soldered onto the earring. The piece is buffed and in every way finished, then the paddle is pressed into place with the fingers of each side fitting into the holes in the joint

487

(which may need to be bent open slightly to receive them). The tension of the mechanism is created as the center tine of the paddle rubs against the flat section at the top of the joint.

An alternate style uses a loop of wire as a paddle, two versions of which are shown. In this case the springiness of the loop of wire is used to make the mechanism work. In the example shown in 12.75b, the joint is made with tubes that will hold the ends of the wire. The angle at which the tubes are sawn is what determines the position at which the tension is greatest. In the other version, 12.75c, the curved shape of the joint achieves the same effect, holding the wire down on the ear through the spring tension of the wire itself.

Threaded mechanisms

One solution to the uncomfortable pinching of a clip-on mechanism is to replace it with a screw like the one shown in figure 12.76. This also pinches the lobe but at least offers some control over the force.

The construction of this mechanism requires a threading die or pre-threaded screws and nuts that are commercially available. The male threads are cut into a wire and the opposite threads are cut into a thick-walled tube. Solder the tube to a straight piece of wire and attach a rounded pad to one end of the threaded rod. Screw the rod into position and solder

a textured nut onto the other end, a piece large enough to grip but not so big it overpowers the earring. As before, a bulge is soldered onto the point opposite the threaded rod to create increased pressure at the point of contact.

Ear cuffs

This very simple ornament has no mechanism, per se, but is simply a band of metal that is pressed onto either the lobe or the shell of the ear. It has the shape of a miniature cuff bracelet and like that, has no moving parts. A proper fit can usually be found simply by wearing the cuff on a different part of the ear or by opening or closing the form slightly.

12.7
Cuff-links

Cuff links provide a variety of design challenges that can be stimulating or frustrating depending on your point of view. Consider the requirements: the cuff link must allow one-handed insertion; it must close easily and securely but be relatively easy to remove. It should be reasonably easy to make, should look good, and should not get in the way of arm movement. In some designs the links must be made as a mirror image of each other.

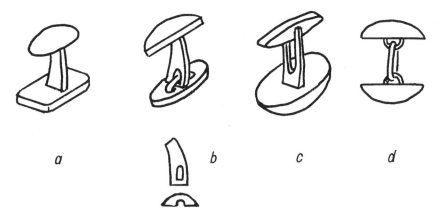

Figure 12.77
Cuff link mechanisms.
a) rigid toggle, b) folding toggle, c) hinged toggle, d) linked.

Figure 12.77a

A stem of sheet metal at least 1 mm thick (18 gauge) is soldered between the front and the back plate of the cuff link. This stem should be slightly curved to accommodate the shape of the sleeve and lie tight against it. The size of the back plate (or cross bar) is determined by the length of the buttonhole – it should just pass through the hole. Among cuff link mechanisms, this is probably the most troublesome to use.

Figure 12.77b

This mechanism works well and lends itself to being made by hand. As with any cuff link, the length of the stem must be sufficient to pass through the layers of a French cuff. In this case the fabric is pressed flat to allow the hinged crossbar to flip from laying flat against the stem to sitting at a right angle to it. This is what locks the cuff link in place.

The trestle, or piece that attaches to the back of the cuff link, is soldered into place after being hooked through the stem. For the mechanism to work it is of course important that the stem not be accidentally soldered stiff. To prevent this, make two short sawcuts next to the round opening in the trestle – this will prevent the solder from flowing past that point.

Figure 12.77c

The cross bar in this version contains a leaf spring that allows it to snap into place at both the vertical and horizontal orientations. Though these can be made by hand, they are also available in industrially produced versions. These often come in the form of a small joint similar to a pin joint that can be hard soldered onto the cuff link. The mechanism (which has a tempered steel spring and therefore cannot be soldered in place) is held on with a rivet that passes through the joint.

Figure 12.77d

In this simple solution, the two plates of the cuff link are connected with a jump ring that passes through rings attached to each of the other units. This three-link chain can be reduced even further to a two-link arrangement. As in all other cases, the proportions require that the cuff link and back fit only snugly through the button-holes, and that the links accommodate the thicknesses of fabric in the cuff.

Repair Work

13.1
General Principles

There is no reason to degrade goldsmiths who are mainly involved with repair work. It takes knowledge, ability, experience and resourcefulness to maintain an old piece, particularly since it might also be necessary to remove earlier repair mistakes made by a less capable predecessor. A real expert and competent goldsmith knows that new production and repairs are two sides of the same coin and he will make every effort to do his best in both areas.

Part of the service of a goldsmith should include an appropriate amount of time for carrying out repairs. It would be false to consider this merely a tiresome necessity that hinders creative activity. Instead it should be viewed as an opportunity for growth and a genuine service to a customer. A goldsmith who repairs a treasured heirloom is likely to be remembered when a customer needs a new piece or wants a discriminating gift. We expect, after all, that craftsmen in other professions show the same willingness to take on repairs when, for example, our car, washing machine or shoes need work.

Goldsmiths who develop their skills at repair work will not only be financially compensated, but have the additional satisfaction of seeing the joy on a customer's face when they receive a favorite piece of jewelry back again.

Repairs can be necessary for the following reasons:

- Unavoidable wear and tear occurs to every piece of jewelry through contact with its environment. Polished surfaces will become dull through minute scratches, stone settings will become thinned and engraved ornamentation will wear down.
- Moving parts such as clasps on earrings, chains and bracelets become worn down through friction of the parts.
- Parts can become dented and ripped when a jewelry piece is hit against a hard surface or caught on something.
- Production defects can cause a piece to wear out prematurely if, for example, the parts are made too thin or improperly soldered.
- Defects in the material itself can cause damage. Fortunately, this is only very rarely the cause of a broken piece.

Though perhaps sad, it's worth noting that every functional object has a finite life expectancy. Through improving or exchanging worn out parts, its useful life can be extended but at some point it becomes scrap! This general experience is accepted in clothing and in household goods but strangely not accepted with jewelry. This has to do with special features of jewelry.

We can only guess that this stems from the fact that jewelry often carries idealized, sentimental associations, for instance because it was inherited or received as a gift. Because of the intrinsic value and aesthetic worth, jewelry is set apart from things like toasters – we forget that the same rules of metal fatigue apply!

And unlike toasters, the life expectancy of jewelry is also related to fashion. When a piece has gone out of style it is often given a new lease on life by being modernized, as for instance when stones are reset in a new mounting. Though not technically a repair, it is again the job of a diligent and caring goldsmith to affect this transformation.

Before undertaking a repair job a goldsmith should take into consideration several factors such as the potential risk to the piece, the likelihood of the piece to soon need some other repair, and the reasons for the repair in the first place. A repair that is acceptable to one customer ("I know you can't make it look like new, but I just want it so I can wear it again.") will not be enough for another ("If it doesn't look like new, I'm not interested.") Clarity from the outset is very important and can prevent anger and disappointment later on.

Finally, keep in mind that a slipshod repair does no one any good. The customer feels cheated, the reputation of the goldsmith is damaged, and the work is compromised, making a genuine repair that much harder. How much damage has been done by novice jewelers who took an easy way out! How many hours have been spent repairing their repairs!

There is a difference between repair and historical restoration such as one might undertake for a museum. In the latter case the mission is not to fix a problem so a piece can be worn, but to restore a piece to a former state, and to do so with a technology that mimics as closely as possible the original manufacture of the piece.

13.2
Acceptance of Repair Work

Before a piece is accepted for repair, the goldsmith should examine it carefully in the presence of the customer in order to establish the actual condition of the object and to evaluate the extent of the repair. He must determine, for example, whether the repair will be made more difficult by the presence of tin solder, whether heat sensitive stones must be removed from their settings, and whether plated surfaces will need to be renewed after the repair is competed. This detailed examination should only be made after the piece has been thoroughly cleaned because the oils and debris that naturally accumulate when jewelry is worn can hide many problems.

It is of mutual interest to inform the client of the approximate repair costs. In some cases the value of the piece or the price of a new one must be compared to the repair costs so that the client can decide whether the repair is worthwhile.

It builds trust with the client when the length of the chain, number of pearls, or even the weight of the jewelry piece and size of the gems and pearls are determined in the presence of the client and noted on the repair envelop. If the repair work could endanger the gems, the customer is advised of such and should sign a waiver stating that the risks are understood.

Actually many clients still approach goldsmiths with mistrust, mainly because the lay person lacks the knowledge of what actually occurs with his or her jewelry piece in the goldsmith's studio. He or she doesn't know the compositions of precious metal alloys and may have exaggerated ideas of their value.

Where mistrust exists, it is the responsibility of the goldsmith to respond professionally, by listening to the concern and offering detailed explanations of what is involved in the repair. To do this it is necessary to take time with the customer and answer his or her questions in an understandable manner and inform the customer about the necessary expenditures. Any form of arrogance by the specialist toward the lay person is inappropriate.

In addition to the customer's name and address, the repair tag should include a clear description of the intended work and any unusual details about the piece. If there is a pre-existing flaw such as a chipped stone, point it out to the customer and write it down on the tag. If special features come to light in the process of repair, or if unusual measures are taken, these should also be noted and discussed with the owner when the piece is picked up. The tags should be filed away in case a question or complaint arises later.

The finished repairs should only be given out after the receipt has been presented. If the receipt has been lost, information about the person picking up the work should be kept in a control book.

13.3
Gems in the Work Place

There are numerous specialized books on gemstones that describe in detail the characteristics of precious stones and the devices and methods for telling them apart. Serious goldsmiths will no doubt find themselves consulting such resources at some point in their careers.

For our purposes here, we will offer a few hints about dealing with precious stones in the goldsmith's studio. Wherever possible stones should be removed from a jewelry piece before soldering – exposure to heat always involves some risk! Even in the stones listed in Table 13.1 as capable of withstanding high temperatures, there can be problems from inclusions or micro fractures within the gems.

Where the table describes resistance to acids and bases, reference is being made to the usual chemicals found in a goldsmith's studio such as pickle, patina solutions, cleaning and plating baths. It is understood, of course that any heated stone should be allowed to cool to room temperature as slowly as possible. Even a tough stone will shatter if quenched!

It is important to understand the difference between hardness and toughness. Some stones can be very hard (resistant to penetration and scratching) but still brittle, or easily broken along natural lines of cleavage. It is best to work under the assumption that all stones are delicate and should be treated with care.

Here are some general statements about specific gemstones.

Name	Cleavage	Sensitivities to:			
		Bases	Acids	Heat	Color changes
Agate	no	no	no	slight	no
Alexandrite	very much	yes	no	no	no
Amazonite	no	no	no	slight	no
Amber	no, but brittle	no	no	burns	softens
Amethyst	no	no	yes	slight	yes
Aquamarine	no	no	hydroflouric	slight	slight
Chalcedony	no	no	no	slight	no
Chrysoberyl	very much	yes	no	no	no
Chrysoprase	no	no	no	yes	melts
Citrine	no	no	hydroflouric	no	no
Coral	no	no	dissolves	very much	yes
Corundum	no	no	no	no	seldom
Diamond	very much	no	no	no	over 850°
Emerald	no, brittle	no	yes	yes	yes
Fluorspar	very much	no	very much	slight	no
Garnet	no	no	no	no	no
Hematite	no	no	hydrochloric	slight	no
Kunzite	very much	no	hydroflouric	no	no
Lapis Lazuli	no	no	very much	very much	yes
Malachite	no	no	dissolves	very much	destroyed
Marcasite	no	no	nitric	very much	destroyed
Moonstone	very much	no	no	yes	no
Nephrite	no	no	no	slight	no
Opal	no, but brittle	yes	yes	very much	yes
Pearl	yes, flakes	no	dissolves	very much	yes
Tiger eye	no	no	yes	slight	yes
Topaz	very much	no	sulfuric	no	no
Tourmaline	no	no	no	slight	yes
Turquoise	no	no	very much	very much	yes
Spinel	no	no	no	no	no
Zircon	yes	no	yes	no	no

Table 13.1
Common gem materials showing properties that might affect the way they are handled during repairs.

Diamond

Though they are the hardest stones on earth, even diamonds can be split if force is applied in the direction of their octahedral surface. For this reason a setter should be careful not to slip while tapping a prong into position.

Diamonds are, of course, pure carbon and since this has a melting point greater than 3500°C (6300°F), one would assume that there is no danger in soldering around a diamond. In fact diamonds can be damaged by a torch at only 850°C (1560°F), where it might accumulate a dull white coating that can only be removed through polishing.

To protect against this, coat the diamond with boric acid. Avoid direct heating of the stone and if possible pack the gem in insulating material. Acids, even in concentrated form, will not affect diamonds.

Corundum

Whereas rubies can be readily exposed to heat, blue sapphires must be handled carefully because the color can be lost through heating.

Chrysoberyl

This stone will withstand soldering heat and exposure to acids but has a definite cleavage.

Spinel

Heating can cause loss of color, but as the stone cools the color usually reappears. It is not damaged by acids and even though it does not have a pronounced cleavage it is brittle and care must be exercised while mounting.

Topaz

Heating can change the color. Because of its pronounced cleavage, topaz is at risk even while being worn. It can be attacked by concentrated sulfuric acid, but will not be damaged by pickle.

Beryl

Aquamarine is resistant to heat up until 750°C (1380°F). Higher temperatures can change the color so, it must be protected when soldering. Emeralds cannot be exposed to heat at all because the inclusions, cracks and hollow spaces leave the stone particularly vulnerable. For the same reasons, emeralds are sensitive to external forces. It is best to use softer alloys for mountings for emeralds to avoid breaking the stone while setting it. By contrast, aquamarine is hardly sensitive to pressure. All beryls are resistant to acids.

Zircon

The color changes at the relatively low temperature of 500°C (930°F) so all zircons are considered to be heat sensitive. They are also vulnerable to cleavage and should not be exposed to sharp blows. Zircons are only affected by concentrated sulfuric acid with prolonged heating.

Tourmaline

All tourmalines are resistant to soldering heat, acids and pressure.

Garnet

Pyrope and almadine, both deep red in color, are the garnets most commonly used in jewelry. Whereas pyropes are quite resistant to heat, almadines may lose their color and crack when heated. Garnets are resistant to acid and pressure.

Quartz

Rock crystal is quite heat resistant. Amethysts and darker citrines can change their color as low as 250°C. (480°F). Smoky quartz is resistant to about 1000°C (1830°F). Citrines are pressure sensitive when mounting. All of the quartz gems should be protected when soldering because they can lose their color and crack. Chrysoprase and rose quartz fade when heated. Opal is particularly sensitive to heat because of the moisture trapped in its interior. Quartz gems are mildly affected by hydrofluoric acid but are otherwise resistant to acids. Opals and citrines are at risk while setting, all others however, are rather tough.

Pyrite, malachite and hematite.

These are all sensitive to heat and acids.

Turquoise, lapis lazuli, malachite
These can change color and crack with heat; they will be attacked by acids. Because of sensitivity to oils, turquoise must be treated carefully while polishing with tripoli.

Moonstone, amazonite
These stones are heat sensitive and have pronounced cleavage.

Jadite
Flames can melt the edges and will turn the stone yellow. It is resistant to pressure and acids.

Jade
Because of its toughness this stone was used in pre-historic times for tools; it is resistant to heat and acid.

Amber
This is not a stone at all, but fossilized tree sap. It will be damaged by even low heat and will dissolve in acid.

Synthetic stones
Laboratory-grown gems behave much as the corresponding genuine stones, but will generally stand up to high temperatures.

Doublets
These are artificially made gems that consist of two thin layers that have been bonded together. They will not withstand high temperatures because the glue breaks down.

Glass gems
In soldering heat they are not always stable; after heating they need to be cooled slowly. Red glass is particularly stable at high temperatures. With the exception of flouric acid, glass stones are resistant to acids. They can easily crack if stressed when being mounted.

Pearls, Coral, Ivory
As with other organic materials these gems will change color in moderate heat and be quickly destroyed by a torch flame. They are usually set today with epoxy, which avoids the risk of heat altogether. They are at risk in pickle and will be damaged by any acid.

13.4
General Repair Work

13.4.1 CLEANING JEWELRY

Regardless of what the damage that brought the work in for repair, you can usually count on the fact that jewelry and hollowware will need to be cleaned. Normal exposure to use and atmosphere in the case of hollowware, and wear and everyday chemicals like perfume and lotions are enough to leave work looking unattractive. In addition, such debris can hide problems that need to be repaired.

For this reason the first step when a piece is brought in should be a complete cleaning and the last step before it leaves is a total repolishing. It should become automatic to perform certain checks, even if these are not the items that the customer mentions as the problem. In the case of jewelry, see that prongs are not worn or lifted and that stones have not been chipped. Make sure clasps lock securely and hinges are operating smoothly. For hollowware, inspect legs, ferrules and spouts to be certain they are well attached, and make sure the piece sits flat and level.

Instruct the customer about proper care for their valuables, which might included periodic scrubbing with a toothbrush and soapy water, or use of a rouge cloth. Thick build up of tarnish can be removed with chemical solutions available from jewelry stores and are often worth mentioning. Your concern for the appearance of the work will earn you the respect of the customer – involving them in its care will help them appreciate the repairs you do.

13.4.2 BROKEN PARTS

One aspect of repair is the reattachment of parts that have been broken off. This should be approached not as a "make do" effort, but with the same care for permanence that was used when the piece was made. If the piece was hard soldered on and eventually broke off, it seems clear that a less durable soft solder or epoxy attachment is doomed to early failure!

Repair work requires more sensitivity and flame control than when making a piece from scratch. It is particularly important to watch the metal because in most cases you don't know for certain about its content and melting point. When building a piece from raw materials, the goldsmith knows exactly what grades of solder are used for each joint, but when a piece comes in for repairs this information is unavailable. For this reason it is always best to heat as locally as possible, aiming the torch away from the rest of the piece. Use insulating materials wherever possible to prevent previous joints from coming unsoldered.

Complicated repair work should only be carried out by an experienced goldsmith – an apprentice should only practice on simpler and less risky things! When repairing gold pieces, a coating of boric acid will maintain the surface and save time in refinishing.

13.4.3 BENT PARTS

Parts that are bent out of shape during use can sometimes be corrected with pliers. Be careful to select exactly the right tool for the job, matching the contours of the pliers to the shape being bent. The jaws of the tools should be polished to avoid making unwanted marks. It might be necessary to locally anneal an area to be reshaped. It is better to err on the side of caution here, annealing even if it proved unnecessary rather than skipping this step to save a minute only to find the piece has broken off. Reattachment is always a bigger chore!

13.4.4 WORN OUT SETTINGS

Among the most common repairs to come across a goldsmith's bench is the need to retip or replace prongs. There is no mystery why these are so vulner-

able: by definition a prong is a delicate bit of metal positioned where it will get the most wear. Even in light use the prong will be worn away. With the active lifestyles of many people, prongs are daily exposed to dozens of opportunities to be snagged, bent, and worn away.

Depending on wear and the original shape of the prong, it often happens that when one prong is worn out the others are similarly in need of repair. The first assessment, then, is to decide whether it is more efficient to retip a single prong or replace the entire head. The amount of labor is not significantly different so it can happen that a full replacement is cheaper in the long run than several retippings. And both are probably cheaper than replacing a lost stone.

If a single prong is to be retipped, the stone is removed and the prong cut off at midpoint. It is filed at an angle here to increase the surface area presented for attaching a length of wire that will then be filed to shape as a prong.

If a setting is severely worn it might be worth introducing the option of a bezel instead of a prong. Even these can wear out, however, in which case the stone must be removed, the bezel cut away and replaced with an entirely new unit.

13.4.5 LOOSE STONES

If a stone has become loose in its mounting it can audibly rattle when the jewelry is shaken. The mounting might be entirely intact, the problem being a matter of incorrect setting procedures. In most cases it is sufficient to press the prongs or the bezel more snugly around the stone, but sometimes the stone must be removed and the seat recut.

Tall cabochons are subject to a special problem related to the relatively short distance the bezel is pushed in setting such stones. The metal is only elastically deformed, which means it rebounds or springs back. Even though the bezel might be sufficiently angled to hold the stone there might still be a rattle. Use a millegrain tool (beading roulette) to press the very edge down on the stone. If the texture left by this tool is unwanted, follow this with a burnisher or the gentle use of a planishing punch. If this doesn't work, use a dab of adhesive on the underside of the stone to prevent it's moving around. Bear in mind however that the purpose of the glue is only to eliminate the rattle – the stone is still secured into the piece by the bezel.

13.4.6 GLUING OF PRECIOUS STONES AND OTHER ELEMENTS

Wherever possible it is best if a mechanical attachment such as prongs or bezels are used. There are cases, however, when this option is impossible or too costly, as for instance in the case of costume jewelry. Other situations arise in which organic materials such as wood, ivory, pearl, or artificial materials as used to embellish jewelry.

In these cases adhesives should be used, but still with the care and attention that is given to traditional workmanship. In gluing, as in soldering, it's possible to do the job well or poorly. Elements can be reliably attached with glue if the necessary requisites are met. These include:

- Sufficiently large contact area.
- A protective border or bezel that will protect against sideward shearing and bending forces.
- Roughing up of the contact surfaces.
- Selection of the appropriate glue.
- Use of glue according to directions.

There are many adhesives available today, each with its unique advantages. Read labels carefully to determine the best glue for each situation, and follow manufacturer's instructions precisely. In two-part glues like epoxies, measure and mix the parts with care to guarantee success. Pay attention also to recommended temperature ranges, proper cleaning and set-up times.

Gluing pearls

Pearls are mounted and glued exactly as they were in the original mountings, assuming of course these were adequate. One frequent cause of loose pearls is the fact that they were originally mounted on wires that were too thin. In these cases, the original post should be replaced with a thicker wire that is soldered into place.

Completely remove the old glue and redrill the hole if necessary to match up with a thicker post. Use a glue like epoxy or pearl cement that is made for porous surfaces – the inside of a pearl is powdery and will not adhere to the anaerobic adhesives like Super Glue.

13.4.7 TIN SOLDER

No goldsmith working in repairs will go very long before encountering a piece that has been previously repaired with a tin-based solder. This is often used by amateurs because it melts at a low temperature and therefore avoids the difficulties of removing stones, repolishing and so on. Unfortunately, the solder is unsightly and weak, which is often why the piece comes to a goldsmith in the end anyway. Now there are two problems – getting rid of the soft solder and repairing the original problem!

It is critical that every trace of the tin-based solder be removed before the piece is heated to the temperatures needed for proper silver or gold soldering. Failure to do this will trigger a reaction when the tin is overheated; it will diffuse into the precious metal to create an alloy that makes deep pits. Once the damage is done there is no way to correct this poisoning effect except to completely cut away the damaged portion and solder a new panel of metal in its place. This is tedious and costly.

Remove every bit of solder in any way you can. Usually the first step is to scrape the solder with a knife blade, scraper or similar tool. Follow this with sandpaper or a bur. In the case of noble metals that will resist acid, such as high karat gold or platinum, immerse the piece in a warm a 1:4 solution of nitric acid. Allow the work to soak for several hours, rinse well and examine under magnification to be sure all the tin is gone. Even then it is wise to heat the work slowly, watching for the telltale gray shine of the solder. If you see any, stop immediately and remove it.

Despite the reservations regarding the use of tin solder it's use is sometimes appropriate, particularly when precious metals are not involved. In those cases, be certain to provide plenty of contact surface and to see that it is scraped clean. Use an appropriate flux (described in detail in chapter 8), and warm the metal with either a soldering iron or a torch. Be careful not to overheat the metal, remembering that these solders melt at less than a third the temperatures needed for silver brazing.

13.5
Special Repair Work

13.5.1 MECHANICAL REPAIRS

It is not uncommon for moving parts to wear out. This is to be expected because of increased friction as parts rub against one another. A common example can be found in connecting rings such as the jump rings that attach a charm to a bracelet or a pendant to a chain.

If a section of the ring is worn thin it is usually best to discard the old ring and replace it with a new one. Circular rings are preferred over ovals because they rotate naturally during use and distribute wear around the entire loop. Wherever possible such loops should be soldered closed.

Another common repair involves springs that loose their tension over the years. This might be due to several factors, ranging from something as easy as a bent part to something as complicated as annealed or broken springs. Before undertaking any repairs to a moving part, study it to be certain you understand the mechanism. Consider every possibility – What will happen if I file this away? If I tighten this rivet? and so on – before trying anything. Not only is the process thereby made more efficient, but you avoid the risk of replacing one problem with another!

Each situation deserves unique consideration, so our comments here must be general. If a rivet must be removed, file the head off one end and use a needle to push the rivet free. Do not try to reuse this wire, but replace it with the same gauge.

Always try the simplest solution first. It might be possible to renew springiness simply by bending parts into tighter curves. If this doesn't work, try rehardening a piece by bending and straightening or by lightly planishing it. Continue in this way, each time checking your results to see if the problem has been fixed.

13.5.2 BROOCHES

The following details will be found in a properly made brooch. Where any of these is not the case, the repair task is obvious.

• The pin must easily move without rattling.
• The pin should open at least 90 degrees.
• The pin must securely fit in the catch with enough tension so that it is securely fastened.
• The pin stem should be straight and pointed so that it easily penetrates clothing by pushing aside the fibers rather than snagging through them.

If the pin has gotten bent, use flat pliers to straighten it or lay the shaft on a flat steel surface and tap it with a small hammer or plastic mallet, taking care not to create unnecessary hammer marks. To complete the repair, tap the rivet at the joint to make a tight fit and burnish the tip to restore its shape.

If the joint unit has come loose, the pin should be removed before the joint is reattached so it does not get annealed. Of course stones on the front of the brooch will also need to come out. When soldering on a safety catch (also called a ball catch), avoid using too much flux or solder because they might flow up into the mechanism and seize it. For the same reason, direct the heat mostly on the brooch, remembering that solder will flow toward heat. In this case you don't want the solder to be attracted to the pin catch before it has had a chance to spread itself out on the brooch. The moving part of the catch can also be protected from being soldered by applying a drop of oil with a needle between the walls.

In cases where the brooch cannot withstand the heat of soldering, prepare a piece of sheet metal that will integrate with the back of the piece, using sterling, nickel silver or brass to match the piece. Solder the pin joint and catch onto this, then after cleaning it, use glue or soft solder to connect it to the pin.

13.5.3 CHAINS

Most repair shops will agree that the most common job they see is the repair of chains. Not only are these subject to a sharp tug, sometimes by a child or by accident when taking off a jacket, but they also consist of nothing but elements that constantly rub against each other. Especially in the case of delicate chains, it is only a matter of time before the links wear thin.

A good repairman will start by examining the chain closely. If many of the links are worn it is probably useless to make the repair – the chain will just break again soon at some other place. Take the time to show the worn links to the customer and allow them to reach the inevitable conclusion themselves.

When repairing a chain, isolate the broken link with a needle or locking tweezers and lay it open so its ends can be properly prepared for soldering. Though the joint is small, or perhaps just because it is so small, it is important to follow the rules for soldering fully. If you can locate the solder joints in the adjacent links, turn them in such a way that the solder does not touch any other link.

Lay the intact chain on a soldering block, perhaps marking the location of the joint by drawing a line across the block, and apply a very small chip of solder on the joint. Solder with a pointed flame. Commercially made chains use special wire that has the solder – typically a very low melting alloy! – inside the wire itself. This explains why even a 14K (Au 585) chain seems to crumple at what seems to be a usual soldering temperature. Always proceed cautiously and use the lowest temperature solder available.

It is also possible to protect adjacent links with an insulating material like yellow ocher or soldering investment, but most professional repairmen disdain the practice. It is tedious and as often as not, useless. The protecting material flows into the intended joint and prevents the solder from closing the link. In the end your best bet is to prepare the joint well and pay close attention when you solder.

It is often the practice in repair studios to work on several chains at once. There is something about the scale and sensitivity of the repair that suggests that once you get into the rhythm, you should stick with it. If several chains are laid out on the block at the same time, remember to mark each with a tag so you will be able to return it to the proper repair envelope!

13.5.4 BRACELETS

Many repairs deal with closures. When a box clasp no longer holds, it is usually the result of the tongue having lost its elasticity. The problem can be quickly but only temporarily solved by putting a knife into the tongue to raise it; after a short time the problem will reappear and the tongue can easily break off.

It is better to grasp the end of the tongue with flat pliers and bend only the remaining portion of the tongue upward with a knife; this will protect the tip from breaking. If the tongue is broken it is best to replace it with a new one. Soldering it together will cause the metal to be soft. In this case it will be necessary to work harden the piece by hammering so that it will obtain the necessary springiness. In some cases the tongue is large enough to allow the parts to be riveted together, in which case the original springiness can be retained.

Just as with necklace chains, link bracelets are subject to wear as the elements rub against each other. Again it is necessary to examine the bracelet to determine if a single loop is at fault or if most of the links are worn thin. The former case allows a link to be strengthened by soldering a bit of extra metal to the thin spot; a worn chain should be replaced.

There is a style of bracelet in which the sections are held together by a hinge. If the bracelet has been well cared for, these hinges can last several generations before showing wear. Of course some people are harder on their jewelry than others, and a hasty or clumsy person can put a lot of stress on a hinge by torquing it sideways.

If the hinge is simply loose, it might be possible to tap on the ends of the rivet pin to tighten it up. If the hinge is broken or the tubing worn through, the entire hinge will need to be rebuilt from scratch.

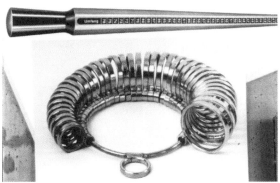

Figure 13.1
Ring stick and ring sizers.

13.6
Determination of Ring Sizes

A ring fits well when it is no longer felt on the finger. If in the course of time the size of the finger changes or if the ring is to be fitted for another wearer, a sizing of the ring is necessary. The first step is to determine the finger size, which is done with a ring sizer, a set of about 30 steel rings in graduated sizes, figure 13.1. If the customer has a comfortable ring to use as a guide, its size is measured on a graduated ring stick.

In Germany, ring sizes are described by the diameter of the finger hole or inside circumference; in France and the United States, sizes measured by a number, with higher numbers indicating larger sizes. The systems are compared in figure 13.2.

Selecting a correct ring size is not as straightforward as it might at first appear. For one thing, fingers are not round but instead have a cross section like the first image in figure 13.3. In addition, we all know that our fingers swell slightly in the course of the day – for some people this can be a significant change. And of course on hot days our fingers swell even more, while in cold weather our fingers might seem to shrink. No wonder it's difficult to make rings fit well!

There is an additional challenge for people with slim, bony fingers. The ring must of course be large enough to slip over the knuckle, but if there is little skin at the base of the finger the ring slips around uncomfortably. Also, wider bands will need to be a

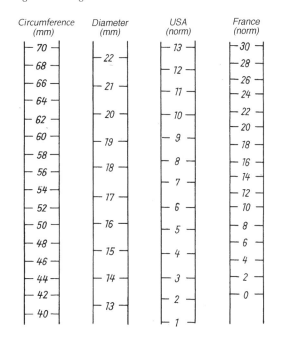

Figure 13.2
Different measurement standards for ring sizes.

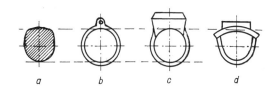

Figure 13.3
Possible measurement mistakes.
a) finger form, b) ring size, c) ring with projecting pointed stone,
d) non-circular shanks.

little larger in size than narrow ones because the wide bands trap skin beneath them. Bands that have an opening under a stone or in some other way allow the finger skin to swell upward can afford to be a little smaller than the same ring without that opening.

Figure 13.4
Reading the ring stick.
(Size 52)

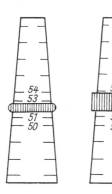

Figure 13.5
Cutting with the ring cutter.

Perhaps it would be better if all rings took the actual shape of the finger rather than a perfect circle, but for better or worse, that is the system that is in widest use. In the end what matters is to create a comfortable fit, regardless of its size. Customers who insist that they wear a specific size are condemning themselves to a poor fit. Similarly, when a ring size is handed over as a length of string or a mark on a strip of paper, this information must be taken only loosely since those devices have more flexibility than the metal of the final ring.

When a ring size is checked on a ring stick, the measurement is read at the edge that makes contact with the ring stick (figure 13.4). Though it should not happen that the culet of a stone projects into the finger area of a ring, it sometimes occurs, nevertheless. Such rings can be measured on a ring stick that has a groove running along its vertical axis.

13.6.1 SAWING RINGS OPEN

Though it's not truly jewelry repair, it sometimes falls to a goldsmith to cut away a ring that can no longer be taken off a finger. This most often happens because an injury or illness has caused the hand to swell, but it might be a matter of simply "growing attached" to your jewelry.

The first alternative is to hold the finger under cold

water and to coat it with liquid soap. Hold the hand vertically in the air, allowing the blood to drain from it, and try one last time to remove the ring. If that fails the ring will need to be cut.

One solution is to use a jewelers sawframe with a coarse blade. Insert a blade upside down so the teeth point toward the back of the frame and slide the blade between the skin and ring shank. Cut by sawing upward away from the hand.

A better solution is to use a ring cutter made for this express purpose, shown here in figure 13.5. The lever pressed here with the left thumb presses the ring up against a circular saw that is turned with the other hand to cut through the ring. Ring forming pliers are then used to bend the ring open enough to allow it to be slipped off.

13.6.2 ENLARGING WEDDING RINGS

When a plain band needs to be enlarged slightly it is often possible to achieve this through mechanical stretching. The number and variety of tools made to achieve this give some indication of how common a repair this is! Stretching is faster and less aggressive than the alternative of inserting an extra piece of metal and should always be considered.

One device uses an attachment for a rolling mill to redistribute the metal in such a way that the ring is made larger. If the shank is made thinner, the metal

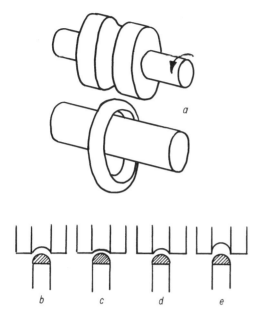

Figure 13.6
Sizing (stretching) machine.
a) mode of action, b) matching profile, c) too flat a profile, d) too narrow
a profile, e) too deep a profile.

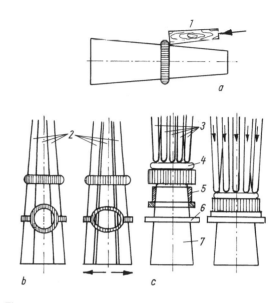

Figure 13.7
Enlarging by stretching.
a) ring mandrel b) stretching mandrel (before and after stretching),
c) spring head of the enlarging mandrel (before and after stretching).

that use to be seen as "thickness" has gone some-where. Where? It has been pushed outwards, or con-verted to length, making the ring slightly larger.

Another alternate is to anneal the ring, then slide it onto a lightly oiled steel ring mandrel. Tap the ring gently with a wooden, leather or plastic mallet as shown in figure 13.7a to stretch it. Because of the tapered nature of the mandrel it is important to take the ring off periodically, invert it, and repeat the process.

A variation on this that avoids the possibility of marring a ring with mallet blows is the use of a tool called the Schwaan Ring Stretcher. The tool consists of a tapered mandrel with a hollow core that has been split into four vertical segments (figure 13.7b). The ring is put onto this rod and a smaller solid steel taper is driven into the first unit with a mallet. This has the effect of stretching the petals (and therefore the ring), though there is no direct contact with the ring itself. This has to be done slowly with great care so that the ring doesn't break.

Figure 13.7c shows a stretching machine developed

by the Fisher Company in Pforzheim. The machine uses a internal bushing of the intended size to prevent the stretching process from going too far, and includes a copper ring that protects the jewelry piece from being damaged.

No matter how sophisticated the tool, any stretch-ing will stress the metal and there is always a risk of the ring snapping. More than that, there is a limit to how far a ring can be stretched. As mentioned, it's always worth considering but there are many cases where a more radical technique will be needed.

13.6.3 ENLARGEMENT OF GEM RINGS
Rings with stones cannot be stretched on a mandrel because of the stress this puts on the stone. There is a danger of breaking the gem, or at least popping it out of its setting. When stones are involved, and if the enlargement is slight, a tool like the one shown at fig-ure 13.8 is recommended.

The device has a number of dies of different shaped grooves that mimic the cross section of the ring shank. Select the one that corresponds to the ring

503

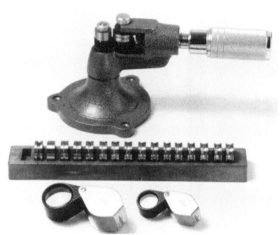

Figure 13.8
Ring enlargement machine (J. Schmalz Company, Pforzheim).

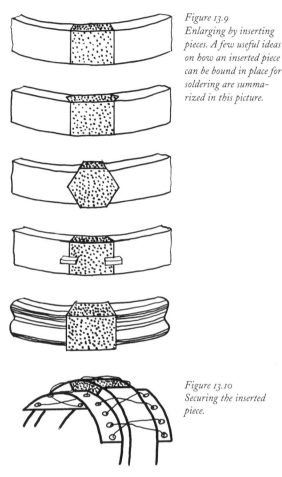

Figure 13.9
Enlarging by inserting pieces. A few useful ideas on how an inserted piece can be bound in place for soldering are summarized in this picture.

Figure 13.10
Securing the inserted piece.

being stretched and attach it to the vertical post of the machine. The ring is then forced against this to locally "forge" the shank. As mentioned above, the action exchanges thickness for length, pressing the ring in such a controlled way that the change is unnoticeable. Of course there is a limit to the stretching that can be done this way, not only because the metal hardens at it is stretched, but the shank could eventually be made too thin.

If these methods cannot be used – most commonly because the desired increase in size is too great – then a piece of metal must be inserted into the shank. First examine the shank closely to see if a solder line is already present. A shank can be lightly heated to reveal the color difference at the solder line. If a line is present, saw the ring open on that existing seam. It there doesn't seem to be a previous joint, cut the ring open at the point opposite the stone, making certain that you don't cut through any hallmarking or engraving.

Insert a piece of metal that perfectly matches in color and makes a tight seam at both ends (figure 13.9). It is not critical that the cross section of the insert match; in fact there is an advantage to having it a little larger than the shank. After soldering the excess is filed away to blend the pieces together. In most cases it is possible to file the insert so it snaps into place, and while this might take some work, the

resulting invisible seam is worth the effort. When the new section cannot be made to stay in place, use a thin piece of steel and binding wire as shown in figure 13.10 to hold the pieces together for soldering.

If the ring contains heat sensitive stones then this complicates soldering. Amber, coral and pearls are so sensitive that such stones need to be removed if a normal soldering flame is used. Other sensitive stones should be taken out if possible. If this is not possible, then they need to be protected against heat. Numerous possibilities have been recommended, all of which are based on the concept that the stone is packed in moist material so that the heat of soldering boils the water instead of being transmitted to the stone.

Though primitive, one solution is to protect the stones by packing them in a raw potato. Cut a hole

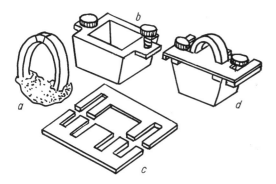

Figure 13.11
Apparatus for soldering of stone rings.
a) Prepared ring, b) opened apparatus, c) lid of apparatus, d) closed apparatus with ring ready for soldering.

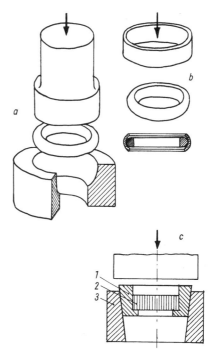

Figure 13.12
Reduction of wedding ring.
a) punch and reducing plate, b) compression of copper sheath, c) reduction with plastic liner: 1) plastic liner, 2) ring, 3) cone-shaped reduction hole.

and press the stone and mounting into it, adding shreds of potato to bury them completely.

A variety of moldable insulating materials are commercially available through tool and supply companies. These can be packed around the stone like modeling clay. A variation that is best used in conjunction with a heat insulator is shown in figure 13.11. The lid pieces (c) are slid over the ring and attached to the box (b) which is either filled with water or an insulating paste. The assembled unit is shown in 13.11d, ready for soldering.

It is always best if a small, very hot flame can be used in repairs that include gemstones. The microtorch is able to heat the metal so quickly that the heat does not have time to flow from the joint area to the rest of the piece. The motto is to get in and out as quickly as possible.

Allow these repairs to air cool, even if you think the heat has not reached the stone. It is a terrible mistake to correctly complete a repair solder without damaging a gem only to have impatience crack the stone because of thermal shock!
Remember that:

- A thick shank conducts heat more quickly than a thin one.
- A silver shank conducts heat better than a gold one.
- Even heat resistant stones can crack and break due to internal structural problems.

13.6.4 SIZING DOWN PLAIN BANDS
When a basic wedding band or similar ring needs to be made a little smaller, the first method of choice is to compress it. Like its corresponding partner, stretching, this is fast, efficient and the least intrusive process. And like stretching, it can only be used when the change in size is small.

A ring sizing machine consists of a series of conical or hemispherical cavities and a flat anvil that is used to press the ring into them. Anneal the ring and select an opening that is just large enough to contain the ring, as seen in figure 13.12a. Apply some pressure to the ram, then flip the ring over and repeat the process. Check periodically to be certain you don't go too far, and remember to anneal periodically if you are compressing a lot.

If the ring is made of several metals, for instance of white gold and yellow gold, this method is limited and might even result in breaking the two metals

505

apart because they have different rates of compression. If the outer surface of the ring is faceted, chased or engraved, protect it by putting a copper band around the ring to absorb the stress at the point of contact figure 13.12b). A variation on this device, shown in figure 13.12c uses a bushing to protect the ring's outer surface.

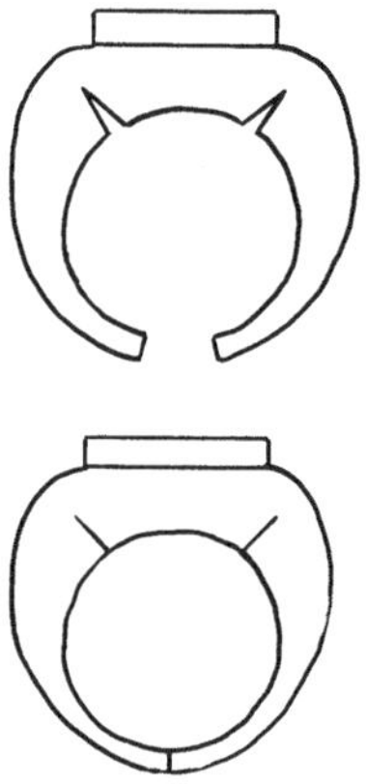

13.6.5 SIZING DOWN GEM RINGS

The stone or stones are taken out and the ring shank cut, again exactly where previous joints have been made if there are any. Remember to check the inside of the band for hallmarks and engraving and to work around them. The shank is bent so the ends come together to make a tight seam, and here again it is important to file the surfaces so they make a clean joint. Failure to do this will make an imperfect soldering that will leave irregularities or pits; in the process of filing these away it is easy to make the shank too small. In the case of thin shanks, file the two butting surfaces at an angle to increase the surface contact and thereby make a stronger joint.

In the case of massive mens' rings, it can be very difficult or even impossible to bend the shanks down to the intended size. In such cases it is advisable, as is shown in figure 13.13, to take out a wedge-shaped piece.

With larger stone settings and delicate ring heads there is a danger that the head of the ring will be bent out of shape and deformed on any of the methods described above. The shanks can break off at the head of the ring or from its shoulders where the solder joints are stressed. It also happens sometimes that a thin shank is simply worn so thin it can no longer be repaired with an isolated joint.

A proven method for dealing with a thin shank consists of soldering a piece on the inside of the ring to strengthen it and to simultaneously decrease the inside diameter (figure 13.14). Though not nearly as good as soldering, this solution can also be achieved with a strong adhesive.

Figure 13.13
Tightening thick-walled rings.

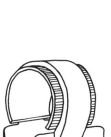

Figure 13.14
Narrowing inside diameter by insertion of inside ring.

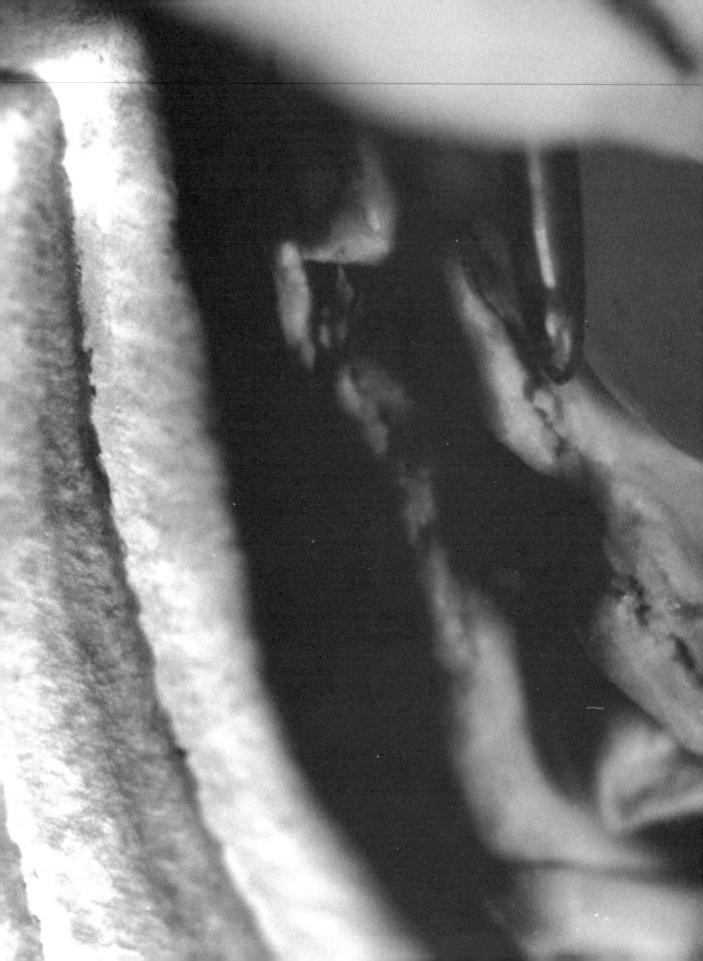

APPENDIX

––––––––––––

ALLOY DATA

Symbol	Name	Au	Ag	Cu	Zn	Other	melting points °C	°F	specific gravity
Al	Aluminum					100 Al	660	1220	2.7
Sb	Antimony					100 Sb	631	1168	6.6
Bi	Bismuth					100 Bi	271	520	9.8
260	Brass (cartridge)		70	30			954	1749	8.5
226	Jewelers Bronze		88	12			1030	1886	8.7
220	Red Brass			90	10		1044	1910	8.8
511	Bronze			96		4 Sn	1060	1945	8.8
Cd	Cadmium					100Cd	321	610	8.7
Cr	Chromium					100 Cr	1890	3434	6.9
Cu	Copper			100			1083	1981	8.9
Au	Gold (fine)	100					1063	1945	19.3
920	22K yellow gold	92	4	4			977	1790	17.3
900	22K coinage	90	10				940	1724	17.2
750	18K yellow	75	15	10			882	1620	15.5
750	18K yellow	75	12.5	12.5			904	1660	15.5
750	18K green	75	25				966	1770	15.6
750	18K rose	75	5	20			932	1710	15.5
750	18K white	75				25 Pd	927	1700	13.7
580	14K yellow	58	25	17			802	1476	13.4
580	14K green	58	35	7			835	1535	13.6
580	14K rose	58	10	32			827	1520	13.4
580	14K white	58				42 Pd	927	1700	13.7
420	10K yellow	42	12	41	5		786	147	11.6
420	10K yellow	42	7	48	3		876	1609	11.6
420	10K green	42	58				804	1480	11.7
420	10K rose	42	10	48			810	1490	11.6
420	10K white	42				58 Pd	927	1760	11.8
Fe	Iron					100 Fe	1535	2793	7.9
Pb	Lead					100 Pb	327	621	11.3
Mg	Magnesium					100 Mg	651	1204	1.7
	Monel metal			33		60 Ni, 7 Fe	1360	2480	8.9
Ni	Nickel					100 Ni	1455	2651	8.8
752	Nickel silver			65	17	18 Ni	1110	2030	8.8
Pd	Palladium					100 Pd	1774	3225	21.4
	Old pewter					80 Pb. 20 Sn	304	580	9.5
Pt	Platinum					100 Pt	1774	3225	21.4
Ag	Silver (fine)		100				961	1762	10.6
925	Sterling		92.5	7.5			920	1640	10.4
800	Con silver		80	20			890	1634	10.3
	Mild steel					99 Fe, 1 C	1511	2750	7.9
	Stainless steel					91 Fe, 9 Cr	1371	2500	7.8
Sn	Tin					100 Sn	232	450	7.3
Ti	Titanium					100 Ti	1800	3272	4.5
Zn	Zinc				100		419	786	7.1

TEMPERATURE CONVERSIONS

To convert Celsius to Fahrenheit:
- multiply by 9,
- divide this answer by 5,
- add 32 to this result.

To convert Fahrenheit to Celsius:
- subtract 32 from the degrees Fahrenheit,
- multiply by 5,
- divide the result by 9.

°C	°F	°C	°F	°F	°C	°F	°C
0	32	600	1112	32	0	1200	649
50	122	625	1157	100	38	1250	677
75	167	650	1202	150	66	1300	704
100	212	675	1247	200	93	1350	732
125	257	700	1292	250	121	1400	760
150	302	725	1337	300	149	1450	788
175	347	750	1382	350	177	1500	816
200	392	775	1427	400	204	1550	843
225	437	800	1472	450	232	1600	871
250	482	825	1517	500	260	1650	899
275	527	850	1562	550	288	1700	927
300	572	875	1607	600	316	1750	954
325	617	900	1652	650	343	1800	982
350	662	925	1697	700	371	1850	1010
375	707	950	1742	750	399	1900	1038
400	752	975	1787	800	427	1950	1066
425	797	1000	1832	850	454	2000	1093
450	842	1025	1877	900	482	2050	1121
475	887	1050	1922	950	510	2100	1149
500	935	1075	1967	1000	538	2150	1177
525	977	1100	2012	1050	566	2200	1204
550	1022	1125	2057	1100	593	2250	1232
575	1067	1150	2102	1150	621	2300	1260

RELATIVE SIZES

B&S	MM	Inches thousandths	Inches fraction	Drill Size
0	8.5	.325	21/64	
1	7.35	.289	9/32	
2	6.54	.250	1/4	
3	5.83	.229	7/32	1
4	5.19	.204	13/64	6
5	4.62	.182	3/16	15
6	4.11	.162	5/32	20
7	3.67	.144	9/64	27
8	3.26	.129	1/8	30
10	2.59	.102		38
11	2.30	.090	3/32	43
12	2.05	.080	5/64	46
13	1.83	.072		50
14	1.63	.064	1/16	51
15	1.45	.057		52
16	1.29	.050		54
17	1.15	.045	3/64	55
18	1.02	.040		56
19	.912	.036		60
20	.813	.032	1/32	65
21	.724	.029		67
22	.643	.025		70
23	.574	.023		71
24	.511	.020		74
25	.455	.018		75
26	.404	.016	1/64	77
27	.361	.014		78
28	.330	.013		79
29	.279	.011		80
30	.254	.010		

CONVERSIONS

Multiply the known unit by the factor to the right of the unit of measure you are seeking.

carats				pennyweights (dwt.)		
to grains	x	3.0865		to grains	x	24
to grams	x	.2		to grams	x	1.5551
to milligrams	x	200		to oz. avoir.	x	.05486
grains				lb. avoirdupois		
to carats	x	.324		to grains	x	7000
grams	x	.0648		to grams	x	453.59
to milligrams	x	64.799		to kilograms	x	.4536
to oz. avoir.	x	.002286		to oz. troy	x	14.5833
to oz., troy	x	.00208		lb. troy		
to pennyweight	x	.04167		to grams	x	373.242
grams				to kilograms	x	.3732
to carat	x	5		to oz, avoir.	x	.82286
to grains	x	15.4324		feet		
to oz. avoir.	x	.03527		to centimeters	x	30.48
to oz., troy	x	.03215		to meters	x	.3048
to pennyweight	x	.64301		meters		
kilograms				to feet	x	3.2808
to oz, avoir.	x	35.274		to inches	x	29.37
to oz. troy	x	32.1507		to yards	x	1.0936
to pennyweight	x	643.015		millimeters		
to lb. avoir.	x	2.2046		to feet	x	.00328
to lb. troy	x	2.6792		to inches	x	.03937
oz. avoirdupois				inches		
to grains	x	437.5		to centimeters	x	2.54
to grams	x	28.3495		to meters	x	.0254
to oz., troy	x	.91146		to millimeters	x	25.4
to pennyweight	x	18.2291		cubic centimeters		
to lb. troy	x	.07595		to cubic inches	x	.061
oz., troy				to US fluid oz.	x	.0338
to grains	x	480		cubic inches		
to grams	x	31.1035		to cubic cm	x	16.387
to oz., avoir.	x	1.0971		to liters	x	.01639
to pennyweight	x	20		to US fluid oz.	x	.554
to lb. avoir.	x	.06857		US gallons		
US fluid ounces				to liters	x	3.785
to cu. cm	x	29.5737		to cubic inches	x	231
to cu inches	x	1.80469		to cubic feet	x	.1337
to liters	x	.02957		liters		
				to US gallons	x	.2642
				to US quarts	x	1.0567

EQUIVALENT NUMBERS

Fractions	Inches	Millimeters	Fractions	Inches	Millimeters
1/64	.0156	0.3969	17/64	.2656	6.7468
1/32	.0313	0.7937	9/32	.2812	7.1437
3/64	.0469	1.1906	19/64	.2969	7.5405
1/16	.0625	1.5875	5/16	.3125	7.9374
5/64	.0781	1.9843	21/64	.3281	8.3343
3/32	.0937	2.3812	11/32	.3438	8.7312
7/64	.1094	2.7781	23/64	.3594	9.1280
1/8	.1250	3.1750	3/8	.3750	9.5249
9/64	.1406	3.5718	25/64	.3906	9.9217
5/32	.1562	3.9687	13/32	.4062	10.3186
11/64	.1719	4.3656	27/64	.4219	10.7155
3/16	.1875	4.7624	7/16	.4375	11.1124
13/64	.2031	5.1593	29/64	.4531	11.5092
7/32	.2187	5.5562	15/32	.4687	11.9061
15/64	.2344	5.9530	3194	.44844	12.3030
1/4	.2500	6.3499	1/2	.5000	12.6999

SAWBLADE & DRILL SIZES

Number	Thickness	Depth	Drill Equivalent	Recommended for…
8/0	.0060	.0130	80	26 gauge B&S
6/0	.0070	.0140	79	24
4/0	.0085	.0170	77	22
2/0	.0100	.0200	75	22
0	.0110	.0230	73	20
1	.0115	.0250	71	20
3	.0140	.0290	68	18
5	.0160	.0340	65	16
7	.0200	.0480	55	12

FINENESS OF GOLD

Gold alloys are described either as parts per thousand or as "karats", a proportion based on 24ths.

Karat	%gold	1000	Karat	%gold	1000	Karat	%gold	1000
24	100	1000	16	67%	.666	8	33%	.333
23	96%	.958	15	63%	.625	7	29%	.292
22	92%	.916	14	58%	.583	6	25%	.250
21	88%	.875	13	54%	.541	5	21%	.208
20	83%	.833	12	50%	.500	4	17%	.166
19	79%	.791	11	46%	.458	3	13%	.125
18	75%	.750	10	42%	.416	2	8%	.083
17	71%	.708	9	38%	.375	1	4%	.042

THICKNESS OF COPPER SHEET

Ounces	Pounds	Inches	B&S	Stubbs	Ounces	Pounds	Inches	B&S	Stubbs
–	16	.3456	00	00	56	3 ½	.0756	13	15
–	15	.3240	0	0	48	3	.0648	14	16
–	14	.3024	1	1	44	2 ¾	.0594	15	17
–	13	.2808	1	2	40	2 ½	.0540	15	17
–	12	.2592	2	3	36	2 ¼	.0486	16	18
–	11	.2376	3	4	32	2	.0432	17	19
–	9 ½	.2052	4	6	28	1 ¾	.0378	19	20
–	9	.1944	4	6	24	1 ½	.0324	20	21
–	8 ½	.1836	5	7	20	1 ¼	.0270	21	22
–	8	.1728	5	8	18	1 ⅛	.0243	22	23
–	7 ½	.1620	6	8	16	1	.0216	23	24
–	7	.1512	7	9	14	⅞	.0189	25	26
–	6 ½	.1404	7	10	12	¾	.0162	26	27
–	6	.1296	8	10	10	⅝	.0081	32	33
–	5 ½	.1188	9	11	8	½	.0108	29	31
80	5	.1080	10	12	6	⅜	.0081	32	33
72	4 ½	.0972	10	13	4	¼	.0054	35	35
64	4	.0864	11	14	2	⅛	.0027	–	–

WEIGHT CONVERSION FACTORS

To find the weight of a given object in a different metal than it is now, multiply by the factors shown below. Example: I have a sterling ring tha twights 6 dwts. This is the *known* ingredient. My *query* is "How much will is weight n 18K gold?" Answer: 6 x 1.48 (from the table) = 8.8 dwt.

Query	Known	Factor
18K yellow	18K white	1.064
	platinum	.723
	brass	1.885
	sterling	1.480
14K yellow	18K white	.842
	14K white	1.035
	patinum	.609
	brass	1.589
	sterling	1.248
10K yellow	18K yellow	.745
	14K white	.884
	platinum	.539
	brass	1.406
	sterling	1.104

Query	Known	Factor
Platinum	palladium	1.758
	iridium	.953
	10% irid. plat	.995
	15% irid. plat	.993
	rhodium	1.717
	ruthenium	1.771
	sterling	2.046
Sterling	fine silver	.984
	coin silver	1.004
	18K yellow	.675
	14K yellow	.801
	10K yellow	.905
	platinum	.488
	brass	1.273
Coin silver	fine silver	.980
	sterling	.995

BIBLIOGRAPHY

FINEGOLD AND SEITZ: *Silversmithing.* Radnor, Pennsylvania: Chilton Publishing, 1983.

HARDY AND ALLEN: *The Jewelry Engraver's Manual.* New York: Van Nostrand Reinhold, 1976 (orig. 1954).

HUGHES, RICHARD AND ROWE, MICHAEL: *Colouring, Bronzing and Patination of Metals.* New York: Watson-Guptill, 1982.

LEWTON-BRAIN, CHARLES: *The Jewelry Workshop Safety Report.* Calgary, Alberta: Brain Press, 1998.

LEWTON-BRAIN, CHARLES: *Hinges and Hinge-based Catches for Jewelers and Goldsmiths.* Calgary, Alberta: Brain Press, 1997.

MCCREIGHT, TIM: *The Complete Metalsmith: An Illustrated Handbook.* 2d edition. Worcester, Massachusetts: Davis Publications, 1991.

MCCREIGHT, TIM: *Practical Casting.* 2d edition. Portland, Maine: Brynmorgen Press, 1986.

REVERE, ALAN: *Professional Goldsmithing: A Contemporary Guide to Traditional Jewelry Techniques.* San Francisco: RAJA Press, 1991.

SMITH, ERNEST A.: *Working in Precious Metals.* London: N.A.G. Press Limited, 1935.

STARK, JEAN: *Classical Loop-in-Loop Chains and Their Derivatives.* 2d edition. Portland, Maine: Brynmorgen Press, 1999.

UNTRACT, OPPI: *Jewelry, Concepts and Technology.* New York: Doubleday, 1982.

UNTRACT, OPPI: *Metal Techniques for Craftsmen.* New York: Doubleday, 1968.

VON NEUMAN, ROBERT: *Design and Creation of Jewelry.* Radnor, Pennsylvania: Chilton Publishing, 1961.

Jewelry Supplies

Allcraft Jewelry Supply
135 W 29th Street, Rm 402
New York, NY 10001
    212 279 7077
    800 645 7124

Frei & Borel
PO Box 796
126 Second Street
Oakland, CA 94607
    800 772 3456
    800 900 3734 fax
    510 832 0355
    510 834 6217 fax
        www.ofrei.com
        info@ofrei.com

Jules Borel & Co
1110 Grand Blvd
Kansas City, MO 64106
    800 333 4646
    816 421 6110
    800 333 4083

Metalliferous
34 West 46th Street
New York, NY 10036
    212 944 0909
    212 944 0644 fax

Rio Grande
7500 Bluewater Road NW
Albuquerque, NM 87121
    800 545 6566
    800 965 2329 fax
        www.riogrande.com
        info@riogrande.com

William Dixon
"a division of Grobet"
750 Washington Avenue
Carlstadt, NJ 07072
    201 935 0100
    800 847 4188
    800 243 2432 fax
        www.grobetusa.com
        dental@grobetusa.com

Metals

Bayshore Metals Inc
244 Napoleon Street
San Francisco, CA 94124
    800 533 2493
    415 647 7981
    415 285 5759
        www. bayshoremetals.com
        baymetals@aol.com

Hauser & Miller Co
Box 500700
St Louis, MO 63150
    800 462 7447
    800 535 3829 fax
    314 487 1311
        www.hauserandmiller.com
        support@hauserandmiller.com

Hoover & Strong
10700 Trade Road
Richmond, VA 23236
    800 759 9997 phone & fax
    804 794 3700
    804 794 5687 fax
        www.hooverandstrong.com
        info@hooverand strong.com

United Precious Metal Refining
2781 Townline Road
Alden, NY 14004
    800 999 FINE
    800 533 6657 fax
        www.unitedpmr.com
        sales@unitedpmr.com

Miscellaneous

Blacksmithing equipment & books
Centaur Forge
117 N. Spring Street
Burlington, WI 53105
    800 666 9175
    262 763 9175
    262 763 8350 fax
        www.centaurforge.com
        centforge1@aol.com

Titanium, niobium, findings and specialty tools
Reactive Metals Studio
Box 890
Clarkdale, AZ 86324
    800 876 3434
    520 634 3434
    520 634 6734 fax
        www.reactivemetals.com
        reactive@sedona.net

Small fasteners
J. I. Morris Company
394 Elm Street
Southbridge, MA 01550
    508 764 4394
    508 764 7350 fax
        www.jimorris.thomasregister.com

Pitch for repoussé
Northwest Pitchworks
1317 Roland Street
Bellingham, WA 98226
    360 715 1772
        www.northwestpitchworks.com
        northwest_pitchworks@yahoo.com

Specialty materials and tools
Small Parts
13980 NW 58th Court
PO Box 4650
Miami Lakes, FL 33014
    800 220 4242
    800 423 9009 fax
    305 557 7955
    305 558 0509 fax
        www.smallparts.com

Studio chemicals
Bryant Labs Inc
1101 Fifth Street
Berkeley, CA 94710
    800 367 3141
    510 526 3141
    510 528 2948 fax
        www.sirius.com/~bry_lab
        bry_lab@sirius.com

Index

527

COLOPHON

The Theory and Practice of Goldsmithing
was edited in Microsoft Word and formatted in
QuarkXpress 3.3. The body text was set in 10 pt.
Adobe Caslon with Brynmorgen Greek. The
chapter titles were set in Expo Sans. Printed in
China on 100gsm wood free paper.